SADLIER-OXFORD

Fundamentals of Algebra

PRACTICE BOOK

Alfred S. Posamentier

Catherine D. LeTourneau

Edward William Quinn

Sadlier-Oxford
A Division of William H. Sadlier, Inc.
www.sadlier-oxford.com

Photo Credits

Cover: **Alamy/Scott Camazine:** computer generated glass icosidodecahedron; **Getty Images/Photographer's Choice/Joe Drivas:** space shuttle; **Getty Images/Stone/Gerben Oppermans:** snowflake; **iStockphoto.com/ PhotoEuphoria:** protractor; **Punchstock/Stockbyte:** basketball. Interior: **Alamy/imagebroker/Guenter Fischer:** 341 right; **Alamy/Paul Springett:** 341 center; **Alamy/UK Stock Images Ltd/Grantly Lynch:** 341 left.

. . . .

𝕊® is a registered trademark of William H. Sadlier, Inc.

Printed in the United States of America.

ISBN: 978-0-8215-8227-5

3 4 5 6 7 WEBC 20 19 18 17

Contents

Chapter 3

Inequalities

Chapter 4

Rational Numbers: Decimals

Chapter 5

Rational Numbers: Fractions

Chapter 6

Ratio and Proportion

Chapter

Percent and Consumer Applications

Use with SOURCEBOOK pages 173–206.

Chapter

Data Analysis and Statistics

Use with SOURCEBOOK pages 207–238.

Chapter 9

Two-Dimensional Geometry

Use with SOURCEBOOK pages 239–270.

Chapter 10

Two-Dimensional Geometry and Measurement Applications

Use with SOURCEBOOK pages 271–300.

Chapter  11

Three-Dimensional Geometry

Chapter  12

Probability

Chapter 13

Patterns, Relations, and Functions

Chapter 14

Polynomials, Equations, and Inequalities

Gridded-Response Form

Name _____ Date _____

1-1 Integers and Absolute Value

Name _____ Date _____

> The set of integers contains the set of whole numbers and their opposites.
>
> Negative Integers — Zero — Positive Integers
>
> -8 -7 -6 -5 -4 -3 -2 -1 0 1 2 3 4 5 6 7 8
>
> A — -4 B — 4
>
> **Remember:** The opposite of 0 is 0.
>
> Point A is at -4, or negative 4. -4 and 4 are opposites.   Point B is at 4, or positive 4.
>
> The *absolute value* of a number is its distance from zero on a number line.
> The absolute value of -4 is equal to the absolute value of 4. $|-4| = |4| = 4$.

Write each as an integer.

1. 7 meters forward __**+7 or 7**__

2. at sea level _____

3. 8° C below 0° C _____

4. loss of 6 points _____

5. 90 meters below sea level _____

6. $4 gain _____

Write the opposite of each. (*Hint:* First evaluate the expression. Then find its opposite.)

7. 5
  __**−5**__

8. -9
  _____

9. -32
  _____

10. $-|18|$
  _____

11. $-|-23|$
  _____

12. $-(-15)$
  _____

Write the integer for each exercise.

13. $|7|$
  __**7**__

14. $|0|$
  _____

15. $|-8|$
  _____

16. $|-5|$
  _____

17. (-3)
  _____

18. $-(-2)$
  _____

Use the number line for exercises 19–31.
Name the letter that matches each integer on the number line.

A B C D E F G H I J K L M N O P Q

-3 -2 0 1 4 6

19. -1
  __**H**__

20. -6
  _____

21. -5
  _____

22. -4
  _____

23. 2
  _____

24. 3
  _____

Name the integer that matches each letter on the number line.

25. P
  __**7**__

26. B
  _____

27. N
  _____

28. L
  _____

29. Q
  _____

30. A
  _____

31. What integer would be 2 units to the right of E? _____

Use the number line to name the integer that matches each letter.

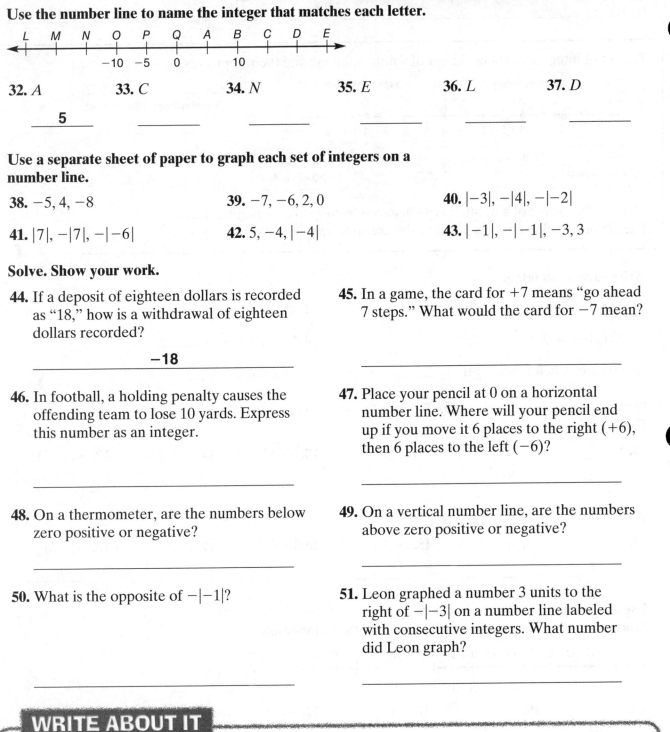

32. *A*   **33.** *C*   **34.** *N*   **35.** *E*   **36.** *L*   **37.** *D*

_____5_____   _____   _____   _____   _____   _____

Use a separate sheet of paper to graph each set of integers on a number line.

38. $-5, 4, -8$

39. $-7, -6, 2, 0$

40. $|-3|, -|4|, -|-2|$

41. $|7|, -|7|, -|-6|$

42. $5, -4, |-4|$

43. $|-1|, -|-1|, -3, 3$

Solve. Show your work.

44. If a deposit of eighteen dollars is recorded as "18," how is a withdrawal of eighteen dollars recorded?

_____-18_____

45. In a game, the card for $+7$ means "go ahead 7 steps." What would the card for -7 mean?

_____

46. In football, a holding penalty causes the offending team to lose 10 yards. Express this number as an integer.

_____

47. Place your pencil at 0 on a horizontal number line. Where will your pencil end up if you move it 6 places to the right $(+6)$, then 6 places to the left (-6)?

_____

48. On a thermometer, are the numbers below zero positive or negative?

_____

49. On a vertical number line, are the numbers above zero positive or negative?

_____

50. What is the opposite of $-|-1|$?

51. Leon graphed a number 3 units to the right of $-|-3|$ on a number line labeled with consecutive integers. What number did Leon graph?

_____

WRITE ABOUT IT

52. Can the graph of an absolute value be negative? Explain your reasoning.

_____

_____

_____

1-2 Compare and Order Integers

Name _____ Date _____

Integers increase in value as you move from left to right on a horizontal number line.

$$\longleftarrow \underset{-10\,-9\,-8\,-7\,-6\,-5\,-4\,-3\,-2\,-1\ \ 0\ \ 1\ \ 2\ \ 3\ \ 4\ \ 5\ \ 6\ \ 7\ \ 8\ \ 9\ \ 10}{\vdash\!+}\longrightarrow$$

-4 is to the right of -10, so -4 is greater than -10.
Write $-4 > -10$.

5 is to the right of -7, so 5 is greater than -7.
Write $5 > -7$.

On a horizontal number line:
- To order from least to greatest, start with the integer farthest to the left.
  $-10, -7, -4, 5$
- To order from greatest to least, start with the integer farthest to the right.
  $5, -4, -7, -10$

Write the integer for each exercise.

1. -3 __**−3**__   **2.** (4) _____   **3.** $|18|$ _____   **4.** $-|5|$ _____   **5.** $|-7|$ _____   **6.** $-|-1|$ _____

Write the integer that comes just before and just after each number.

7. -1
   __**−2 and 0**__

8. -19
   _____

9. -8
   _____

10. -50
   _____

11. 0
   _____

12. 79
   _____

13. $-(-10)$
   _____

14. $|-6|$
   _____

Compare. Write <, =, or >.

15. 4 __<__ 7 **16.** 3 ___ 1 **17.** 2 ___ 0 **18.** 0 ___ -4

19. -1 ___ 1 **20.** 3 ___ -6 **21.** -6 ___ -3 **22.** -3 ___ -8

23. -14 ___ -12 **24.** -42 ___ -50 **25.** -25 ___ -26 **26.** -58 ___ -59

27. -17 ___ $-(-13)$ **28.** -18 ___ $-(-18)$ **29.** $-(-36)$ ___ 36 **30.** $-(-100)$ ___ 1000

31. 5 ___ $|-5|$ **32.** 2 ___ $-|2|$ **33.** $-|-7|$ ___ -7 **34.** -14 ___ $-|-5|$

35. $-(-4)$ ___ $|-4|$ **36.** $|-8|$ ___ $-(-8)$ **37.** $-(-51)$ ___ $-|22|$ **38.** $-(-22)$ ___ $-|-51|$

True or False. Explain.

39. A positive integer is always greater than 0.

   True: Positive integers are always to the right of 0 on a number line and are > 0.

40. A negative integer is not less than 0.

_____

41. A negative integer is always less than a positive integer.

_____

42. A positive integer is never greater than a negative integer.

_____

Order from least to greatest.

43. $0, -6, 5, 3, -3$

$\underline{-6, -3, 0, 3, 5}$

44. $-7, 0, -3, -5, 6$

45. $27, -15, 11, -11, 0$

46. $21, -16, -3, -1, |-19|$

47. $3, -6, |-4|, -3$

48. $-321, -415, 321, 163$

Order from greatest to least.

49. $-8, -3, -5, -1$

$\underline{-1, -3, -5, -8}$

50. $-16, -19, -9, -6$

51. $-4, -6, -8, 1, 0$

52. $-5, -3, -16, -12$

53. $-(-8), 18, -28, -10$

54. $20, 25, 40, -|-20|$

Solve. Show your work.

55. Meteorology The TV weather forecaster recorded the daily low temperatures for the week: $-10°C, 5°C, 8°C, -4°C, -11°C, 4°C,$ and $-1°C$. List these Celsius temperatures from highest to lowest.

Order from highest to lowest
Positive: 8, 5, 4
Negative: −1, −4, −10, −11
$\underline{\qquad 8, 5, 4, -1, -4, -10, -11}$

56. Chemistry Order the melting points of these elements in degrees Celsius from least to greatest: hydrogen, $-259°C$; chlorine, $-103°C$; helium, $-272°C$; and oxygen, $-218°C$.

57. Topography The Dead Sea is 1312 feet below sea level. Death Valley is 282 feet below sea level. Which point is lower?

58. The temperature on Wednesday was 4 degrees Celsius. On Thursday the temperature was -5 degrees Celsius. Which temperature was higher?

TEST PREPARATION

59. Which set of integers is ordered from greatest to least?

    A. $-1, 2, 0, -3$

    B. $0, -1, 2, -3$

    C. $-3, 2, -1, 0$

    D. $0, -1, -2$

60. Which absolute value has the least value?

    F. $|14|$

    G. $|-18|$

    H. $|-27|$

    J. $|23|$

1-3 Add Integers

Name _____ Date _____

To add integers with *like signs*, add the absolute values of the addends and use the sign of the addends for the sum.

Add: $-2 + (-6)$

Think $|-2| + |-6| \rightarrow 2 + 6 = 8$

$-2 + (-6) = -8$ The addends are negative, so the sum is negative.

Add: $2 + 6$

Think $|2| + |6| \rightarrow 2 + 6 = 8$

$2 + 6 = 8$ The addends are positive, so the sum is positive.

To add integers with *unlike signs*, subtract the lesser absolute value from the greater absolute value. Use the sign of the addend with the greater absolute value for the sum.

Add: $-2 + 6$

Think $|6| - |-2| \rightarrow 6 - 2 = 4$

$-2 + 6 = 4$ $|6| > |-2|$, so the sum is positive.

Add: $2 + (-6)$

Think $|-6| - |2| \rightarrow 6 - 2 = 4$

$2 + (-6) = -4$ $|-6| > |2|$, so the sum is negative.

Add.

1. $-4 + (-2)$ ___**−6**___

2. $7 + (-16)$ _____

3. $-11 + 12$ _____

4. $0 + (-3)$ _____

5. $7 + (-15)$ _____

6. $-7 + 5$ _____

7. $-4 + (-6)$ _____

8. $9 + (-6)$ _____

9. $-17 + (-8)$ _____

10. $-11 + (-16)$ _____

11. $18 + (-3)$ _____

12. $-14 + (-12)$ _____

13. $16 + 17$ _____

14. $-13 + (-13)$ _____

15. $-11 + 19$ _____

16. $-45 + 45$ _____

17. $-45 + 12$ _____

18. $23 + (-18)$ _____

19. $-14 + (-34)$ _____

20. $43 + 9$ _____

21. $-39 + (-4)$ _____

22. $19 + (-23)$ _____

23. $47 + 29$ _____

24. $35 + 56$ _____

25. $-67 + 54$ _____

26. $-14 + (-32)$ _____

27. $28 + (-31)$ _____

28. $-50 + 35$ _____

29. $24 + (-19)$ _____

30. $-81 + (-11)$ _____

31. $-213 + (-327)$ _____

32. $121 + (-232)$ _____

33. $-453 + 112$ _____

Find the sum.

34. $15 + 19 + (-23)$
$\quad\quad\quad 34 + (-23)$
$\quad\quad\quad\quad\quad 11$

35. $-9 + (-13) + (-17)$

36. $-12 + 12 + (-4)$

37. $-17 + (-49) + 5$

38. $15 + 78 + 34$

39. $-19 + 16 + (-42)$

40. $-23 + 14 + (-33)$

41. $-7 + (-19) + 32$

42. $102 + (-345) + 234$

43. $-78 + (-56) + 679$

44. $178 + (-129) + 96$

45. $-312 + (-154) + 283$

Complete the addition table.

	Rule: +	−5	20	−17	6
46.	12	$12 + (-5) = 7$			
47.	−8				
48.	15				

Use mental math to compare. Write <, =, or >.

49. $-7 + (-8) \underline{\;=\;} -8 + (-7)$

50. $-4 + 8 \underline{\quad\quad} 4 + (-8)$

51. $-2 + (-3) \underline{\quad\quad} 2 + 3$

52. $15 + (-12) \underline{\quad\quad} 12 + (-15)$

53. $-22 + 22 \underline{\quad\quad} 4 + (-4)$

54. $-33 + 0 \underline{\quad\quad} 0 + 33$

Solve. Check to justify your answers.

55. Meteorology As of 2006, California's record high temperature was 179 degrees above its record low. If the record low temperature is $-45°F$, what is the state's record high temperature?

56. Sports On the first four possessions of the game, the Blue Hawks football team made the following plays: a 1-yard loss, a 3-yard gain, a 4-yard loss, and no gain. How many yards did the football team lose or gain after the first four possessions?

WRITE ABOUT IT

57. When adding two integers, how can you tell if a sum will be positive, negative, or zero without actually adding? Use examples to explain.

1-4 Subtract Integers

Name _____ Date _____

To subtract integers, add the opposite (additive inverse)
of the subtrahend.

$9 - 7$	$9 - (-7)$	$-9 - 7$	$-9 - (-7)$
$9 + (-7)$	$9 + 7$	$-9 + (-7)$	$-9 + 7$
2	16	-16	-2

Remember: The subtrahend
is the number you subtract.

$$9 - \mathbf{7} = ?$$

$$\begin{array}{r} 9 \\ -\ \mathbf{7} \leftarrow \text{subtrahend} \\ \hline ? \end{array}$$

Find the difference. (*Hint:* Rewrite each expression using the
opposite, or additive inverse. Then compute.)

1. $25 - 6$
  $25 + (-6)$
  19

2. $9 - 9$

3. $27 - 27$

4. $0 - 9$

5. $17 - 28$

6. $38 - 56$

7. $40 - (-40)$

8. $7 - (-7)$

9. $34 - (-17)$

10. $30 - (-70)$

11. $-18 - 12$

12. $-32 - 64$

13. $-16 - 18$

14. $-32 - 75$

15. $-45 - 39$

16. $-98 - 134$

17. $-4 - (-4)$

18. $-3 - (-8)$

19. $-5 - (-8)$

20. $-12 - (-25)$

21. $-7 - (-6)$

22. $-11 - (-14)$

23. $-45 - (-12)$

24. $-34 - (-23)$

25. $-112 - (-56)$

26. $12 - |8|$

27. $23 - |11|$

28. $|15| - 7$

29. $|108| - 67$

30. $-|4| - 9$

Subtract. (*Hint:* Rewrite each expression using the additive inverse. Then compute.)

31. $-25 - 10 - 5$
$-25 + (-10) + (-5)$
-40

32. $-6 - 11 - 23$

33. $37 - 18 - 9$

34. $19 - 4 - 31$

35. $15 - (-3) - (-12)$

36. $39 - (-53) - (-42)$

Compute. (*Hint:* Rewrite each expression using the additive inverse. Then compute.)

37. $-8 + 3 - 5 + (-3) - (-6)$
$-8 + 3 + (-5) + (-3) + 6$
-7

38. $-7 - 9 + (-2) + 7 + 4$

39. $-2 + (-3) - 4 + (-5) - 6$

40. $2 - (-3) - (-4) + 5 + 6$

41. $80 + (-60) - 80 + 70$

42. $-72 + (-43) - 6 - 14$

Solve. Check to justify your answers.

43. Money Management Jana's credit card has a balance of $0. If she buys groceries for $250, what integer represents the balance on her credit card?

$0 + (-250) = -250$
The integer is -250.
Check: $-250 + 250 = 0$

44. Finance The price of a share of stock was $23 on Monday and $19 on Tuesday. What is the difference in price of those two days? Write an integer to represent the change in the price of the stock.

45. History If years B.C. are represented by negative numbers and years A.D. by positive numbers, how many years are there from 40 B.C. to 4 B.C.?

46. Sports The football referee calls a penalty of 5 yards against a team in addition to a loss of 3 yards. If another referee calls an additional penalty of 10 yards, what is the team's net loss in yards?

CHALLENGE

47. Insert negative signs, and addition and subtraction symbols to make each sentence true. Example: $1 = 1 + (-2) + (-3) + 4 + (-5) + 6$

  a. $7 =$ 1 2 3 4 5 6 **b.** $3 =$ 1 2 3 4 5 6

  c. $-1 =$ 1 2 3 4 5 6 **d.** $-11 =$ 1 2 3 4 5 6

1-5 Multiply Integers

Name _____ Date _____

The product of two integers with *like signs* is positive.

positive • positive = positive
$2 • 3 = 6$
negative • negative = positive
$-2 • (-3) = 6$

The product of two integers with *unlike signs* is negative.

positive • negative = negative
$2 • (-3) = -6$
negative • positive = negative
$-2 • 3 = -6$

When the number of negative factors is *even*, the product is positive.
$-2 • (-2) • (-2) • (-2) = 16$

When the number of negative factors is *odd*, the product is negative.
$-2 • (-2) • (-2) = -8$

Remember: Multiplication can be shown different ways:
$3 \times 4 = 3 • 4 = 3(4) = (3)(4).$

Find the product.

1. $5 • 8$ ___**40**___

2. $9 • 6$ _____

3. $3(11)$ _____

4. $6(12)$ _____

5. $0 • 14$ _____

6. $-16(0)$ _____

7. $-3 • (-8)$ _____

8. $-2(-34)$ _____

9. $-8 • (-12)$ _____

10. $(-9)(-18)$ _____

11. $7 • (-9)$ _____

12. $5 • (-10)$ _____

13. $34(-2)$ _____

14. $-9 • 9$ _____

15. $8(-14)$ _____

16. $(-49)(38)$ _____

17. $23 • |-10|$ _____

18. $-36 • |-1|$ _____

19. $|-2| • |-29|$ _____

20. $|4| • (54)$ _____

21. $|-8 • 13|$ _____

Tell whether the product will be positive or negative.
Then find the product. (*Hint:* Count the negative factors.)

22. $3 • (-3) • (-3)$ ___**positive; 27**___

23. $4 • (-4) • (-4) • (-4)$ _____

24. $1 • (-1) • 1 • (-1) • 1$ _____

25. $(-2) • (-3) • (-4) • (-5)$ _____

26. $8(-1)(-2)(-3)$ _____

27. $-9(-1)(3)(-1)(-2)$ _____

28. $(-4)(3)(2)(-1)(0)$ _____

29. $-1(5)(6)(7)(8)$ _____

Find the product.

30. $(-6)(8)(2)$ ___**−96**___

31. $-8 • (2)(2)$ _____

32. $9 • (-2)(2)$ _____

33. $-5 • 0 • (-12)$ _____

34. $(-3)(-4)(9)$ _____

35. $-3(-2)(-4)$ _____

36. $-3 • 5 (4 • 2)$ _____

37. $-9(13 • 0 • 2)$ _____

38. $2 • (-5) • 2 • (-2)$ _____

39. $-6 (-11)(1)(2)$ _____

40. $-2 • (-4)(-7) • (-3)$ _____

41. $8(16) • (-2)(-1)$ _____

Use mental math to solve. Then write the missing factor.

42. $7 \cdot \underline{\quad 4 \quad} = 28$

43. $35 = 7(\underline{\quad\quad})$

44. $15 = (\underline{\quad\quad})(5)$

45. $8 \cdot \underline{\quad\quad} = 0$

46. $\underline{\quad\quad} \cdot (-5) = 0$

47. $-9 = -3 \cdot \underline{\quad\quad}$

48. $(\underline{\quad\quad})(25) = -25$

49. $-27 = (-3) \cdot \underline{\quad\quad}$

50. $-6 \cdot \underline{\quad\quad} = 54$

51. $(\underline{\quad\quad})(-7) = 63$

52. $-15(\underline{\quad\quad}) = 90$

53. $(\underline{\quad\quad})(-6) = 18$

54. $-42 = -7(\underline{\quad\quad})$

55. $-8(\underline{\quad\quad}) = -72$

56. $-40 = (\underline{\quad\quad})(10)$

Solve. Check to justify your answer.

57. A diet plan claims that people who follow the diet lose an average of 2 pounds per week. If this claim is true, what is the average change in weight for people who follow the diet for 4 weeks? Use an integer in your answer.

$$-2(4) = -8$$
The average weight change is −8 pounds.

58. Sports On each of four consecutive plays in a football game, a team lost 11 yards. If lost yardage is interpreted as a negative integer, write this information as a product of integers, and determine the total number of yards lost.

59. One section of a city sinks an average of 3 inches each year. What is the average amount the elevation changes in this city over 5 years? Use an integer in your answer.

60. Every year, 20 fewer students eat in the school cafeteria. Assuming this trend continues, write a multiplication expression to show the change in the number of students over the next 5 years. Express the change as an integer.

CRITICAL THINKING

61. An oceanographer dives at an average speed of four meters every 10 minutes from sea level. A mountaineer climbs at an average speed of two meters every three minutes from sea level.

If the mountaineer begins her climb at 11:07 A.M., and the oceanographer begins his dive at 11:17 A.M., what distance will the mountaineer be from the oceanographer at 11:37 A.M.? Explain your answer. (*Hint:* 1 hour = 60 minutes.)

1-6 Divide Integers

Name _____ Date _____

The quotient of two integers with *like signs* is positive.	The quotient of two integers with *unlike signs* is negative.
positive ÷ positive = positive $\quad 32 \div 8 = 4$	positive ÷ negative = negative $30 \div (-6) = -5$
negative ÷ negative = positive $\quad \dfrac{-21}{-3} = 7$	negative ÷ positive = negative $\dfrac{-18}{9} = -2$

The quotient of any nonzero integer and 1 is that integer. $\quad 12 \div \mathbf{1} = 12$

The quotient of any nonzero integer and -1 is the opposite of that integer. $\quad 12 \div (\mathbf{-1}) = -(12) = \mathbf{-12}$

The quotient of zero and any nonzero divisor is zero. $\quad \mathbf{0} \div 12 = \mathbf{0}$

The quotient of any nonzero integer and zero is undefined. $\quad 12 \div \mathbf{0}$ is undefined.

Find the quotient.

1. $56 \div 8$

_____ 7 _____

2. $\dfrac{99}{9}$

3. $\dfrac{27}{3}$

4. $0 \div 9$

5. $20 \div 0$

6. $-30 \div (-5)$

7. $-48 \div (-6)$

8. $\dfrac{-35}{-5}$

9. $\dfrac{-49}{-1}$

10. $\dfrac{-36}{-6}$

11. $\dfrac{-143}{-13}$

12. $40 \div (-2)$

13. $27 \div (-9)$

14. $52 \div (-4)$

15. $\dfrac{3}{-3}$

16. $\dfrac{14}{-1}$

17. $\dfrac{63}{-9}$

18. $\dfrac{144}{-12}$

19. $-54 \div 18$

20. $-92 \div 4$

21. $-(60 \div 1)$

22. $-(121 \div 11)$

23. $\dfrac{-72}{8}$

24. $\dfrac{-96}{8}$

25. $\dfrac{|-64|}{|-8|}$

26. $\dfrac{|-25|}{|-5|}$

27. $\dfrac{-36}{|-12|}$

28. $-|15| \div 3$

29. $|-8 \div 2|$

30. $|-10 \div -(-10)|$

Use mental math to solve. Then write the quotient.

31. $-8 \div 2 \div 2$

_____ **−2** _____

32. $-1 \div (-1) \div (-1) \div (-1) \div (-1)$

_____

33. $-1000 \div 10 \div 10 \div (-10)$

_____

34. $-3000 \div 30 \div -10 \div -10$

_____

35. $48 \div (-8) \div (-3)$

_____

36. $108 \div (-3) \div (-4)$

_____

37. $-144 \div (-12) \div (-6)$

_____

38. $-360 \div 3 \div (-12)$

_____

39. $-150 \div -2 \div (-3) \div 5$

_____

40. $-9600 \div 100 \div (-2) \div 4 \div (-4)$

_____

Solve. Check to justify your answers.

41. An oil rig is anchored to the sea floor 96 feet below sea level. A drill on the oil rig can cut down through 24 feet of rock each hour. Today, a newly drilled well is 96 feet below the sea floor. What integer represents the number of hours it took to drill that well?

_____

42. An architect is designing a new glass-faced skyscraper that is 1050 feet tall. If she designs every floor to be 15 feet above the previous one, how many floors are in the building? Use an integer in your answer.

_____

43. Six large floral displays each included the same number of carnations. If 540 carnations were used in all, how many were in each display? Use an integer in your answer.

_____

44. Sports If a football player lost a total of 66 yards in 11 plays, how many yards, on average, did he lose on each play? Express this loss as an integer.

_____

MENTAL MATH

45. The expression $a \bullet 10$ has a value of -40. The expression $b \div 10$ also has a value of -40. Which has a greater value, factor a or dividend b? Let a and b represent integers.

_____

_____

_____

1-7 Properties

Name _____ Date _____

Properties can help you compute mentally with integers.

Commutative Property of Addition	**Commutative Property of Multiplication**
$6 + (-3) = (-3) + 6$ $7 + 2 = 2 + 7$	$-4(5) = 5(-4)$
Associative Property of Addition	**Associative Property of Multiplication**
$(-6 + 5) + 3 = -6 + (5 + 3)$	$-7(2 \bullet 4) = (-7 \bullet 2)4$
Identity Property of Addition	**Identity Property of Multiplication**
$0 + 7 = 7$ $7 + 0 = 7$	$1 \bullet (-5) = -5$ $-5 \bullet 1 = -5$
Inverse Property of Addition	**Zero Property of Multiplication**
$3 + (-3) = 0$ $-3 + 3 = 0$	$0 \bullet (-2) = 0$ $-2 \bullet 0 = 0$
Distributive Property of Multiplication over Addition	**Distributive Property of Multiplication over Subtraction**
$2(-4 + 7) = [2 \bullet (-4)] + (2 \bullet 7)$	$3(5 - 9) = (3 \bullet 5) - (3 \bullet 9)$

Name the property used.

1. $0 \bullet -7 = 0$
Zero Property of
Multiplication

2. $(8 \bullet 5) - (8 \bullet 3) = 8(5 - 3)$
Distributive Prop of Multi
div

3. $8 + (-8) = 0$
inverse prop
of add

4. $-3 \bullet 1 = -3$
Identity of
Multi

5. $(1 + 2) + 3 = 1 + (2 + 3)$
Associative Prop of
Addition

6. $3(7 + 9) = 3 \bullet 7 + 3 \bullet 9$
Associative prop
of Multi

7. $6 \bullet -2 = -2 \bullet 6$
commutative prop
of Mult

8. $0 + (-4) = -4$
Identity of
Add

$\cancel{9.}$ $(5 \bullet 1) \bullet (-3) = 5[1 \bullet (-3)]$
Associative prop
of Multi

Name the property and find the value of the missing integer.
Let '?' represent each missing integer.

10. $-7 \bullet ? = -7$
Identity Property of
Multiplication; 1

11. $6(8 - 2) = (6 \bullet ?) - (6 \bullet 2)$
Distributive Prop
of Multi
Sub

12. $? = -2 \bullet 0$
prop of Multi
0

13. $6[4 + (-5)] = 4 + 6 \bullet ?$
Assoc Prop of

14. $(3 \bullet 7) \bullet ? = 3 \bullet [7 \bullet (-8)]$
Associative Multi prop
of Multi prop

15. $9 + 0 = ?$
9
Identity of Add

16. $(5 + 9) + 7 = 5 + (9 + ?)$
Associative prop of
Add of Multi

17. $? + (-13) = 0$
13
inverse prop
of add

18. $0 + ? = 6$
6
Identity prop
of Add

19. $8 + (5 + 4) = (5 + ?) + 8$
4
Commutive prop
of add

20. $(11 \bullet 6)(7 \bullet 12) = (7 \bullet 12)(11 \bullet ?)$
Commutive prop of
Multi

Compute mentally. Then name the property or properties you use.

21. $-33 \cdot 1$
   -33; Identity Property of
      Multiplication

22. $16 \cdot 8 \cdot 0$

23. $-19 + 0$

24. $27 + (-27) + 5$

25. $32 - 12 - 32$

26. $-12 \cdot 1 \cdot (-6 + 6)$

Find the value of the missing integer. Name the property you use.
Let '?' represent each missing integer.

27. $-13 + ? = -13$
   ? = 0
   **Identity Property of
      Addition**

28. $5[3 + (-7)] = 5 \cdot ? + 5 \cdot (-7)$

29. $(? \cdot 8) \cdot (-9) = 4 \cdot [8 \cdot (-9)]$

30. $? \cdot 12 = 12 \cdot 4$

31. $4(-6) + 4(?) = 4(-6 + 9)$

32. $0 = 178 + ?$

Problem Solving

33. Jorge has 5 pens in his left hand and 4 pens in his right. Kendra has 2 pens in her left hand and 7 pens in her right hand. How many pens should Kendra move from one hand to the other to match Jorge? What property does this illustrate?

34. The Office Supply Store is selling 4 packages of 8 markers for $5.00. The Marker Time Store sells 8 packages of 4 markers for $5.00. Which store offers the better deal? Explain.

CHALLENGE

35. How many integers are between the two given integers? (*Hint:* Do not include the given integers in your answer.)

   a. -10 and 0 _____

   b. -20 and 20 _____

   c. -100 and 0 _____

   d. 200 and 300 _____

   e. Describe the method you used to find the answer to parts **a.–d.**

36. If B.C. years are represented by negative numbers and A.D. years by positive numbers, how many years are there from the first date to the second date? (*Hint:* There is no year zero in our calendar system.)

   a. 40 B.C. and 4 B.C. _____

   b. 44 A.D. and 67 A.D. _____

   c. 40 B.C. and 67 A.D. _____

   d. Describe the method you used to find the answers to parts **a.–c.**

1-8 Closure Property

Name _____   Date _____

When an operation is performed using two elements in a set and the result is *always* an element in the set, then the set is *closed* under that operation.

- Only one counterexample is needed to prove that a set is *not* closed under an operation.

- One confirming example does *not* prove that a set is closed under that operation.

Closure Property for Whole Numbers

The set of whole numbers is closed under addition because the sum of any two whole numbers is a whole number.

Example: $3 + 4 = 7$ ◀— whole number

Whole numbers are *not* closed under subtraction.

Counterexample: $6 - 8 = -2$ ◀— *not* a whole number

Closure Property for Integers

The set of integers is closed under addition, subtraction, and multiplication because the sum, difference, or product of two integers is an integer.

Examples: $5 + 7 = 12$ ◀— integer
$6 - 9 = -3$ ◀— integer
$-2 \bullet 4 = -8$ ◀— integer

Integers are *not* closed under division.
Counterexample: $1 \div 2 = 0.5$ ◀— *not* an integer

Mrs. Anderson gave   correct answers   True = closed
False = not closed

Tell whether each set is closed under the given operation. If the set is *not* closed under that operation, provide a counterexample. *to 12*

1. Set: odd whole numbers
Operation: addition

> Odd whole numbers are not
> closed under addition.
> $3 + 5 = 8$; The sum is not odd.

2. Set: even whole numbers
Operation: addition

True
~~False~~

3. Set: integers
Operation: subtraction

True

4. Set: negative integers
Operation: multiplication

~~True~~
~~False~~
False

5. Set: positive integers
Operation: subtraction

False

6. Set: whole numbers
Operation: division

False

7. Set: whole numbers
Operation: multiplication

True

8. Set: whole numbers > 9
Operation: subtraction

False

9. Set: integers
Operation: multiplication

True

10. Set: integers
Operation: division

False
~~True~~

11. Set: integers < −5
Operation: addition

~~False~~
~~True~~
True

12. Set: integers < −5
Operation: subtraction

~~False~~
~~True~~
False

Use with SOURCEBOOK Lesson 1-8, pages 16–17.

Tell whether each set is closed under the given operation. If the set is *not* closed under that operation, provide a counterexample.

13. Set: numbers 0 and 1
   Operation: addition

   not closed
   1 + 1 = 2

14. Set: numbers 0 and 1
   Operation: subtraction

   closed not
   0 - 1 = -1

15. Set: numbers 0 and 1
   Operation: division

   closed

16. Set: numbers −1 and 1
   Operation: division

   closed

17. Set: even integers < 12
   Operation: division

   closed

18. Set: odd integers < 11
   Operation: subtraction

   not closed

True or false? If false, provide a counterexample.

19. The sum of two whole numbers is a whole number.

   True

20. The set {−3, 0, 3} is closed under subtraction.

   True

21. The set {−3, 0, 3} is closed under multiplication.

   False

22. The difference of any two odd whole numbers is an odd whole number.

   false

23. The product of two even whole numbers is an even whole number.

   True

24. The sum of odd prime numbers is an odd prime number.

   False

25. The quotient of two whole numbers is a whole number.

   false

26. The set {1, −1} is closed under multiplication.

   True

27. The set {1, −1} is closed under addition.

   True

Problem Solving

28. A tour group has 112 people. If they hire three charter buses that have exactly 40 passenger seats each to transport the group, will there be any empty seats? Use the closure property to show why or why not.

29. A store sells eggs in cartons of one dozen. Lauren needs 26 eggs to make several batches of cookies. Can Lauren buy the exact number of eggs she needs without having any left over? Explain your answer.

TEST PREPARATION

30. Which set of numbers is closed under subtraction?

   A. numbers 1, 2 and 3
   B. numbers −5, 0
   C. prime numbers
   D. integers

31. Which set of numbers is *not* closed under addition?

   F. odd integers
   G. negative integers
   H. positive integers
   J. even integers

1-9 Powers and Laws of Exponents

Name _____   Date _____

An *exponent* tells how many times a number, called the *base*, is used as a factor.

Numbers that can be written using exponents are called *powers*.

exponential form: $(-8)^3$
factored form: $-8 \cdot (-8) \cdot (-8)$
standard form: -512

$-8 \cdot (-8) \cdot (-8) = (-8)^3$ ←exponent

↑
base

The laws of exponents can help you simplify multiplication and division expressions that include powers with the *same bases*.

Law of Exponents for Multiplication

For $a \neq 0$, $a^m \cdot a^n = a^{m+n}$

$4^2 \cdot 4^6 = 4^{2+6} = 4^8$

Law of Exponents for Division

For $a \neq 0$ and $m > n$, $a^m \div a^n = a^{m-n}$

$6^7 \div 6^4 = 6^{7-4} = 6^3$

Law of Exponents for Zero

For $a \neq 0$, $a^0 = 1$

$18^0 = 1$

Remember:
For $a \neq 0$, $a^1 = a$

Write each in exponential form.

1. $6 \cdot 6 \cdot 6 \cdot 6 \cdot 6$

    6^5

2. $3 \cdot 3 \cdot 3 \cdot 3 \cdot 3 \cdot 3 \cdot 3$

    3^7

3. $7 \cdot 7 \cdot 7 \cdot 5 \cdot 5 \cdot 5 \cdot 5$

    $7^3 \cdot 5^4$

4. $9 \cdot 9 \cdot 9 \cdot 4 \cdot 4$

    $9^3 \cdot 4^2$

5. $-(7 \cdot 7 \cdot 7 \cdot 7)$

    -7^4

6. $-(16 \cdot 16 \cdot 16 \cdot 16 \cdot 16 \cdot 16)$

    -16^6

7. $-5 \cdot (-5) \cdot (-5) \cdot (-4)$

    $-5^3 \cdot (-4^1)$

8. $-9 \cdot (-9) \cdot (-2) \cdot (-2) \cdot (-2)$

    $-9^2 \cdot (-2^3)$

9. $-21(-21)(-21)(-21)(-21)$

    -21^5

Write each in factored form. Then evaluate.

10. 2^0

    1

11. 3^4

    $3 \cdot 3 \cdot 3 \cdot 3 = 81$

12. -7^3

    $-1(-7)(-7) \cdot (-7) = 343$

13. -5^3

    $(-5) \cdot (-5) \cdot (-5) = 12$
    -125

14. $-(4)^3$

    $-1(-4)(-4)(-4) = 64$

15. $(-4)^4$

    $(-4) \cdot (-4) \cdot (-4) \cdot (-4) =$
    $+256$

16. $(-2)^4$

    $(-2) \cdot (-2) \cdot (-2) \cdot (-2) =$
    $+16$

17. $(-6)^3$

    $-6 \cdot (-6) \cdot (-6) = -216$

Add or Subtract. (*Hint:* First write each power in standard form.)

18. $2^3 + 2$

    $8 + 2$
    10

19. $7^2 + 7$

    $49 + 7 = 56$

20. $5^3 - 6^0$

    $125 - 1 = 124$

Multiply or Divide. (*Hint:* First write each power in standard form.)

21. $2^3 \cdot 7^2$

$2 \cdot 2 \cdot 2 \cdot 7 \cdot 7$
392

22. $5^2(-1)^3$

$25(-1) = -25$

23. $-5^2(-2)^3$

$-25 \cdot (-8) = 200$

24. $10^3 \div 5^2$

25. $\frac{27^2}{3^3}$

26. $\frac{-20^2}{-2^3}$

Use the laws of exponents to simplify each expression.

27. $\frac{12^5}{12^3}$

$12^{5-3} = 12^2$

28. $\frac{9^4}{9^0}$

$9^4 - 9^{4-0} = 9^4$

29. $\frac{13^8}{13^2}$

$13^{8-2} = 13^6$

30. $\frac{24^7}{24^3}$

$24^{7-3} = 24^4$

31. $8^0 \div 8^0$

$8^{0-0} = 8^0 = 1$

32. $30^6 \div 30^5$

$30^{6-5} = 30^1$

33. $14^6 \cdot 14^8$

$14^{6+8} = 14^{14}$

34. $38^0 \cdot 38^5$

$38^{0+5} = 38^5$

Write an expression using powers. Then answer the questions using numbers in standard form.

35. A crate contains 5 cartons. Each carton contains 5 boxes. Each box contains 5 canisters. Each canister contains 5 tubes. How many tubes are in the crate?

36. A photo album has 6 sections. Each section contains 6 pages and each page holds 6 photos. How many photos can be placed in the album?

37. Sam invites two friends to his house. Each friend calls two friends and invites them to come along. Then each of those friends invites two friends. How many people (including Sam) are invited in all?

38. Callie's parents said that she cannot have more than 35 guests at her party. Callie invites three friends to her party. Each friend invites three friends, and those friends each invite three friends. Does Callie meet the guest limit? Explain.

WRITE ABOUT IT

39. Lana says there are 4^3 eggs in a dozen. Patrick says there are 3^4 eggs in a dozen. Is either person correct? Explain your reasoning.

1-10 Order of Operations

Name _____ Date _____

To simplify the expression $7 + (4 + 8) \div 2^2$, follow the order of operations.

Grouping symbols: parentheses ( )
brackets [ ]
When an expression contains multiple grouping symbols, begin computing with the innermost set.

Order of Operations
• First compute operations within grouping symbols.
• Next simplify exponents.
• Then multiply or divide from left to right.
• Last add or subtract from left to right.

$7 + (4 + 8) \div 2^2$ ⟵ Compute operations within grouping symbols.

$7 + (12) \div 2^2$ ⟵ Simplify exponents.

$7 + 12 \div 4$ ⟵ Divide.

$7 + 3$ ⟵ Add.

10 ⟵ Simplify.

Remember: You can write division expressions of the form $\frac{a}{b}$ as $a \div b$.

Evaluate each expression.

1. $3 + (3 \bullet 3)$

$3 + 9$
12

2. $6 + (20 \div 4)$

$6+5$
11

3. $(4 \bullet 3) + (16 - 2)$

$12+14$
26

4. $(6 \bullet 8) - (8 \div 2)$

$48 - 4$
44

5. $7(26 - 26 + 3)$

$7(3)$
21

6. $7(4 \bullet 4 - 2)$

$7(16-2)$
98

7. $18 \div (4 + 5)$

2

8. $(6 + 18) \div (-8)$

$24 \div (-8)$
-3

9. $(-2 \bullet 8) \div (-16 \div 2)$

$-6 \div -8$
$8 \quad 2$

10. $(5^2 + 0) \div (5 - 10)$

-5

11. $3 \bullet 3^2 - 0 + (10 \div 2)$

32

12. $11 - (8 \div 4)^3 - 5$

2

13. $(20 + 2 \bullet 8 - 6) \div (-6)$

-5

14. $(8 + 9 \bullet 4 - 4) \div (-4)$

$= 10$

15. $[3^4 \bullet (-6)] + (15 \div 3)$

$-486 + 5$
-481

16. $5 + [2 - (4^2 \div 2)] \bullet 3$

$[2 - (16 \div 2)] \bullet 3$
27
-13

17. $\dfrac{36}{18 \bullet 2 - 4 \bullet 12}$

$36 - 48$
$12 - 3$

18. $\dfrac{(5^2 + 9 \bullet 3)}{2 \bullet 13}$

$\dfrac{52}{26} = 2$

Find the value of each expression.

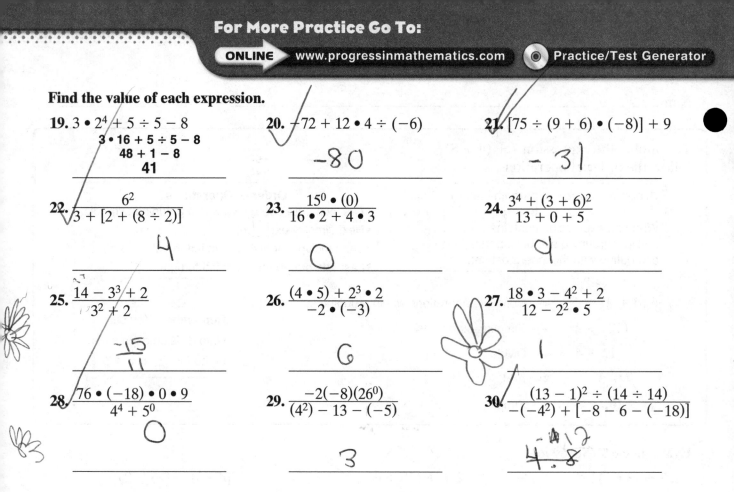

19. $3 \cdot 2^4 + 5 \div 5 - 8$

$3 \cdot 16 + 5 \div 5 - 8$

$48 + 1 - 8$

41

20. $-72 + 12 \cdot 4 \div (-6)$

-80

21. $[75 \div (9 + 6) \cdot (-8)] + 9$

-31

22. $\dfrac{6^2}{3 + [2 + (8 \div 2)]}$

4

23. $\dfrac{15^0 \cdot (0)}{16 \cdot 2 + 4 \cdot 3}$

0

24. $\dfrac{3^4 + (3 + 6)^2}{13 + 0 + 5}$

9

25. $\dfrac{14 - 3^3 + 2}{3^2 + 2}$

$\dfrac{-15}{11}$

26. $\dfrac{(4 \cdot 5) + 2^3 \cdot 2}{-2 \cdot (-3)}$

6

27. $\dfrac{18 \cdot 3 - 4^2 + 2}{12 - 2^2 \cdot 5}$

1

28. $\dfrac{76 \cdot (-18) \cdot 0 \cdot 9}{4^4 + 5^0}$

0

29. $\dfrac{-2(-8)(26^0)}{(4^2) - 13 - (-5)}$

3

30. $\dfrac{(13 - 1)^2 \div (14 \div 14)}{-(-4^2) + [-8 - 6 - (-18)]}$

$\dfrac{4 \cdot 12}{4 \cdot 8}$

Solve. Check to justify your answers.

31. Mr. Tanner took his family to the movies. The tickets cost $5 each for three adults and $3 for four children. How much did Mr. Tanner pay?

32. Health Studies show that a person burns about 11 calories per minute riding a bicycle and about 10 calories per minute swimming. Brian rides a stationary bike for 30 minutes and then swims for 20 minutes. How many calories does he burn?

33. Eighty students and some adults went on a 3-day camping trip. Each adult was responsible for five students. How many people went on the trip?

34. Marianne figured out that her father's age is her age plus five to the power of four, less 365, minus 22, all divided by six. If her father is 42, how old is Marianne?

CHALLENGE

35. Insert grouping symbols in the equations below to make the statements true.

    a. $-32 \div (-3) + (-5) - 2 \cdot (-3) = 10$

    b. $-6 \div (-3) + 2 \cdot 5 \div 5 + (-7) \cdot (-2) = 18$

1-11 The Coordinate Plane

Name _____ Date _____

Together the *x-axis* and *y-axis* are called the *coordinate axes*. They divide the coordinate plane into four quadrants. The intersection point of the axes is called the *origin* (0,0).

The *coordinates*, or *ordered pair*, (*x*, *y*), for a point identify its location on the coordinate plane.

Point *A*(−3, 3), lies in Quadrant II.
Point *B*(0, 2), lies on the *y*-axis.
Point *C*(3, 0), lies on the *x*-axis.

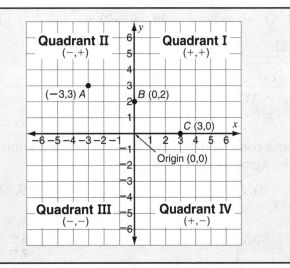

Use the coordinate plane at the right for exercises 1–18.
For exercises 1–12, give the coordinates of each point.
Then name the quadrant or axis on which each point lies.

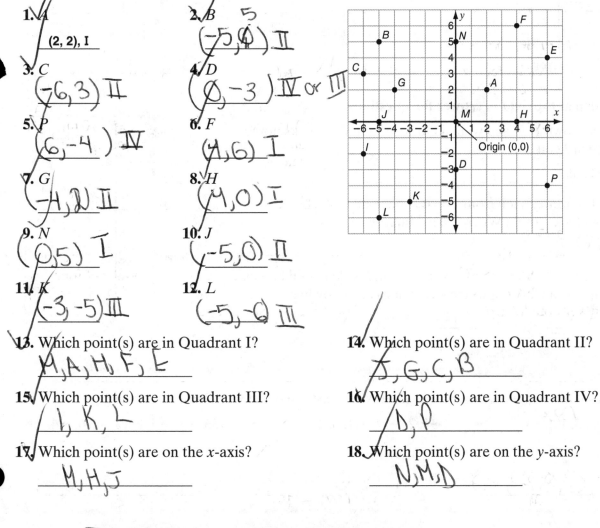

1. A
   (2, 2), I

2. B
   (−5,6) II

3. C
   (−6,3) II

4. D
   (0,−3) IV or III

5. P
   (6,−4) IV

6. F
   (4,6) I

7. G
   (−4,2) II

8. H
   (4,0) I

9. N
   (0,5) I

10. J
    (−5,0) II

11. K
    (−3,−5) III

12. L
    (−5,−6) III

13. Which point(s) are in Quadrant I?
    M, A, H, F, E

14. Which point(s) are in Quadrant II?
    J, G, C, B

15. Which point(s) are in Quadrant III?
    I, K, L

16. Which point(s) are in Quadrant IV?
    D, P

17. Which point(s) are on the *x*-axis?
    M, H, J

18. Which point(s) are on the *y*-axis?
    N, M, D

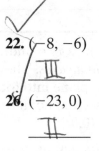
Identify the quadrant or axis that indicates the location of each point.

19. $(-1, 5)$ 20. $(8, -2)$ 21. $(3, -6)$ 22. $(-8, -6)$

   II   IV   IV   III

23. $(0, -15)$ 24. $(-9, -12)$ 25. $(11, 7)$ 26. $(-23, 0)$

   II or III   III   I   II

Graph and connect the points in order on each coordinate plane. Name the figure formed.

27. $A(-5, 3), B(6, 3), C(4, -3),$ 28. $A(0, 0), B(0, 5), C(4, 0)$ 29. $A(2, 2,), B(-2, 2),$
    $D(-3, -3)$ $C(-2, -2), D(2, -2)$

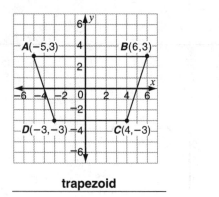

trapezoid

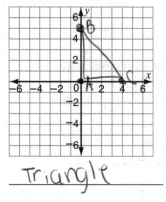

Triangle

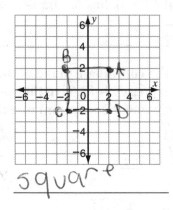

square

Use the map at the right to answer the questions.

30. Start at Town Hall and walk 6 blocks east and 3 blocks north. Where are you?

   At the bank.

31. To get to Marty's job from Town Hall, walk 6 blocks west, then 4 blocks south. Where does Marty work?

   Hospital

32. Jeff lives 5 blocks north of Town Hall and Kyle lives 6 blocks east of Town Hall. On which street does each boy live?

   They lif live in the Northeast
   Jeff lives in Road. Kylie on Streeties
   on Streeties

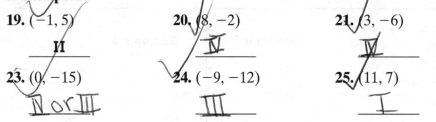

SPIRAL REVIEW

List each set of integers in order from greatest to least. Then list from least to greatest.

33. $6, -12, 3, 12, -3$ 34. $2, -11, -1, 0, 4, -3$ 35. $-9, -1, -12, 3, 16, -4$

   12, 6, 3, -3, -12   4, 2, 0, -1, -3, -11   16, 3, 1, -4, -9, -12

1-12 Problem-Solving Strategy:
Guess and Test

Read > Plan > Solve > Check

Name _____ Date _____

Solve by using the strategy Guess and Test.

1. 62 is half of one less than the cube of a whole number.
   What is the number?

   _____

2. The sum of the squares of two consecutive numbers is 145.
   What are those two numbers?

   _____

3. What is the only odd single-digit number greater than 1 whose
   cube is a perfect square?

   _____

4. Shaine has twice as many nickels as dimes and twice as many
   dimes as quarters. The total value of these coins is $2.60. How many
   of each coin does Shaine have?

   _____

5. Helena has the same number of $1, $5, and $10 bills. The total
   value of these bills is $128. How many of each bill does she have?

   _____

6. Rafiq made a mistake on the homework problem at the right. He incorrectly answered 63 because he reversed the Order of Operations. A stray ink mark now covers one of the numbers in the problem. What is the missing number, and what is the correct answer to the problem?

$$4 + 5 \times \blacklozenge = \underline{\quad 63 \quad}$$

_____

7. Twelve cases are discovered in an abandoned mine in Arizona. Some of them hold $40,000 in silver, and the rest hold $200,000 in gold! The combined value of the cases is $1,280,000. How many cases hold silver, and how many hold gold?

_____

8. Bruno has seven more dollar bills than quarters. His money totals $13.25. How many of each does he have?

_____

9. Susan and Judy shared the driving on a trip. Of the 810 miles they drove, Susan drove twice as far as Judy. How many miles did Susan drive?

_____

10. When a number is subtracted from half of its own square, the result is 60. What is the number?

_____

Enrichment:
Sequence Sums

Name _____ Date _____

Find the sum of the multiples of 5 from 5 to 500:

$5 + 10 + 15 + \ldots + 490 + 495 + 500$

First, add the first and the last numbers in the sequence to find the sum of the pairs. The sum of the pairs is 505.

Second, find the number of pairs with that sum. The multiples of 5 are every fifth number from 0 to 500. There are $500 \div 5 = 100$ numbers in this sequence. Divide that number by two to get the number of pairs. There are 50 pairs in the sequence with the sum 505.

Third, multiply 505 by 50 to obtain 25,250, which is the sum of the numbers in the sequence.

Find the sum.

1. Find the sum of the odd numbers from 1 to 35.

**1 + 35 = 36; 18 odds, so 9 pairs sum to 36.
Sum of sequence is 36 • 9 = 324**

2. Find the sum of the even numbers from 2 to 36.

_____

3. Find the sum of the odd numbers from 35 to 101.

_____

4. Find the sum of the even numbers from 36 to 102.

_____

5. Find the sum of the numbers from 51 to 500.

_____

6. Find the sum of the numbers from 101 to 1000.

_____

7. Find the sum of the multiples of 3 from 36 to 153.

_____

8. Find the sum of the multiples of 4 from 92 to 240.

_____

9. Find the sum of the numbers from 1949 to 2006.

_____

10. Find the sum of the multiples of 5 from 5550 to 15,555.

_____

Problem Solving

11. As part of Joe's workout schedule, he plans to increase the number of sit-ups he does by 5 each day. If he starts with a workout of 30 sit-ups, what is the total number of sit-ups Joe does over a 14-day period?

_____

12. As part of her savings plan, Darcy plans to increase the amount she deposits by ten dollars each week. If she starts with ten dollars the first week of the year, how much will she have deposited over the full year?

_____

Vocabulary Development

Name _____ Date _____

Chapter 1 Vocabulary

absolute value	exponent
additive inverse	Identity Property of Addition
Associative Property of Addition	Identity Property of Multiplication
Associative Property of Multiplication	integers
base	inverse operations
Closure Property	Inverse Property of Addition
Commutative Property of Addition	ordered pair
Commutative Property of Multiplication	origin
counting numbers	powers
Distributive Property of Multiplication over Addition	quadrants
	whole numbers
Distributive Property of Multiplication over Subtraction	zero pair
	Zero Property of Multiplication

From the vocabulary list above, choose the term(s) that best complete each sentence. Write the term(s) in the space(s) provided.

1. In the expression 5^2, the number 5 is the _____ and the

   number 2 is the _____.

2. The _____ of a number n is the distance from 0 to n on the number line.

3. Multiplication and division are _____.

4. A number and its opposite are called _____ because their sum is zero.

5. The _____ states that the product does not change when you change the order of the factors.

6. The product of any two integers is an integer, is an example of the _____.

7. The point at which the x-axis and y-axis meet is the _____.

Choose two terms from the list that you did not use in Questions 1–7. For each term, write a definition in your own words and give an example.

8. _____

   _____

   _____

Test Prep: Multiple-Choice Questions
Strategy: Understand Distractors

Name _____ Date _____

Distractors are incorrect answer choices in multiple-choice questions. These are often the result of common errors.

To solve the problem, try using these strategies:

- Underline important words.
- Restate the question.
- Apply appropriate rules, definitions, or properties.
- Analyze and eliminate answer choices.

Sample Test Item

Which is equivalent to $7 - 2^3$?

A. 125 ← Did not follow the order of operations. Subtracted first. Eliminate this choice.

B. 15 ← Did not follow the order of operations. Did not simplify the exponent correctly. Eliminate this choice.

C. 1 ← Followed the order of operations, but combined the integers incorrectly. Eliminate this choice.

D. −1 ← Followed the order of operations. Simplified the exponent correctly. This is the correct choice.

Choose the correct answer. *TIP: Use the time you have left to review your answers.*

1. What is the value of the expression?

$$-2(3)^2 - 6(1 - 6)$$

A. −48   **C.** −42

B. 12   **D.** 18

2. Which expression is equivalent to $5^3 \bullet 5^4$?

F. 5^7 **H.** 5^{12}

G. 25^7 **J.** 25^{12}

3. Which of the following statements is true?

F. $(6)(6)(6) = 3(6)$

G. $(-4)^3(-4)^2 = (-4)^6$

H. $\dfrac{2^8}{2^4} = 2^2$

J. $\dfrac{(-5)^5}{(-5)^2} = (-5)^3$

4. Which point is the correct graph of the number −6?

A. A   **C.** C

B. B   **D.** D

5. Which of the following expressions results in a negative number?

A. $8 - (-3)$ **C.** $-8 - (-3)$

B. $-3 - (-8)$ **D.** $3 - (-8)$

6. Simplify the expression below.

$$(6 - 24 \div 3) + 3^2 \bullet 2$$

F. 6   **H.** 12

G. 14   **J.** 16

---

7. Simplify.

$$\frac{(-6)^3 \cdot 3}{-6 \cdot 3^2}$$

    A. −12   **C.** 3

    B. 2   **D.** 12

8. At 5:00 A.M., the temperature was −6 degrees Celsius. The temperature steadily increased 2 degrees each hour. What was the temperature at noon?

    F. −8°C   **H.** 8°C

    G. −4°C   **J.** 14°C

9. Which equation shows the Distributive Property of Multiplication over Addition?

    F. $(5 + 2) + 7 = 7 + (5 + 2)$

    G. $5(2 + 7) = 5(2) + 5(7)$

    H. $5 + (2 + 7) = (5 + 2) + 7$

    J. $5 + 2 + 0 = 5 + 2$

10. Which list of values is in order from greatest to least?

    A. $|2|, |4|, |-6|, |-10|$

    B. $|4|, |2|, |-6|, |-10|$

    C. $|-10|, |-6|, |2|, |4|$

    D. $|-10|, |-6|, |4|, |2|$

11. Which property is demonstrated by the equation?

$8(15 - 12) = (15 - 12)8$

    A. The Commutative Property of Multiplication

    B. The Associative Property of Multiplication

    C. The Distributive Property

    D. The Inverse Property of Multiplication

12. Which point has coordinates $(2, -3)$?

    F. *F*   **H.** *H*

    G. *G*   **J.** *J*

13. A diver is 800 ft below sea level. The diver descends 220 ft and then rises 650 ft. Where is the diver in relation to sea level? Let sea level = 0 ft.

    F. −1650 feet   **H.** −370 feet

    G. −1230 feet   **J.** 70 feet

14. Which expression has the least value?

    A. $|-12|$ **C.** $|-20|$

    B. $|7|$ **D.** $|15|$

15. Which expression simplifies to −20?

    A. $-5 + |-15|$ **C.** $5 + |-15|$

    B. $-5 - |-15|$ **D.** $5 - |-15|$

16. Simplify.

$3(4^2 - 9) + 5$

    F. 2   **H.** 20

    G. 26   **J.** 44

Practice Chapter 1 Test

Name _____ Date _____

Write each as an integer.

1. 12 feet above sea level

2. 6 degrees below zero

3. 5 above par

_____

_____

_____

Evaluate each expression. Then write its opposite.

4. $-(2)^3$

5. $-(-4)$

6. $|-37|$

_____

_____

_____

Compare. Write <, =, or >.

7. -9 _?_ -12

8. 2 _?_ -2

9. -1 _?_ $|-1|$

_____

_____

_____

Order from least to greatest.

10. $-9, -12, -3, 4$

11. $-5, 3, 6, -2$

12. $-17, -21, -12, -43$

_____

_____

_____

Compute.

13. $-34 + (-9)$

14. $-78 + 94$

15. $64 + (-67) + (-17)$

_____

_____

_____

16. $-3 \cdot 15$

17. $-28 \div (-7)$

18. $-(-6) \cdot (-18) \cdot (-1)$

_____

_____

_____

Name the property used.

19. $-6 \cdot 8 = 8 \cdot (-6)$

20. $-3 + (-2 + 4) = [-3 + (-2)] + 4$

21. $-5 \cdot 0 = 0$

_____

_____

_____

Tell whether the set is closed under the given operation. If the set is *not* closed under the operation, give a counterexample to show it is not closed.

22. Set: $-2, 0, 2$
   Operation: subtraction

23. Set: numbers 0 and 1
   Operation: multiplication

24. Set: whole numbers
   Operation: addition

_____

_____

_____

25. Set: whole numbers
   Operation: subtraction

26. Set: prime numbers
   Operation: addition

27. Set: prime numbers
   Operation: multiplication

_____

_____

_____

Evaluate each expression.

28. $3 \cdot 3^4 \cdot 3 \cdot 3^2$

29. $-8(6 + 3) \div 12 + (4 \cdot 5)$

30. $\dfrac{4 + (7 \cdot 2) - 5^2}{-(3^0)}$

_____

_____

_____

Identify the quadrant or axis that indicates the location of each coordinate.

31. $(7, 3)$

32. $(9, -5)$

33. $(0, -6)$

_____

_____

_____

34. $(-8, 0)$

35. $(-6, 2)$

36. $(-9, -1)$

_____

_____

_____

Solve. Check to justify your answers.

37. A music store sells CDs for $12 each and DVDs for $18 each. Rachel bought 5 CDs and 2 DVDs. She paid with a $100-dollar bill. How much change did she receive?

_____

38. The high temperature was 28°F on Friday. The high temperature was −2°F on Saturday. What is the difference in these temperatures?

_____

39. From a wind-chill chart Louise found that an air temperature of 20°F feels like 3°F at a wind speed of 10 mph. However, 20°F feels like −10°F at 20 mph. What is the difference in the wind-chill temperatures?

_____

40. The number of students who ride a bus to school has been decreasing at a rate of 16 each year. Assuming that this trend continues, what will be the change in the number of students that ride the bus over the next 5 years?

_____

Tell About It

Explain how you solve each problem. Show all your work.

41. Karl told three friends about the secret place to find fossil seashells. Each of these friends told three friends, and each of these three friends told three more friends. How many people know Karl's secret place to find fossil seashells?

_____

42. Sarah draws a rectangle *MNST* on a coordinate plane. If $M(-3, -5)$, $N(-3, 2)$, and *S* is 5 units right of *N*. What are the coordinates of *S* and *T*?

_____

Cumulative Review: Chapter 1

Name _____ Date _____

Circle the best answer.

1. Evaluate.

$-|-4| + |6| - |-4| + |6|$

    A. -10 **B.** 10
    C. 4   **D.** -4

2. Which group of numbers is arranged in order from greatest to least?

    F. $-5, -7, 2, 1$
    G. $-6, -4, -2, 2$
    H. $3, 0, -4, -3$
    J. $4, 2, 0, -1$

3. Add.

$-57 + (-23)$

    A. -80
    B. -34
    C. 34
    D. 80

4. Subtract.

$-28 - (-49)$

    F. -71
    G. -21
    H. 21
    J. 71

5. Multiply.

$-9 \cdot 5$

    A. -45
    B. -4
    C. 4
    D. 45

6. Divide.

$-84 \div (-7)$

    F. -14
    G. -12
    H. 12
    J. 14

7. Find the value of the missing number.

$5(8 + 4) = 5(8) + 5(?)$

    A. -4 **B.** 4
    C. 12   **D.** 60

8. $7 + (-7) = 0$ is an example of which property?

    F. Identity Property of Addition
    G. Commutative Property of Addition
    H. Associative Property of Addition
    J. Inverse Property of Addition

9. Which set is closed under addition?

    A. prime numbers
    B. even numbers
    C. odd numbers
    D. $0, 1, 2, 3, 4, 5$

10. Write in exponential form.

$-5 \cdot (-5) \cdot (-5) \cdot (-5)$

    F. -5^4
    G. 5^4
    H. $(-5)^4$
    J. 4^{-5}

11. Write in factored form.

2^4

    A. $2 \cdot 4$
    B. $2 + 2 + 2 + 2$
    C. $4 + 4$
    D. $2 \cdot 2 \cdot 2 \cdot 2$

12. Simplify.

$-22 \div (3 + 2 \cdot 4) + (-7)$

    F. -9
    G. -5
    H. -4
    J. 5

13. What is the value of 12^0?

    A. 0   **B.** 1
    C. 12   **D.** undefined

14. Which point lies in Quadrant II?

    F. $(-3, -8)$ **G.** $(-6, 4)$
    H. $(5, -2)$ **J.** $(-2, 0)$

15. Evaluate.

$$\frac{2^3 \cdot (6 + 3)}{-4 \cdot (12 - 3)}$$

    A. -2 **B.** 2
    C. 3   **D.** 8

16. Divide.

$4 \div 0$

    F. 0   **G.** 4
    H. -4 **J.** undefined

17. Simplify.

$6^2 \cdot 6^3$

    A. 6   **B.** 6^5
    C. 6^6 **D.** 36^5

18. Add.

$-17 + (-23)$

    F. (-40) **G.** (-6)
    H. 6   **J.** 40

19. In which quadrant is $(8, -3)$ located on the coordinate plane?

    A. I   **B.** II
    C. III   **D.** IV

20. What number is equivalent to $-(-5)$?

    F. -5 **G.** 5
    H. $2(5)$ **J.** 5^0

21. Simplify.

$$\frac{5^9}{5^4}$$

    A. 5^{36} **B.** 5^{13}
    C. 1^5 **D.** 5^5

22. Which has the least value?

    F. -12 **G.** 0
    H. $|-12|$ **J.** -2

Tell About It

Explain how you solve each problem. Show all your work.

23. Dina had $35 saved at the beginning of July. During July, she spent $15 at the mall, earned $30 baby-sitting, and spent $12 at the movies. How much money did Dina have at the end of the month?

24. The drama club's first production was sold out. Half of the 180 tickets were sold to students and teachers. Half of the remaining tickets were sold to parents. The leftover tickets were sold to the members of the public. How many tickets were sold to the public?

2-1 Mathematical Expressions

Name _____ Date _____

Mathematical expressions can be numerical expressions or algebraic expressions. *Mathematical expressions* do not contain comparison symbols.

Numerical expressions contain numbers.

Word Phrase	Numerical Expression
the sum of 3 and 5	$3 + 5$
the product of 5 and 9	$5 \cdot 9$
the difference between 11 and 4	$11 - 4$
twenty-six divided by 2	$26 \div 2$

Algebraic expressions contain one or more variables and may also have numbers.

A *variable* is a symbol, usually a letter, used to represent a number.

Word Phrase	Algebraic Expression
three more than a number, r	$r + 3$
23 subtracted from a number, q	$q - 23$
a number, n, times -12	$-12 \cdot n$
The quotient of a number, t, and 4	$t \div 4$ or $\dfrac{t}{4}$

Write each as a numerical expression.

1. the sum of 8 and 4

$\underline{\qquad 8 + 4 \qquad}$

2. 53 increased by 39

$\underline{\quad 53 + 39 \quad}$

3. the absolute value of -62

$\underline{\quad |-62| \quad}$

4. 7 cubed times -8

$\underline{\quad 7^3 \cdot (-8) \quad}$

5. half the sum of 11 and -3

$\underline{\quad \dfrac{11 + 3}{2} \quad}$

6. 42 divided by 13

$\underline{\quad \dfrac{42}{13} \quad}$

7. 4 less than the product of 3 and 9

$\underline{\quad (3 \cdot 9) - 4 \quad}$

8. 9 more than the quotient of 12 and 4

$\underline{\quad \dfrac{12}{4} + 9 \quad}$

9. the square of the sum of 8 and 7

$\underline{\quad 8 + 7 \quad}$

Write a word phrase for each expression.

10. $a + 21$

$\underline{\textbf{a number, } \textit{a}\textbf{, increased by 21}}$

11. $d \div 7$

_____

12. $8c - 6$

_____

13. $w[8 + (-5)]$

_____

14. $9(f + 2)$

_____

15. $4j + (-6)$

_____

16. $\dfrac{g + 3}{6}$

_____

17. $\dfrac{18 - s}{4}$

_____

18. $7(5 - v)$

_____

Write each as an algebraic expression. Use *n* as the variable.

19. sixty more than twice a number

$2n + 60$

20. three times a number, plus 2

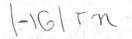
$3n + 2$

21. nine less than half a number

$\frac{n}{2} - 9$

22. a number decreased by the square of 9

$n - 9$

23. a number added to the absolute value of -16

$|-16| + n$

24. the absolute value of negative eight minus twice a number

$|-8 - 2n|$

25. a number times the sum of 9 and 3

$(9 + 3)n$

26. the product of twenty-two minus five and a number.

$22 - 5n$

27. a number times the difference of 4 and 3

$n(4 - 3)$

28. seven multiplied by the sum of a number and three

$7(n + 3)$

29. the quotient when -19 plus a number is divided by 10

$\frac{-19 + n}{10}$

30. the quotient when the sum of two and a number is divided by four

$\frac{2 + n}{4}$

Write an expression that models each situation.

31. Ada has seventeen dollars. If she earns *q* dollars more, how much will she have?

32. Ben is *r* years old. His sister is three times as old as he is. How old is his sister?

33. Sports Over the course of his career in major league baseball, Willie Mays hit 58 more than double the number of home runs Roger Hornsby hit. How many home runs did Mays hit?

34. Lian has *z* pennies. How many dollars does she have?

TEST PREPARATION

35. By car, Chicago is 363 miles closer to Atlanta than Boston. Let *x* equal the distance from Boston to Atlanta. Which mathematical expression shows the distance from Chicago to Atlanta?

A. $363 - x$ **C.** $x - 363$

B. $x + 363$ **D.** $x \div 363$

36. Which value is equivalent to $\frac{5^8}{5^2}$?

F. 4

G. 6

H. 5^4

J. 5^6

2-2 Simplify and Evaluate Algebraic Expressions

Name _____ Date _____

To evaluate $3(x - y)$ when $x = 2$ and $y = 5$, first substitute the values given for the variables. Then follow the order of operations to compute.

$3(x - y)$
$3(2 - 5)$
$3 \cdot (-3)$
-9

Remember: *Constants,* or terms that do not contain a variable, are also like terms.

So the value of the expression $3(x - y)$ is -9 when $x = 2$ and $y = 5$.

Each part of an expression that is separated by a $+$ or $-$ sign is called a *term*. *Like terms* have the same variable parts.

A *coefficient* is the numerical factor of a term containing a variable.

To simplify, combine like terms and use properties.

$6x + 3y + 2(9x - 4y)$
$6x + 3y + 18x - 8y$ ◂— Distributive Property
$6x + 18x + 3y - 8y$ ◂— Commutative Property; Combine like terms.
$24x + (-5y)$ ◂— Simplify.

Evaluate each expression using the values of the variables given in the chart.

s	t	v	a	b	c	n
1	3	-9	20	-5	6	-12

1. $4 + t$

$4 + 3$
7

2. $v + |-14|$

5

3. $t + 7 - n$

-2

4. $|s| + t + v$

$1 + 3 + -9$
-5

5. $a \cdot (b + c)$

-600

6. $n(a - t)$

-84

7. $(a + 4s) \div n$

$20 + 4(1) = -12$
-2

8. $(b - s) \div t$

$-5 - 1 \div 3$
1.8

9. $8^2 + n$

$64 + -12$
52

10. $-v + 5b$

$-9 + 5(-5)$
20

11. $(a \div b + s) \div t$

$\frac{20}{-5} + 1$
1.6

12. $(b^2 - c + 1) \div a$

$-5^2 - 6 + 1$
26

13. $a \cdot s + c \cdot t^3$

$20 \cdot 1 + 6 \cdot 3^3$
102

14. $5(6b - 2n)$

$-150 - 2(-12)$
$= 126$

15. $8s - 4(3s - 2v)$

$1 - 12 - (-18)$
-29

16. $\frac{c \cdot t}{|v|}$

2

17. $-\dfrac{|b| \cdot n}{s + t}$

15

18. $\dfrac{s(n + a)}{t^2 - s}$

1

19. $\dfrac{-t + n + b + a}{v^2}$

$= 3 + -12 - 5 + 20$
0

20. $-\dfrac{t(b + a)}{t(n - v)}$

900
-63

Simplify each expression. Use properties and combine like terms.

21. $6x + 9 + 5x - 7$

$11x + 2$

22. $(9 \cdot 2w) + 6w + 5$

[handwritten:] $18w + 6w + 5$
$24w + 5$

23. $6g^2 + 5h^2 - 3g^2 - 8h^2$

[handwritten:] $-5gh \cdot 3g^2 + -3h^2$
$2g^2$

24. $-13rs - 12s + 6rs$

[handwritten:] $-7rs - 12s$

25. $4c + 5cd - 4(c + d)$

[handwritten:] $0c + 5cd + 4d$

26. $4(f + 2g) - 4g + f$

[handwritten:] $4f + 8g - 4g + f$
$5f + 4g$

27. $7 + 3p - 4(2p) + 6$

[handwritten:] $7 + 3p \quad 8p + 6$
$13 + (-5p)$

28. $5g(9m - 2) + 3g$

[handwritten:] $8g \cdot 9m - 2$

29. $4(w^2z + 2wz) - (w^2z - 5wz)$

[handwritten:] $4w^2z + 8wz$
$5w^2z - 3wz$

Solve. Show your work.

30. Cory earns d dollars for every hour he works after school. On the weekends, his hourly wage is three times the sum of his after school wage and $2.

   a. Write and simplify an expression that represents Cory's weekend wage.

     _____

   b. Write and simplify an expression that represents the total amount of money Cory earns each week if he works 12 hours after school and 8 hours during the weekend.

     _____

31. One adult's ticket to an amusement park costs d dollars. One child's ticket costs $19 less than twice the cost of an adult's ticket. Write and simplify an expression for the cost of one child's ticket. If an adult's ticket is $28, what is the cost of a child's ticket?

_____

CHALLENGE

32. Use patterns to complete the chart.

x	y
6	12
15	21
34	40
	52
67	
x	

33. Use patterns to complete the chart.

x	y
5	10
10	20
21	
37	
	112
	y

2-3 Equations

Name _____ Date _____

Numerical equations contain only numbers and operations. They are *closed sentences;* that means they are *either* true or false.

Word Sentence	Numerical Equation
The sum of 8 and 9 is 17.	$8 + 9 = 17$
−6 is equal to the product of −2 and 3.	$-6 = -2 \cdot 3$

Algebraic equations contain one or more variables. They are *open sentences;* that means they are *neither* true nor false.

Word Sentence	Algebraic Equation
A number, *n*, divided by 3 is 12.	$n \div 3 = 12$
52 is equal to 18 less than a number, *p*.	$52 = p - 18$

To determine whether given values are solutions of an equation, use substitution.
Evaluate: $z^2 - 12 = 88$ for $z = 10$ and $z = 12$.

$10^2 - 12 \stackrel{?}{=} 88$

$100 - 12 \stackrel{?}{=} 88$

$\qquad 88 = 88$ True

So 10 is a solution of the equation.

$12^2 - 12 \stackrel{?}{=} 88$

$144 - 12 \stackrel{?}{=} 88$

$\qquad 132 \neq 88$

So 12 is *not* a solution of the equation.

Write an equation for each sentence. Label each equation *numerical* or *algebraic*.

1. Two less than twice a number is equal to ten.

$\underline{\qquad 2n - 2 = 10 \qquad}$

$\underline{\qquad \textbf{algebraic} \qquad}$

2. Seventeen is one more than twice a number.

_____

3. Four times nine is thirty-six.

_____

4. Eight less than 23 is fifteen.

_____

5. One more than three times seven is twenty-two.

_____

6. One sixth of forty-two is seven.

_____

7. Six less than three times a number is equal to twenty.

_____

8. Two dollars off the regular price of a calculator is $9.

_____

9. A number is equal to 5 times 2.

_____

10. Negative 48 is the product of the opposite of four and twelve.

_____

11. Four is the quotient of −32 and −8.

_____

12. When 15 minus 3 is multiplied by a number, the product is 2.

_____

13. A number times the sum of 5 and 8 is 42.

_____

14. Nine is the quotient when 12 plus 6 is divided by 2.

_____

15. Negative 4 is the product of −2 and the difference between 5 and 3.

_____

16. The sum of two consecutive whole numbers is 25.

_____

17. The sum of two consecutive integers is −3.

_____

18. The difference between 11 and a number is the subtrahend plus 1.

_____

Identify whether the equation is *open* or *closed*. If it is closed, identify if it is *true* or *false*. Then explain why.

19. $d + 9 = 14$

_____
open

20. $33 \div 3 = 9$

21. $63 - 8 = 55$

22. $-\dfrac{8f}{3} = 24$

Determine whether either of the given values is a solution of the equation.

23. $6w = 18$
when $w = 3$, $w = 9$

$$6(3) \overset{?}{=} 18 \qquad 6(9) \overset{?}{=} 18$$
$$18 = 18 \qquad\qquad 54 \neq 18$$
solution: $w = 3$

24. $5n = -125$
when $n = 25$, $n = -25$

25. $18 = f + 9$
when $f = 8$, $f = 18$

26. $-12 = q + (-14)$
when $q = -26$, $q = 2$

27. $-5 + 10 \div p = 0$
when $p = 10$, $p = 2$

28. $10 + 55 \div (-f) = -1$
when $f = 5$, $f = -11$

Solve. Show your work.

29. Evaluate the equation $8x = 480$ when $x = 60$, and when $x = 80$. Explain why each value of x is or is not a solution of the equation.

30. A machine produces x widgets per hour and 540 widgets in 6 hours. Write an equation that represents this information. Decide whether the equation is open or closed. If it is closed, tell why it is true or false.

31. Caleb earns $12 for every lawn he mows. After mowing 6 lawns, Caleb will be paid $75. Write an equation that represents Caleb's statement. Tell whether the equation is open or closed. If it is closed, explain why it is true or false.

32. Karen is k years old. Morgan is 3 years older than Karen. Jasmine is 1 year younger than Karen. The sum of their ages is 35. Write and simplify an equation that you could use to find Karen's age.

SPIRAL REVIEW

Use the order of operations and properties of addition and multiplication to simplify each expression.

33. $6(9 + 7) \div 12(-4 + 2)$

34. $[(9 + 9) + 41] \cdot 10 + 5(4 - 5)$

2-4 Solve Addition Equations

Name _____ Date _____

The Subtraction Property of Equality
When the same number is subtracted from both sides of an equation, the result is a true statement.

> **Remember:** Addition and subtraction are inverse operations. Inverse operations "undo" each other.

Solve: $p + 34 = 79$

$p + 34 - \mathbf{34} = 79 - \mathbf{34}$ ← Subtract 34 from both sides to isolate the variable.

$p = 45$

Check: Use substitution.

$p + 34 = 79$

$45 + 34 \stackrel{?}{=} 79$

$79 = 79$ True

So 45 is the solution of the equation $p + 34 = 79$.

Solve and check.

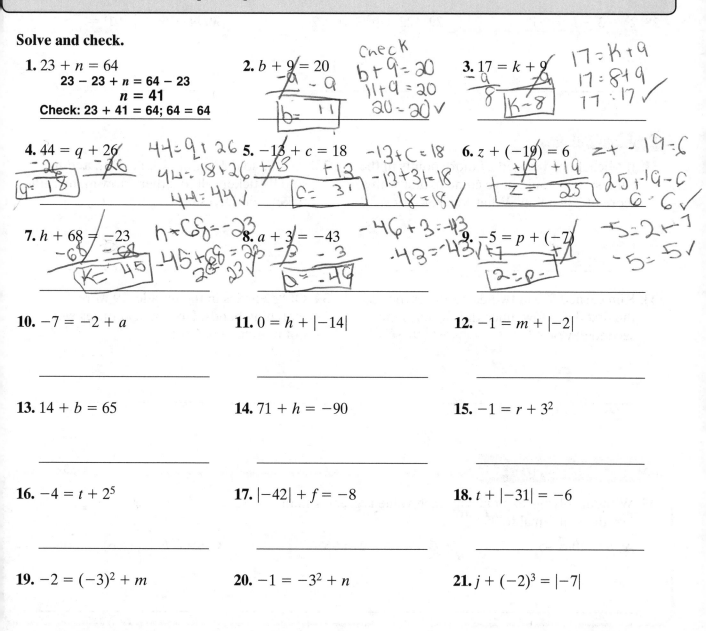

1. $23 + n = 64$
$23 - 23 + n = 64 - 23$
$n = 41$
Check: $23 + 41 = 64$; $64 = 64$

2. $b + 9 = 20$

3. $17 = k + 9$

4. $44 = q + 26$

5. $-13 + c = 18$

6. $z + (-19) = 6$

7. $h + 68 = -23$

8. $a + 3 = -43$

9. $-5 = p + (-7)$

10. $-7 = -2 + a$

11. $0 = h + |-14|$

12. $-1 = m + |-2|$

13. $14 + b = 65$

14. $71 + h = -90$

15. $-1 = r + 3^2$

16. $-4 = t + 2^5$

17. $|-42| + f = -8$

18. $t + |-31| = -6$

19. $-2 = (-3)^2 + m$

20. $-1 = -3^2 + n$

21. $j + (-2)^3 = |-7|$

Solve. (*Hint:* First combine the numerical terms.)

22. $x + 4 + 8 = 10$
$x + 12 = 10$
$x + 12 - 12 = 10 - 12$
$x = -2$

23. $v + 20 + 12 = -51$

24. $83 = 8 + z + 7$

Estimate the solution, then find the exact answer.

25. $n + 42 = 79$
$n + 40 = 80;$ so $n \approx 40$
$n + 42 = 79$
$n + 42 - 42 = 79 - 42$
$n = 37$

26. $-93 = c + (-7)^2$

27. $0 = 6 + 2^3 + g$

28. $2^5 - 3 + h = -1^6$

29. $122 + 6^2 + n = 2$

30. $m - 6^2 + |-91| = -5$

Problem Solving

31. If Michele had scored 27 more points in the contest, she would have come in first with a score of 279 points. What was her score?

32. Arthur sold 43 raffle tickets. Dan and he sold 94 tickets all together. How many raffle tickets did Dan sell?

33. Kim earned $23 in two days. She earned $9 the first day. How much did she earn the second day?

34. Of 85 entries in the parade, 19 were marching bands. How many entries were not marching bands?

MENTAL MATH

35. Without solving, explain why each value is greater than, less than, or equal to 95.

A. $p + 40 = 95$

B. $n + 2 - 2 = 95$

C. $95 = k + (-56)$

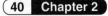

2-5 Solve Subtraction Equations

Name _____ Date _____

The Addition Property of Equality
When the same number is added to both sides
of an equation, the result is a true statement.

> **Remember:** Addition and subtraction
> are inverse operations.

Solve: $t - 28 = 13$

$t - 28 + 28 = 13 + 28$ ← Add 28 to both sides
to isolate the variable.

$t = 41$

Check: Use substitution.

$t - 28 = 13$

$41 - 28 \overset{?}{=} 13$

$13 = 13$ True

So 41 is the solution of the equation $t - 28 = 13$.

Solve and check.

1. $j - 17 = 28$
$j - 17 + 17 = 28 + 17$
$j = 45$
Check: $45 - 17 \overset{?}{=} 28$
$28 = 28$

2. $h - 32 = 38$
$+32 \quad +32$
$h = 70$

3. $154 = m - 31$
$+31 \quad +31$
185
$185 = m$

4. $0 = n - 78$
$+78 \quad +78$
$78 = n$

5. $-14 = z - 6$
$+6 \quad +6$
$-8 = z$

6. $-51 = v - 9$
$+9 \quad +9$
$-42 = v$ ✓

7. $16 = c - (-12)$
$+12 \quad +12$
$28 = c$

8. $r - (-56) = -3$
$+56 \quad +56$
$r = 53$

9. $t - |-32| = 5$
$+32 \quad +32$
37
$t = 37$

10. $-38 = m - 15$
$+15 \quad +15$
-23
$m = -23$

11. $-5 = b - 19$
$+19 \quad +19$
$14 = b$

12. $z - 29 = 76$
$+29 \quad +29$
105
$z = 105$

13. $r - 43 = -68$

14. $48 = g - (-32)$

15. $4 = w - (-5^2)$

Solve and check. (*Hint:* First combine numerical terms.)

16. $9 + 3^2 - 1 + f = -43$
$9 + 9 - 1 + f = -43$
$17 + f = -43; f = -60$
Check: $9 + 3^2 - 1 + (-60) \overset{?}{=} -43$
$-43 = -43$ True

17. $77 = 11 - 2^0 + 2^0 + e$

18. $-1 = 32 - 4^2 + t$

Use number sense to select a reasonable value for *z* from the box at the right. Use substitution to check.

z = 30	z = 18	z = −106
z = 92	z = 24	z = −30

19. $34 = 4 - z$

$34 = 4 - (-30)$
$z = -30$

20. $11 = 35 - z$

21. $7 - z = -11$

22. $0 - z = -30$

23. $z - (-30) = 0$

24. $z - (-81) = 173$

Estimate the solution, then find the answer.

25. $t - 19 = -32$

$t - 20 = -30; t \approx -10$
$t - 19 + 19 = -32 + 19$
$t = -13$

26. $d - 14 = 12$

27. $s - 15 = -127$

Problem Solving

28. Last Saturday, George worked three hours fewer than Sutapa. George worked six hours. How many hours did Sutapa work?

29. Charlene is twenty-five years younger than Nina. Charlene is thirty-nine. How old is Nina?

30. Two groups of tourists fly to Japan. It takes the first group 4 hours less than the second to fly there. If it takes the first group 17 hours, how many hours does it take the second group?

31. Fred's final score on a computer game is 520 points. He scored some points in the first half and lost 205 points in the second half. How many points did Fred score in the first half?

WRITE ABOUT IT

32. How can you show that the solution of an equation is correct?

2-6 Solve Multiplication Equations

Name _____ Date _____

The Division Property of Equality

When both sides of an equation are divided by the same number, the result is a true statement.

> **Remember:** Multiplication and division are inverse operations.

Solve: $12t = -84$

$$\frac{12t}{12} = \frac{-84}{12}$$ ← Divide both sides by 12 to isolate the variable.

$$\frac{\overset{1}{\cancel{12}}t}{\underset{1}{\cancel{12}}} = \frac{\overset{-7}{\cancel{-84}}}{\underset{1}{\cancel{12}}}$$

$$t = -7$$

So -7 is the solution of the equation $12t = -84$.

Check: $12t = -84$

$$12 \bullet (-7) \overset{?}{=} -84$$

$$-84 = -84 \text{ True}$$

Solve and check.

1. $4r = 28$

$$\frac{\overset{1}{\cancel{4}} \bullet r}{\underset{1}{\cancel{4}}} = \frac{\overset{7}{\cancel{28}}}{\underset{1}{\cancel{4}}}; r = 7$$

Check: $4(7) = 28$
$28 = 28$ True

2. $9d = 27$

$\frac{9}{9}$ $\frac{27}{9}$

$d = 3$

3. $h \bullet 9 = -72$

$\frac{}{9}$ $\frac{}{9}$

-8

4. $n \bullet 15 = -150$

-10

5. $-3 \bullet y = 42$

-14

6. $-15 \bullet k = 30$

-2

7. $-8x = 48$

$\frac{}{-8}$ $\frac{}{8}$

-6

8. $-20q = 120$

$\frac{}{-20}$ $\frac{}{-20}$

-6

9. $-55 = 5v$

-11

10. $-90 = 6z$

-15

11. $0 = x \bullet 10$

0

12. $0 = n \bullet 4$

0

13. $-63 = f \bullet 9$

14. $152 = w \bullet (-4)$

15. $168 = r \bullet (-56)$

16. $-56 = c \bullet (-14)$

17. $-e \bullet 8 = 96$

18. $-j \bullet 2 = -62$

Combine like terms to solve, then check.

19. $12b - b = 77$

$11b = 77; \dfrac{11b}{11} = \dfrac{77}{11}$

$b = 7$

20. $-39s - s = -80$

21. $27 = 2v + 7v$

22. $88 = 6k + 5k$

23. $-6 = 7b - b$

24. $20 = 7h - 12h$

25. $76 = -2t - (-21t)$

26. $120 = -6z - (-18z)$

27. $-(2^3)p + (-6p) = -112$

28. $-2z - 0z = -2^1$

29. $4t + 7t - 2t = 72$

30. $9g - 4g - 8g = -15$

Combine like terms to solve. Then check.

31. $24d + 12d = 90 + 90$

$36d = 180; \dfrac{36d}{36} = \dfrac{180}{36}$

$d = 5$

32. $5a + 12a = -37 - 14$

33. $-48 - 8 = 2a - 9a$

Problem Solving

34. Nathan helps out in the family pet shop on Saturdays. He must separate a shipment of 112 fish into nine bowls. Does Nathan have enough bowls if each bowl can fit no more than 12 fish? Explain why.

35. The school librarian must place no more than 28 books on each shelf. She arranged 150 books in all. How many shelves did the librarian use?

CRITICAL THINKING

36. Imam has 6 packs of cards. Mateo has 10 packs of cards. Between the two of them, they have 128 sports cards. How many sports cards does each child have? Explain your answer.

2-7 Solve Division Equations

Name _____ Date _____

The Multiplication Property of Equality
When both sides of an equation are multiplied
by the same number, the result is a true statement.

> **Remember:** Multiplication and division
> are inverse operations.

Solve: $\dfrac{m}{3} = 18$

$\dfrac{m}{3} \bullet 3 = 18 \bullet 3 \longleftarrow$ Multiply both sides by 3
to isolate the variable.

$m = 54$

Check: Use substitution.

$\dfrac{m}{3} = 18$

$\dfrac{54}{3} \overset{?}{=} 18$

$18 = 18$ True

So 54 is the solution of the equation $\dfrac{m}{3} = 18$.

Solve and check.

1. $\dfrac{b}{4} = 8$

$\dfrac{b \bullet \overset{1}{\cancel{4}}}{\underset{1}{\cancel{4}}} = 8 \bullet 4;\ b = \mathbf{32}$

Check: $\dfrac{\mathbf{32}}{\mathbf{4}} = 8;\ 8 = 8$

2. $\dfrac{h}{7} = 8$

56

3. $57 = \dfrac{b}{19}$

1083

4. $0 = \dfrac{i}{8}$

0

5. $\dfrac{d}{4} = -25$

-100

6. $\dfrac{k}{5} = -3$

-15

7. $\dfrac{v}{-4} = 6$

-24

8. $\dfrac{z}{-7} = 23$

-161

9. $\dfrac{y}{-11} = -6$

66

10. $\dfrac{n}{-7} = -5$

11. $-5 = \dfrac{a}{-12}$

12. $-3 = \dfrac{n}{-4}$

12

13. $7 = k \div 18$

126

14. $7 = m \div 21$

15. $|-6| = \dfrac{c}{-25}$

16. $-|-1| = \dfrac{t}{15}$

17. $|3| = f \div 13$

18. $r \div 12 = |12|$

Solve and check.

19. $\dfrac{e}{-9} = 10$

$\dfrac{e}{-9}(-9) = 10(-9)$

$e = -90$

20. $\dfrac{s}{-7} = -7$

21. $0 = \dfrac{x}{100}$

22. $-1 = \dfrac{m}{-63}$

23. $\dfrac{p}{-34} = -|2|$

24. $\dfrac{z}{-5} = -|-8|$

25. $\dfrac{64}{4} = \dfrac{v}{-1}$

26. $\dfrac{2000}{50} = -\dfrac{p}{3}$

27. $\dfrac{36}{-2} = \dfrac{b}{|-3|}$

Problem Solving

28. Carol's car seats one third the number of people that Joan's car can seat. Two people can be seated in Carol's car. How many people can Joan's car seat?

29. Larry shared his baseball cap collection equally among 8 friends. Each friend received 15 caps. How many caps did Larry give away?

30. A school collected x food items and divided them equally among 6 charities. Each charity received 250 items. How many items did the school collect?

31. There are 12 chairs at each table for the annual parents' night dinner. Thirty-two tables are set up. How many people can be seated at these tables?

TEST PREPARATION

32. The adult population of Sparta is 9850. The local satellite TV company believes it can sell a satellite dish to one fifth of this population. Which mathematical sentence describes the number of projected sales?

   A. $9850 \div 5 = n$ **B.** $\dfrac{5}{9850} = n$ **C.** $5 \bullet 9850 = n$ **D.** $\dfrac{9850}{15} = n$

2-8 Solve Two-Step Equations

Name _____   Date _____

To solve a *two-step equation*, use two properties of equality
to isolate the variable.

Solve: $2x + 17 = 29$

$2x + 17 - \mathbf{17} = 29 - \mathbf{17}$ ← Use the Subtraction Property of Equality.

$2x = 12$ ← Simplify.

$\dfrac{\overset{1}{\cancel{2}}x}{\underset{1}{\cancel{2}}} = \dfrac{\overset{6}{\cancel{12}}}{\underset{1}{\cancel{2}}}$ ← Use the Division Property of Equality.

$x = 6$ ← Simplify.

So 6 is the solution of the equation $2x + 17 = 29$.

Check: $2x + 17 = 29$

$2(6) + 17 \overset{?}{=} 29$

$12 + 17 \overset{?}{=} 29$

$29 = 29$ True

Solve and check.

1. $2b - 8 = 80$

$2b - 8 + 8 = 80 + 8$

$2b = 88; \dfrac{2b}{2} = \dfrac{88}{2}; b = 44$

Check: $2(44) - 8 = 80$

$88 - 8 = 80; 80 = 80$

2. $3h - 10 = 35$

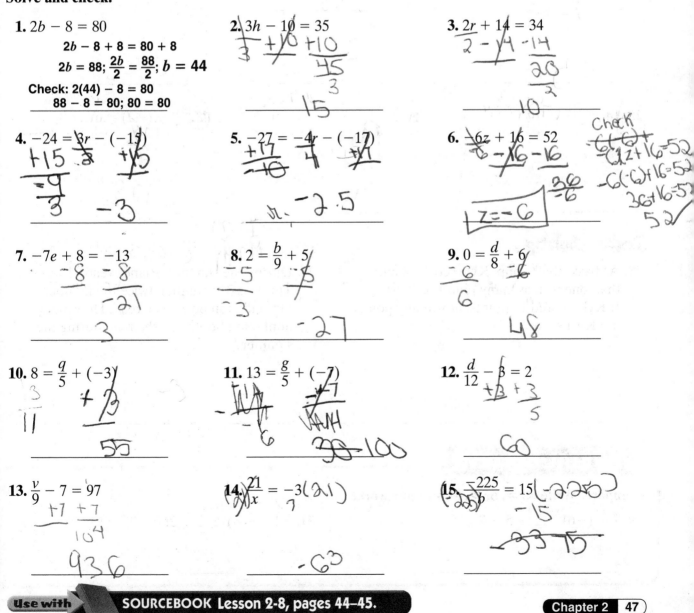

3. $2r + 14 = 34$

4. $-24 = 3r - (-15)$

5. $-27 = -4r - (-17)$

6. $-6z + 16 = 52$

7. $-7e + 8 = -13$

8. $2 = \dfrac{b}{9} + 5$

9. $0 = \dfrac{d}{8} + 6$

10. $8 = \dfrac{q}{5} + (-3)$

11. $13 = \dfrac{g}{5} + (-7)$

12. $\dfrac{d}{12} - 3 = 2$

13. $\dfrac{v}{9} - 7 = 97$

14. $\dfrac{21}{x} = -3$

15. $\dfrac{-225}{b} = 15$

Solve and check.

16. $10 = 6 + \dfrac{a}{2}$

$10 - 6 = 6 - 6 + \dfrac{a}{2}$

$4 = \dfrac{a}{2}; \ 4(2) = \dfrac{a}{2}(2)$

8 = a

17. $15 = 8 + \dfrac{m}{3}$

21

18. $-9 = \dfrac{t}{3} + (-1)$

-24

19. $-4 = \dfrac{w}{2} + 15$

38

20. $\dfrac{k}{7} - (-5) = |-17|$

-84

21. $\dfrac{n}{6} - |-5| = 11$

96

22. $\dfrac{d}{5} - (-1) = 0$

5

23. $-\dfrac{y}{13} - 2 = 1$

-39

24. $6 = \dfrac{42}{x}$

256

25. $14 = \dfrac{70}{-c}$

-5

26. $\dfrac{6}{q} - 1 = 2$

27. $\dfrac{16}{p} - (-2) = 6$

128

Problem Solving

28. At basketball camp, Kyle scored 4 more than one fifth as many points as Kurt. If Kyle scored 12 points, how many points did Kurt score?

29. During the summer, Bianca read 11 novels. This was 3 more than twice the number of nonfiction books she read. How many nonfiction books did she read during the summer?

SPIRAL REVIEW

Compare. Write <, =, or >. Show your work.

30. $7 + (-6) \underline{\hspace{1cm}} -5 + 2$

31. $-1(5 - 6) \underline{\hspace{1cm}} -2(7 - 9)$

2-9 Formulas

Name _____   Date _____

The interior dimensions of a restaurant refrigerator are 8 feet high,
6 feet wide, and 3 feet deep. How many cubic feet of space are
in the refrigerator?

To solve, use the formula for the volume of a
rectangular prism.

$V = \ell wh$

$V = 8 \cdot 6 \cdot 3$ ← Substitute the known values.

$V = 144$ ← Simplify.

There are 144 cubic feet of space inside the refrigerator.

> **Remember:** *Volume* is measured in cubic units (units³).
> *Area* is measured in square units (units²).
> *Perimeter* is measured in units.

Use the volume formula for a rectangular prism, $V = \ell wh$, to solve.

1. Find V when $\ell = 4$, $w = 6$, and $h = 2$.

$V = 4 \cdot 6 \cdot 2$
$V = 48$ units³

2. Find V when $\ell = 50$, $w = 30$, and $h = 15$.

$V = \ell wh$
$V = 50(30)\,15$
$V = 22\,500$ un³

3. Find h when $V = 54$, $\ell = 6$, and $w = 3$.

4. Find h when $V = 512$, $\ell = 8$, and $w = 8$.

5. Find w when $V = 360$, $\ell = 9$, and $h = 5$.

$V = \ell wh$ check
$360 = 9(w)(5)$ $V = \ell wh$
$360 = 45w$ $V = 9(8)5$
$\frac{360}{45} = \frac{45w}{45}$ $V = 360$ un³ ✓
$8 = w$

6. Find w when $V = 48$, $\ell = 2$, and $h = 6$.

7. Find ℓ when $V = 108$, $w = 6$, and $h = 2$.

$V = \ell wh$ check
$108 = \ell(6)2$ $V = \ell wh$
$\frac{108}{12} = \frac{12\ell}{12}$ $V = 6(9)2$
           $\ell = 9$ $V = 108$ un³ ✓

8. Find ℓ when $V = 1000$, $h = 10$, and $w = 10$.

Use the area formula for a rectangle, $A = \ell w$, to solve.

9. Find A when $\ell = 24$ and $w = 3$.

$A = 24 \cdot 3$
$A = 72$ units²

10. Find A when $\ell = 9$ and $w = 11$.

11. Find w when $A = 225$ and $\ell = 25$.

12. Find w when $A = 64$ and $\ell = 8$.

13. Find ℓ when $w = 4$ and $A = 104$.

14. Find ℓ when $w = 13$ and $A = 65$.

Use the perimeter formula for a rectangle, $P = 2(\ell + w)$ or $P = 2\ell + 2w$, to solve.

15. Find P when $\ell = 71$ and $w = 33$.

$P = 2(71) + 2(33)$
$P = 142 + 66$
$P = 208$ units

16. Find P when $\ell = 24$ and $w = 4$.

$P = 2\ell + 2w$ Check
$P = 2(24) + 2(4)$ $24 + 24 + 4 + 4$
                  56 ✓
$P = 48 + 8$
$P = 56$ units

17. Find w when $\ell = 1$ and $P = 6$.

18. Find ℓ when $P = 24$ and $w = 4$.

Use a formula to solve for the missing dimension.

19. Luke's graphing calculator is a rectangular prism with dimensions 2 centimeters by 8 centimeters by 17 centimeters. What is the calculator's volume?

20. A rectangular prism has a length of 20 inches and a width of 12 inches. If its volume is 1440 cubic inches, what is its height?

21. A field has an area of 5000 square yards. If its width is 50 yards, what is its length?

22. The area of a lawn is 37,600 square centimeters. If its length is 188 centimeters, what is its width?

23. The fence around a rectangular rose garden is 18 meters. If the length of the garden is 3 meters, what is its width?

24. A professional basketball court has a perimeter of 288 feet. If its width is 50 feet, what is its length?

CHALLENGE

25. If the perimeter of a rectangle is known, can its area be found? If the perimeter of a square is known, can its area be found? Explain your reasoning.

2-10 Problem Solving Strategy: Organize Data

Read ⟩ Plan ⟩ Solve ⟩ Check

Name _____ Date _____

Solve by using the strategy Organize Data.

1. A team's jersey comes in any of three sizes (small, medium, or large), two different colors (blue or gold), and sleeve length (short or long). How many different types of jerseys are available for purchase?

2. Two islands are connected by a bridge. When traveled by boat, a trip between the islands takes one-twentieth the time it would take to swim the same distance. When traveled by car, the same trip takes two-thirds the time it would take by boat. When traveled by helicopter, the trip takes one-fourth the time it would take by car. A helicopter can fly between the islands in 52 seconds. How long would it take to swim between the islands?

3. While delivering holiday presents, Sylvia drove 8 miles east, 4 miles south, 3 miles east, 6 miles north, 7 miles west, and 5 miles south. How many miles, in each of the compass directions, is she now from her starting point?

4. Luís and Al are competing in a table tennis match. The first person to win either three consecutive games or a total of four games wins the match. In how many different ways can their match be played?

5. Justin, Kyeung, Leonard, and Maia each have a different weekly chore. Their chores are putting out the trash, cleaning the dishes, doing the laundry, and walking the dog. Use the following clues to determine each person's chore:
   Clue 1: Leonard does his chore inside.
   Clue 2: Justin is allergic to detergent and liquid soap.
   Clue 3: Kyeung spends 30 minutes outside during her chore.
   Clue 4: Maia's chores do not involve food or dishes.

6. A sports league has two divisions of eight teams each. Each team plays every other team within its division 12 times, but it plays only 6 games with each team from the other division. In all, how many games are played by a single team for the season?

7. Melissa has four types of marbles, and 120 marbles of each type. She trades two-fifths of the first type, three-eighths of the second type, five-sixths of the third type, and three-quarters of the fourth type. Of the original 480 marbles, how many does Melissa trade?

8. In how many different ways can the three slots _ _ _ be filled if you can use either 1 or 2 in the first slot, A or B in the second, and $ or ¢ in the third?

9. Use a stem-and-leaf plot to order these twenty scores from least to greatest:

63, 84, 47, 32, 68, 71, 39, 41, 63, 70, 88, 76, 55, 57, 47, 81, 65, 72, 82, 59

10. Of the 38 males that attended the Astronomy Club meeting, 6 wore neither a tie nor glasses, 22 wore ties, and 8 of those who wore ties also wore glasses. In all, how many males in attendance wore glasses?

Enrichment:
Be a Math Magician

Name _____ Date _____

The first column gives the steps of a number trick. Follow the steps of the trick for the number 7 and for any number, x.

Step	Number	Variable
1. Pick a number or variable.	7	x
2. Subtract 2.	$7 - 2 = 5$	$x - 2$
3. Multiply by 6.	$6(5) = 30$	$6(x - 2)$
4. Add 15.	$30 + 15 = 45$	$6(x - 2) + 15$
5. Divide by 3.	$\frac{45}{3} = 15$	$\frac{6(x - 2) + 15}{3} = 2(x - 2) + 5$
6. Add 4.	$15 + 4 = 19$	$2(x - 2) + 5 + 4 = 2x + 5$
7. Subtract twice your original number.	$19 - 2(7) = 5$	$2x + 5 - 2x = 5$

The right column shows that the puzzle will always yield the number 5.

For exercises 1–9: In the first two empty columns follow the steps of the trick for two different numbers you choose. In the last column, follow the steps starting with the variable x. Describe the result of the trick.

1.

Step	Number	Number	Variable
a. Pick a number or a variable.			
b. Multiply by 4.			
c. Add 6.			
d. Add 22.			
e. Divide by 4.			
f. Subtract 7.			
Result			

2.

Step	Number	Number	Variable
a. Pick a number or a variable.			
b. Add 2.			
c. Multiply by 15.			
d. Subtract 51.			
e. Divide by 3.			
f. Add 11.			
g. Subtract five times the original number.			
Result			

3.

Step	a. Pick a number or a variable.	b. Subtract 4.	c. Multiply by 6.	d. Add 30.	e. Divide by 2.	f. Subtract 3.	Result
Number							
Number							
Variable							

4.

Step	Number	Number	Variable
a. Pick a number or a variable.			
b. Add next integer.			
c. Add 9.			
d. Divide by 2.			
e. Subtract original number.			
Result			

5.

Step	Number	Number	Variable
a. Pick a number or a variable.			
b. Add 1.			
c. Multiple by 3.			
d. Subtract 15.			
e. Divide by 3.			
f. Add 4.			
Result			

6.

Step	Number	Number	Variable
a. Pick a number or a variable.			
b. Multiply by 5.			
c. Add 8.			
d. Add 22.			
e. Divide by 5.			
f. Subtract 6.			
Result			

7.

Step	Number	Number	Variable
a. Pick a number or a variable.			
b. Add 7.			
c. Multiply by 4.			
d. Subtract 14.			
e. Divide by 2.			
f. Subtract 7.			
Result			

8.

Step	Number	Number	Variable
a. Pick a number or a variable.			
b. Multiply by 5.			
c. Add 3.			
d. Multiply by 5.			
e. Add 15.			
f. Divide by 5.			
g. Subtract 11.			
h. Divide by 5.			
Result			

9.

Step	Number	Number	Variable
a. Pick a number or a variable.			
b. Multiply by 2.			
c. Add 3.			
d. Add 7.			
e. Multiply by 7.			
f. Subtract 56.			
g. Divide by 2.			
h. Subtract 7.			
Result			

Come up with a magic number trick of your own that satisfies the given results. Try it out with two numbers.

10. The answer is the original number.

11. The answer is five greater than the original number.

12. The answer is three less than twice the original number.

Test Prep: Multiple-Choice Questions

Strategy: Try All the Answers

Name _____ Date _____

Sometimes you can *work backward* and try each of the answer choices to solve multiple-choice questions.

To solve the problem, try using these strategies:

- Underline important words.
- Restate the question.
- Use the Test-Prep Strategy.
- Apply appropriate rules, definitions, or properties.
- Analyze and eliminate answer choices.

Sample Test Item

When $w = 4$ and $x = -5$, what value of y makes the equation $wx + 8 = 3y$ true?

A. $y = -5$ ← The left side of the equation equals -12, but $3(-5) \neq -12$. Eliminate this choice.

B. $y = -4$ ← $4(-5) + 8 = -12$ and $3(-4) = -12$. This is the correct choice.

C. $y = 4$ ← The left side of the equation equals -12, but $3(4) \neq -12$. Eliminate this choice.

D. $y = 3$ ← The left side of the equation equals -12, but $3(3) \neq -12$. Eliminate this choice.

Choose the correct answer. *TIP: Avoid spending too much time on any one question.*

1. Which value of n results in a positive number when substituted in the expression below?

$$2n - 6$$

A. $n = -3$ **C.** $n = 0$

B. $n = 2$ **D.** $n = 4$

2. Which statement is true for $s = -3$?

F. $2 - 5s = -11$ **H.** $5s - 2 = -11$

G. $2s - 5 = -11$ **J.** $5 - 2s = -11$

---

3. What are the coordinates of point K?

F. $(-2, -2)$ **H.** $(3, 1)$

G. $(-3, 2)$ **J.** $(1, -3)$

4. The expression below represents the total amount it would cost, including admission, to go on r rides, at an amusement park.

$$4r + 9$$

What is the total cost to go to the park and go on 3 rides?

A. $12   **C.** $13

B. $16   **D.** $21

---

5. What value of x makes the equation true?

$$\frac{x}{8} + 3 = 7$$

A. 4   **C.** 32

B. 64   **D.** 80

6. Which expression has the same value as 3^4?

F. $3 \cdot 4$ **H.** $3 + 3 + 3 + 3$

G. $4 \cdot 4 \cdot 4$ **J.** $3 \cdot 3 \cdot 3 \cdot 3$

Name _____   Date _____

Chapter 2 Vocabulary

addition equation

addition expression

Addition Property of Equality

algebraic equation

algebraic expression

closed sentence

coefficient

constant

division equation

division expression

Division Property of Equality

equation

evaluate

formula

like terms

mathematical expression

multiplication equation

multiplication expression

Multiplication Property of Equality

numerical equation

numerical expression

open sentence

simplest form

solution

subtraction equation

subtraction expression

Subtraction Property of Equality

terms

two-step equation

variable

From the vocabulary list above, choose the term(s) that best complete(s) each sentence. Write the term(s) in the space(s) provided.

1. To solve the equation $x + 5 = 12$, use the _____ Property of Equality.

2. In the expression $3m + 56$, the 3 is a _____ and

the 56 is a _____.

3. To represent an unknown number, use a _____.

4. A(n) _____ becomes a(n) _____ when a variable is given a value.

5. To solve $\frac{c}{-21} = -4$, use the _____ Property of Equality.

6. To solve $26m = -13$, use the _____ Property of Equality.

Tell whether each statement is *true* or *false*. If it is false, change it to make it true.

7. To simplify means to substitute given values for variables and then compute.

_____

8. Terms with no variables are also like terms.

_____

9. An equation shows a specific mathematical relationship between two or more quantities.

_____

Use after   **SOURCEBOOK Lessons 2-1–2-9, pages 30–47.**

Practice Chapter 2 Test

Name _____ Date _____

Evaluate each expression when $a = -9$ and $b = 16$.

1. $36 - b$

2. $\dfrac{a}{3}$

3. $b - a$

4. $2a + b$

_____ _____ _____ _____

Write each word phrase as an algebraic expression or equation.

5. fourteen less than a number

_____

6. Ten times a number is four less than the number.

_____

7. a number divided by nine

_____

8. Twice a number plus ten is 50.

_____

9. six times a number added to four

_____

10. Triple a number minus eight is -12.

_____

Solve and check.

11. $21 + a = 33$

12. $-14 = j + 2$

13. $z - 7 = 12$

_____ _____ _____

14. $-25 = y - 19$

15. $10x = -120$

16. $4 = -4b$

_____ _____ _____

17. $6 = \dfrac{d}{8}$

18. $\dfrac{a}{4} = -36$

19. $m + |-10| = 70$

_____ _____ _____

20. $26 = n - |-4|$

21. $4 + 3m = -2$

22. $-17 = -3 - 2n$

_____ _____ _____

23. $54 = 17n - (-3)$

24. $7x - (-2) = 30$

25. $\dfrac{m}{-2} + (-6) = 13$

_____ _____ _____

26. $34 = 9 - \dfrac{w}{-2}$

27. $-10 = 2d - 2^3$

28. $2n - 3^2 = 53$

_____ _____ _____

Solve and check.

29. $6w - 2w = 44$

30. $-6b - b = 56$

31. $30 = \dfrac{t}{5} - 10$

_____   _____   _____

Write an equation. Then solve and check.

32. Teri lost four pounds over the summer. This is four more than half the weight she wants to lose by December. How much does Teri want to lose?

33. Twelve seventh graders entered the library poster contest. This was three less than five times the number of eighth graders who entered. How many eighth graders entered the contest?

_____   _____

Problem Solving

Solve and check.

34. A rectangle has a perimeter of 70 centimeters and a length of 21 centimeters. What is its width?

35. How many square meters of contact paper are needed to cover a poster measuring 10 meters by 20 meters?

_____   _____

36. Elliott is building a toy box for his nephew that will be 52 inches long, 36 inches wide, and 10 inches deep. How much space will be inside the toy box?

37. Mark needs to build a roof for his dog's house. He found a board with a perimeter of 24 inches. If it has a length of 8 inches, what is the area of the board?

_____   _____

Tell About It

Explain how you solve the problem. Show all your work.

38. Paul and Mike work at the refreshment stand at the county fair. The owner of the stand pays them $\dfrac{1}{6}$ of whatever they sell. In the first hour, Paul sells $42 worth of refreshments. Paul's earnings are half of Mike's. How much does Mike earn in the first hour?

_____

_____

_____

Cumulative Review: Chapters 1–2

Name _____   Date _____

Circle the best answer.

1. Which shows 2^6 expressed in standard form?

    A. 12
    B. 26
    C. 36
    D. 64

2. Which of the following expressions is *not* positive?

    F. $(-2)3(-1)(2)$
    G. $-3(-2)(-3)4$
    H. $5(-2)(-4)10$
    J. $-1(-5)(-2)(-4)$

3. A rectangular water tank has a capacity of 64 cubic meters. The length is two meters, and the height is eight meters. What is the width of the tank?

    A. 2 meters
    B. 4 meters
    C. 8 meters
    D. 16 meters

4. Simplify.

$4 + 35 - 27 \bullet 2^3$

    F. 96   **G.** 177

    H. -27 **J.** -177

5. The sum of two integers is -5. Their product is four. What are the integers?

    A. $-3, 2$ **B.** $-4, -1$

    C. $-5, 0$ **D.** none of these

6. Which is the algebraic equation for "negative twenty is twelve less than a number"?

    F. $-20 = n - 12$
    G. $12 + n = -20$
    H. $n - 20 = 12$
    J. $n - 12 = 20$

7. Which list is in order from least to greatest?

    A. $-11, 10, -7, 5$
    B. $-11, 10, 5, -7$
    C. $-11, -7, 5, 10$
    D. none of these

8. Which pair of values will make the equation $x^2 + 2y + 3 = 13$ true?

    F. $x = 2, y = 5$
    G. $x = 2, y = 3$
    H. $x = 3, y = 2$
    J. $x = 4, y = -4$

9. If you graph a point at $(2, 5)$ and then subtract nine from each coordinate, in what quadrant is the new point?

    A. I
    B. II
    C. III
    D. IV

10. The perimeter of a square is 16 feet. What is its area?

    F. 8 ft^2 **G.** 16 ft^2

    H. 32 ft^2 **J.** 64 ft^2

11. A prism has a volume of 540 cubic yards, a width of six yards, and a height of 10 yards. What is the length of the prism?

    A. 6 yd   **B.** 9 yd

    C. 54 yd   **D.** 90 yd

12. A rug has an area of 48 square feet. If it has a length of eight feet, what is its width?

    F. 8 ft
    G. 7 ft
    H. 6 ft
    J. 5 ft

13. A football field has an approximate area of 5350 square meters. If it has a width of 50 meters, what is the field's approximate length?

    A. 5400 m
    B. 5300 m
    C. 117 m
    D. 107 m

14. Which is the solution of $25 + 2y = 35$?

    F. $y = 5$
    G. $y = 15$
    H. $y = 40$
    J. $y = 80$

15. Find the sum.

$$-4 + 12 - |-3|$$

    A. -19
    B.   5
    C. 11
    D. 19

16. Simplify.

$$-(-8)^2$$

    F. -16 **G.** -64

    H. 16   **J.** 64

17. Which is the solution of $\frac{x}{5} - 6 = -7$?

    A. -5 **B.** -1
    C.   5   **D.** 65

18. The point $(-6, 4)$ lies in which quadrant?

    F. I
    G. II
    H. III
    J. IV

19. Which set is closed under subtraction?

    A. negative numbers
    B. positive numbers
    C. even integers
    D. whole numbers

20. The sum of two consecutive integers is 49. Which equation represents the sum?

    F. $x + (x + 1) = 49$
    G. $x + (x + 2) = 49$
    H. $x(x + 1) = 49$
    J. $x(x + 2) = 49$

21. Which is equivalent to $x \bullet x \bullet x \bullet x \bullet x$?

    A. $5x$ **B.** x^5

    C. $\frac{x}{5}$ **D.** $x + 5$

22. Which is the value of $d^2 - 7c + cd$ when $c = -2$ and $d = 5$?

    F. -14 **G.**   1
    H.   21   **J.** 29

Tell About It

Explain how to solve the following problem. Show all your work.

23. Casey paid $45 for one new tire and one used tire for his bicycle. The new tire costs $17 more than the used tire. How much did the new tire cost?

_____

_____

_____

3-1 Inequalities

Name _____ Date _____

An inequality is a mathematical sentence that uses symbols
to compare two expressions.
Word sentences can be written as inequalities.
A number is at least 12. $\longrightarrow m \geq 12$
Inequalities can be written as word sentences.
$x - 4 < 3 \longrightarrow$ A number minus 4 is less than 3.
Inequalities with variables are *open sentences*;
they are neither true nor false. When a value is substituted for
the variable, the inequality becomes a closed sentence; then the
inequality is true or false for that value.

> **Remember:**
> **Inequality Symbols**
> $<$ *is less than*
> $>$ *is greater than*
> $\neq$ *is not equal to*
> $\leq$ *is less than or equal to*
> $\geq$ *is greater than or equal to*

Represent each situation by an inequality.
(*Hint:* Use any variable to represent *a number*.)

1. 2 is less than a number.

2 < d

2. The temperature is no more than $-15°F$.

$t \leq -15$

3. 5 is not equal to the sum of a number and 2.

$5 \neq n + 2$

4. Three times a number does not exceed 50.

$3n < 50$

5. Triple a value is less than or equal to 20.

$3v \leq 20$

6. A number minus 7 is greater than or equal to 2.

$n - 7 \geq 2$

7. The sum of *n* and 3 is greater than or equal to 6.

$n + 3 \geq 6$

8. One fifth of the band members is more than 18.

$\frac{1}{5} b > 18$

Write each inequality as a word sentence.

9. $6 > m$

6 is greater than *m*.

10. $z \leq 32$

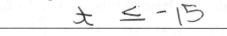
z is greater than or equal to 32.

11. $y \neq 5$

y is not equal to 5.

12. $-12 \neq t$

-12 is not equal t.

13. $x + 3 \geq 4$

x plus 3 is greater than or equal to 4

14. $43 > -2p$

43 is greater then -2 times p

15. $|v| > 9$

the absolute value is greater than 9.

16. $6 > b \div 19$

6 is greater than b divded by 19.

17. $t - 12 \geq -20$

t minus 12 is greater than or equal to -20

18. $16 > c \div 12$

16 is greater than c divided by 12

19. $89 > e \div (-7)$

89 is greater than e divided by

20. $\frac{n}{-9} \leq -4$

n divided by 9 less than or equal -4

Write <, =, or > to make a true sentence.

21. 65 _?_ 60

    >

22. −7 _?_ 7

    <

23. $|-9|$ _?_ 9

    =

24. 11 _?_ $-|-11|$

    >

25. −6 + 5 _?_ −5 + 7

    <

26. 8 + (−11) _?_ 9 + (−7)

    >

27. 2 − 2 _?_ 0 − 1

    ≥

28. 1 − 5 _?_ 0 − (−3)

    ≤

29. −3 • (−3) _?_ 3 • 3

    <

30. 12(−6) _?_ 13(−5)

    <

31. 24 ÷ 6 _?_ 14 ÷ 7

    ≥

32. −6 ÷ (−2) _?_ 6 ÷ (−2)

    ≤

33. $|-6| + 2$ _?_ $|-6 + 2|$

    >

34. $|-4| - |-5|$ _?_ $|-4 + 5|$

    <

35. $|3(-4)|$ _?_ $|3| • |-4|$

    =

Tell whether the inequality is true or false for each given value.

36. $m + 10 \neq 55$, when $m = 15$
    substitute 15 for m
    15 + 10 ≠ 55; 25 ≠ 55; True

37. $p - (-40) < 52$ when p is −18

    false

38. $-3a > 5$, when $a = -2$

    false

39. $d ÷ (-3) \geq -3$ when d is −9

    true

40. $c^2 + 14 < 15$ when c is −5

    false

41. $x - |-9| > 3$ when $x = 0$

    true

Problem Solving

Write and simplify an inequality using ≤ or ≥, then answer each question.

42. Cameron has a summer job selling magazine subscriptions. He earns $4 for each subscription he sells. He hopes to earn at least $100 over the summer. If he sells 26 subscriptions, will he meet his goal?

43. Zoe's father told her she could invite no more than 12 people to her birthday party. She has 6 people she wants to invite for sure. If she invites 7 more, will she be within the limit her father set?

SPIRAL REVIEW

44. Use mental math to evaluate each expression.

    a. 3 (−9)   **b.** −27 ÷ 9   **c.** 27 ÷ (−9)   **d.** −27 ÷ (−9)   **e.** 7 − 8   **f.** −3 + (−5)

3-2 Graph Inequalities on a Number Line

Name _____ Date _____

Find the solution set for the inequality $x \geq 35$,
when the replacement set is the set of whole numbers.

$R = \{0, 1, 2, \ldots\}$ ⟵ The replacement set, R, is the set of whole numbers.
$x \geq 35$ ⟵ given inequality
$S = \{35, 36, 37, 38, 39, \ldots\}$ ⟵ Solution set of all possible values from the replacement set that make the inequality true.

You can graph the solution set on a number line.

The *solution set* for an inequality can be *one, some, all,* or *none* of the values in the replacement set.
Graph the inequality $x > 35$ for the same replacement set on a number line.

34 35 36 37 38 39 40

35 is a solution for the set

34 35 36 37 38 39 40

35 is not a solution for the set

Remember:
- ● the number is in the solution set
- ○ the number is *not* in the solution set
- ∅ empty set, no number makes the inequality true

Find the solution set for each inequality.

Inequality	Replacement Set, R	Solution Set, S
1. $x > 8$	$\{2, 4, 6, 8, 10, 12\}$	**{10, 12}**
2. $a < 16$	$\{14, 15, 16, 17\}$	_____
3. $j \geq 9$	$\{1, 10, 100\}$	_____
4. $c \leq 90$	$\{40, 50, 60, 70, 80, \ldots\}$	_____
5. $d \geq -1$	$\{-3, -2, -1, 0, 1, 2, 3\}$	_____
6. $g < 12$	$\{-4, -2, 0, 2, 4, 6, \ldots\}$	_____
7. $h > 10$	$\{10, 20, 30, 40, \ldots\}$	_____
8. $k < 6$	$\{$positive multiples of 4$\}$	_____
9. $l > 100$	$\{$whole numbers$\}$	_____
10. $f < 60$	$\{60, 61, 62, 63, \ldots\}$	_____
11. $n + 2 > 20$	$\{2, 4, 6, 8, 10\}$	_____
12. $p - 4 \geq 10$	$\{9, 13, 17, 21\}$	_____
13. $5t > -15$	$\{-4, -3, -2, -1, 0, 1, 2\}$	_____
14. $\dfrac{g}{-3} \leq 4$	$\{-24, -18, -12, -6, 0, 6\}$	_____

Find the solution set for each replacement set where $x \leq 4$.

15. $R = \{0, 1, 2, 3, 4, \ldots\}$

$\underline{\quad S = \{0, 1, 2, 3, 4\} \quad}$

16. $R = \{0, 2, 4, 6, 8, \ldots\}$

17. $R = \{1, 3, 5, 7, 9, \ldots\}$

18. $R = \{1, 10, 100, 1000, \ldots\}$

19. $R = \{1, 4, 8, 12, 16, \ldots\}$

20. $R = \{6, 8, 10, 12, 14, \ldots\}$

Write an inequality to describe the graph.

21.

−2 −1 0 1 2 3

$\underline{\quad x \geq -1 \quad}$

22.

−3 −2 −1 0 1 2

23.

0 1 2 3 4 5

24.

−3 −2 −1 0 1 2

25.

−14 −13 −12 −11

26.

5 6 7 8 9 10

Graph each inequality on a number line.

27. $x \geq 5$

28. $x \leq 4$

29. $-15 > x$

30. $-2 > x$

31. $x > -3$

32. $x \geq 100$

Problem Solving

33. Ben and Jim's combined score on a science project is no more than 168. They each scored at least 78. What are the possible combined scores they could have received?

34. The total number of laps needed to complete a bike marathon is 75. Kayla completed at least 68 laps. How many possible complete laps could Kayla have completed?

WRITE ABOUT IT

35. Compare and contrast the graphs of the inequalities $x > 7$ and $x \geq 7$.

3-3 Model Properties of Inequality

Name _____ Date _____

You can use algebra tiles and number lines to model
the following properties that are true for all inequalities.

Addition Property of Inequality
When you add the *same number* to both sides
of an inequality, you get a true statement.
If $a < b$, then $a + c < b + c$.

Subtraction Property of Inequality
When you subtract the *same number* from both
sides of an inequality, you get a true statement.
If $a > b$, then $a - c > b - c$.

Multiplication Property of Inequality
When you multiply both sides of an inequality
by the *same positive number*, you get a true
statement.
If $a \leq b$, and c is positive, then $ac \leq bc$.

When you multiply both sides by the *same
negative number*, you get a true statement
when you *reverse* the inequality symbol.

Division Property of Inequality
When you divide both sides of an inequality
by the *same positive number*, you get a true
statement.
If $a \geq b$, and c is positive, then $\frac{a}{c} \geq \frac{b}{c}$.

When you divide both sides by the *same
negative number*, you get a true statement
when you *reverse* the inequality symbol.

**Draw the result and write the inequality.
Then tell which property is illustrated.**

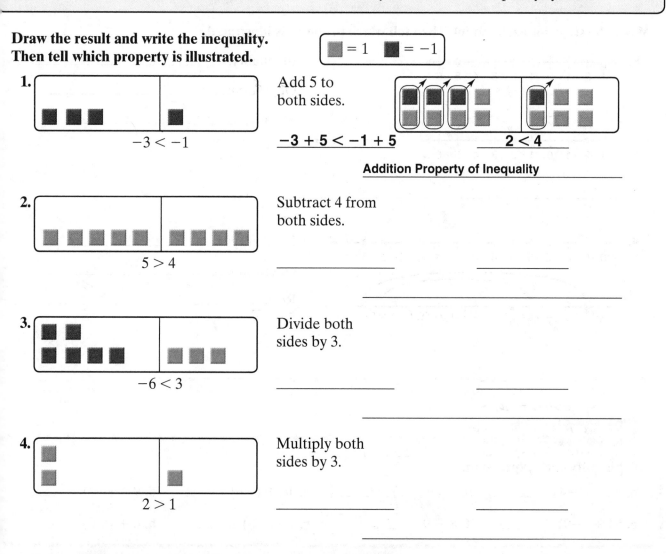

$\blacksquare = 1$ $\blacksquare = -1$

1. $-3 < -1$

Add 5 to both sides.

$-3 + 5 < -1 + 5$ $2 < 4$

Addition Property of Inequality

2. $5 > 4$

Subtract 4 from both sides.

_____   _____

_____

3. $-6 < 3$

Divide both sides by 3.

_____   _____

_____

4. $2 > 1$

Multiply both sides by 3.

_____   _____

_____

Draw the result and write the inequality.
Then tell which property is illustrated.

5.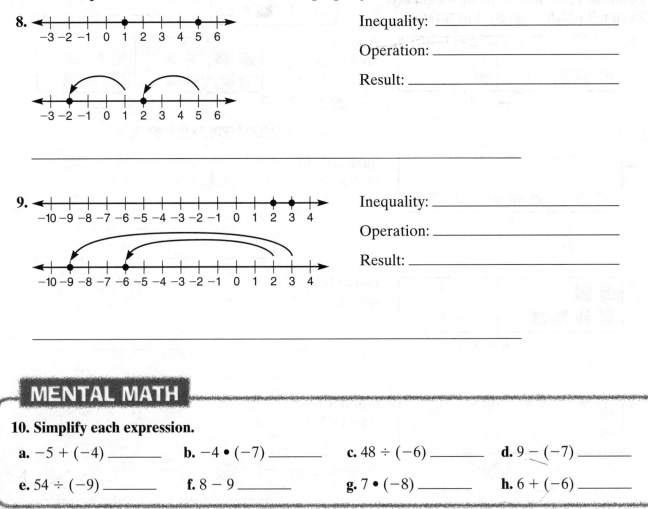

$-3\ -2\ -1\ \ 0\ \ 1\ \ 2\ \ 3\ \ 4$

$0 > -2$

Multiply both
sides by -4.

_____ _____

_____

6.

$-7\ -6\ -5\ -4\ -3\ -2\ -1\ \ 0$

$-5 < -2$

Subtract 2 from
both sides.

_____ _____

_____

7.

$-18\ -12\ -6\ \ \ 0\ \ \ 6\ \ 12\ \ 18$

$-12 < 6$

Divide both
sides by 6.

_____ _____

_____

Write the steps for each model. Then tell which property is illustrated.

8.

$-3\ -2\ -1\ \ 0\ \ 1\ \ 2\ \ 3\ \ 4\ \ 5\ \ 6$

$-3\ -2\ -1\ \ 0\ \ 1\ \ 2\ \ 3\ \ 4\ \ 5\ \ 6$

Inequality: _____

Operation: _____

Result: _____

_____

9.

$-10\ -9\ -8\ -7\ -6\ -5\ -4\ -3\ -2\ -1\ \ 0\ \ 1\ \ 2\ \ 3\ \ 4$

$-10\ -9\ -8\ -7\ -6\ -5\ -4\ -3\ -2\ -1\ \ 0\ \ 1\ \ 2\ \ 3\ \ 4$

Inequality: _____

Operation: _____

Result: _____

_____

MENTAL MATH

10. Simplify each expression.

a. $-5 + (-4)$ _____   **b.** $-4 \bullet (-7)$ _____   **c.** $48 \div (-6)$ _____   **d.** $9 - (-7)$ _____

e. $54 \div (-9)$ _____   **f.** $8 - 9$ _____   **g.** $7 \bullet (-8)$ _____   **h.** $6 + (-6)$ _____

3-4 Solve Inequalities Using Addition and Subtraction

Name _____ Date _____

To solve inequalities involving addition, use the *Subtraction Property of Inequality*.

Solve: $p + 7 \leq 9$

$p + 7 - 7 \leq 9 - 7$ ← Subtract 7 from both sides.

$p \leq 2$ ← Simplify.

The solution set contains {numbers less than or equal to 2}.

Check: According to the solution set, 2 is a solution and 4 is not.

Let $p = 2$.

$2 + 7 \overset{?}{\leq} 9$

$9 \leq 9$ True

Let $p = 4$.

$4 + 7 \overset{?}{\leq} 9$

$11 \leq 9$ False

To solve inequalities involving subtraction, use the *Addition Property of Inequality*.

Graph the solution set for $p \leq 2$.

Remember: The graph of an inequality containing < or ≤ has a ray that points left. The graph of an inequality containing > or ≥ has a ray that points right.

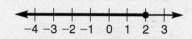

Check: According to the solution set, both 2 and 0 are solutions. So there must be a dot on point 2 and the ray must point left.

So the graph is correct.

Solve the inequality. Check to justify your answer. Then write the solution set, S, using words.

1. $n + 4 \leq 10$

$n + 4 - 4 \leq 10 - 4$

$n \leq 6$

Check: $6 + 4 \leq 10$; $10 \leq 10$

$S = \{$numbers less than or equal to 6$\}$

2. $-9 + b \leq 45$

-9 -9

36

54

check

$-9 + 53 \leq 45$

3. $x - 4 \geq -11$

$+4$ $+4$

$x \geq -7$

check

$-6 - 4 \geq -11$

4. $3 + h \geq 31$

-3 -3

$h \geq 29$

Check

$3 + h \geq 31$

$3 + 29 \geq 31$

5. $-13 > k - 8$

$+8$ $+8$

-5

$-5 > k$ $k < -5$

Check

$-13 > k - 8$

6. $24 > f - 6$

$+6$ $+6$

30

$30 > f$

Check

$24 > f - 6$

$24 > 29 - 6$

$24 > 29 - 6$

Combine terms to solve. Check to justify your answer. Then write the solution set, S, using words.

7. $(8 - 2) + t > 8$

$(6) + t > 8$; $6 - 6 + t > 8 - 6$

$t > 2$

$S = \{$numbers greater than 2$\}$

8. $(6 - 5) + g > 1$

$1 + g > 1$

$g > 1$

9. $5 \geq j + (2 - 4)$

$5 \geq j + -2$

$+2$ $+2$

$3 \geq j$

10. $-4 \geq p + (-2 - 1)$

$-4 \geq p + -3$

$+3$ $+3$

$-7 \geq p$

11. $-22 < t - 3 - 1$

$-22 < t - 2$

$+2$ $+2$

$-20 < t$

12. $-1 < b - 10 + (-2)$

$-1 < b - 8$

$+8$ $+8$

$7 < b$

Solve and graph each inequality. Check to justify your answer.

13. $x + 5 < 12$

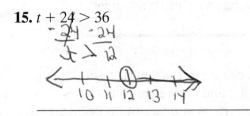

$x + 5 - 5 < 12 - 5; \ x < 7$

Check: 0 is less than 7
So (0) + 5 < 12; 5 < 12 True

14. $20 + x < -5$

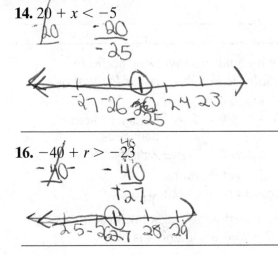

15. $t + 24 > 36$

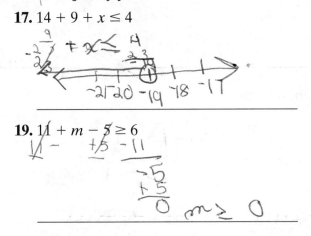

16. $-40 + r > -23$

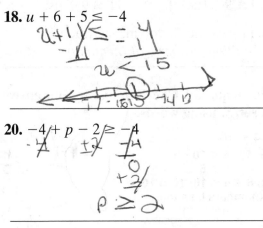

Combine like terms to solve. Then graph the solution set. Check to justify your answer.

17. $14 + 9 + x \le 4$

18. $u + 6 + 5 \le -4$

19. $11 + m - 5 \ge 6$

20. $-4 + p - 2 \ge -4$

Problem Solving

21. A certain aircraft can carry a maximum cargo weight of 1300 pounds. If the baggage weighs no more than 210 pounds, what is the limit of the combined weight of the pilot and passengers?

22. Celia has $20 to spend at the grocery store. She needs milk, bread, and fruit. If milk cost $3 and bread costs at least $2, how much can she spend on fruit?

CRITICAL THINKING

23. Is the inequality $z > z - 2$ true for any value of z? Explain your answer.

3-5 Solve Inequalities Using Multiplication

Name _____ Date _____

To solve inequalities involving division,
use the *Multiplication Property of Inequality*.

Solve: $\frac{t}{-6} \leq 1$

$\left(\frac{t}{-6}\right)(-6) \leq 1(-6)$ ←Multiply both sides by -6.

$t \geq -6$ ←Simplify.

The solution set contains
{numbers greater than or equal to -6}.

Graph and check the solution set.

Check: According to the solution set, both -6 and 0 are solutions.
So there must be a closed circle at -6 and the ray starting
at -6 must point right.

Check: According to the solution set,
0 is a solution and -12 is not.

Let $t = 0$.   Let $t = -12$

$0 \div (-6) \overset{?}{\leq} 1$ $-12 \div (-6) \overset{?}{\leq} 1$

$0 \leq 1$ True $2 \leq 1$ False

Remember:
If $a < b$, and c is *positive*, then $ac < bc$.
If $a < b$, and c is *negative*, then $ac > bc$.
A similar statement can be written
for $a > b$, $a \leq b$, and $a \geq b$.

**Solve each inequality and write the solution set, *S*, using words.
Check to justify your answer.**

1. $7 < \frac{n}{2}$

$7(2) < \frac{n}{2}(2)$; $14 < n$ (or $n > 14$)

Check: $7 < \frac{15}{2}$; $7 < 7.5$ True

$S = $ {numbers greater than 14}

2. $-1 < \frac{n}{6}$

3. $8 \leq \frac{d}{4}$

4. $\frac{x}{-4} \leq 3$

5. $\frac{x}{-7} > 2$

6. $2 > \frac{b}{3}$

7. $\frac{p}{15} \geq 0$

$p \geq 0$

8. $\frac{x}{11} \geq -5$

9. $\frac{m}{-8} \leq -3$

10. $\frac{h}{-11} \leq -2$

11. $5 > \frac{t}{-13}$

12. $11 > \frac{s}{-17}$

**Solve each inequality. Check to justify your answer.
Then graph each solution set.**

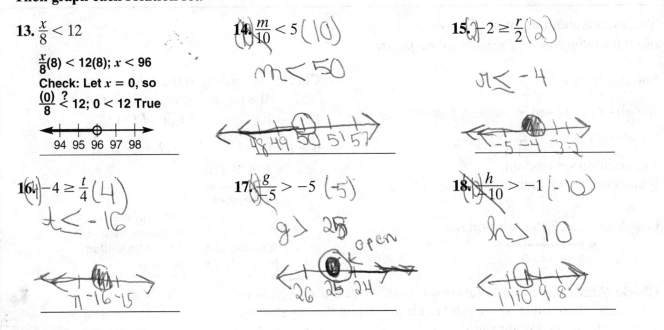

13. $\frac{x}{8} < 12$

$\frac{x}{8}(8) < 12(8)$; $x < 96$

Check: Let $x = 0$, so
$\frac{(0)}{8} \overset{?}{<} 12$; $0 < 12$ **True**

94 95 96 97 98

14. $\frac{m}{10} < 5$ (10)

$m < 50$

48 49 50 51 57

15. $-2 \geq \frac{r}{2}$ (2)

$r \leq -4$

-5 -4 -3 -2

16. $-4 \geq \frac{t}{4}$ (4)

$t \leq -16$

-17 -16 -15

17. $\frac{g}{5} > -5$ (-5)

$g > 25$

open

26 25 24

18. $\frac{h}{10} > -1$ (-10)

$h > 10$

11 10 9 8

Problem Solving

19. Jen and two friends divide the cost of an art project evenly. If each person pays no more than $15, what does the project cost?

20. Twenty-five people split an inheritance equally. If each person receives no more than $500, could the total inheritance be $12,000?

21. Mel divides his baseball cards evenly among 7 cousins. If each cousin gets more than 20 cards, could 119 cards be the total number of cards that Mel gives away?

22. Five students share the writing of a term paper evenly. If each person writes more than six pages, how long is the paper?

CHALLENGE

Express the situation as an inequality. Then solve. You may have to use more than one property of inequality.

23. Ola is less than one fourth of his father's age minus 6 years. If Ola is 2 years old, could his father, Jide, be 34 years old?

3-6 Solve Inequalities Using Division

Name _____ Date _____

To solve inequalities involving multiplication, use the *Division Property of Inequality*.

Solve: $15m > 45$

$$\frac{15m}{15} > \frac{45}{15}$$ ←Divide both sides by 15.

$$m > 3$$ ←Simplify.

The solution set contains {numbers greater than 3}.

Check: According to the solution set, 5 is a solution and 0 is not.

Let $t = 5$.

$$15(5) \overset{?}{>} 45$$
$$75 > 45 \text{ True}$$

Let $t = 0$.

$$15(0) \overset{?}{>} 45$$
$$0 > 45 \text{ False}$$

Graph the solution set.

2 3 4 5

Check: According to the solution set, 5 is a solution, but 3 is not. So there must be an open circle at 3 and the ray starting at 3 must point right.

Remember:
If $a < b$, and c is *positive*, then $\frac{a}{c} < \frac{b}{c}$.

If $a < b$, and c is *negative*, then $\frac{a}{c} > \frac{b}{c}$.

A similar statement can be written for $a > b$, $a \le b$, and $a \ge b$.

Solve each inequality and write the solution set, S, using words. Check to justify your answer.

1. $32 < 8a$

$$\frac{\overset{4}{\cancel{32}}}{\underset{1}{\cancel{8}}} < \frac{\overset{1}{\cancel{8a}}}{\underset{1}{\cancel{8}}}; \ 4 < a \text{ (or } a > 4)$$

Check: $5 > 4$, so $32 < 8(5)$
$32 < 40$ True
$S = \{\text{numbers greater than 4}\}$

2. $0 < 5x$

$$\frac{}{5} \quad \frac{}{5}$$

$$x > 0$$

3. $8p \le -64$

$$\frac{\cancel{8}}{\cancel{8}} \quad \frac{}{8}$$

$$p \le -8$$

4. $6i \le -42$

$$\frac{}{6} \quad \frac{}{6}$$

$$i \le -7$$

5. $-6v > 36$

$$\frac{}{-6} \quad \frac{}{-6}$$

$$v > 6$$

6. $-32f > 64$

$$\frac{}{-32} \quad \frac{}{-32}$$

$$f > -2$$

7. $-56 \le -7d$

8. $-143 \ge -13q$

9. $-(-51) > -17c$

10. $-(-120) > -24b$

11. $-|-16|t \ge -304$

12. $-|-23|v \ge -391$

Solve each inequality. Check to justify your answer. Then tell whether the given value is in the solution set. (*Hint:* First combine like terms.)

13. $-25 \geq 3p + 2p$

$5p \leq -25$

$p \leq -5$

Is −5 a solution? _yes_

14. $-5w - 3w > -80$

$-2w > -80$

w 40

Is 10 a solution? _No_

Solve each inequality. Check to justify your answer. Then graph each solution set.

15. $87 > 29v$

$\frac{87}{29} > \frac{29v}{29}$; $3 > v$ or $v < 3$

Check: $0 < 3$, so $87 > 29(0)$

$87 > 0$ **True**

16. $-8w \leq -24$

$\frac{-8w}{-8} \quad \frac{-24}{-8}$

$w \leq 3$

17. $-35 \geq -3w - 4w$

$-1w$

$w \leq 35$

Problem Solving

18. Tina charges $12 for each lawn she mows. She hopes to earn at least $360 in all. How many lawns must she mow?

19. The temperature of a sample of water is 0°C and changes by −6° each hour. After how many hours will the temperature be less than −54°C?

CRITICAL THINKING

Solve each inequality. Check to justify your answer. Then graph each solution set. Explain your process.

20. $\frac{21}{x} < 3$

21. $\frac{81}{c} \geq 9$

3-7 Problem-Solving Strategy:
Find a Pattern

Name _____   Date _____

Solve by using the strategy Find a Pattern.

1. What digit is in the 31st place after the decimal point in the decimal representation of $\frac{26}{111}$?

   _____

2. Pressing fewer than eight calculator keys, determine the value of
   $2 + 2 + 4 + 8 + 16 + 2^5 + 2^6 + 2^7 + \ldots + 2^{17} + 2^{18}$.

   _____

3. What is the ones digit in the standard form of of 9^{24}?

   _____

4. Each of 20 sheets of paper has an A on one side and a B on the other. These are placed on the floor with sides facing up in an alternating pattern: A, B, A, B, A, B, A, B, etc. Twenty students perform the following in order:

   - The first student flips every single card.
   - The second student flips every card beginning with the second card.
   - The third student flips every card beginning with the third card.
   - The fourth student flips every card beginning with the fourth card.

   This process continues for each of the 20 students. Describe what the cards show at the end of this activity.

   _____

5. For the year 2008, Selwyn resolved to deposit $25 in his savings account on each day of the month that is a multiple of 4. If Selwyn followed through on his resolution, how much money would he have added to his savings for the year?

   _____

6. How many line segments (vertical or horizontal) are used in this design?

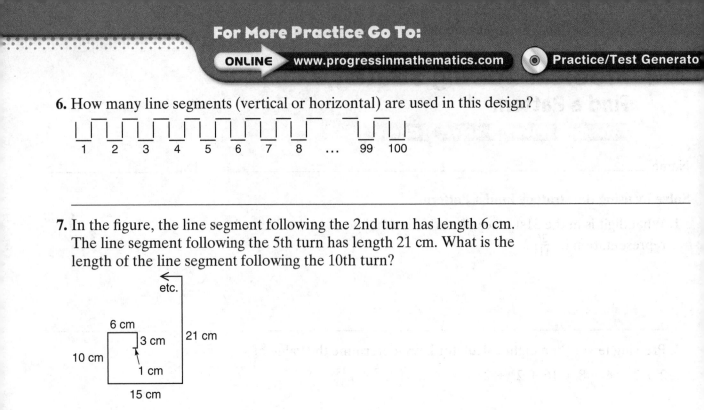

1   2   3   4   5   6   7   8   ...   99   100

7. In the figure, the line segment following the 2nd turn has length 6 cm. The line segment following the 5th turn has length 21 cm. What is the length of the line segment following the 10th turn?

8. If the pattern below continues, how many dots are in the 20th row of the design?

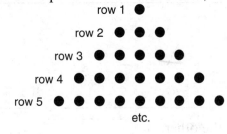

etc.

9. How many dots will be present in the 50th stage?

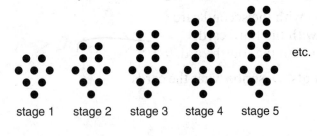

etc.

stage 1   stage 2   stage 3   stage 4   stage 5

10. About half the time a coin is flipped, it lands on heads. To show this, a teacher has 16 of her students bring 4 coins to class. She has each student flip all 4 coins at once. About how many students would you predict will have all 4 coins land on heads?

Enrichment:
Define, Substitute, and Compute

Name _____ Date _____

For all real numbers a and b, $a \$ b = 2(a + b)$.
a. Find $a \$ b$ for at least five pairs of numbers.
b. Is the operation commutative?

a.

a	b	$a \$ b$
0	2	$2(0 + 2) = 4$
1	3	$2(1 + 3) = 8$
2	2	$2(2 + 2) = 8$
−3	6	$2(−3 + 6) = 6$
−25	−33	$2(−25 + (−33)) = −116$
6.4	2.2	$2(6.4 + 2.2) = 17.2$

b. $a \$ b = 2(a + b)$
$2(b + a) = b \$ a$
So the operation $ is commutative.

For Problems 1–3, use the following information.
For all real numbers a and b, $a £ b = 2(a + 3b)$.

1. Find $a £ b$ for at least five pairs of numbers.

2. Is the operation commutative? If so, explain
how you know. If not, give a counterexample.

_____

3. Is the operation associative? If so, explain how
you know. If not, give a counterexample.

_____

a	b	$a £ b$

Problem Solving

4. Consider an operation ¥ that is defined for only
six whole numbers: 0, 1, 2, 3, 4, 5. The result $a ¥ b$
is the remainder when $a + b$ is divided by 6.
Complete the table to the right for the operation.

_____

¥	0	1	2	3	4	5
0						
1						
2						
3						
4						
5						

CHALLENGE

5. Create an operation that is commutative and associative.

_____

_____

Vocabulary Development

Name _____ Date _____

Chapter 3 Vocabulary

Addition Property of Inequality

compound inequality

Division Property of Inequality

empty set

inequality

Multiplication Property of Inequality

open sentence

replacement set

solution set

Subtraction Property of Inequality

From the vocabulary list above, choose the term(s) that best complete each sentence. Write the term(s) in the space(s) provided.

1. The _____ states that when you add the same number to both sides of an inequality, you get a true statement.

2. A _____ is a set of numbers that can be used as possible values for the variable in a particular situation.

3. A mathematical sentence that compares two expressions is called

   an _____.

4. The _____ states that when you divide both sides of an inequality by the same positive number, you get a true statement.

5. The _____ for an inequality contains all the values of the variable that make the inequality true.

6. The solution set is called an _____, if no numbers from the replacement set make the inequality true.

7. The _____ states that when you subtract the same number from both sides of an inequality, you get a true statement.

8. The _____ states that when you multiply both sides of an inequality by the same negative number, you must reverse the inequality to form a true statement.

Choose two terms from the list that you did not use in Questions 1–8. For each term, write a definition in your own words and give an example.

9. _____

   _____

   _____

   _____

   _____

Use after ▶ **SOURCEBOOK Lessons 3-1–3-6, pages 54–65.**

Test Prep: Short Answer Questions
Strategy: Show All Your Work

Name _____ Date _____

When you need to write an equation or inequality to solve a problem, you may find it helpful to *write a verbal model* first.

To solve the problem, try using these strategies:

- Reread the test item.
- Use the Test-Prep Strategy.
- Apply appropriate rules, definitions, or properties.
- Analyze your answers.

Sample Test Item

The temperature today will be greater than 65°F. If the temperature is 60°F, how many more degrees can the temperature be expected to rise? **Show all your work.**

Write a verbal model:

$$\frac{\text{current}}{\text{temperature}} + \frac{\text{temperature}}{\text{increase}} > \frac{\text{temperature}}{\text{forecast}}$$

Write and solve an algebraic inequality.

Let t = temperature increase.

$60 + t > 65$ ← Substitute 60 for the current temperature, and 65 for the temperature forecast.

$60 + t - 60 > 65 - 60$ ← Subtract 60 from both sides.

$t > 5$ ← Simplify.

Answer: The temperature can be expected to rise more than 5°F.

Solve. *TIP: Show your work. Even if your answer is wrong, you might get partial credit.*

1. A river raft holds at most 8 people. The guide and 2 people are already on board. How many more people can board the raft?

Show all your work.

Answer _____

2. Three students clean the park. They share the money earned equally. They earn more than $18 each. How much do all the students earn?

Show all your work.

Answer _____

3. At least 15 students must enroll to hold tennis camp. So far 9 students have enrolled. How many more students must enroll for tennis camp to be held?

Show all your work.

Answer _____

4. A trail is less than 12 miles long. Kyle has already hiked 9 miles. How much farther does Kyle have to hike to complete the trail?

Show all your work.

Answer _____

5. Twelve teammates share the cost of their coach's gift equally. Each person contributes $4 towards the gift. How much in all do the teammates collect for the coach's gift?

Show all your work.

Answer _____

6. Halle is making a keychain from blue and green beads. The number of blue beads is no fewer than 10 less than three times the number of green beads. If she uses 110 blue beads, how many green beads will she use?

Show all your work.

Answer _____

7. An aquarium can hold at most 10 gallons of water. Tory has put 7 gallons of water in the tank. How much more water can she put in the aquarium?

Show all your work.

Answer _____

8. Dale wants to work less than 15 hours this week. If he works the same number of hours on each of 3 days, what is the most he must work each day?

Show all your work.

Answer _____

9. Santiago starts a savings account with $20. Each month he deposits $15 more into the account. Santiago wants to save at least $80. Write an inequality that represents this situation.

Show all your work.

Answer _____

10. Shelby buys four shirts. Each shirt is the same price. She uses a coupon that is worth $8 off her total purchase. She pays less than $52 with the coupon. Write an inequality that represents the cost of one shirt.

Show all your work.

Answer _____

11. Alissa needs to save at least $75 to buy a new snowboard. She has already saved $32. Write an inequality to show how much more Alissa needs to save to buy a new snowboard.

Show all your work.

Answer _____

12. Connor needs more than $70 for a class trip. He has $22. He can earn $8 an hour doing yard work. How many hours must Connor work to have the money he needs?

Show all your work.

Answer _____

Practice Chapter 3 Test

Name _____ Date _____

Use a variable to write each sentence as an inequality.

1. Dimitri has more than 6 pet ferrets.

_____

2. The area of the square is less than 63 cm^2.

_____

3. The temperature is at least $-8°$F.

_____

4. Swavek read at most 120 minutes this week.

_____

5. Four times a number is at least 24.

_____

6. Four hundred is less than one third of a number.

_____

7. Marcus is 62 inches tall. This is at least 4 inches taller than Darnell.

_____

8. Kamel is younger than 34 years old, but older than 17.

_____

Use each replacement set, R, to find the solution set, S, for $h \leq -6$.

9. $R = \{-10, -9, -8, -7, -6, \ldots\}$

_____

10. $R = \{$negative even numbers$\}$

_____

Express the solution set in words for each inequality.

11. $a \leq 6$

_____

12. $10 < g$

_____

Write an inequality to describe each graph.

13.

14.

Solve each inequality. Check to justify your answer. Then tell whether the given value is in the solution set.

15. $-28 \leq m - 14$

_____

Is -10 a solution? _____

16. $45 \geq 15 + j$

_____

Is 30 a solution? _____

17. $3c > 18$

_____

Is 6 a solution? _____

18. $9w < -81$

_____

Is 0 a solution? _____

19. $7 \geq \dfrac{f}{4}$

_____

Is 32 a solution? _____

20. $-4 \leq -\dfrac{h}{8}$

_____

Is 32 a solution? _____

Write an inequality and find the solution set, S, for each. Then answer the question.

21. Kris checked out more than 5 library books. The maximum number of books he could check out was 10. How many books could he have checked out?

22. Ruth planted at most 8 tomato plants. How many could she have planted?

_____

Solve each inequality. Check to justify your answer. Then write the solution set, S, using words.

23. $-7 > c + 6$

24. $7 < z - 8$

25. $44 < -4t$

26. $-104 < -13t$

27. $-\dfrac{a}{25} \le 5$

28. $\dfrac{m}{-7} \ge -1$

Solve each inequality. Check to justify your answer. Then graph the solution set.

29. $10 + c \le 9$

30. $-3d > 9$

31. $-4 \ge \dfrac{p}{-12}$

Problem Solving

32. The addition Maria is building on her house will add 300 square feet to the floor area. After the addition is complete, the floor area of the house will be more than 2,400 square feet. What was the floor area before the addition?

33. Theo watched two movies today. He claims that the second movie ran at least 30 minutes shorter than the first. The second movie ran 82 minutes. How many minutes could the first movie have run?

Tell About It

Explain how you solved the problem. Show all your work.

34. So far this week, Jan has worked out on the treadmill more than 3 times as much as she did last week. She worked out no more than 240 minutes on the treadmill this week. Could Jan have worked out 2 hours last week? (1 hr = 60 minutes)

Cumulative Review: Chapters 1–3

Name _____ Date _____

Circle the best answer.

1. Simplify.

$-46 - (-8)$

    A. -54
    B. -38
    C. 38
    D. 54

2. Simplify. $5 \cdot (3 + 1)^2 + 6 - 2$

    F. 44   **G.** 84
    H. 260   **J.** 404

3. Multiply.

$-12 \cdot 8$

    A. -96
    B. -4
    C. 4
    D. 96

4. The ordered pair $(15, -8)$ lies in which quadrant?

    F. I
    G. II
    H. III
    J. IV

5. Find the sum.

$|-24| + (-9) + |11|$

    A. -66
    B. -22
    C. 4
    D. 26

6. Evaluate.

$-(5)^4$

    F. -625 **G.** -40
    H. 40   **J.** 625

7. The following is an example of which property?
$-6(4 - 2) = (-6 \cdot 4) - (-6 \cdot 2)$

    A. Associate Property of Multiplication
    B. Commutative Property of Addition
    C. Distributive Property of Multiplication over Subtraction
    D. Identity Property of Multiplication

8. Simplify. $4^1 \cdot 4^2 \cdot 4^0$

    F. 0   **G.** 12
    H. 64   **J.** 256

9. Each side of a cube has a length of 9 centimeters. What is the volume of the cube?

    A. 27 cm^3
    B. 81 cm^3
    C. 486 cm^3
    D. 729 cm^3

10. What is the area of a rectangular stage that is 48 feet long and 30 feet wide?

    F. 78 ft^2
    G. 144 ft^2
    H. 1440 ft^2
    J. 3204 ft^2

11. Gary scored 898 points in an electronic game. Which equation can be used to show how many points he needs so that he can tie with his opponent, who has 1025 points?

    A. $898 - p = 1025$
    B. $898 + p = 1025$
    C. $p - 1025 = 898$
    D. $p - 898 = 1025$

12. Jen has half as many siblings as Mark. Jen has three siblings. Which equation can be solved to find the number of siblings Mark has?

    F. $3m = 2$ **G.** $2m = 3$
    H. $\dfrac{m}{3} = 2$ **J.** $\dfrac{m}{2} = 3$

13. Which values for p and q make $p + q = |{-17}|$ true?

    A. $p = 12, q = 5$
    B. $p = 15, q = 8$
    C. $p = 32, q = 32$
    D. $p = -13, q = -4$

14. Which is the solution of $-6 + \dfrac{c}{8} = -12$?

    F. $c = -144$
    G. $c = -96$
    H. $c = -48$
    J. $c = -6$

15. Which is the solution of $b + 5 \geq -13$?

    A. $b \geq -8$
    B. $b \leq -8$
    C. $b \leq -18$
    D. $b \geq -18$

16. A hallway is 72 feet long. The length is less than 12 times the width. Which inequality could be used to find the hallway width?

    F. $w - 12 < 72$
    G. $72 < 12w$
    H. $12w < 72$
    J. $w < 12 \cdot 72$

17. A rectangle's length is 5 centimeters greater than its width. The perimeter of the rectangle is 46 centimeters. Which equation could be used to find the width?

    A. $4w + 5 = 46$
    B. $4w + 10 = 46$
    C. $2w + 5 = 46$
    D. $2w + 10 = 46$

18. Solve $-42 > 14n$.

    F. $n < 3$
    G. $n > -3$
    H. $-3 < n$
    J. $-3 > n$

19. Solve $-6d \geq 30$.

    A. $d \leq -5$
    B. $d \geq -5$
    C. $d \leq 5$
    D. $d \geq 5$

20. Which is a solution of $25 < x - 5$?

    F. $x > 30$
    G. $x < 20$
    H. $x > -30$
    J. $x > -20$

21. Which is a solution of $200 < 15x - 5x$?

    A. $x < 10$
    B. $x > 20$
    C. $x > -10$
    D. $x < -20$

22. Which is the solution of $-75 \geq -15a$?

    F. $a \geq -5$
    G. $a \leq -5$
    H. $a \geq 5$
    J. $a \leq 5$

Tell About It

Explain how you solve the following problem. Show all your work.

23. Dr. Root records measurements of a vine she is studying. Compared to the first measurement, the vine has quadrupled in length. It is now more than 48 centimeters long. Use an inequality to show how long the vine might have been when Dr. Root first measured it.

4-1 Rational Numbers

Name _____ Date _____

A *rational number* is any number that can be written in fraction form $\frac{a}{b}$, where a and b are integers and b is not equal to 0.

0.55 is a *terminating decimal* and 0.166... or $0.1\overline{6}$ is a *repeating decimal*.

Think $\frac{-a}{b} = \frac{a}{-b} = -\frac{a}{b}$

Rational Numbers

natural numbers
whole numbers
integers
terminating decimals
repeating decimals

fractions
mixed numbers

Write in decimal form:

$-59 = -59.0$

$\frac{4}{9} = 4 \div 9 \longrightarrow 9\overline{)4.0000...}$ ($0.4444...$)

$= 0.4444...$ or $0.\overline{4}$

Write one of the following terms that best describes each number: natural number, whole number, integer, terminating decimal, repeating decimal, fraction, or mixed number. If a number is not rational, write *not rational*.

1. -5

_____integer_____

2. 0

_____

3. $\frac{1}{4}$

_____

4. $\frac{16}{1}$

_____

5. $3\frac{1}{2}$

_____

6. $-7\frac{10}{13}$

_____

7. 9.75

_____

8. $0.\overline{92}$

_____

9. 3.14... or π

_____

Write each fractional number in decimal form. Then identify the decimal as terminating or repeating.

10. $\frac{3}{8}$

$3 \div 8 = 0.375$
terminating

11. $\frac{4}{6}$

_____

12. $\frac{1}{-9}$

_____

13. $\frac{125}{8}$

_____

14. $\frac{12}{36}$

_____

15. $\frac{2}{4}$

_____

16. $\frac{21}{99}$

_____

17. $\frac{25}{100}$

_____

18. $\frac{6}{11}$

_____

19. $\frac{1}{-5}$

_____

20. $\frac{5}{8}$

_____

21. $\frac{7}{30}$

_____

22. $\frac{15}{16}$

_____

23. $\frac{9}{33}$

_____

24. $\frac{11}{20}$

_____

25. $\frac{17}{88}$

_____

Plot each point and its opposite on a number line. Label the points.

26. $1\frac{1}{2}$

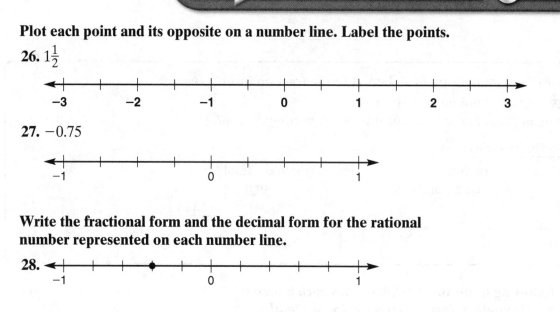

27. -0.75

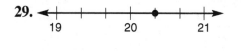

Write the fractional form and the decimal form for the rational number represented on each number line.

28.

29.

Tell whether the statement is true or false. Explain your reasoning.

30. All rational numbers are also integers.

31. Zero is a rational number.

Solve. Check to justify your answer. (*Hint:* To find the average, add the scores and divide the sum by the number of scores.)

32. Sports In softball, a player's batting average is computed by dividing the number of hits by the number of times at bat. So far this season, Charlotte has gotten 18 hits out of 44 times at bat. What is her batting average in decimal form?

33. Shanti's teacher gives a 10-point math quiz every week. On the five quizzes given so far, Shanti's scores were 10, 9, 5, 7, and 10. What is Shanti's average math quiz score?

CRITICAL THINKING

34. Give integer values for *a* and *b*, so that $\frac{a}{b}$ is equivalent to:

   A. an integer

   B. a terminating decimal

   C. a repeating decimal

4-2 Equivalent Rational Numbers

Name _____   Date _____

To *rename a fraction as an equivalent decimal*, divide the numerator by the denominator. Keep the integer part the same.

Write $-6\frac{5}{11}$ in decimal form.

- Divide 5 by 11.

$$11)\overline{5.0000...}^{\,0.4545...}$$

- Use an overbar to show the digits that repeat.

$$-6\frac{5}{11} = -6.\overline{45}$$

To *rename a decimal as an equivalent fraction*, read the decimal. Then write the digits in the decimal part over the place value power of ten.

Write 9.073 in fractional form.

- Read the decimal. 9.073 is read as "nine and seventy-three *thousandths*."

    ↑ numerator   ↑ denominator

- Write the equivalent fraction.

$$9.073 = 9\frac{73}{1000}$$

Write each fraction or mixed number as an equivalent decimal.

1. $\frac{45}{100}$

_____ **0.45** _____

2. $\frac{3}{100}$

_____

3. $2\frac{7}{10}$

_____

4. $8\frac{17}{1000}$

_____

5. $\frac{25}{8}$

_____

6. $\frac{11}{3}$

_____

7. $\frac{3}{8}$

_____

8. $\frac{2}{5}$

_____

9. $-\frac{68}{10,000}$

_____

10. $-\frac{9}{100}$

_____

11. $-\frac{8}{25}$

_____

12. $\frac{-11}{20}$

_____

13. $\frac{-1}{9}$

_____

14. $\frac{-7}{11}$

_____

15. $97\frac{43}{50}$

_____

16. $-8\frac{4}{15}$

_____

17. $-2\frac{17}{18}$

_____

18. $32\frac{14}{16}$

_____

19. $\frac{41}{45}$

_____

20. $15\frac{7}{12}$

_____

Write each decimal as an equivalent fraction or mixed number.

21. 0.61

_____ $\frac{61}{100}$ _____

22. 0.09

_____

23. 0.083

_____

24. −0.302

_____

25. 4.01

_____

26. −0.0104

_____

27. −12.031

_____

28. −4.0300

_____

29. −4.58

_____

30. 5.011

_____

31. 0.28

_____

32. −7.45

_____

Find the equivalent decimal or fraction. Then graph each rational number on the number line. Label each point as a decimal and a fraction.

33. $\frac{4}{5}$ **34.** $-\frac{1}{2}$ **35.** $\frac{11}{5}$ **36.** $1\frac{2}{5}$ **37.** -1.9 **38.** -1.1

$4 \div 5$

_0.8_

_____   _____   _____   _____   _____   _____

Problem Solving

39. The camp cook made 18 quarts of soup to divide equally among 48 campers. If a quart contains 4 cups, is the soup serving per camper more or less than two cups?

_____

40. Health and Fitness To calculate someone's body mass index (BMI) use the expression $\frac{703w}{h^2}$, where w is weight in pounds and h is height in inches. People with a BMI less than 18.5 are considered underweight. Jo is 66 inches tall and weighs 110 pounds. Is she underweight?

41. Jack flipped a coin 50 times. He flipped heads 32 times. Express the portion of the flips that were tails as a fraction, and as a decimal.

_____

42. Mrs. Moon baked 45 carrot cupcakes to divide equally among 12 groups of students. If each group has 3 students, does every student get a whole cupcake?

_____

WRITE ABOUT IT

43. Use long division to rename $\frac{1}{11}$, $\frac{2}{11}$, $\frac{3}{11}$, and $\frac{4}{11}$ as decimals. Describe any patterns that you see. Predict the decimal equivalents of $\frac{6}{11}$ and $\frac{8}{11}$. Check your predictions by dividing.

_____

_____

_____

_____

4-3 Compare and Order Decimals

Name _____ Date _____

To compare decimals -5.136 and -5.1367:
- Write one number under the other and align the place values. Insert zeros, as needed.
- Start with the greatest place and compare digits moving right until the digits are not the same.

$$-5.136\mathbf{0}$$
$$-5.136\mathbf{7} \leftarrow \boxed{-7 < 0}$$

Remember:
Comparison symbols:
$<$ *is less than*
$>$ *is greater than*

So $-5.1367 < -5.136$

To compare rational numbers $\frac{1}{5}$ and $0.\overline{2}$:
- Rename the rational numbers in like form.
- Compare numbers.

$$\frac{1}{5} = 1 \div 5 = 0.2 \text{ and } 0.\overline{2} = 0.22\ldots$$
$$0.2 \underline{\ ?\ } 0.22$$
$$0.2\mathbf{0}$$
$$0.2\mathbf{2}\ldots \leftarrow \boxed{0 < 2}$$

So $0.20 < 0.22\ldots$ or $\frac{1}{5} < 0.\overline{2}$.

Compare these numbers. Write $<$, $=$, or $>$. (*Hint:* Visualize the number line to compare negative numbers.)

1. 0.027 __<__ 0.039 **2.** 0.43 _____ $0.4\overline{4}$ **3.** $4.\overline{4}$ _____ 4.421

4. -5.9 _____ -5.987 **5.** 1.081 _____ 1.0810 **6.** $-0.\overline{5}$ _____ $0.0\overline{5}$

7. 0.984 _____ 0.99 **8.** 5.013 _____ 5.01 **9.** -7.002 _____ -7.0020

Compare these numbers. Write $<$, $=$, or $>$. (*Hint:* Use numbers in like form.)

10. $9.33\ldots$ __=__ $9.\overline{3}$ **11.** $\frac{1}{4}$ _____ 0.250 **12.** $0.09\overline{9}$ _____ $0.111\ldots$

13. $-6\frac{1}{8}$ _____ -6.18 **14.** 0.0750 _____ $\frac{7}{10}$ **15.** 0.23 _____ $-\frac{2}{9}$

16. 0.75 _____ $\frac{3}{4}$ **17.** 8.25 _____ $8\frac{1}{2}$ **18.** 2.3 _____ $\frac{1}{3}$

Order from least to greatest. (*Hint:* Use the decimal point to line up the numbers vertically, then compare the digits from left to right.)

19. 0.6118; 0.61; 0.618; 0.6128

_____0.61; 0.6118; 0.6128; 0.618_____

20. 2.453; 2.345; 2.435; 2.445

_____

21. -0.05; -0.058; -0.625; -0.063

_____

22. -3.33; -3.034; -2.871; -2.08

_____

23. -45.05; -44.05; -40.97; -44.096

_____

24. -0.04; 0.09; 0; -0.9; -0.49

_____

25. 7.11024; 7.10124; 7.01142; 7.1102

_____

26. -60.0163; -66.0361; -66.061; -60.016

_____

Order from greatest to least.

27. 9.678; 9.876; 9.786; 9.089

      9.876; 9.786; 9.678; 9.089

28. 2.4132; 2.413; 2.31; 2.$\overline{43}$; 2.44

29. 0.7; 0.717; 0.0772; 0.72

30. 0.532; 0.542; 0.53; 0.5342

31. −4.081; −4.018; −5.3; −5.043

32. −15.06; −15.045; −13; −13.054

33. −0.0684; −0.631; −0.0067; −0.008

34. −0.025; −0.0528; −0.0248; −0.08

35. −0.608; 0.068; −0.68; 0.6; −6

36. −4; 4.692; −3.999; 3.994; 4.0964

37. 0.8; 0.812; 0.083; 0.85

38. 1.53; 1.053; 1.5; 1.35

Solve. Check to justify your answer.

39. The relative atomic masses of nickel, cobalt, and iron are 58.70, 58.9332, and 55.847, respectively. Which element has the greatest mass? The least mass? (*Hint:* Order the masses.)

40. During a week in February, a weather station recorded these daily low temperatures:

Mon.	Tues.	Wed.	Thurs.	Fri.
−4.75°C	−1.5°C	4.25°C	−4.9°C	−1.75°C

Which temperature is the highest? The lowest? (*Hint:* Order the temperatures.)

CHALLENGE

41. Write three decimal numbers that lie between $\frac{1}{8}$ and 0.123. Explain how you found these numbers.

4-4 Estimate Decimal Sums and Differences

Name _____ Date _____

To use rounding to estimate a sum or difference, find the place to which you are rounding, and look to the digit to the right of that place. If the digit is less than 5, round down. If the digit is greater than or equal to 5, round up. Then add or subtract.

26.57 + (8.453) to the nearest whole

26.5**7** + (8.4**5**3) ◄── 5 ≥ 5, so round up
                          4 < 5, so round down

27 + **8** = 35
So 26.57 + (8.453) ≈ 35

To use clustering to estimate a sum, determine a number that approximates each addend. Then multiply this number by the number of addends.

8.4 + 8.1 + 7.9

3 • 8 = 24 ◄── All *three* addends are about 8.

The estimated sum is 24.

To use front-end estimation to estimate a sum or difference, add or subtract the front digits in the *greatest* nonzero place of the greatest number. For addition only, you can adjust the estimate by using the digits in the place value to the right.

65.845 + 42.13 ──►
                           65.845
                      +42.13
                      100 ◄── Estimated sum

        65.845 ≈ 6
       + 42.13 ≈ 2
                8 ◄── Estimated adjustment

Adjusted Estimate: **100** + **8** = 108.
So 65.845 + 42.13 ≈ 108

Estimate each sum or difference by rounding. (*Hint:* When rounding negative numbers, round the absolute value of the number. Then multiply the negative number by −1.)

1.   54.6 ≈ 50
    + 35.2 ≈ 40
           ≈ 90

2.   36.5
    + 45.8

3.   86.2
   − (−7.7)

4.   36.8
   + 298.4

5.   355.45
   −246.75

6. 475.49 − 49.76

7. −19.54 + (−2857.6)

8. −17.788 + (−909.64)

Estimate each sum or difference. Complete the chart.

	round to tens place	round to ones place	round to tenths place
67.1 + 85 + 12.67 + 1.43 ≈	**9.** _____	**10.** _____	**11.** _____
225.58 − 6.49 ≈	**12.** _____	**13.** _____	**14.** _____
−99.6 + (−76.46) + (−34.25) ≈	**15.** _____	**16.** _____	**17.** _____
−340.845 − 57.5 ≈	**18.** _____	**19.** _____	**20.** _____

Estimate each sum or difference by using front-end estimation.

21. 9.7 + 12.82

$0 + 10 = 10$
$9.7 + 2.82 \approx 13$
adjusted: $10 + 13 = 23$

22. 45.23 + 6.341

23. −8 + (−17.99)

24. −55.2 + (−9.36)

25. 16.975 − 4.408

26. 78.98 − 38.12

Estimate each sum by clustering.

27. 8.4 + 7.75 + 7.99

$3 \cdot 8 = 24$

28. 7.5 + 6.9 + 7.125

29. −38.1 + (−41.67) + (−40.09) + (−39.5)

30. −74.6 + (−76.22) + (−75.24) + (−73.75)

Estimate each result using mental math.

31. 4.8 + (−2.4) + 7.01 + (−4.8)

$5 + (−2) + 7 + (−5) \approx 5$

32. −8.299 + 45.46 + 7.89 + 24.912

33. 8.1 + 12.03 + (−3.57) + (−1.9)

34. 21.73 + 13.02 + (−11.61) + 10.604

Problem Solving

35. A Girl Scout troop earned the following amounts from its cookie sale: $65.83, $67.99, $68.50, $67.02, $63.90, and $72.16. About how much more does the troop need to sell to reach its goal of $500?

36. About how much change should Mr. Wilcox expect from a $50 bill if he purchased painting supplies for $29.75, $6.25, $10.99, and $1.09?

WRITE ABOUT IT

37. Show and explain how to use rounding and additive inverses to estimate the value of the following expression:
−0.1525 + 0.2075 + (−0.04375) − 0.21 − (−0.148) − 0.0635.

4-5 Add and Subtract Decimals

Name _____ Date _____

To add or subtract decimals with *unlike signs*, line up the decimal points and subtract the absolute values of the addends.

Add: $2.2 + (-5.8)$

```
  5.8   ← |-5.8| = 5.8
- 2.2   ← |2.2| = 2.2
-----
 -3.6   ← |-5.8| > |2.2|, so the sum is negative
```

Check: Compare with an estimate: $2 + (-6) = -4$
-3.6 is close to -4. The sum is reasonable.

To add or subtract decimals with *like signs*, line up the decimal points and add or subtract the same way as with integers.

Subtract: $-3.08 - 6.81$

Think
Subtract by *adding the opposite.*

$-3.08 - 6.81 = -3.08 + (-6.81)$

```
  -3.08   ← |-3.08| = 3.08
+ -6.81   ← |-6.81| = 6.81
-------
  -9.89   ← Use the sign of the addends.
```

Add.

1. $20.95 + 13.87$

34.82

2. $14.57 + 39.26$

3. $0.89 + 1.970$

4. $15.01 + 3.592$

5. $-12.38 + (-1.74)$

6. $-17.23 + (-2.58)$

7. $-4.7 + (-2.68)$

8. $-52.43 + (-34)$

9. $8.01 + (-3.46)$

10. $-7.119 + 4.02$

11. $19.61 + (-26.52)$

12. $-119.14 + 89.480$

Subtract.

13. $6.1 - 3.5$

$6.1 + (-3.5)$
2.6

14. $7.000 - 0.359$

15. $2.4 - 1.06$

16. $3.407 - 2.0098$

17. $28.14 - (-19.31)$

18. $15.72 - (-13.18)$

19. $-3.24 - (-9)$

20. $-16.35 - (-17.9)$

21. $-4.8 - 2.6$

22. $-36.17 - 23.46$

23. $-14.3 - 16.41$

24. $-101.3 - 37.83$

25. $-9.3 - (-4.5)$

26. $-38.2 - (-13.9)$

27. $-20.1 - (-5.121)$

28. $-271.36 - (-131.74)$

Simplify $a + b + c$ for the given values.

29. $a = -2.5, b = 3.3, c = -5.8$

$$(-2.5) + 3.3 + (-5.8)$$
$$-8.3 + 3.3 = -5$$

30. $a = 90.1, b = 88.3, c = -212.4$

31. $a = -16.6, b = -12.2, c = 98.5$

32. $a = 88.44, b = 39.73, c = -23.03$

33. $a = 25.6, b = -7.9, c = 43.2$

34. $a = -14.7, b = -11.3, c = 15.1$

35. $a = 43.5, b = -23.8, c = 7.9$

36. $a = 83.1, b = -73.4, c = -64.6$

Problem Solving

37. Anne put her dog Simon on a diet for three weeks. Simon lost 3 pounds the first week, gained 1.75 pounds the second week, and lost 2.5 pounds the third week. What was his net weight gain or loss?

38. A submarine dove 132.58 meters to reach a resting depth of 700 meters below sea level. What was its original depth?

39. After buying school supplies, Hazel has $1.79 in change. She bought a notebook for $3.49 and a box of pens for $2.98. How much money did she originally have?

40. The highest point of elevation in the United States is Mount McKinley at about 6193.54 meters above sea level. The lowest point is Death Valley at about 85.95 meters below sea level. What is the elevation difference between the highest point and the lowest point?

SPIRAL REVIEW

Solve each equation.

41. $c - 12 = -3$

$$c - 12 + 12 = -3 + 12$$
$$c = 9$$

42. $-7x = 28$

43. $\frac{n}{4} + 5 = 2$

44. $-5 + 8z = 27$

4-6 Multiply Decimals

Name _____ Date _____

To multiply decimals:
- Multiply as you would with integers.
- Count the *total number* of decimal places in all of the factors.
- From the right, mark off the same number of decimal places in the product.
- Use the same sign rules as with integers.

> **Remember: Multiplication properties**
> commutative property: $ab = ba$
> associative property: $a(bc) = (ab)c$
> distributive property: $a(b + c) = ab + ac$
> $a(b - c) = ab - ac$

Multiply: $2.75 \bullet 7.9$
First estimate by rounding: $3 \bullet 8 = 24$.
Then multiply.

$$
\begin{array}{r}
2.75 \quad \leftarrow \text{2 decimal places} \\
\times \ 7.9 \quad \leftarrow \text{1 decimal place} \\
\hline
2475 \\
19250 \\
\hline
21.725 \quad \leftarrow \text{3 decimal places}
\end{array}
$$

21.725 is close to the estimate of 24.
The answer is reasonable.

Multiply. Use an estimate to check.

1. 3.2
  $\times$ 0.4
  _____
  1.28
  Check: $3 \bullet 0.4 = 1.2$
  $1.28 \approx 1.2$

2. 3.4
  $\times$ 0.7

3. 4.7
  $\times$ 1.9

4. 2.9
  $\times$ 1.6

5. 3.7
  $\times$ 1.6

6. -3.8
  $\times$ (-2.9)

7. -1.5
  $\times$ (-3.9)

8. 5.03
  $\times$ 0.27

9. 7.3
  $\times$ 0.6

10. 5.1
  $\times$ 3.5

11. -1.9
  $\times$ (-0.8)

12. 0.3
  $\times$ 9.8

13. $33.29(-0.3)$

14. $21.01(-0.7)$

15. $(1.28)(-0.11)$

16. $(-4.97) \bullet 0.008$

17. $(-3.8) \bullet 0.009$

18. $-0.87(1.6)$

Find each product. (*Hint:* Use properties to multiply factors.)

19. $85.3 \bullet (0.8 \bullet 1.1)$

20. $(-1.84 \bullet 0.5)(-9.1)$

21. $-1.3(-7.2)(-2.3)(-1)$

Simplify $a \cdot (b + c)$ for the given values.

22. $a = 0.24, b = 1.7, c = 3.3$

<u>   **0.24(1.7 + 3.3) = 1.2**   </u>

23. $a = -0.19, b = 0.4, c = 1.6$

24. $a = 9.0, b = 8.8, c = -21.2$

25. $a = 3.2, b = 0.2, c = -8.2$

26. $a = 8.3, b = 0.7, c = 1.6$

27. $a = -0.5, b = 3.1, c = 9.2$

28. $a = 3.7, b = 0.8, c = 7.7$

29. $a = 7.4, b = -6.2, c = -1.3$

Problem Solving

30. A certain stock showed a loss of 3.2 points per share, or $3.20 per share, on Monday. On Tuesday each share of that stock lost four and a quarter times Monday's loss. What was the loss on Tuesday?

31. Phil bought asparagus that costs $2.60 per pound. If he bought six and three quarter pounds of asparagus, what was the total cost?

32. The temperature in Anchorage, Alaska, was −6.4 degrees Celsius. In four months the temperature will rise by two and one half times. What will be the temperature in four months?

33. Carley's little brother has $0.81 in his piggy bank. He told their mom that his piggy bank would contain 12 times that amount in six months. At the end of six months, he reached his savings goal. How much money was in the bank?

MENTAL MATH

Use the distributive property to compute the product mentally. (*Hint:* Sometimes the Distributive Property of Multiplication over Subtraction is useful.)

34. 5($6.09) **35.** 8($11.03) **36.** 6($2.99) **37.** 3($5.95)

4-7 Estimate Decimal Products and Quotients

Name _____ Date _____

To *estimate products of decimals*, round each factor to its greatest nonzero place. Then multiply.

Estimate: 0.37 • 2.34

Think: 0.37 ≈ 0.4   0.4 • 2 = 0.8
         2.34 ≈ 2

So 0.37 • 2.34 ≈ 0.8

> You can also use compatible numbers to estimate products of decimals.

To *estimate quotients of decimals*, use compatible numbers. *Compatible numbers* are estimates that are easy to compute with mentally. To compute with compatible numbers use division facts.

Estimate: 43.73 ÷ 0.0683
43.73 ≈ 42
0.0683 ≈ 0.06
42 ÷ 0.06 ⟶ 42.00 ÷ 0.06 = 700

So 43.73 ÷ 0.0683 ≈ 700.

> **Think**
> Use a division fact.
> 42 ÷ 6 = 7

> **Remember:** Use a power of 10 to move the decimal point to make the divisor an integer.

Estimate each product. Show the rounded numbers you use.

1. 247.23 • 3.83

250 • 4 = 1000

2. 7.888 • 8777

3. 62.45 • 42.8

4. 219.3 • 58.8

5. 751.15 • 4.08

6. 0.091 • 0.18

7. 8669 • 0.00105

8. 0.077 • 32,355

9. 0.668 • 0.43

10. 4430 • 2.68

11. 0.083 • 0.0179

12. 0.0038 • 0.57

13. (18.59)(0.00053)

14. (0.76)(5.13)

15. (305.07)(0.99)

16. (43.75)(1.83)

17. (0.62)(0.036)

18. (29.05)(3.11)

19. (56.81)(4.29)

20. (418.6)(12.3)

21. (0.39)(11.76)

22. (74.86)(1.87)

23. (128.07)(2.96)

24. (506.9)(14.26)

Place the decimal point for a reasonable answer.

25. 0.98134 • 0.0506

0 0 0 0 0 0 0 0 0 5

26. 0.81128 • 0.30798

0 0 0 0 0 0 2 4

27. 0.00928 • 1723

0 0 0 0 0 0 1 8 0

28. 0.5555 • 0.05555

0 0 0 0 0 0 0 3 6

29. 0.2458 • 4.09

0 0 0 0 0 0 0 0 8 0 0

30. 0.0065 • 0.048

0 0 0 0 0 0 3 5

Estimate each quotient. Show the compatible numbers you use.

31. $34.72 \div 8.6$

$$36 \div 9 = 4$$

32. $26.809 \div 4.24$

33. $0.00438 \div 0.00072$

34. $0.02848 \div 0.00579$

35. $0.7889 \div 9.05$

36. $0.382 \div 40.7$

37. $705.3 \div 8.01$

38. $622.9 \div 7.75$

39. $1.731 \div 0.95$

40. $5.51 \div 8.213$

41. $0.269 \div 0.42$

42. $0.709 \div 92$

Solve. Check to justify your answer.

43. Rex bought 3.25 pounds of broccoli for $1.79 per pound. About how much did he pay?

44. Los Angeles has a land area of 1200.64 square kilometers and a population of about 3.8 million. What is the approximate population density?

45. On the treadmill at the gym, Erin ran 3.44 kilometers in 22 minutes. What was her average running speed in kilometers per hour? (*Hint:* 1 hour = 60 minutes.)

46. Ji Young bought 12.7 gallons of gas for $2.72 per gallon. If she has at least $40, does she have enough money to pay for the gas?

CRITICAL THINKING

47. Use compatible numbers to find two numbers that the quotient of $2.11 \div 0.44$ is between. Verify your method.

4-8 Divide Decimals

Name _____ Date _____

To divide with decimals:

- Multiply both the dividend and the divisor by the least power of 10 to form an integer divisor.
- Align the decimal point in the quotient with the decimal point in the dividend.
- Divide as with integers.
- Add placeholder zeros in the dividend and quotient as necessary.

Divide: $64.452 \div (-2.46)$

$64.452(100) = 6445.2$
$-2.46(100) = -246$

$$
\begin{array}{r}
-26.2 \\
-2.46\overline{)64.45.2} \\
\end{array}
$$

$$
\begin{array}{r}
-\ 492 \\
\hline
1525 \\
-\ 1476 \\
\hline
492 \\
-\ 492 \\
\hline
0
\end{array}
$$

Check by multiplying.

-26.2 ←—1 decimal place
$\times\ -2.46$ ←—2 decimal places
$\overline{1572}$
10480
$+\ 52400$
$\overline{64.452}$ ←—3 decimal places

The product matches the dividend so the quotient is true.

Put the decimal point in the correct position for the quotient to create a true statement.

1. $6 \div 0.3$

0 0 2 0. 0 0

2. $8 \div 0.2$

0 0 0 4 0 0 0

3. $72 \div 0.09$

8 0 0 0 0 0

4. $0.30 \div 0.08$

3 7 5 0 0 0

5. $7.488 \div 1.3$

5 7 6 0 0

6. $1.925 \div 7.7$

0 0 0 2 5 0 0 0

7. $0.2160 \div 0.74$

0 0 0 2 9 1 8 9

8. $0.6867 \div 0.63$

0 0 0 1 0 9 0 0 0

Find each quotient. Check to verify your answer.

9. $0.6\overline{)78}$

$780 \div 6 = 130$
Check: $130 \cdot 0.6 = 78$

10. $22.4\overline{)134.4}$

11. $0.36\overline{)18}$

12. $0.65\overline{)91}$

13. $0.16\overline{)1}$

14. $0.48\overline{)0.24}$

15. $0.72\overline{)0.0216}$

16. $-0.5\overline{)-219}$

17. $-0.9\overline{)-373.5}$

18. $-0.31\overline{)-0.124}$

19. $-10.8\overline{)0.027}$

20. $4.05\overline{)32.4}$

21. $0.08\overline{)64}$

22. $0.7\overline{)0.56}$

23. $-20.8\overline{)0.052}$

Divide. Round each quotient to the nearest hundredth.

24. $3.26 \div 0.06$

$$326 \div 6 = 54.3\overline{3}$$
$$\approx \mathbf{54.33}$$

25. $5.485 \div 1.13$

26. $-5.7 \div (-0.07)$

27. $-0.8654 \div (-0.24)$

28. $4 \div (-0.03)$

29. $0.412 \div (-0.13)$

Simplify $\frac{a}{b} + c$ for the given values.

30. $a = 0.22, b = 4.4, c = 3.8$

31. $a = 0.091, b = 0.07, c = 1.3$

Select the best estimate.

32. $-65.615 \div 0.05$ is about

    F. -13
    G. -130
    (H.) -1300
    J. -150

33. $7741.9 \div 515.3$ is about

    A. 15
    B. 150
    C. 200
    D. 250

34. $8.742 \div 0.047$ is about

    F. 18
    G. 180
    H. 1800
    J. 20

Explain how you solve each problem. Show all your work.

35. Bianca earned \$399.60 after working for 18.5 hours. How much did she earn for one hour?

36. Mr. Shaw paid \$38.86 for 11.5 gallons of gasoline. How much did he pay per gallon?

37. An Olympian ran 1.5 miles in 5.56 minutes. To the nearest tenth of a minute, how long did it take him to run one mile?

38. A car averages 6.3 kilometers per liter of gasoline. To the nearest liter, how much fuel will be needed for a 110.5 kilometer trip?

MENTAL MATH

39. Divide mentally.

    A. $4.2 \div 0.6$
    B. $4.2 \div 0.06$
    C. $0.42 \div 0.6$
    D. $0.42 \div 0.06$

4-9 Negative Exponents

Name _____ Date _____

You can express decimals as powers with negative exponents.

Write 0.001 as a power.

$0.001 = \frac{1}{1000}$ ←Write as a fraction.

$= \frac{10^0}{10^3}$ ←Write the numerator and denominator as powers of 10.

$= 10^{(0-3)}$ ←Apply the Law of Exponents.

$= 10^{-3}$ ←Simplify.

You can express powers with negative exponents as decimals or fractions.

> For any integer n, and any nonzero number a, $a^{(-n)} = \frac{1}{a^n}$ and $\frac{1}{a^{-n}} = a^n$.

Write $10^{(-1)}$ as a decimal.

$10^{(-1)} = \frac{1}{10^1}$ ←Rule for negative exponents.

$= \frac{1}{10}$ ←Simplify.

$= 0.1$ ←Write as a decimal.

You can also use the Laws of Exponents to compute powers with negative exponents and like bases.

> **Remember:** $x^0 = 1$ when $x \neq 0$.

$5^{-1} \cdot 5^{-2} = 5^{-1+(-2)} = 5^{-3}$ ←Law of Exponents for Multiplication; $a^m \cdot a^n = a^{m+n}$

$\frac{2^{(-7)}}{2^{(-4)}} = 2^{(-7)-(-4)} = 2^{(-7)+4} = 2^{-3}$ ←Law of Exponents for Division; $a^m \div a^n = a^{m-n}$

Complete the table to find the equivalent forms.

	Decimal form	Fraction form	Fraction form with powers of 10	Power of 10 with negative exponent
1.	0.01	_____	_____	_____
2.	_____	$\frac{1}{100,000}$	_____	_____
3.	0.000001	_____	_____	_____

Evaluate each expression. (*Hint*: Use factor form.)

4. 36^{-1}

$\frac{1}{36^1} = \frac{1}{36}$
_____

5. 4^{-1}

_____

6. 2^{-2}

_____

7. 6^{-2}

_____

8. $\frac{1}{3^{-2}}$

_____

9. 8^{-3}

_____

10. $\frac{1}{5^{-3}}$

_____

11. 4^{-3}

_____

12. $\frac{1}{6^{-2}}$

_____

13. $\frac{1}{9^{-3}}$

_____

14. 5^{-4}

_____

15. 2^{-3}

_____

Use with SOURCEBOOK Lesson 4-9, pages 88–89.

Evaluate. Write each product or quotient in fraction form.

16. $5^{-3} \cdot 5^{-1}$

$5^{-3 + (-1)} = 5^{-4} = \dfrac{1}{625}$

17. $7^{-2} \cdot 7^{-2}$

18. $20^{-2} \cdot 20^{-3}$

19. $2^{-5} \cdot 2^{-1}$

20. $(3^{-1})(3^{-2})$

21. $(4^{-1})(4^{-2})$

22. $(6^{-2})(6^{-1})$

23. $(8^{-2})(8^{-2})$

24. $9^{-1} \cdot 9^{-1}$

25. $\dfrac{9^{-4}}{9^{-3}}$

26. $\dfrac{8^{-3}}{8^{-1}}$

27. $\dfrac{10^{-9}}{10^{-4}}$

28. $\dfrac{6^{-2}}{6^{-2}}$

29. $\dfrac{8^0}{8^{-2}}$

30. $\dfrac{6^{-8}}{6^{-9}}$

31. $\dfrac{5^{-2}}{5^{-4}}$

32. $\dfrac{11^{-7}}{11^{-6}}$

33. $\dfrac{7^0}{7^{-3}}$

34. $\dfrac{2^{-4}}{2^{-5}}$

35. $\dfrac{4^{-5}}{4^{-7}}$

36. $\dfrac{3^{-1}}{3^{-1}}$

37. Solve. Write the answer in decimal form. Check to justify your answer.

A. A computer takes 10^{-9} seconds to do a mathematical calculation. _____

B. The thickness of a metallic layer in a circuit board is 10^{-4} centimeters. _____

SPIRAL REVIEW

38. Write and solve equations using numbers in exponential form.

A. Susan wants to put 5^6 apples equally into baskets of 25. How many baskets does she need?

B. If an author types about 10^3 words on one manuscript page, how many words will be on 10^2 pages?

4-10 Scientific Notation

Name _____   Date _____

Numbers written in scientific notation are expressed as the product of two factors:

(a number x, such that $x \geq 1$ and $x < 10$) × (a power of 10)

$285000 = 2.85 \times 10^5$

5 decimal places

Numbers greater than 1 have *positive* exponents.

$0.0004062 = 4.062 \times 10^{-4}$

4 decimal places

Numbers less than 1 and greater than 0 have *negative* exponents.

To express numbers written in scientific notation in *standard form*,

move the decimal point   or   multiply the two factors in standard form.

$8.064 \times 10^7 = 8.0640000 = 80,640,000$

Move the decimal point 7 places to the *right*.

$5.27 \times 10^{(-4)} = 0.0005.27 = 0.000527$

Move the decimal point 4 places to the *left*.

$8.064 \times 10^7 = 8.064 \times 10,000,000$
$\qquad\qquad\quad = 80,640,000$

$5.27 \times 10^{(-4)} = 5.27 \times 0.0001$
$\qquad\qquad\quad\; = 0.000527$

Remember:
$10^1 = 10,\ 10^0 = 1,\ 10^{-1} = 0.1$

Write the power of 10 in standard form. Then multiply the factors.

1. 6.4×10^3

6.4 × 1000

6400

2. 8.36×10^7

_____

3. 2.5×10^{-3}

_____

4. 1.09×10^{-5}

_____

5. 7.83×10^0

_____

Write in scientific notation.

6. 531,000

5.31 × 10⁵

7. 6,100,000

_____

8. 0.0426

_____

9. 0.0075

_____

10. −48,060

_____

11. −54,200,000

_____

12. −0.00000062

_____

13. −0.0000909

_____

Write in standard form.

14. 7×10^7

70,000,000

15. 9×10^{10}

_____

16. 3.7×10^4

_____

17. 2.925×10^{-2}

_____

18. 7.374×10^{-2}

_____

19. 4.04×10^{-9}

_____

20. -1.065×10^9

_____

21. -5.15×10^{-5}

_____

22. 4.36×10^5

_____

23. 7.1×10^{-4}

_____

24. 9×10^{-6}

_____

25. 6×10^7

_____

Compare. Write <, =, or >. (*Hint:* First compare the signs of the decimal factors. Then compare the powers of 10. Finally, compare the decimal factors.)

26. 5.21×10^4 ___<___ 5.21×10^5

$10^4 < 10^5$; $52,100 < 521,000$

27. 6.051×10^6 _____ 6.51×10^6

28. 1.623×10^{-7} _____ 1.623×10^{-9}

29. -6.79×10^{-3} _____ -6.098×10^{-3}

Order from least to greatest. (*Hint:* first convert all of the numbers to like form, either scientific notation or standard form.)

30. 9.6667×10^{-9}; $7,020,000$; 6.975×10^6; 1×10^8

$7,020,000 = 7.020 \times 10^6$
9.6667×10^{-9}; 6.975×10^6; $7,020,000$; 1×10^8

31. $515,000$; 5.15×10^{-6}; 5.9×10^4; 4.5×10^6

32. -5.45×10^{-6}; 4.77×10^{-9}; -0.000007; -5.3×10^{-7}

33. 1.875×10^2; -2.77×10^2; $-3,225$; 319

Problem Solving

34. Geography The Mariana Trench has been measured at 1.0923×10^4 meters below sea level. The peak of Mt. Everest is 8.848×10^3 meters above sea level. Which of these is a greater distance from sea level?

35. Biology A dust mite has a diameter of about 2×10^{-4} meters. Ragweed pollen has a diameter of about 2×10^{-5} meters. Which of these has a larger diameter? How many times larger?

CHALLENGE

36. Rank the numbers below from greatest to least. Explain how you found your answer.

500×10^{-3}; $500,000 \times 10^{-7}$; 0.0005×10^5

4-11 Operations with Scientific Notation

Name _____ Date _____

Simplify. Write each answer in scientific notation.

1. $2(8 \times 10^6)$

16×10^6
$1.6 \times 10^1 \times 10^6$
$1.6 \times 10^{1 + 6}$
1.6×10^7

_____

2. $3(7 \times 10^3)$

_____

3. $(8 \times 10^9)(0.9)$

_____

4. $(0.7)(3.4 \times 10^5)$

_____

5. $6(5.1 \times 10^{-12})$

_____

6. $4(9.4 \times 10^{-6})$

_____

7. $(2.67 \times 10^{-9})(0.03)$

_____

8. $(3.85 \times 10^{-21})(0.002)$

_____

Simplify. Write each answer in scientific notation.

9. $\dfrac{1.08 \times 10^5}{12}$

0.09×10^5
$9 \times 10^{-2} \times 10^5$
$9 \times 10^{-2 + 5}$
9×10^3

_____

10. $\dfrac{1.05 \times 10^7}{15}$

_____

11. $\dfrac{9.9 \times 10^{20}}{9900}$

_____

12. $\dfrac{5.2 \times 10^{12}}{2600}$

_____

13. $\dfrac{6 \times 10^{-2}}{240}$

_____

14. $\dfrac{7.29 \times 10^{-6}}{900}$

_____

15. $\dfrac{4.608 \times 10^{-22}}{0.96}$

_____

16. $\dfrac{8.064 \times 10^{-36}}{0.0056}$

_____

Tell whether each equation is *true* or *false*. If false, write the inequality in like terms, using < or >.

17. $(9.5 \times 10^{-5}) \times 4 = 3.8 \times 10^{-6}$

18. $(9.3 \times 10^{-17}) \times 6 = 5.58 \times 10^{-16}$

_____

_____

19. $(7.8 \times 10^{12}) \times 800 = (7.8 \times 10^{10}) \times 80{,}000$

20. $\dfrac{1.32 \times 10^{-10}}{11} = 1.2 \times 10^{-10}$

_____

_____

21. $\dfrac{4.8 \times 10^8}{4{,}800} = \dfrac{4.8 \times 10^6}{48}$

22. $45 \times (9.2 \times 10^{-3}) = \dfrac{4.14 \times 10^1}{100}$

_____

_____

Solve. Write each answer in scientific notation.

23. Biology A scientist looks at a cell through a microscope. The actual diameter of the cell is 2.5×10^{-5} meters. What is the diameter of the image of the cell if it is magnified 400 times?

24. Astronomy The average surface temperature of a red giant star is much cooler than that of a white dwarf star. Suppose a white dwarf star has a surface temperature of 1.2×10^4 Kelvin (abbreviated K), which is 4 times the temperature of a red giant star. What is the surface temperature of the red giant star?

_____

_____

CHALLENGE

25. Physics The average time it takes light to travel from the Sun to Earth is about 8.3 minutes. The speed of light is approximately 3×10^8 meters per second. What is the average distance between the Sun and Earth? Write your answer in scientific notation, and explain how you found your answer. (*Hint:* Speed $= \dfrac{\text{distance}}{\text{time}}$ and 1 minute $= 60$ seconds.)

_____

_____

_____

4-12 Addition and Subtraction Equations with Decimals

Name _____ Date _____

To solve an addition equation, use the *Subtraction Property of Equality*.

> **Remember:** Addition Property of Equality
> If $a = b$, then $a + c = b + c$.

$$a + 45.6 = 73.2$$
$$a + 45.6 - \mathbf{45.6} = 73.2 - \mathbf{45.6}$$
$$a = \mathbf{27.6}$$

Check: Use substitution. $\mathbf{27.6} + 45.6 = 73.2$

$$\mathbf{73.2} = 73.2 \text{ True}$$

To solve a subtraction equation, use the *Addition Property of Equality*.

> **Remember:** Subtraction Property of Equality
> If $a = b$, then $a - c = b - c$.

$$b - 12.2 = 67.5$$
$$b - 12.2 + \mathbf{12.2} = 67.5 + \mathbf{12.2}$$
$$b = \mathbf{79.7}$$

Check: Use substitution. $(\mathbf{79.7}) - 12.2 = 67.5$

$$\mathbf{67.5} = 67.5 \text{ True}$$

When the variable is the number being subtracted, write a related sentence.

$$2.4 - \mathbf{c} = 1.8 \longrightarrow 1.8 + \mathbf{c} = 2.4$$

Solve and check each addition equation.

1. $s + 3.3 = 4.9$
$s + 3.3 - 3.3 = 4.9 - 3.3; s = 1.6$
Check: $1.6 + 3.3 = 4.9; 4.9 = 4.9$ True

2. $-8.1 + r = 7.3$

3. $2.8 + m = 9.6$

4. $7.2 = -14.1 + t$

5. $x + (-11.64) = -6.96$

6. $158.72 + w = -45.3$

Solve and check each subtraction equation.

7. $n - 15.8 = 7.9$
$n - 15.8 + 15.8 = 7.9 + 15.8; n = 23.7$
$23.7 - 15.8 = 7.9; 7.9 = 7.9$ True

8. $17.52 = y - 9.4$

9. $v - 14.4 = -20.5$

10. $-15.25 = x - 4.080$

11. $b - (-80.77) = 48.57$

12. $m - (-0.631) = -0.96$

Solve. Check to justify your answer.

13. $-5.204 - z = -18.148$
$-18.148 + z = -5.204$
$z = 12.944$
Check: $-5.204 - 12.944 = -18.148$
$-18.148 = -18.148$ True

14. $36.25 - d = -40.3$

15. $32.3 - a = 8.4$

16. $-3.2 - q = 11.2$

17. $51.6 - w = 32.1$

18. $23.71 - t = 15.03$

Combine numerical terms, then solve each equation.

19. $(10.09 + 30.07) + w = -8.25$

$$40.16 + w = -8.25$$
$$40.16 - 40.16 + w = -8.25 - 40.16$$
$$w = -48.41$$

20. $(3.0075 - 6.0215) + t = -2.105$

21. $16.7 = 0.624 + x - 0.058$

22. $38.56 + g + 99.41 = 86.68$

23. $-5.04 = [-18.48 - (-20.09)] + z$

24. $[-22.04 - (-18.48)] + z = 35.77$

25. $11.7 + f + 16.25 = 33.1$

26. $(76.02 - 70.5) + c = -3.4$

27. $3.01 = [-2.8 - (-4.7)] + e$

28. $53.7 = 26.5 + h - 0.76$

Problem Solving

29. Geometry The two congruent sides of an isosceles triangle each have the length of 4.625 inches. If the perimeter of the triangle is 16.375 inches, what is the length of the base?

30. Regina has a bank account. After she wrote a check for $44.32, and deposited $25.50, her balance was $116.08. How much money did she have in her account originally?

TEST PREPARATION

31. Mark needs to collect money from his paper route. He collected $12.95 on Monday and $11.55 on Tuesday. If his total must be $30.00, how much more money does he need to collect?

    A. $1.40   **B.** $5.50   **C.** $17.05   **D.** $24.50

4-13 Multiplication and Division Equations with Decimals

Name _____ Date _____

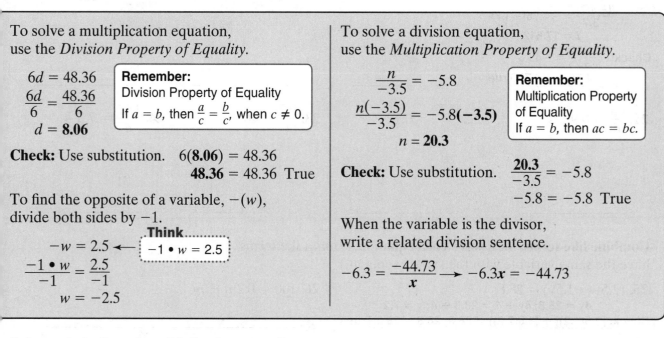

To solve a multiplication equation, use the *Division Property of Equality.*

$6d = 48.36$

$\dfrac{6d}{6} = \dfrac{48.36}{6}$

$d = 8.06$

Remember:
Division Property of Equality
If $a = b$, then $\dfrac{a}{c} = \dfrac{b}{c}$, when $c \neq 0$.

Check: Use substitution. $6(8.06) = 48.36$
$48.36 = 48.36$ True

To find the opposite of a variable, $-(w)$, divide both sides by -1.

$-w = 2.5$ ← **Think** $-1 \cdot w = 2.5$

$\dfrac{-1 \cdot w}{-1} = \dfrac{2.5}{-1}$

$w = -2.5$

To solve a division equation, use the *Multiplication Property of Equality.*

$\dfrac{n}{-3.5} = -5.8$

$\dfrac{n(-3.5)}{-3.5} = -5.8(-3.5)$

$n = 20.3$

Remember:
Multiplication Property of Equality
If $a = b$, then $ac = bc$.

Check: Use substitution. $\dfrac{20.3}{-3.5} = -5.8$
$-5.8 = -5.8$ True

When the variable is the divisor, write a related division sentence.

$-6.3 = \dfrac{-44.73}{x} \longrightarrow -6.3x = -44.73$

Solve and check each multiplication equation.

1. $6.2q = 139.5$

$\dfrac{6.2q}{6.2} = \dfrac{139.5}{6.2}; q = 22.5$
Check: $6.2(22.5) = 139.5$
$139.5 = 139.5$ True

2. $7.5d = 56.25$

3. $8.032 = -25.1a$

4. $6.975 = -15.5x$

5. $-18.6 = 2.4s$

6. $1.24k = -3.72$

7. $-0.42y = -2.142$

8. $-0.006v = -0.135$

Solve and check each division equation.

9. $\dfrac{n}{10} = 1.6$

$\dfrac{n(10)}{10} = 1.6(10); n = 16$
Check: $\dfrac{16}{10} = 1.6; 1.6 = 1.6$ True

10. $80 = \dfrac{d}{0.1}$

11. $\dfrac{y}{-2} = 66.3$

12. $\dfrac{w}{-0.06} = 8.48$

13. $\dfrac{n}{-10.2} = 0.137$

14. $\dfrac{d}{3.9} = -11.9$

15. $\dfrac{z}{-1.4} = 9.2$

16. $\dfrac{y}{53.075} = -1$

Solve. Check to justify your answer.

17. $\frac{i}{-3.7} = -4.76$

$\frac{i(-3.7)}{-3.7} = -4.76(-3.7)$

$i = 17.612$

Check: $\frac{17.612}{-3.7} = -4.76$

$-4.76 = -4.76$ **True**

18. $\frac{-(z)}{1.4} = -8.8$

19. $\frac{k}{-8.8} = -12.9$

20. $7.6 = \frac{-(y)}{2.2}$

21. $\frac{45}{e} = 0.9$

22. $\frac{0.72}{d} = 0.12$

23. $\frac{9.2}{t} = 46$

24. $\frac{18.6}{a} = 7.5$

Combine like terms, then solve each equation. (*Hint:* Like terms have the same variable with the same exponent.)

25. $(2.5y + 1.5y) = 28.8$

$4y = 28.8; \ 4y \div 4 = 28.8 \div 4; \ y = 7.2$

Check: $[2.5(7.2)] + [1.5(7.2)] = 28.8; \ 28.8 = 28.8$ **True**

26. $100 = 0.2m - m$

27. $(4.3b - 0.5b) = 31.16$

28. $75 = 3.8r + 3.7r$

29. $481 = (7.6n - 11.3n)$

30. $0.2y + 7.8y = 54.6$

Solve. Check to justify your answer.

31. If one pen costs $3.75, how many pens can you buy for $67.50?

32. Mr. Kwan spent $33.41 on gas. If the gas cost $2.57 per gallon, how many gallons did he buy?

CRITICAL THINKING

33. Write another division sentence and a multiplication sentence related to

$\frac{5.76}{x} = 6.4$. For which of the three sentences is it easiest to find the solution? Explain.

4-14 Solve Two-Step Equations with Decimals

Name _____ Date _____

To solve a two-step equation, apply the order of operations and the Properties of Equality to isolate the variable, the unknown value.

> **Remember:** Properties of Equality
> If $a = b$, $a + c = b + c$.
> If $a = b$, $a - c = b - c$.
> If $a = b$, $ac = bc$.
> If $a = b$, $\dfrac{a}{c} = \dfrac{b}{c}$, when $c \neq 0$.

Solve: $50 + 9.85a = 79.55$

$50 - 50 + 9.85a = 79.55 - 50$

$9.85a = 29.55$

$\dfrac{9.85a}{9.85} = \dfrac{29.55}{9.85}$

$a = 3$

Check: Use substitution.

$50 + (9.85 \bullet 3) = 79.55$

$50 + (29.55) = 79.55$

$79.55 = 79.55$ True

Solve. Check to justify your answer.

1. $36.3 = 8.3 + 4s$

$36.3 - 8.3 = 8.3 - 8.3 + 4s$

$28 = 4s$

$\dfrac{28}{4} = \dfrac{4s}{4}; 7 = s$

Check: $36.3 = 8.3 + 4(7)$

$36.3 = 36.3$ True

2. $8.5p + 6 = 40$

_____

3. $19.5 = 0.5t + 14$

_____

4. $186.8 = 43k + 32$

_____

5. $0.6w + 6 = 23.4$

_____

6. $88.7a - 15 = 19.593$

_____

7. $16.6 = 0.8x - 17$

_____

8. $46.0365 = 7.3g + 46$

_____

9. $-2.46j - 15 = -12.54$

_____

10. $(r \div 1.2) + 7.5 = 45$

_____

11. $26 = \dfrac{n}{6.4} + 4.3$

_____

12. $(b \div 2.8) + 83 = 39$

_____

13. $\dfrac{y}{0.25} + 12 = 77$

_____

14. $0.89 = \dfrac{w}{7.9} - (-0.14)$

_____

15. $\dfrac{z}{3.6} - 0.65 = -0.15$

_____

Simplify by combining like terms, then solve.

16. $(0.7n + 0.2n) + 0.8 = -2.8$
$0.9n + 0.8 = -2.8$
$0.9n + 0.8 - 0.8 = -2.8 - 0.8$
$0.9n = -3.6$
$\dfrac{0.9n}{0.9} = \dfrac{-3.6}{0.9}; n = -4$

17. $32.5 = 4.3r + 16 - r$

18. $5.3c - 3c + 15 = 16.84$

19. $8.12 = -1.5f - 8.12 - f$

20. $11.3\ell - 10.1\ell + 7 = 13.24$

21. $(5.9p + 0.3p) + 7.1 = -2.2$

Problem Solving

22. Sports At the July 1980 Olympics, the record for the women's shot put was 22.41 meters, which was 5.09 meters less than double the 1948 Olympic winning distance. What was the women's winning shot put distance in the 1948 Olympics?

23. Stephanie set her rental car trip meter at 0, while the odometer read 4962.8. She drove the same route round-trip from the airport to her hotel. When Stephanie returned the car, the odometer read 5554 miles. What was the car trip meter reading after her trip from the airport to the hotel?

24. Astronomy The average density of Earth is 5.5 g/cm^3, which is 0.1 g/cm^3 less than 8 times that of Saturn. What is the average density of Saturn?

25. Zoology The Wilson's Storm Petrel has a wingspan of 0.41 meter, which is 0.15 meter less than one fourth the wingspan of the Black-browed Albatross. What is the wingspan of the Black-browed Albatross?

CHALLENGE

Does the given value make the equation true? If false, tell what value makes the equation true.

26. $9 \overset{?}{=} (3m + 7m + 8) \div 2$, when $m = 2.8$

27. $-1 \overset{?}{=} \dfrac{2h + 11 - 3h}{3}$, when $h = 1.4$

4-15 Rename Metric Units of Measure

Name _____ Date _____

Metric Units of Length, Capacity, and Mass						
thousands	hundreds	tens	ones	tenths	hundredths	thousandths
1000	100	10	1	0.1	0.01	0.001
Length kilometer (km)	hectometer (hm)	dekameter (dam)	meter (m)	decimeter (dm)	centimeter (cm)	millimeter (mm)
Capacity kiloliter (kL)	hectoliter (hL)	dekaliter (daL)	liter (L)	deciliter (dL)	centiliter (cL)	milliliter (mL)
Mass kilogram (kg)	hectogram (hg)	dekagram (dag)	gram (g)	decigram (dg)	centigram (cg)	milligram (mg)

To rename large units as smaller units, *multiply* by a power of 10. To rename smaller units as larger units, *divide* by a power of 10.

32.5 cm = _?_ hm **Think**

1 m = 100 cm and 1 hm = 100 m
so 1 hm = 100 • 100 = 10,000 cm

= 32.5 ÷ 10,000 = 0.00325 hm

You can also move the decimal point the same number of places and in the same direction as the places between the given unit and the new unit on the metric place-value chart.

7.8 dg = _?_ mg **Think**

decigrams to milligrams ⟶
2 places to the right

7.8 dg ⟶ 7.80. ⟶ 780 mg

Complete the chart so that each row shows equivalent units of length.

	km	hm	dam	m	dm	cm	mm
1.	0.001	0.01	0.1	1	___	___	___
2.	___	___	5	___	500	___	___
3.	___	7	___	___	___	___	___
4.	0.06	___	___	___	___	___	___
5.	___	___	___	___	___	250	___

Rename each unit of capacity and mass.

6. 8000 cL = __80__ L

7. 1.75 kL = _____ L

8. 70,500 L = _____ kL

9. 240 mL = _____ cL

10. 7 g = _____ mg

11. 29 cg = _____ mg

12. 38.6 dg = _____ mg

13. 91.3 cg = _____ dag

14. 0.51 cg = _____ kg

15. 42.1 mg = _____ dg

16. 4.16 cL = _____ mL

17. 5.01 dag = _____ dg

Cross out the measure in each row that is *not* equivalent to the others.

18. 5 L   ~~5000 cL~~   500 cL   50 dL

19. 17 m   0.017 km   1.7 dam   1700 dm

Compare. Write <, =, or >.

20. 0.09 g ___<___ 90 cg   **21.** 4200 kg _____ 4.2 g   **22.** 9.4 mg _____ 0.0094 g

23. 47 daL _____ 0.05 hL   **24.** 335 mL _____ 33 cL   **25.** 2000 cL _____ 100 hL

Complete the chart of equivalent measures.

	Volume of a Cube	Capacity	Mass
26.	_____ cm³ of water	12 mL of water	_____ g of water
27.	_____ dm³ of water	43 L of water	_____ kg of water
28.	3 dm³ of water	_____ mL of water	_____ g of water
29.	_____ cm³ of water	_____ mL of water	5 kg of water

Solve. Check to verify your answer.

30. On Monday Albert ran 700 meters; on Tuesday he ran 6 hectometers; on Wednesday he ran 5 kilometers; and on Thursday he ran 17,000 meters. How many kilometers did Albert run?

31. In the laboratory, Dr. Joon drew 27 centiliters from a full liter container of a solution. How many liters are now in the container?

32. A European cake recipe calls for 7.5 cL of fresh lemon juice. If a baker wants to make a dozen of these cakes, how many liters of fresh lemon juice are needed?

33. Sara has 7.8 kg of tiny beads. She wants to make packages containing 24 grams of beads each. How many packages can she make?

CRITICAL THINKING

34. A metric ton is a unit of mass equivalent to 1000 kilograms. During the summer, each adult blue whale consumes approximately 40 million krill, or a total of more than 3.6 metric tons of krill each day. Antarctic krill are at least 34.5 millimeters long. How many grams of krill does one adult blue whale eat in one week?

4-16 Problem-Solving Strategy:
Review of Strategies

Name _____ Date _____

Solve. Show your work.

1. In the repeating decimal $0.\overline{14253}$, what digit is in the 1003rd place after the decimal point?

_____

2. Below are the points scored by 28 football teams during the first game of the new season. Arrange them in order from least to greatest: 14, 31, 28, 10, 18, 24, 20, 7, 32, 28, 31, 21, 10, 27, 17, 10, 35, 20, 42, 20, 31, 21, 24, 17, 3, 16, 17, 28

_____

3. In how many ways can three students be selected from a group of five students?

_____

4. Of 140 patrons of a Chicago restaurant, 62 say they are White Sox fans but not Cubs fans. Forty-three say they are Cubs fans but not White Sox fans. Seven say they are neither White Sox fans nor Cubs fans. How many said they were fans of both the White Sox and Cubs?

_____

5. Below are the first 5 stages of a design made out of toothpicks. How many toothpicks are required to make the 20th stage of this design?

stage 1   stage 2   stage 3   stage 4   stage 5

_____

6. In how many distinguishable ways can you arrange the letters in AAABB?

_____

7. The sum of the squares of three consecutive numbers is 110. What are these squares?

_____

8. Suppose each dimension of a rectangle is a whole number of feet and its area is 80 square feet. What are the largest and smallest possible perimeters?

_____

9. How many diagonals does a 9-sided polygon have?

_____

10. In how many ways can you select two people from a group of 9 people?

_____

Enrichment:
Binary Numbers

Name _____ Date _____

Write the decimal number 144 as a binary number.
144 ⟶ The greatest power of 2 that is less than or equal to 144 is 128, or 2^7. $144 - 128 = 16$.
16 ⟶ The greatest power of 2 that is less than or equal to 16 is 16, or 2^4. $16 - 16 = 0$.
So the binary representation is $1001\ 0000_{two}$.

Write the binary number 1010 1011 as a decimal number.
$1010\ 1011_{two} = (1 \times 2^7) + (0 \times 2^6) + (1 \times 2^5) + (0 \times 2^4) + (1 \times 2^3) + (0 \times 2^2) + (1 \times 2^1) + (1 \times 2^0)$
$1010\ 1011_{two} = 128 + 32 + 8 + 2 + 1$
$1010\ 1011_{two} = 171$

Convert each decimal number to a binary number.

1. 18
$2^4 = 16 \le 18;\ 18 - 2^4 = 2$
$2^1 = 2 \le 2;\ 2 - 2^1 = 0$
$\underline{1\ 0010_{two}}$

2. 23

3. 41

4. 67

5. 73

6. 80

7. 92

8. 100

Convert each binary number to a decimal number.

9. 0101_{two}

$(1 \times 2^2) + (1 + 2^0) = 5$

10. 0110_{two}

11. 1001_{two}

12. $1010\ 1010_{two}$

Problem Solving

13. Write your birth year as a binary number.

14. The Santiago Bernabeu Stadium in Madrid, Spain, holds about $1\ 0011\ 1000\ 1000\ 0000_{two}$ people, when its capacity is expressed as a binary number. Rewrite this as a decimal number.

CHALLENGE

15. The time of day can be described in minutes instead of in hours and minutes. For example if it is 10:30 A.M., you could also say that it is 630 minutes after midnight. Write the current time of day in minutes after midnight and then write this value as a binary number.

Vocabulary Development

Name _____   Date _____

Chapter 4 Vocabulary

capacity	front-end estimation	negative exponent	repeating decimal
clustering	length	negative power of 10	scientific notation
compatible numbers	mass	positive exponent	subtraction principle
decimal number	metric system of measurement	rational number	terminating decimal

From the vocabulary list above, choose the term(s) that best complete each sentence. Write the term(s) in the space(s) provided.

1. A deciliter is a metric unit of _____.

2. A kilogram is a metric measure of _____.

3. A hectometer is a metric measure of _____.

4. When a lesser integer is divided by a greater integer, the quotient will be a _____.

5. $9.333\ldots$ or $9.\overline{3}$ is called a _____.

6. 8.5 is called a _____.

7. _____ is a more compact method of expressing large numbers and very small decimal numbers.

8. A _____ is a number that can be written in the form $\frac{a}{b}$, where a and b are integers and b is not 0.

9. When estimating $74.89 \div 7.7$ by finding the quotient of $72 \div 8$, you are using _____.

True or False. If the statement is false, change it to make it true.

10. The number 34.7×10^4 is written in scientific notation.

_____

11. The number $\frac{11}{20}$ in decimal form is a terminating decimal.

_____

12. The Subtraction Principle states that to subtract a number, you should add its absolute value.

_____

Use after   SOURCEBOOK Lessons 4-1–4-15, pages 72–101.

Test Prep: Extended-Response Questions
Strategy: Organize Information

Name _____ Date _____

When you answer extended-response questions, it is helpful to *make notes* about the steps you must complete. The notes help to organize your thinking.

To find the answer, try using these strategies:
- Reread the item.
- Use the Test-Prep Strategy.
- Apply appropriate rules, definitions, properties, or strategies.
- Analyze your answers.

Solve. *TIP: Avoid leaving blank answers. Write down as much as possible.*

1. Rachel mixes 750 mL of mango juice, 650 mL of orange juice, and 325 mL of pineapple juice. She adds sparkling water to fill a punch bowl that has a capacity of 2.5 L.

Part A

How many liters of juice does Rachel use?
Show all your work.

Part B

How much sparkling water does Rachel add to the punch bowl? Give your answer in liters and milliliters.
Show all your work.

Answer _____

Answer _____

2. The table shows geographic information about Africa.

Africa	
Area	3.0065×10^7 square kilometers
Highest elevation	5.895×10^3 meters
Lowest elevation	-1.56×10^2 meters

Part A

Write the area and the highest and lowest elevations in Africa in standard form.

Area _____

Highest Elevation _____

Lowest Elevation _____

Part B

What is the difference in the elevation between the highest and lowest points in Africa?
Show all your work.

Answer _____

Part C

Death Valley is the lowest point in North America. It lies 70 meters above the lowest point in Africa. Write the elevation of Death Valley in scientific notation.
Show all your work.

Answer _____

3. This week, Claire hiked 8.5 kilometers less than twice the distance she hiked last week.

Part A

Write an expression to represent the number of kilometers Claire hiked this week.

Answer _____

Part B

If Claire hiked 12.75 kilometers last week, how far did she hike this week?

Show all your work.

Part C

If Claire hiked 32.5 kilometers this week, how far did she hike last week? Explain your answer.

Show all your work.

Answer _____

Answer _____

---

4. Mr. Lee has two pieces of ribbon. One piece is 2.8 meters long and the other is 1.26 meters long.

Part A

Mr. Lee cuts 75 millimeters from each end of the shorter ribbon. How many meters long is the remaining part of that ribbon?

Show all your work.

Part B

Mr. Lee cuts the longer ribbon into 8 pieces that are the same length. What is the length of each piece of the cut ribbon in centimeters?

Show all your work.

Answer _____

Answer _____

---

5. A nature magazine sells 3,400,000 copies each month.

Part A

The sales of a sports magazine are 0.1% of the nature magazine. Write the monthly sales of the sports magazine in standard form and in scientific notation.

Show all your work.

Part B

How many nature magazines are sold each year? Write the answer in standard form and in scientific notation.

Show all your work.

Standard Form _____

Standard Form _____

Scientific Notation _____

Scientific Notation _____

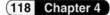

Practice Chapter 4 Test

Name _____   Date _____

Tell whether each number is rational or not rational.

1. π

2. $-6.\overline{144}$

3. $\frac{4}{9}$

4. $0.20020002\ldots$

_____   _____   _____   _____

Write as an equivalent decimal. Tell whether the number is a terminating or repeating decimal.

5. $-\frac{3}{100}$

6. $3\frac{4}{5}$

7. $4\frac{2}{9}$

8. $\frac{-11}{20}$

_____   _____   _____   _____

Write as an equivalent fraction or mixed number.

9. -0.7

10. 4.81

11. 0.006

12. -17.39

_____   _____   _____   _____

Compare. Write <, =, or >.

13. 0.563 _____ 0.569

14. -6.125 _____ $-6\frac{1}{5}$

15. $\frac{4}{5}$ _____ 0.8

16. -7.09 _____ $-7.\overline{09}$

Order from least to greatest.

17. $\frac{2}{5}, 0.\overline{12}, 0.1\overline{2}, 0.\overline{4}$

18. $-5.17, 5\frac{4}{9}, -5.040, -5.71$

_____   _____

Estimate. Then find the actual sum, difference, product, or quotient.

19. $-30.76 + 16.09$

20. $-56.04 - 35.88$

21. $(47.9)(-2.3)$

22. $-0.2156 \div 0.77$

_____   _____   _____   _____

Evaluate each expression.

23. 8^0

24. 9^{-2}

25. $7^{-2} \bullet 7^{-2}$

26. $\frac{5^{-2}}{5^{-1}}$

_____   _____   _____   _____

Compute. Write each answer in scientific notation.

27. $50(4.26 \times 10^{-4})$

28. $\frac{1.335 \times 10^9}{500}$

_____   _____

29. $33(1.04 \times 10^{-6})$

30. $\frac{6.17 \times 10^7}{125}$

_____   _____

Solve. Check to justify your answer.

31. $-33.5 = a - 19.72$

32. $1.703 + b = 3.48$

33. $-4.6c = 27.6$

34. $\dfrac{x}{6.12} = 0.8$

_____ _____ _____ _____

35. $-17.2m = 159.96$

36. $0.173 + g = 0.703$

37. $1.18 = s + 3.09$

38. $\dfrac{p}{2.05} = 6.71$

_____ _____ _____ _____

Rename each unit of measure.

39. 2.9 kg = _____ g

40. 9.8 mm = _____ m

41. 11.2 hL = _____ kL

42. 445 dm = _____ km

43. 1000 cL = _____ L

44. 23.2 cg = _____ dag

45. 9.3 kL = _____ L

46. 56.1 dg = _____ mg

47. 9 g = _____ mg

48. 0.011 cg = _____ kg

49. 1.75 cL = _____ mL

50. 36,700 L = _____ kL

Problem Solving

51. The blue whale, presently the largest mammal, weighs about 2.27 times more than the largest dinosaur. Blue whales weigh about 1.362×10^5 kilograms. Using scientific notation, about how much did the largest dinosaur weigh?

52. Dana bought a sweater on sale for half its original price. Including $1.96 sales tax, she paid $26.45. What was the original price of the sweater?

_____ _____

Tell About It

Explain how you solve the problem. Show all your work.

53. Marcos is 25 years old. The difference between his age and 5×10^{-2} times his sister's age is $\dfrac{12}{0.5}$. How many years apart are Marcos and his sister's age?

_____

_____

_____

_____

Cumulative Review: Chapters 1–4

Name _____   Date _____

Circle the best answer.

1. Which has the least value?

    A. $|-9| - |4|$ **B.** $|-9 - 4|$

    C. $|4| - |-9|$ **D.** $|4| - (-9)|$

2. Which is *not* equal to 74 centimeters?

    F. 740 mm
    G. 0.74 m
    H. 0.0074 hm
    J. 0.0074 km

3. Which point is in Quadrant II?

    A. $(-5, 9)$
    B. $(5, 9)$
    C. $(5, -9)$
    D. $(-5, -9)$

4. Simplify.

$$3a^2b + 2a - a^2b - 5a$$

    F. $2a^2b - 3a$
    G. $4a^2b + 7a$
    H. $2a^2b - 7a$
    J. $4a^2b + 3a$

5. Bhin's age is two years less than three times Tom's age. If Bhin is 16, which equation would you use to find Tom's age?

    A. $16 = 3t - 2$ **B.** $t = 3 \cdot 16 - 2$
    C. $16 - 2 = 3t$ **D.** $16 = (3 - 2)t$

6. Which fraction can be written as a repeating decimal?

    F. $\frac{1}{4}$ **G.** $\frac{7}{15}$

    H. $\frac{9}{20}$ **J.** $-\frac{36}{225}$

7. Which set is closed under the given operation?

    A. integers under division
    B. negative integers under subtraction
    C. odd integers under multiplication
    D. negative integers under multiplication

8. Which graph shows the solution of $x + 4 \geq 3$.

    F. 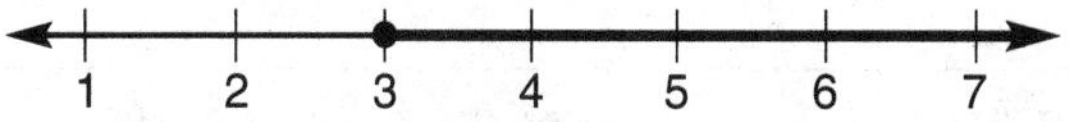 number line from 1 to 7, closed dot at 3
    G. 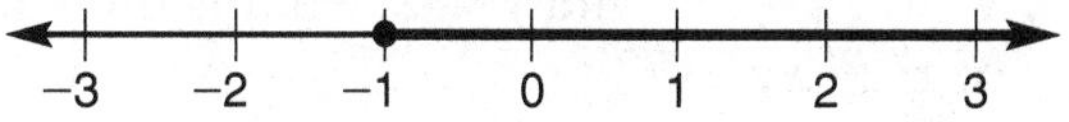 number line from -3 to 3, closed dot at -1
    H. 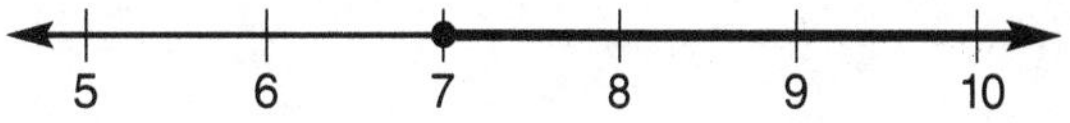 number line from 5 to 10, closed dot at 7
    J. 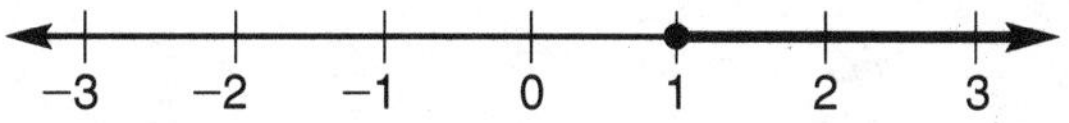 number line from -3 to 3, closed dot at 1

9. Which is the product $3(4.2 \times 10^4)$ expressed in scientific notation?

    A. 12.6×10^4
    B. 1.26×10^3
    C. 1.26×10^5
    D. 1.26×10^{12}

10. Evaluate.

$$m \div 0.8 - (0.2)^2 = 8.96$$

    F. $m = 7.2$ **G.** $m = -7.2$
    H. $m = 9.0$ **J.** $m = 7.136$

11. Which algebraic sentence represents the statement, "a number divided by 3 is no more than 4"?

    A. $\frac{n}{3} \geq 4$ **B.** $\frac{n}{3} \leq 4$

    C. $\frac{n}{3} > 4$ **D.** $\frac{n}{3} < 4$

12. The formula for the perimeter of a rectangle is $P = 2(\ell + w)$. If $\ell = 4$ and $P = 14$, what is the value of w?

    F. 3   **G.** 7
    H. 10   **J.** 14

13. Simplify.

$-5 + 35 \div y = -12$

    A. -7 **B.** 7
    C. -5 **D.** 5

18. Which inequality represents this graph?

    F. $x < -2$ **G.** $x > -2$
    H. $x \leq -2$ **J.** $x \geq -2$

14. Evaluate.

3^{-3}

    F. -27 **G.** -9
    H. $\frac{1}{27}$ **J.** $\frac{1}{9}$

19. Which is the solution of $-\frac{1}{3}x = 9$?

    A. -27 **B.** -3
    C. 3 **D.** 27

15. When $x = -3$ and $y = 2$, what is the value of $x^2 - xy + 7$?

    A. -8 **B.** 4
    C. 10 **D.** 22

20. Find the solution set for $-(x) > -2$ if the replacement set is $R = \{-3, -2, -1, 0, 1, 2, 3\}$.

    F. $\{-1, 0, 1, 2, 3\}$
    G. $\{-3\}$
    H. $\{-3, -2, -1, 0, 1\}$
    J. $\{3\}$

16. Suppose p is a positive integer and n is a negative integer. Which of the following results in a positive number?

    F. pn
    G. n^3
    H. $n - p$
    J. $n \div (-p)$

21. Which is an example of the Identity Property of Addition?

    A. $1 \bullet 6 = 6$
    B. $0 + (-3) = -3$
    C. $12 + (-12) = 0$
    D. $(5 + 1) = (1 + 5)$

17. Which is not a rational number?

    A. $0.0\overline{39}$ **B.** $-\frac{737}{945}$
    C. -3.659 **D.** $0.12345\ldots$

22. Simplify.

$3.6 + 7.2 \div 0.4 - (0.6)^2$

    F. 21.24 **G.** 2.124
    H. 212.4 **J.** 0.2124

Tell About It

Explain how you solve each problem. Show all your work.

23. Zelda bought pears that cost $1.72 per pound. If she has $10, what is the greatest number of pounds of pears she can buy, to the nearest quarter pound?

24. Mr. Park pays $1000 per month in rent. Before depositing his paycheck, his checking account balance was $359.47. After the deposit, it was $1441.33. Will Mr. Park have enough money to pay his rent?

5-1 Prime Factorization

Name _____ Date _____

To find the *prime factorization* of 528, use a factor tree and the divisibility rules.

528 ◄— Divisible by 4.
/ \
4 • **132** ◄— Composite numbers.
/ \ / \
2 • 2 • 3 • **44** ◄— Divisible by 4.
/ / / / \
2 • 2 • 3 • **4** • 11 ◄— Divisible by 2.
/ / / / \ \
2 • 2 • 3 • 2 • 2 • 11 ◄— All prime numbers.

Check: 2 • 2 • 3 • 2 • 2 • 11 = 528 True

Another way to find the prime factorization is to divide by prime numbers until the quotient is 1.

2	528	or	3	528
2	264		2	176
2	132		2	88
2	66		2	44
3	33		2	22
11	11		11	11
	1			1

prime factorization

So the prime factorization of 528 is 2 • 2 • 2 • 2 • 3 • 11 in factor form and $2^4 • 3 • 11$ in exponential form.

Tell how you know whether each number is prime or composite.

1. 49
Divisible by 7
composite

2. 93
_____

3. 19
_____

4. 29
_____

5. 74
_____

6. 47
_____

7. 83
_____

8. 51
_____

9. 27
_____

10. 127
_____

11. 315
_____

12. 57
_____

13. 21
_____

14. 87
_____

15. 211
_____

Rewrite each prime factorization using exponential form. Then find the product.

16. 2 • 2 • 5
$2^2 • 5 = 20$

17. 2 • 7 • 7
_____

18. 3 • 3 • 3
_____

19. 5 • 5 • 5
_____

20. 5 • 2 • 5 • 3
_____

21. 3 • 3 • 3 • 5
_____

22. 7 • 2 • 3 • 2 • 3
_____

23. 2 • 2 • 2 • 2
_____

24. 2 • 2 • 2 • 3
_____

25. 7 • 3 • 3 • 2
_____

26. 2 • 2 • 5 • 5
_____

27. 5 • 2 • 3 • 5 • 2
_____

28. 3 • 3 • 5 • 2
_____

29. 2 • 8 • 3 • 8
_____

30. 2 • 2 • 2 • 9
_____

31. 6 • 8 • 6 • 6
_____

Use a separate sheet of paper and draw two different factor trees for each number. Then write the prime factorization of each number in exponential form.

32. 48

$2^4 \cdot 3$

33. 45

34. 1100

35. 1575

Divide by prime numbers to find the prime factorization of each number. Then write it in exponential form.

36. 18

$2 \cdot 3^2$

37. 42

38. 90

39. 70

40. 135

41. 36

42. 175

43. 84

Write the prime factorization of each number in exponential form.

44. 81

3^4

45. 64

46. 20

47. 50

48. 72

49. 108

50. 56

51. 34

52. 171

53. 240

54. 385

55. 286

Problem Solving

Use prime factorization to help you solve each problem.

56. A landscaper has 105 small shrubs to plant on the grounds of a park. He wants to plant the shrubs in equal groups. What different sized groups could he make?

57. Brenda is meeting 2, 4, or 5 friends at the park. She is bringing 30 cookies to share with them. If Brenda distributes all of the cookies, can she give an equal amount of whole cookies to herself and each of her friends?

CRITICAL THINKING

58. If a number, *n*, is divisible by 42, what other numbers greater than 1 is it divisible by? Use prime factorization to explain your answer.

5-2 Greatest Common Factor

Name _____   Date _____

Here are two ways to find the GCF of 54 and 90:
- List all the factors of each number, then choose the greatest common factor.
  Factors of 54: **1**, **2**, **3**, **6**, **9**, **18**, 27, 54
  Factors of 90: **1**, **2**, **3**, 5, **6**, **9**, 10, 15, **18**, 30, 45, 90
  Common factors: 1, 2, 3, 6, 9, 18. The GCF is 18.

- Find the prime factorization of each number, then multiply the common factors.
  $$54 = 2 \cdot 3 \cdot 3 \cdot 3$$
  $$90 = 2 \cdot 3 \cdot 3 \cdot 5$$

Multiply the common factors: $2 \cdot 3 \cdot 3 = 18$. So the GCF is 18.

Remember: Every number has 1 as a factor. A prime number has exactly two factors, itself and 1.

A fraction is in simplest form when its numerator and denominator have a GCF of 1.

Here are two ways to write $\frac{54}{90}$ in simplest form:

Divide the numerator and denominator by the GCF.	Use prime factorization.
$\frac{54 \div 18}{90 \div 18} = \frac{3}{5}$	$\frac{54}{90} = \frac{\overset{1}{2} \cdot \overset{1}{3} \cdot \overset{1}{3} \cdot 3}{\underset{1}{2} \cdot \underset{1}{3} \cdot \underset{1}{3} \cdot 5} = \frac{3}{5}$

To write equivalent fractions for $\frac{54}{90}$, multiply or divide both numerator and denominator by the same nonzero number.

Multiply. $\frac{54 \cdot 2}{90 \cdot 2} = \frac{108}{180}$ Divide. $\frac{54 \div 9}{90 \div 9} = \frac{6}{10}$

List the factors of each number. Then find the GCF for each pair of numbers.

1. 24 _____**1, 2, 3, 4, 6, 8, 12, 24**_____

18 _____**1, 2, 3, 6, 9, 18**_____

GCF: _____**6**_____

2. 36 _____

20 _____

GCF: _____

3. 42 _____

14 _____

GCF: _____

4. 96 _____

36 _____

GCF: _____

Find the GCF. Use prime factorization.

5. 30 and 54

$30 = 2 \cdot 3 \cdot 5$
$54 = 2 \cdot 3 \cdot 3 \cdot 3$
GCF: $2 \cdot 3 = 6$

6. 27 and 90

_____

7. 14 and 28

_____

8. 35 and 28

_____

9. 17 and 19

_____

10. 43 and 13

_____

11. 25 and 50

_____

12. 50 and 75

_____

13. 8 and 20

_____

Find the GCF. List the factors or use prime factorization.

14. 9, 24, 27

GCF: 3

15. 15, 45, 60

16. 13, 15, 22

17. 56, 72, 40

18. 36, 63, 72

19. 64, 48, 32

20. 48, 60, 84

21. 42, 75, 90

Write each fraction in simplest form. Use the GCF or prime factorization.

22. $\frac{6}{18}$

$$\frac{6 \div 6}{18 \div 6} = \frac{1}{3}$$

23. $\frac{12}{24}$

24. $\frac{15}{20}$

25. $\frac{16}{20}$

26. $\frac{36}{45}$

27. $\frac{35}{90}$

28. $\frac{42}{56}$

29. $\frac{39}{104}$

Write two equivalent fractions for each given fraction.

30. $\frac{12}{32}$

$$\frac{12}{32} = \frac{3}{8} = \frac{24}{64}$$

31. $\frac{25}{70}$

32. $\frac{32}{112}$

33. $\frac{108}{144}$

34. $\frac{102}{316}$

35. $\frac{14}{21}$

36. $\frac{24}{90}$

37. $\frac{55}{105}$

Solve. Check to justify your answer.

38. Jesse says that all these fractions are in simplest form. Nita says that one is not. Who is correct?

$$\frac{8}{9} \quad \frac{2}{11} \quad \frac{5}{17} \quad \frac{11}{12} \quad \frac{9}{39}$$

39. Sergio says that he can quickly find the GCF of any two consecutive numbers without knowing any of the factors of either number. What is his secret?

CRITICAL THINKING

40. Sometimes a pair of composite numbers has 1 as their only common factor. Find a value of n that is a composite number less than 72 that makes this statement true. Explain how you found the number. For example, if the fraction $\frac{n}{72}$ is in simplest form, then the GCF of n and 72 is 1.

5-3 Least Common Multiple

Name _____ Date _____

Here are two ways to find the LCM of the numbers 9, 12, and 18:

Method 1 List the multiples.
Multiples of 9 = 9, 18, 27, **36**, ...
Multiples of 12 = 12, 24, **36**, ...
Multiples of 18 = 18, **36**, ...
The LCM of 9, 12, and 18 is **36**.

Method 2 Use prime factorization.
9 = 3 • 3   12 = 2 • 2 • 3   18 = 2 • 3 • 3

Write the greatest number of times each factor occurs among all the numbers. The product of the factors is the LCM.

The LCM is 2 • 2 • 3 • 3 = 36.

Find the *least common denominator* (LCD) of $\frac{5}{6}$, $\frac{7}{12}$, and $\frac{3}{8}$.

List the multiples of each denominator. Then find the first common multiple, or LCM.

6: 6, 12, 18, **24**, ...   12: 12, **24**, ...   8: 8, 16, **24**, ...

The LCM of 6, 8, and 12 is 24.
So the LCD of $\frac{5}{6}$, $\frac{7}{12}$, and $\frac{3}{8}$ is 24.

You can also use the prime factorization of each denominator to find the LCD in the same way that you found the LCM.

Two numbers are *relatively prime* when their only common factor is 1. The LCM of relatively prime numbers is their product.

Find the LCM for each set of numbers. List the multiples.

1. 6 and 10

2. 9 and 12

3. 2 and 5

4. 9 and 4

> Multiples of
> 6 = 6, 12, 18, 24, 30
> Multiples of
> 10 = 10, 20, 30
> **LCM: 30**

5. 3, 2, and 8

6. 2, 4, and 6

7. 6, 8, and 4

8. 6, 8, and 9

Find the LCM for each set of numbers. Use prime factorization.

9. 6 and 9

LCM: 18

10. 8 and 12

11. 9 and 18

12. 48 and 12

13. 4, 6, 3, and 9

14. 9, 12, 6, and 18

15. 4, 7, 8, and 14

16. 8, 16, 12, and 48

Use number sense to find the LCD. Describe the pattern in each row.

17. $\frac{10}{13}$ and $\frac{3}{5}$

18. $\frac{3}{7}$ and $\frac{4}{11}$

19. $\frac{1}{5}$ and $\frac{1}{2}$

20. $\frac{3}{7}$ and $\frac{2}{3}$

_____ **LCD: 65** _____ _____ _____ _____

21. The LCD pattern above is to _____

22. $\frac{3}{4}$, $\frac{5}{12}$, and $\frac{2}{3}$

23. $\frac{1}{2}$, $\frac{3}{8}$, and $\frac{3}{4}$

24. $\frac{2}{7}$, $\frac{1}{14}$, and $\frac{9}{28}$

25. $\frac{8}{15}$, $\frac{7}{60}$, and $\frac{1}{12}$

_____ _____ _____ _____

26. The LCD pattern above is to _____

Find the LCD. List the multiples or use prime factorization.

27. $\frac{4}{11}$, $\frac{21}{22}$ and $\frac{53}{88}$

28. $\frac{5}{6}$, $\frac{1}{12}$, and $\frac{2}{11}$

29. $\frac{7}{20}$, $\frac{13}{35}$, and $\frac{2}{14}$

30. $\frac{18}{18}$, $\frac{3}{27}$, and $\frac{5}{45}$

_____ **LCD: 88** _____ _____ _____ _____

31. $\frac{5}{18}$, $\frac{25}{27}$, and $\frac{2}{5}$

32. $\frac{1}{6}$, $\frac{2}{17}$, and $\frac{10}{51}$

33. $\frac{7}{20}$, $\frac{5}{10}$, and $\frac{13}{15}$

34. $\frac{7}{21}$, $\frac{3}{9}$, and $\frac{5}{7}$

_____ _____ _____ _____

Problem Solving

35. Mr. Gupta drew this diagram with prime factors for 30 and 70. Can he use the diagram to find the GCF, and LCM? Explain.

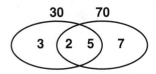
30   70
3 (2   5) 7

36. Louise wants to make cheeseburgers for a company picnic. The hamburger patties come in packs of 24, 18 buns are in a bag, and there are 30 cheese slices per pack. If Louise wants no leftovers, how many packs of each item will she need?

CHALLENGE

37. A pair of numbers has a GCF of 6 and a LCM of 60. What could the numbers be? Explain.

_____

_____

_____

5-4 Fraction Sense: Close to $-1, -\frac{1}{2}, 0, \frac{1}{2}$, or 1

Name _____ Date _____

To determine if a fraction is close to $-1, -\frac{1}{2}, 0, \frac{1}{2}$, or 1, compare the numerator and the denominator.

- A fraction is *close to 0* when the absolute value of the numerator is much less than the absolute value of its denominator.
- A fraction is *close to 1 or −1* when the absolute value of the numerator is about equal to the absolute value of the denominator.
- A fraction is *close to $\frac{1}{2}$ or $-\frac{1}{2}$* when double the absolute value of the numerator is about equal to the absolute value of the denominator.

You can also use compatible numbers to compare a numerator and denominator. $\frac{11}{25}$ is close to $\frac{1}{2}$ because $\frac{12}{24}$ is exactly $\frac{1}{2}$.

Tell whether the fraction is close to 0, $\frac{1}{2}$, or 1. Compare the numerator and denominator.

1. $\frac{29}{30}$

29 is close to 30.

So $\frac{29}{30}$ is close to 1.

2. $\frac{3}{41}$

_____

3. $\frac{19}{20}$

_____

4. $\frac{53}{99}$

_____

Tell whether the fraction is close to $-1, -\frac{1}{2}$, or 0. Compare the numerator and denominator.

5. $\frac{-2}{14}$

close to 0

6. $\frac{-8}{9}$

_____

7. $-\frac{45}{95}$

_____

8. $\frac{-78}{102}$

_____

Use compatible numbers to decide whether the fraction is close to $-1, -\frac{1}{2}, 0, \frac{1}{2}$, or 1.

9. $\frac{11}{100}$

close to 0

10. $\frac{-8}{38}$

_____

11. $\frac{-25}{60}$

_____

12. $\frac{46}{75}$

_____

13. $-\frac{5900}{6000}$

_____

14. $\frac{-29}{32}$

_____

15. $\frac{32}{60}$

_____

16. $-\frac{3210}{5940}$

_____

Estimate to the nearest half.

17. $\frac{13}{28}$

18. $\frac{78}{164}$

19. $\frac{43}{87}$

20. $\frac{497}{989}$

$\frac{13}{28}$ is close to $\frac{15}{30}$.

$\frac{15 \div 15}{30 \div 15} = \frac{1}{2}$

_____   _____   _____

Replace the ? with a number that forms a fraction close to 1.

21. $\frac{80}{?}$

   81 is close to 80
   So $\frac{80}{81}$ is close to 1.

22. $\frac{422}{?}$

23. $\frac{?}{14}$

24. $\frac{?}{23}$

Replace the ? with a number so that the resulting fraction is close to $\frac{1}{2}$.

25. $\frac{?}{16}$

   $\frac{8}{16} = \frac{1}{2}$; so $\frac{7}{16}$

26. $\frac{42}{?}$

27. $\frac{?}{250}$

28. $\frac{?}{38}$

Draw arrows on the number line to show if the fraction is close to −1, 0, or 1.

29. $\frac{8}{10}$

30. $-\frac{5}{11}$

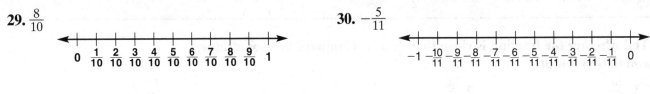

Solve. Check to justify your answer.

31. A socket wrench is needed to remove a bolt so that you can repair a favorite toy. You figure out that the 1-inch socket wrench is too large and the $\frac{1}{2}$-inch socket wrench is too small. There are two wrenches left in your toolbox: a $\frac{3}{8}$-inch socket and a $\frac{3}{4}$-inch socket. Which should you choose? Explain.

32. Tanisha wants to determine which missing numbers might make each fraction below close to, but no greater than, −1. What is the range of possible numbers for each? Explain the strategy you used.

A. $\frac{?}{23}$ _____

B. $\frac{?}{60}$ _____

C. $\frac{80}{?}$ _____

D. $\frac{422}{?}$ _____

WRITE ABOUT IT

33. Are $\frac{5}{12}$ and $\frac{125}{200}$ located in about the same area on a number line? Explain your answer.

5-5 Compare and Order Rational Numbers

Name _____ Date _____

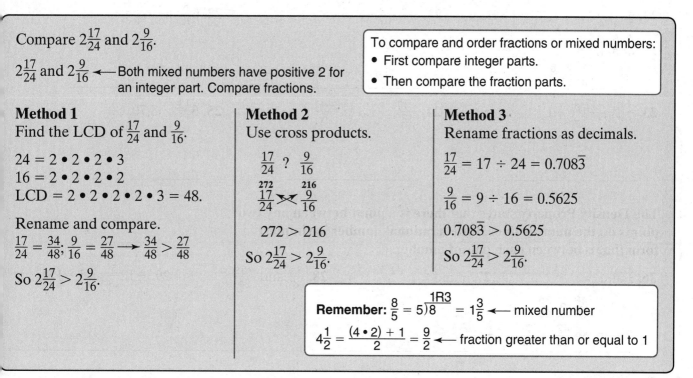

Compare $2\frac{17}{24}$ and $2\frac{9}{16}$.

$2\frac{17}{24}$ and $2\frac{9}{16}$ ← Both mixed numbers have positive 2 for an integer part. Compare fractions.

To compare and order fractions or mixed numbers:
- First compare integer parts.
- Then compare the fraction parts.

Method 1
Find the LCD of $\frac{17}{24}$ and $\frac{9}{16}$.

$24 = 2 \cdot 2 \cdot 2 \cdot 3$
$16 = 2 \cdot 2 \cdot 2 \cdot 2$
$LCD = 2 \cdot 2 \cdot 2 \cdot 2 \cdot 3 = 48.$

Rename and compare.
$\frac{17}{24} = \frac{34}{48}, \frac{9}{16} = \frac{27}{48} \longrightarrow \frac{34}{48} > \frac{27}{48}$

So $2\frac{17}{24} > 2\frac{9}{16}$.

Method 2
Use cross products.

$\frac{17}{24} \; ? \; \frac{9}{16}$

$\overset{272}{\frac{17}{24}} \diagdown \overset{216}{\frac{9}{16}}$

$272 > 216$

So $2\frac{17}{24} > 2\frac{9}{16}$.

Method 3
Rename fractions as decimals.

$\frac{17}{24} = 17 \div 24 = 0.708\overline{3}$

$\frac{9}{16} = 9 \div 16 = 0.5625$

$0.708\overline{3} > 0.5625$

So $2\frac{17}{24} > 2\frac{9}{16}$.

Remember: $\frac{8}{5} = 5\overline{)8}^{\,1R3} = 1\frac{3}{5}$ ← mixed number

$4\frac{1}{2} = \frac{(4 \cdot 2) + 1}{2} = \frac{9}{2}$ ← fraction greater than or equal to 1

Write each fraction greater than or equal to 1 as a mixed number.
Write each mixed number as a fraction greater than or equal to 1.

1. $\frac{3}{2} =$ _____

$3 \div 2 = 1\frac{1}{2}$

2. $\frac{5}{3} =$ _____

3. $\frac{17}{5} =$ _____

4. $2\frac{1}{4} =$ _____

5. $5\frac{4}{7} =$ _____

Compare. Write <, =, or >.

6. $\frac{5}{8}$ and $\frac{7}{12}$

$\frac{15}{24} > \frac{14}{24}$

7. $-\frac{16}{25}$ and $\frac{14}{25}$

8. $\frac{-5}{6}$ and $\frac{-8}{11}$

9. $\frac{-11}{14}$ and $\frac{11}{-14}$

10. $-3\frac{7}{15}$ and $3\frac{12}{25}$

11. $-4\frac{5}{9}$ and $-4\frac{5}{7}$

Compare as like terms in fraction or decimal form. Write <, =, or >.

12. $\frac{2}{5}$ ___<___ 0.6

$\frac{4}{10} < \frac{6}{10}$

13. 0.75 _____ $\frac{3}{5}$

14. $\frac{-1}{6}$ _____ -0.1

15. -0.625 _____ $\frac{-4}{9}$

16. $-7\frac{11}{13}$ _____ 0

17. $-3\frac{7}{10}$ _____ 3.11

18. 8.25 _____ $8\frac{1}{4}$

19. $2\frac{3}{8}$ _____ $\frac{38}{16}$

Write in order from least to greatest. Show the order using the original numbers.

20. $\frac{2}{3}, \frac{5}{6}, \frac{1}{2}$

$\frac{4}{6}, \frac{5}{6}, \frac{3}{6}$

$\frac{1}{2}, \frac{2}{3}, \frac{5}{6}$

21. $\frac{-1}{6}, \frac{-3}{10}, \frac{-1}{4}$

22. $6\frac{5}{12}, 6\frac{5}{6}, 6\frac{3}{4}$

23. $-1\frac{2}{5}, -1\frac{3}{4}, -1\frac{5}{8}$

24. $\frac{-17}{12}, -1.875, \frac{-11}{6}$

25. $6\frac{13}{15}, -8.70, 6\frac{12}{13}$

The Density Property states that there is a point between any two points on the number line. Write a rational number in simplest form that is between each pair of numbers.

26. $\frac{4}{5}$ and $\frac{7}{12}$

$\frac{48}{60}, ?, \frac{35}{60}$

? can be $\frac{42}{60} = \frac{7}{10}$

27. $\frac{3}{4}$ and $\frac{3}{7}$

28. $\frac{-5}{8}$ and $\frac{-19}{24}$

29. $-12\frac{5}{14}$ and $-12\frac{5}{16}$

Problem Solving

30. History A Constitutional amendment may be passed by a $\frac{2}{3}$ vote in each house of Congress and then ratified by at least $\frac{3}{4}$ of the state legislatures. If $\frac{4}{5}$ of the state legislatures approve a proposed amendment, would the amendment be ratified? (*Hint:* Compare the fractions.)

31. Naomi, Will, and Emma all had to wait for an operator to answer when they called customer service. Naomi waited for $\frac{1}{3}$ hour, Will waited for $\frac{2}{5}$ hour, and Emma waited for 30 minutes. Who waited the longest time? Who waited the shortest time?

CRITICAL THINKING

32. Order $5x$, $5.1x$, $\frac{17}{3}x$ and $\frac{1}{5}x$ from least to greatest, where x is greater than 0. Explain your reasoning. (*Hint:* Substitute a value for x.)

5-6 Add and Subtract Fractions

Name _____ Date _____

To add or subtract fractions, use the lowest common denominator (LCD) to rename fractions with like denominators. Apply the sign rules used with integers to add or subtract the numerators. Write the sum or difference in lowest terms.

Add: $\frac{-7}{12} + \frac{8}{9}$

$\frac{-7}{12} = \frac{-21}{36}$ and $\frac{8}{9} = \frac{32}{36}$

$\frac{-21}{36} + \frac{32}{36} = \frac{11}{36}$

So $\frac{-7}{12} + \frac{8}{9} = \frac{11}{36}$

Remember: A fractional number is in *lowest terms* when the only common factor of the numerator and denominator is 1. A fraction greater than or equal to 1 is in *simplest form* (lowest terms) when it is written as an integer or as a mixed number with a fractional part in lowest terms.

Find each sum. Express your answer in lowest terms.

1. $\frac{7}{12} + \frac{1}{12}$

$\frac{7 + 1}{12} = \frac{8}{12} = \frac{2}{3}$

2. $\frac{7}{16} + \frac{5}{16}$

3. $\frac{7}{8} + \frac{11}{12}$

4. $\frac{3}{10} + \frac{10}{10}$

5. $\frac{-3}{8} + \frac{-5}{16}$

6. $-\frac{2}{9} + \frac{-14}{27}$

7. $\frac{-1}{8} + \frac{-9}{10}$

8. $\frac{-7}{9} + \frac{-7}{12}$

9. $\frac{-7}{20} + \frac{7}{10}$

10. $-\frac{5}{12} + \frac{5}{6}$

11. $\frac{3}{5} + \left(-\frac{4}{15}\right)$

12. $\frac{8}{15} + \left(\frac{-7}{30}\right)$

13. $-\frac{12}{25} + \frac{19}{75}$

14. $\frac{-7}{30} + \frac{9}{10}$

15. $\frac{18}{27} + \left(-\frac{7}{9}\right)$

16. $\left(\frac{-21}{48}\right) + \left(\frac{6}{16}\right)$

17. $\frac{3}{8} + \left(\frac{-3}{5}\right)$

18. $\frac{-11}{16} + \frac{2}{3}$

19. $\frac{5}{18} + \left(-\frac{4}{15}\right)$

20. $-\frac{9}{14} + \frac{7}{12}$

Find each sum. Express your answer in simplest form.

21. $\frac{1}{8} = \frac{(1)(2)}{(8)(2)} = \frac{2}{16}$

$+ \frac{15}{16} \qquad = \frac{15}{16}$

$\overline{\frac{17}{16}} \qquad = 1\frac{1}{16}$

22. $\frac{3}{4}$

$+ \frac{2}{3}$

23. $\frac{31}{36}$

$+ \frac{5}{9}$

24. $\frac{3}{5}$

$\frac{1}{2}$

$+ \frac{13}{20}$

25. $\frac{7}{8}$

$\frac{15}{16}$

$+ \frac{1}{4}$

26. $\frac{11}{12}$

$\frac{3}{8}$

$+ \frac{1}{4}$

Find each difference. Express your answer in lowest terms.

27. $\frac{1}{9} - \frac{7}{9}$

$$\frac{1-7}{9} = \frac{-6}{9} = \frac{-2}{3}$$

28. $\frac{7}{15} - \frac{2}{15}$

29. $\frac{2}{3} - \frac{1}{7}$

30. $\frac{6}{33} - \frac{4}{11}$

31. $\frac{4}{13} - \left(\frac{-7}{26}\right)$

32. $\frac{7}{15} - \left(\frac{-11}{12}\right)$

33. $\frac{-1}{6} - \left(\frac{-11}{18}\right)$

34. $-\frac{7}{12} - \left(\frac{-7}{36}\right)$

Find each difference. Express your answer in simplest form.

35. $\frac{5}{6} + \left(\frac{-1}{3} - \frac{1}{4}\right)$

36. $\left(\frac{-1}{8} + \frac{2}{5}\right) - \frac{3}{20}$

37. $\frac{5}{12} - \left(\frac{-1}{6}\right) - \frac{3}{8}$

Evaluate when $a = \frac{-5}{18}$, $b = \frac{7}{12}$, $c = \frac{-3}{4}$, **and** $d = \frac{8}{21}$.

38. $a - c$

$$\frac{-5}{18} - \left(\frac{-3}{4}\right)$$

$$\frac{-10}{36} - \left(\frac{-27}{36}\right) = \frac{17}{36}$$

39. $(a - c) - a$

40. $(a + b) - (c + b)$

Problem Solving

41. Verenda is making salad dressing. She has $\frac{7}{8}$ cup of olive oil. She needs $\frac{1}{3}$ cup for the first recipe and $\frac{1}{4}$ cup for her second recipe. Does she have enough olive oil for both recipes?

42. Claudio has 2 yards of canvas for three projects. One project requires $\frac{3}{4}$ yd, another requires $\frac{1}{2}$ yd, and the third requires $\frac{3}{8}$ yd. Does he have enough? How much canvas does he need for all three projects?

MENTAL MATH

43. Compare mentally. Write <, =, or >.
(*Hint:* Compare each fraction to $\frac{1}{2}$.)

A. $\frac{9}{10} - \frac{1}{5}$ _____ $\frac{1}{2}$

B. $\frac{11}{12} - \frac{1}{3}$ _____ $\frac{1}{2}$

C. $\frac{-7}{12} + \frac{5}{11}$ _____ 0

D. $\frac{3}{5} - \frac{6}{13}$ _____ 0

E. $\frac{7}{11} + \frac{5}{9}$ _____ 1

F. $\frac{4}{9} + \frac{5}{12} + \frac{3}{7}$ _____ $1\frac{1}{2}$

5-7 Add and Subtract Mixed Numbers

Name _____ Date _____

To add mixed numbers, use the LCD to rename the fractional parts with like denominators. Add the fractional parts. Then add the integer parts. For both parts, use the same rules as for adding integers.

Express the sum in simplest form.

$$-7\frac{9}{10} = -7\frac{(9)(4)}{(10)(4)} = -7\frac{36}{40}$$
$$+ -3\frac{3}{8} = -3\frac{(3)(5)}{(8)(5)} = -3\frac{15}{40}$$
$$\overline{}$$
$$-10\frac{51}{40} = -11\frac{11}{40} \leftarrow \text{simplest form}$$

So $-7\frac{9}{10} + \left(-3\frac{3}{8}\right) = -11\frac{11}{40}$

To subtract mixed numbers, use the LCD to rename the fractional parts with like denominators. Then examine the mixed numbers. If necessary, regroup the integer parts. Then subtract using integer rules.

Express the difference in simplest form.

$$4 = 3 + \frac{3}{3} = 3\frac{3}{3}$$
$$-1\frac{2}{3} \rightarrow -1\frac{2}{3}$$
$$\overline{}$$
$$2\frac{1}{3}$$

Remember: To find the difference of two numbers, you can use the Subtraction Principle.
$$4 - 1\frac{2}{3} = 4 + \left(-1\frac{2}{3}\right)$$

Round each mixed number to the nearest integer to estimate the sum or difference.

1. $6\frac{3}{4} + 9\frac{2}{3}$

$\underline{7 + 10 = 17}$

2. $3\frac{5}{9} + \left(-4\frac{5}{8}\right)$

3. $-10\frac{8}{9} + \left(-16\frac{2}{3}\right)$

4. $-18 - 11\frac{9}{14}$

5. $7\frac{5}{12} - 4\frac{7}{10}$

6. $23 + 21\frac{6}{12}$

7. $6\frac{1}{5} - 2\frac{5}{6}$

8. $-16\frac{9}{10} + 3\frac{4}{11}$

Find each sum. Express your answer in simplest form.

9. $3\frac{3}{5} + 7\frac{2}{5}$

$\underline{10\frac{5}{5} = 11}$

10. $13\frac{4}{9} + 5\frac{5}{9}$

11. $-9\frac{5}{8} + \left(-4\frac{7}{8}\right)$

12. $18\frac{1}{2} + 7\frac{3}{8}$

13. $5\frac{1}{9} + 6\frac{1}{18}$

14. $3\frac{7}{15} + 8\frac{4}{5}$

15. $3\frac{5}{6} + 4\frac{5}{12}$

16. $-8\frac{3}{4} + \left(-9\frac{2}{9}\right)$

17. $-6\frac{3}{4} + \left(-9\frac{2}{5}\right)$

18. $34\frac{5}{6} + \left(-10\frac{2}{9}\right)$

19. $108\frac{4}{7} + \left(-45\frac{1}{9}\right)$

20. $-17\frac{7}{12} + \left(29\frac{3}{8}\right)$

Find each difference. Express your answer in simplest form. (*Hint:* You can also rewrite each subtraction problem as an addition problem, then solve.)

21. $5\frac{2}{9} - 8\frac{7}{9}$

$$-3\frac{5}{9}$$
_____

22. $13 - 3\frac{1}{4}$

_____

23. $26\frac{1}{4} - \left(-5\frac{3}{8}\right)$

_____

24. $-5\frac{2}{7} - 4\frac{5}{7}$

_____

25. $-8\frac{2}{15} - 4\frac{7}{15}$

_____

26. $3\frac{8}{15} - 9\frac{2}{5}$

_____

27. $20\frac{3}{5} - \left(-13\frac{9}{10}\right)$

_____

28. $-34\frac{9}{16} - \left(-28\frac{5}{12}\right)$

_____

29. $-42\frac{13}{15} - \left(-39\frac{3}{4}\right)$

_____

Problem Solving

30. At the Grand Canyon, it is a $9\frac{3}{5}$ kilometer walk from the Bright Angel trailhead to Plateau Point. Elena starts at the trailhead, walks to Plateau Point, and comes back. She rests after walking $12\frac{1}{3}$ kilometers. How far is she from the Bright Angel trailhead?

_____

31. Mr. Hawk cuts a square matte board that is $15\frac{1}{2}$ inches on each side. He wants to cut an equal border that is $2\frac{3}{4}$ inches wide. What will be the dimensions of the square hole?

_____

WRITE ABOUT IT

32. Mixed numbers can also be added or subtracted by writing them as *fractions greater than or equal to 1* with like denominators. Use this method to subtract and express the answer in simplest form: $6\frac{2}{5} - 3\frac{4}{5}$. Explain the steps used to find your answer.

_____

_____

_____

_____

5-8 Multiply Fractions

Name _____ Date _____

To multiply fractions, multiply the numerators and denominators. Use the same sign rules as with integers.

$$\frac{-3}{5} \cdot \frac{10}{21} = \frac{-3 \cdot 10}{5 \cdot 21} = \frac{-30}{105}$$

To simplify the product of two fractions,

- Divide the numerator and denominator by the GCF.

$$\frac{-30}{105} = \frac{-30 \div 15}{105 \div 15} = \frac{-2}{7}$$

- or use prime factorization.

$$\frac{-30}{105} = \frac{-1 \cdot 2 \cdot \overset{1}{\cancel{3}} \cdot \overset{1}{\cancel{5}}}{\underset{1}{\cancel{3}} \cdot \underset{1}{\cancel{5}} \cdot 7} = \frac{-2}{7}$$

So $\frac{-3}{5} \cdot \frac{10}{21} = \frac{-2}{7}$.

To simplify a fraction greater than 1, write as a mixed number in lowest terms.

If a numerator of one fraction and a denominator of another have a GCF, divide both numbers by that factor. Then multiply.

$$\frac{\overset{-1}{\cancel{-3}}}{\underset{1}{\cancel{5}}} \cdot \frac{\overset{2}{\cancel{10}}}{\underset{7}{\cancel{21}}} = \frac{-1 \cdot 2}{1 \cdot 7} = \frac{-2}{7}$$

So $\frac{-3}{5} \cdot \frac{10}{21} = \frac{-2}{7}$.

To find $\frac{2}{3}$ of 24, multiply.

$$\frac{2}{3} \cdot 24 = \frac{2}{3} \cdot \frac{24}{1}$$

$$= \frac{2}{\cancel{3}} \cdot \frac{\overset{8}{\cancel{24}}}{\underset{1}{1}} = 16$$

So $\frac{2}{3}$ of 24 is 16.

Write in simplest form. (*Hint*: Use the GCF of pairs of numerator and denominator factors.)

1. $\frac{25 \cdot 4 \cdot 45 \cdot 12}{48 \cdot 9 \cdot 100 \cdot 20} = \underline{\frac{1}{16}}$

2. $\frac{-1 \cdot 2 \cdot 3 \cdot 5 \cdot 7 \cdot 11}{5 \cdot 13 \cdot 2 \cdot 3} = \underline{\hspace{1cm}}$

3. $\frac{12 \cdot 6 \cdot 10 \cdot 14 \cdot 11}{21 \cdot 33 \cdot 15 \cdot 9} = \underline{\hspace{1cm}}$

4. $\frac{15 \cdot 3 \cdot 2 \cdot 24}{9 \cdot 4 \cdot 27 \cdot 10} = \underline{\hspace{1cm}}$

5. $\frac{8 \cdot 12 \cdot 36 \cdot 4}{14 \cdot 18 \cdot 3 \cdot 6} = \underline{\hspace{1cm}}$

6. $\frac{-11 \cdot 5 \cdot 13 \cdot 6}{5 \cdot 26 \cdot 44 \cdot 2} = \underline{\hspace{1cm}}$

Multiply. Express your answer in simplest form.

7. $\frac{5}{3} \cdot \frac{3}{10} = \underline{\frac{1}{2}}$

8. $\frac{2}{3} \cdot \frac{3}{5} = \underline{\hspace{1cm}}$

9. $\left(\frac{-3}{4}\right) \cdot \left(\frac{-5}{8}\right) = \underline{\hspace{1cm}}$

10. $\left(\frac{-4}{5}\right) \cdot \left(\frac{-2}{5}\right) = \underline{\hspace{1cm}}$

11. $\frac{-5}{2} \cdot \frac{-2}{5} = \underline{\hspace{1cm}}$

12. $\frac{4}{5} \cdot \frac{-3}{7} = \underline{\hspace{1cm}}$

13. $\frac{-5}{6} \cdot \frac{-12}{5} = \underline{\hspace{1cm}}$

14. $\frac{2}{3}\left(\frac{-1}{5}\right) = \underline{\hspace{1cm}}$

15. $\frac{-1}{2} \cdot \frac{3}{5} = \underline{\hspace{1cm}}$

16. $\frac{5}{1} \cdot \frac{1}{2} = \underline{\hspace{1cm}}$

17. $\frac{3}{5} \cdot \frac{6}{1} = \underline{\hspace{1cm}}$

18. $-16 \cdot \frac{1}{12} = \underline{\hspace{1cm}}$

19. $-8 \cdot \frac{2}{7} = \underline{\hspace{1cm}}$

20. $5 \cdot \frac{-2}{5} = \underline{\hspace{1cm}}$

21. $\frac{-9}{20} \cdot 20 = \underline{\hspace{1cm}}$

22. $8 \cdot \frac{-3}{4} = \underline{\hspace{1cm}}$

23. $(-60)\left(\frac{-7}{45}\right) = \underline{\hspace{1cm}}$

24. $(36)\left(\frac{5}{8}\right) = \underline{\hspace{1cm}}$

25. $\left(\frac{-36}{70}\right)(-14) = \underline{\hspace{1cm}}$

26. $\left(\frac{-15}{56}\right)(-40) = \underline{\hspace{1cm}}$

27. $(42)\left(\frac{5}{12}\right) = \underline{\hspace{1cm}}$

Multiply to find part of an integer. (*Hint:* "of" means *multiply*.)

28. $\frac{2}{3}$ of 36 = ___24___

$$\frac{2}{3} \cdot \frac{36}{1} = 24$$

29. $\frac{3}{4}$ of 16 = _____

30. $\frac{1}{4}$ of 72 = _____

31. $\frac{5}{9}$ of 48 = _____

32. $\frac{1}{7}$ of −84 = _____

33. $\frac{7}{9}$ of −81 = _____

34. $\frac{3}{8}$ of −112 = _____

35. $\frac{3}{4}$ of −64 = _____

36. $\frac{8}{5}$ of 20 = _____

37. $\frac{3}{2}$ of 5 = _____

38. $\frac{7}{6}$ of 3 = _____

39. $\frac{15}{8}$ of −36 = _____

Find each product when $a = \frac{3}{15}$, $b = -3$, $c = \frac{-5}{9}$, **and** $d = \frac{-5}{36}$.

40. $a \cdot d$

$$\frac{3}{15} \cdot \frac{-5}{36} = \frac{-1}{36}$$

41. $b(c)$

42. ac

43. abd

Find each product when $a = \frac{-7}{8}$, $b = \frac{12}{18}$, $c = \frac{1}{2}$, **and** $d = \frac{7}{26}$.

44. abc

45. $b \cdot d$

46. $c(d)$

47. bc

Problem Solving

48. Marsha has 136 stamps in her collection, $\frac{3}{8}$ of them are foreign stamps. How many stamps are not foreign?

49. Geology In 1980, Mount St. Helen erupted and lost about $\frac{2}{17}$ from its height of 2550 meters. What was Mount St. Helen's height after the eruption?

WRITE ABOUT IT

50. Find the product of $4 \cdot \frac{1}{2}$, in simplest form. Explain why your product is true by rewriting $4 \cdot \frac{1}{2}$ as a repeated addition sentence.

5-9 Multiply Mixed Numbers

Name _____ Date _____

Multiply: $-3\frac{3}{4} \cdot 2\frac{4}{5}$.

$-3\frac{3}{4} = -\frac{(3 \cdot 4) + 3}{4} = \frac{-15}{4}$ ← Rename each factor as a fraction greater than or equal to 1.

$2\frac{4}{5} = \frac{(2 \cdot 5) + 4}{5} = \frac{14}{5}$

$\frac{-15}{4} \cdot \frac{14}{5}$

$\frac{\overset{3}{\cancel{-15}}}{\underset{2}{\cancel{4}}} \cdot \frac{\overset{7}{\cancel{14}}}{\underset{1}{\cancel{5}}}$ ← Simplify. Divide the numerator and the denominator by the GCF.

$\frac{-3 \cdot 7}{2 \cdot 1}$ ← Multiply the numerators.
  ← Multiply the denominators.

$\frac{-21}{2}$ ← Divide to rename as a mixed number. The signs are different, so the quotient is negative.

$-10\frac{1}{2}$

So $-3\frac{3}{4} \cdot 2\frac{4}{5} = -10\frac{1}{2}$.

Round each mixed number to the nearest integer, then estimate each product.

1. $\frac{3}{4} \cdot 4\frac{3}{4} \approx 5$

  $1 \cdot 5 = 5$

2. $4\frac{1}{5} \cdot \left(-1\frac{1}{3}\right)$

_____

3. $-5\frac{4}{10} \cdot \left(-1\frac{4}{7}\right)$

_____

4. $-3\frac{3}{4} \cdot 2\frac{4}{5}$

_____

Multiply. Express each product in simplest form.

5. $8 \cdot 7\frac{1}{8}$

  $\frac{8}{1} \cdot \frac{57}{8} = \frac{57}{1}$

  57

6. $-8\frac{4}{5} \cdot (-10)$

_____

7. $-16\left(4\frac{3}{8}\right)$

_____

8. $-2\frac{4}{9}(18)$

_____

9. $\frac{1}{5}\left(8\frac{1}{3}\right)$

10. $\frac{3}{4}\left(4\frac{3}{4}\right)$

11. $\frac{-3}{4}\left(-12\frac{1}{2}\right)$

12. $\frac{-1}{4}\left(-5\frac{1}{7}\right)$

_____

_____

_____

_____

13. $-2\frac{1}{4} \cdot \frac{1}{3}$

14. $-3\frac{1}{3} \cdot \frac{1}{2}$

15. $8\frac{2}{3} \cdot \left(\frac{-3}{4}\right)$

16. $1\frac{5}{8} \cdot \left(\frac{-4}{7}\right)$

_____

_____

_____

_____

17. $4\frac{2}{3} \cdot (-4)$

18. $-10 \cdot 3\frac{1}{9}$

19. $8\left(-1\frac{1}{5}\right)$

20. $5\left(-3\frac{3}{10}\right)$

_____

_____

_____

_____

Multiply. Express each product in simplest form.

21. $5\frac{0}{7} \cdot 2\frac{1}{3}$

$$\frac{35}{7} \cdot \frac{7}{3} = \frac{35}{3}$$
$$11\frac{2}{3}$$

22. $1\frac{1}{5} \cdot 2\frac{1}{3}$

23. $\left(-16\frac{1}{7}\right)(-3)$

24. $-1\frac{1}{2} \cdot \left(-1\frac{1}{4}\right)$

25. $\left(-3\frac{1}{6}\right)\left(2\frac{2}{3}\right)$

26. $-9\frac{3}{4} \cdot \left(3\frac{1}{9}\right)$

27. $\left(6\frac{2}{3}\right)\left(-1\frac{1}{4}\right)$

28. $\left(2\frac{1}{2}\right)\left(-1\frac{3}{8}\right)$

Find each product when $a = 2\frac{4}{15}$, $b = -10$, $c = 4\frac{2}{3}$, and $d = \frac{-5}{7}$.

29. $a \cdot d$

30. ab

31. $b(c)$

32. abd

$$2\frac{4}{15} \cdot \left(\frac{-5}{7}\right) = -1\frac{13}{21}$$

Find each product when $a = -5\frac{1}{8}$, $b = 16$, $c = 7\frac{3}{4}$, and $d = \frac{9}{14}$.

33. bd

34. $a \cdot c$

35. bcd

36. $a(b)$

Problem Solving

37. Jamie built a dinosaur model seven and one half inches tall. His sister's model dinosaur is one and one fifth times as tall. How tall is his sister's model?

38. Science A skimmer dragonfly is one third the size of a darner dragonfly. If a darner dragonfly is three and three quarters inches long, what is the length of a skimmer?

CHALLENGE

39. Evaluate the expression: $\left(n - \frac{1}{2}\right) \cdot \frac{2}{3}$ when $n = 2\frac{1}{3}$. Explain how you found your answer.

5-10 Divide Fractions

Name _____ Date _____

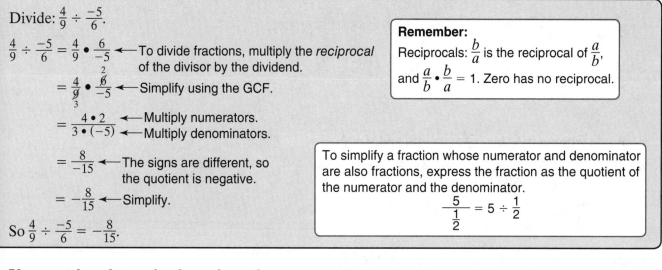

Divide: $\frac{4}{9} \div \frac{-5}{6}$.

$\frac{4}{9} \div \frac{-5}{6} = \frac{4}{9} \cdot \frac{6}{-5}$ ← To divide fractions, multiply the *reciprocal* of the divisor by the dividend.

$= \frac{4}{\cancel{9}_3} \cdot \frac{\cancel{6}^2}{-5}$ ← Simplify using the GCF.

$= \frac{4 \cdot 2}{3 \cdot (-5)}$ ← Multiply numerators.
      ← Multiply denominators.

$= \frac{8}{-15}$ ← The signs are different, so the quotient is negative.

$= -\frac{8}{15}$ ← Simplify.

So $\frac{4}{9} \div \frac{-5}{6} = -\frac{8}{15}$.

Remember:
Reciprocals: $\frac{b}{a}$ is the reciprocal of $\frac{a}{b}$, and $\frac{a}{b} \cdot \frac{b}{a} = 1$. Zero has no reciprocal.

To simplify a fraction whose numerator and denominator are also fractions, express the fraction as the quotient of the numerator and the denominator.
$$\frac{5}{\frac{1}{2}} = 5 \div \frac{1}{2}$$

Use mental math to write the reciprocal.

1. $\frac{6}{11}$ $\frac{11}{6}$

2. $\frac{0}{14}$ _____

3. 16 _____

4. -1 _____

5. $6\frac{1}{8}$ _____

6. $4\frac{2}{3}$ _____

7. $\frac{1}{2}$ _____

8. $\frac{-3}{5}$ _____

9. $3\frac{4}{5}$ _____

10. $5\frac{1}{3}$ _____

11. 9 _____

12. $\frac{0}{13}$ _____

13. $5\frac{3}{21}$ _____

14. $1\frac{9}{9}$ _____

15. $\frac{2}{7}$ _____

Divide. Express your answer in simplest form.

16. $\frac{3}{8} \div \frac{16}{16} =$ _____
$\frac{3}{8} \cdot 1 = \frac{3}{8}$

17. $\frac{3}{5} \div \frac{6}{25} =$ _____

18. $\frac{-1}{10} \div \left(\frac{-2}{3}\right) =$ _____

19. $\frac{-2}{3} \div \left(\frac{-5}{6}\right) =$ _____

20. $\frac{3}{4} \div \left(\frac{-5}{8}\right) =$ _____

21. $\frac{4}{5} \div \left(\frac{-1}{6}\right) =$ _____

22. $0 \div \frac{2}{11} =$ _____

23. $1 \div \frac{3}{4} =$ _____

24. $\frac{\frac{6}{5}}{12} =$ _____

25. $\frac{\frac{0}{9}}{16} =$ _____

26. $\frac{\frac{3}{8}}{-5} =$ _____

27. $\frac{\frac{6}{7}}{-3} =$ _____

28. $\frac{10}{\frac{2}{7}} =$ _____

29. $\frac{\frac{2}{5}}{20} =$ _____

30. $\frac{-6}{\frac{2}{3}} =$ _____

31. $\frac{-9}{\frac{3}{4}} =$ _____

32. $\frac{\frac{3}{4}}{\frac{1}{4}} =$ _____

33. $\frac{\frac{-12}{1}}{\frac{-12}{1}} =$ _____

34. $\frac{\frac{-2}{3}}{\frac{10}{1}} =$ _____

35. $\frac{\frac{7}{9}}{\frac{-2}{3}} =$ _____

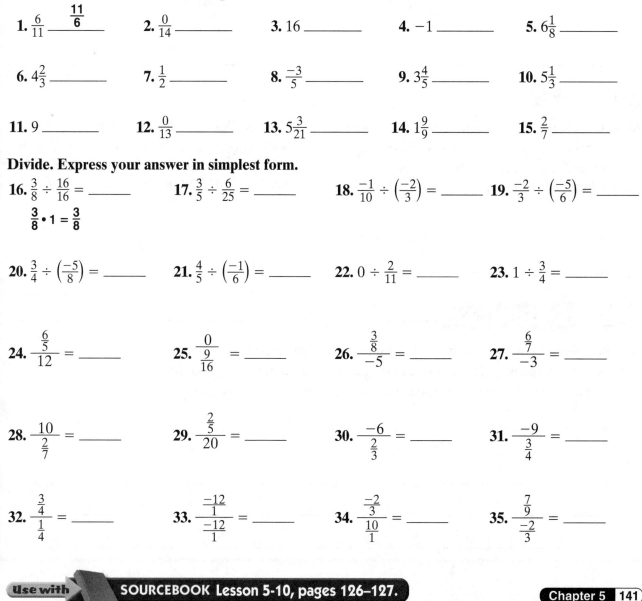

Compare. Write <, =, or >. Show your work.

36. $\frac{3}{2} \div 3 \;\underline{<}\; 3 \div \frac{3}{2}$

$\frac{3}{2} \cdot \frac{1}{3} = \frac{1}{2} < \frac{3}{1} \cdot \frac{2}{3} = 2$

37. $5 \div \frac{1}{2}$ _____ $6 \div \frac{1}{2}$

38. $1\frac{2}{3} \div \frac{5}{3}$ _____ $\frac{17}{17}$

39. $\frac{1}{5} \div 6$ _____ $12 \div \frac{2}{3}$

40. $\frac{2}{7} \div \frac{11}{14}$ _____ $\frac{28}{77}$

41. $\frac{1}{2} \div \frac{8}{12}$ _____ $\frac{3}{4} \div \frac{2}{3}$

Evaluate when $a = \frac{3}{4}$, $b = \frac{-3}{4}$, $c = -8$, and $d = \frac{1}{9}$.

42. $\frac{a}{b}$

$\frac{3}{4} \div \left(\frac{-3}{4}\right)$

$\frac{3}{4}\left(\frac{4}{-3}\right) = \frac{1}{-1} = -1$

43. $\frac{d}{b}$

44. $\frac{a}{c} \cdot c$

Evaluate when $a = \frac{1}{8}$, $b = 4$, $c = \frac{-2}{5}$, and $d = \frac{-3}{10}$.

45. $\frac{c}{a}$

46. $\frac{d}{c} \cdot b$

47. $\frac{a}{b}$

Problem Solving

48. A bicycle path that is $\frac{4}{5}$ mile long is marked in tenths of a mile. If you bicycle $\frac{2}{3}$ of the path and then stop for a break, how many markers will you pass?

49. Biology Water makes up about $\frac{13}{20}$ of human body weight. If 117 pounds of Lavon's body weight is water, about how much does Lavon weigh? (*Hint:* Think about the word *of.*)

WRITE ABOUT IT

50. The value of each U.S. coin is a fractional part of one dollar. A quarter is $\frac{1}{4}$ dollar, a dime is $\frac{1}{10}$ dollar, a nickel is $\frac{1}{20}$ dollar, and a penny is $\frac{1}{100}$ dollar. Simplify the following expressions and describe any patterns you see:

$$\frac{1}{\frac{1}{4}}, \quad \frac{1}{\frac{1}{10}}, \quad \frac{1}{\frac{1}{20}}, \quad \frac{1}{\frac{1}{100}}$$

5-11 Divide Mixed Numbers

Name _____   Date _____

Divide: $4\frac{1}{3} \div 1\frac{1}{6}$.

$4\frac{1}{3} \div 1\frac{1}{6} = \frac{13}{3} \div \frac{7}{6}$ ← Rename mixed numbers as fractions.

$= \frac{13}{3} \cdot \frac{6}{7}$ ← Multiply the reciprocal of the divisor by the dividend.

$= \frac{13}{\cancel{3}_1} \cdot \frac{\cancel{6}^2}{7}$ ← Simplify using the GCF, then multiply.

$= \frac{26}{7}$ ← Divide to rename as a mixed number.

$= 3\frac{5}{7}$

So $4\frac{1}{3} \div 1\frac{1}{6} = 3\frac{5}{7}$

> To simplify a fraction whose numerator and denominator are *mixed numbers*, express the fraction as the quotient of the numerator and the denominator.
>
> $$\frac{4\frac{1}{2}}{3\frac{2}{3}} = 4\frac{1}{2} \div 3\frac{2}{3}$$

Use mental math to rename mixed numbers as fractions greater than 1.

1. $4\frac{1}{10}$ $\frac{41}{10}$

2. $6\frac{5}{8}$ _____

3. $5\frac{2}{7}$ _____

4. $9\frac{3}{8}$ _____

5. $8\frac{9}{10}$ _____

6. $21\frac{1}{3}$ _____

7. $10\frac{5}{6}$ _____

8. $1\frac{11}{12}$ _____

9. $7\frac{5}{8}$ _____

10. $5\frac{3}{4}$ _____

11. $3\frac{7}{9}$ _____

12. $36\frac{1}{2}$ _____

Estimate each quotient. (*Hint:* Use compatible numbers.)

13. $8\frac{1}{2} \div 2\frac{1}{10}$

$\underline{8 \div 2 = 4}$

14. $12\frac{1}{3} \div 6\frac{1}{8}$

_____

15. $\dfrac{14\frac{7}{10}}{2\frac{1}{6}}$

_____

16. $\dfrac{27\frac{2}{3}}{9\frac{3}{5}}$

_____

17. $6\frac{1}{8} \div \frac{15}{16}$

_____

18. $7\frac{4}{5} \div 4\frac{3}{10}$

_____

19. $\dfrac{23\frac{1}{2}}{5\frac{13}{14}}$

_____

20. $\dfrac{16\frac{1}{4}}{7\frac{7}{8}}$

_____

Divide. Write each quotient in simplest form.

21. $17 \div 3\frac{2}{5}$

$\dfrac{17}{1} \div \dfrac{17}{5}$

$\dfrac{17}{1} \cdot \dfrac{5}{17} = \dfrac{5}{1} = 5$

22. $-3\frac{1}{4} \div \left(-\frac{17}{17}\right)$

_____

23. $5\frac{1}{2} \div \left(-\frac{5}{8}\right)$

_____

24. $-2\frac{5}{8} \div \frac{3}{16}$

_____

25. $6\frac{1}{8} \div 2\frac{1}{3}$

26. $-2\frac{1}{7} \div \left(-2\frac{1}{2}\right)$

27. $-3\frac{1}{4} \div 1\frac{1}{2}$

28. $8\frac{3}{4} \div \left(-3\frac{1}{2}\right)$

_____ _____ _____ _____

Divide. Write each quotient in simplest form.

29. $\dfrac{1\frac{5}{8}}{1\frac{1}{2}}$ 30. $\dfrac{11\frac{1}{2}}{8\frac{5}{8}}$ 31. $\dfrac{9\frac{1}{2}}{3\frac{1}{3}}$ 32. $\dfrac{19\frac{3}{8}}{6\frac{1}{5}}$

$1\frac{5}{8} \div 1\frac{1}{2} = \frac{13}{8} \div \frac{3}{2}$

$\frac{13}{8} \cdot \frac{2}{3} = \frac{13}{12} = 1\frac{1}{12}$

33. $\dfrac{-7}{-2\frac{5}{8}}$ 34. $\dfrac{-41\frac{2}{3}}{-7\frac{1}{7}}$ 35. $\dfrac{-20\frac{5}{6}}{11\frac{1}{9}}$ 36. $\dfrac{10\frac{2}{7}}{-3\frac{5}{9}}$

_____   _____   _____   _____

Evaluate when $a = 7\frac{1}{5}$, $b = -\frac{6}{15}$, $c = -1\frac{1}{3}$, and $d = 9$.

37. $\dfrac{a}{b}$ 38. $\dfrac{c \cdot d}{a}$ 39. $\dfrac{b}{d}$

$\dfrac{7\frac{1}{5}}{-\frac{6}{15}}$

$7\frac{1}{5} \cdot \left(-\frac{15}{6}\right) = \frac{36}{5} \cdot \left(-\frac{15}{6}\right) = -\frac{18}{1}$

$\phantom{7\frac{1}{5} \cdot \left(-\frac{15}{6}\right) =} = -18$

40. $\dfrac{c}{b}$ 41. $\dfrac{a}{c} \cdot b$ 42. $\dfrac{d}{a} \div c$

_____   _____   _____

Solve. Check to justify your answer.

43. In a frog-leaping contest, one frog covered a distance of $203\frac{1}{4}$ inches in three leaps. About how far is the average length of one leap?

44. Human hair grows at the average rate of $\frac{1}{3}$ inch per month. Tara wants her hair to grow $4\frac{2}{3}$ inches longer. About how many months will this take?

_____   _____

SPIRAL REVIEW

Solve.

45. $3x - 8 = -20$ 46. $4(-5x + 6x) = -28$ 47. $7 - 3 = 2x - x$ 48. $\frac{1}{5}x + 3 \le 1$

_____   _____   _____   _____

5-12 Properties of Rational Numbers

Name _____ Date _____

	Addition	**Multiplication**
Commutative Property	$\frac{3}{4} + \frac{2}{3} = \frac{2}{3} + \frac{3}{4}$	$\frac{-1}{5} \cdot \frac{4}{7} = \frac{4}{7} \cdot \frac{-1}{5}$
Associative Property	$\left(3\frac{1}{6} + \frac{2}{3}\right) + 1\frac{1}{2} = 3\frac{1}{6} + \left(\frac{2}{3} + 1\frac{1}{2}\right)$	$\left(\frac{1}{4} \cdot 2\frac{3}{8}\right) \cdot \left(-4\frac{2}{3}\right) = \frac{1}{4} \cdot \left[2\frac{3}{8} \cdot \left(-4\frac{2}{3}\right)\right]$
Identity Property	$0 + 4\frac{5}{6} = 4\frac{5}{6} + 0 = 4\frac{5}{6}$	$1 \cdot \left(-\frac{7}{11}\right) = -\frac{7}{11} \cdot 1 = -\frac{7}{11}$
Inverse Property	$-\frac{4}{9} + \frac{4}{9} = \frac{4}{9} + \left(-\frac{4}{9}\right) = 0$ This is the sum of *opposites*.	$\frac{5}{6} \cdot \frac{6}{5} = \frac{6}{5} \cdot \frac{5}{6} = 1$ This is the product of *reciprocals*.

Multiplicative Property of −1	**Zero Property of Multiplication**
$\frac{7}{8} \cdot (-1) = \frac{-7}{8}$ $\quad$ $\frac{-3}{4} \cdot (-1) = \frac{3}{4}$	$0 \cdot \frac{1}{2} = \frac{1}{2} \cdot 0 = 0$ $\quad$ $\frac{-2}{3} \cdot 0 = 0 \cdot \left(\frac{-2}{3}\right) = 0$

Distributive Property of Multiplication Over Addition	**Distributive Property of Multiplication Over Subtraction**
$-\frac{3}{5}\left(2\frac{5}{7} + \frac{1}{3}\right) = -\frac{3}{5} \cdot 2\frac{5}{7} + \left(-\frac{3}{5}\right) \cdot \frac{1}{3}$	$4\frac{1}{2}\left(\frac{2}{3} - 1\frac{3}{5}\right) = 4\frac{1}{2} \cdot \frac{2}{3} - 4\frac{1}{2} \cdot 1\frac{3}{5}$

Name the property used.

1. $0 + 3\frac{1}{3} = 3\frac{1}{3}$

      Identity Property
       of Addition
      _____

2. $4\frac{1}{4}\left(\frac{7}{9} - \frac{3}{4}\right) = \left(4\frac{1}{4} \cdot \frac{7}{9}\right) - \left(4\frac{1}{4} \cdot \frac{3}{4}\right)$ **3.** $\frac{8}{9} \cdot \left(-\frac{3}{4}\right) = -\frac{3}{4} \cdot \frac{8}{9}$

    _____   _____

What number makes each sentence true? Name the property used.

4. $\frac{1}{3} \cdot g = \frac{-1}{3}$

   $g = -1$; **Multiplicative**
     Property of −1
   _____

5. $6\frac{1}{2} + \frac{1}{6} = \frac{1}{6} + m$

   _____

6. $\frac{4}{5} \cdot t = 0$

   _____

Use the properties of rational numbers to compute mentally.

7. $\left(\frac{3}{4} + \frac{1}{3}\right) + \frac{2}{3}$

   $\frac{3}{4} + \left(\frac{1}{3} + \frac{2}{3}\right) = \frac{3}{4} + 1$
         $1\frac{3}{4}$
   _____

8. $\left(1\frac{5}{9} + 5\frac{3}{4}\right) + \left(-5\frac{3}{4}\right)$

   _____

9. $-\frac{1}{5} + \frac{7}{12} + \frac{1}{5}$

   _____

10. $\left(-2\frac{6}{11} \cdot \frac{3}{5}\right) \cdot \frac{5}{3}$

11. $\frac{7}{12}\left(\frac{11}{7} + \frac{1}{7}\right)$

12. $3\frac{2}{3} \cdot 1\frac{6}{7} \cdot 0 \cdot \frac{1}{4}$

   _____   _____   _____

Complete the chart using the additive inverse and the multiplicative inverse of each number.

		Additive Inverses (opposites)	Multiplicative Inverses (reciprocals)
13.	$\frac{1}{2}$	$\frac{1}{2} + \left(\frac{-1}{2}\right) = 0$	$\frac{1}{2} \cdot \frac{2}{1} = 1$
14.	-5		
15.	$1\frac{1}{3}$		
16.	$-3\frac{3}{8}$		
17.	$\frac{15}{18}$		

Problem Solving

18. Don rode his bike $2\frac{3}{4}$ miles directly north to the store. He then rode $\frac{7}{8}$ miles on the same road south to his friend Gary's house. Together they rode $2\frac{3}{4}$ miles south to the park. How far is Don's house from the park?

19. Mr. Smith's car gets about 30 miles per gallon, and holds 13 gallons of gas. He started a trip with a full tank of gas. He used $\frac{3}{4}$ of a tank. About how many more miles can he drive until the tank is totally empty?

20. Cooking Jan mixes $1\frac{1}{3}$ cups of white flour, $1\frac{3}{4}$ cups of whole wheat flour, and $\frac{2}{3}$ cup of rye flour. About what fraction of the mixture is whole wheat flour?

21. Percy is a realtor. He sells a house for $230,000, of which $18,000 is taxes. Percy makes a commission of $\frac{1}{25}$ of the untaxed price of the house. His agency receives the rest. How much did the agency make on this sale?

CHALLENGE

22. Find the number halfway between the two given numbers. (*Hint:* Compute the average of the two numbers.)

A. $-\frac{1}{3}, \frac{1}{3}$ **B.** $\frac{1}{4}, \frac{1}{2}$ **C.** $\frac{3}{5}, 1\frac{4}{5}$ **D.** $-\frac{1}{12}, -\frac{3}{8}$ **E.** $\frac{99}{100}, 1$

5-13 Order of Operations with Rational Numbers

Name _____ Date _____

When *simplifying expressions with rational numbers,* use the order of operations, and follow the sign rules. When there is a division bar, simplify the expressions above and below the bar, then divide the two numbers.

$$\frac{\left(\frac{2}{3}\right)^2 + \frac{4}{9}}{\frac{3}{5} + \frac{1}{3} \cdot \frac{3}{5}} = \frac{\left(\frac{2}{3} \cdot \frac{2}{3}\right) + \frac{4}{9}}{\frac{3}{5} + \frac{1}{\cancel{3}} \cdot \frac{\cancel{3}}{5}} = \frac{\frac{4}{9} + \frac{4}{9}}{\frac{3}{5} + \frac{1}{5}} = \frac{\frac{8}{9}}{\frac{4}{5}}$$

$$\frac{8}{9} \div \frac{4}{5} = \frac{\cancel{8}^2}{9} \cdot \frac{5}{\cancel{4}_1} = \frac{10}{9} = 1\frac{1}{9}$$

Order of Operations
- First, compute operations within grouping symbols.
- Next, simplify exponents.
- Then multiply or divide from left to right.
- Last, add or subtract from left to right.

Simplify Fractions with Exponents

$$\left(\frac{3}{4}\right)^3 = \frac{3 \cdot 3 \cdot 3}{4 \cdot 4 \cdot 4} = \frac{3^3}{4^3} = \frac{27}{64}$$

Simplify.

1. $(0.06)^2 \cdot 10^3$

_____
$\underline{(0.0036)(1000) = 3.6}$

2. $(3 \cdot 2.6) + (1.5 \div 3)$

_____

3. $1.6 + (-1.6) \cdot (-25.2 \div 6 \cdot 3)$

_____

4. $\dfrac{15.8 + (-3)^2}{(2.3 + 1.7) \cdot 2}$

5. $\dfrac{4 + 2.25 - 2.5^2}{24.6 - 33}$

6. $\left(-\frac{3}{4}\right)^2 \cdot \left(\frac{2}{5}\right)^3$

_____

7. $\left(\frac{3}{5}\right)^3 \div \left(\frac{3}{2}\right)^4$

8. $\left(\frac{1}{2}\right)^3 - \frac{3}{4} \cdot \frac{2}{5}$

9. $\frac{5}{6} - \left(\frac{1}{2}\right)^2 \cdot 8$

_____

10. $\left(\frac{1}{2} + 3\frac{1}{4}\right) \cdot 3 + 2\frac{2}{5}$

11. $\dfrac{4\frac{2}{3} + 1\frac{1}{6}}{1\frac{1}{4} + 1\frac{7}{8}}$

12. $\dfrac{5\frac{1}{4} - 2\frac{1}{2}}{7\frac{4}{5} - 6\frac{1}{3}}$

_____

Simplify. Write each answer in fraction form and decimal form.

13. $(-0.5)^5 \cdot \left(\frac{8}{5}\right)^2$

_____
$\underline{-0.03125 \cdot 2.56 = -0.08 = -\frac{2}{25}}$

14. $0.011 + \left(-\frac{2}{5}\right)^3 \div 0.25$

15. $\dfrac{\frac{1}{2} + 2\frac{1}{8} + 1\frac{1}{8}}{2.2 + 2.8}$

16. $10 \div \left(8\frac{1}{3} - 6\frac{1}{4}\right) - 0.3$

17. $\dfrac{5 \cdot 5 + 7}{3^2 \cdot (-1)}$

18. $\dfrac{2^3 + 4}{-\frac{3}{5} \cdot \frac{1}{9}}$

_____

Insert grouping symbols to make the sentence true.

19. $(5 - 4) \bullet \frac{3}{5} - \frac{2}{5} = \frac{1}{5}$

20. $5 - 4 \bullet \frac{3}{5} - \frac{2}{5} = 3$

21. $1\frac{7}{10} + \frac{3}{10} \div \frac{1}{2} - \frac{3}{5} = -20$

22. $1\frac{7}{10} + \frac{3}{10} \div \frac{1}{2} - \frac{3}{5} = 3\frac{2}{5}$

Compare. Write <, = or >.

23. $\frac{1}{2}\left(4 + \frac{1}{8}\right) \underline{\ <\ } \frac{1}{2} \bullet 4 + \frac{1}{8}$

$\frac{4}{2} + \left(\frac{1}{2} \bullet \frac{1}{8}\right) = 2\frac{1}{16}; \frac{4}{2} + \frac{1}{8} = 2\frac{1}{8}$

$2\frac{1}{16} < 2\frac{1}{8}$

24. $2\frac{1}{2} \div \frac{1}{4} \bullet 8 \underline{\qquad} 2\frac{1}{2} \div \left(\frac{1}{4} \bullet 8\right)$

25. $6 \bullet \frac{2}{3} - 5 \bullet \frac{3}{5} \underline{\qquad} 6 \bullet \left(\frac{2}{3} - 5\right) \bullet \frac{3}{5}$

26. $1\frac{7}{9} - \left(\frac{2}{3}\right)^2 \underline{\qquad} \left(1\frac{7}{9} - \frac{2}{3}\right)^2$

Use a formula, then solve. (*Hint:* Let C = Celsius, and F = Fahrenheit.)

27. To convert temperature from Fahrenheit to Celsius, subtract 32 from the Fahrenheit temperature and multiply the result by $\frac{5}{9}$. What is the Celsius temperature if the weather report is 50°F?

$$C = \frac{5}{9}(F - 32); C = \frac{5}{9}(50 - 32) = 10$$

The temperature is 10°C.

28. To convert temperature from Celsius to Fahrenheit, multiply the Celsius temperature by $\frac{9}{5}$, then add 32. What is the Fahrenheit temperature if the weather report is 50°C?

29. To find the length of a woman's foot in inches, based on her shoe size, add 20.5 to her shoe size and divide the result by 3. Let L = foot length and s = shoe size. If a woman wears a size $9\frac{1}{2}$ shoe, how long is her foot?

30. The area formula for a trapezoid is $A = \frac{1}{2}h(b + B)$, where h is the height and b and B are the lengths of the bases. What is the area of a trapezoid with height $\frac{2}{5}$ foot and bases of length $\frac{5}{8}$ foot and $\frac{15}{8}$ foot?

WRITE ABOUT IT

31. Why do you think having a rule for the order of operations is important?

5-14 Addition and Subtraction Equations with Fractions

Name _____ Date _____

To solve addition and subtraction equations with fractions, follow the same rules as you use to add and subtract integers. Rename fractions with common denominators as needed.

Solve: $x - 2\frac{5}{8} = 1\frac{1}{4}$

$x - 2\frac{5}{8} + 2\frac{5}{8} = 1\frac{1}{4} + 2\frac{5}{8}$

$x = 1\frac{2}{8} + 2\frac{5}{8}$

$x = 3\frac{7}{8}$

Check: Use substitution.

$3\frac{7}{8} - 2\frac{5}{8} \stackrel{?}{=} 1\frac{1}{4}$

$1\frac{2}{8} \stackrel{?}{=} 1\frac{1}{4}$

$1\frac{1}{4} = 1\frac{1}{4}$ True

Solve. Check to justify your answer.

1. $\frac{4}{5} = s + \frac{1}{5}$

$\frac{4}{5} - \frac{1}{5} = s + \frac{1}{5} - \frac{1}{5}$

$s = \frac{3}{5}$

2. $x + \left(-\frac{7}{8}\right) = 2\frac{5}{24}$

3. $h + 2\frac{1}{6} = 5\frac{5}{9}$

4. $2 = y - \left(-\frac{3}{5}\right)$

5. $a + 2\frac{1}{3} = 5\frac{2}{3}$

6. $\frac{3}{4} = p - \left(-\frac{1}{2}\right)$

7. $1\frac{3}{4} = c - 3\frac{7}{8}$

8. $7\frac{1}{2} = d - 4\frac{3}{10}$

9. $n - \left(-3\frac{7}{10}\right) = 1\frac{2}{3}$

Solve. Then use substitution to check. (*Hint:* Combine numerical terms.)

10. $\left(-\frac{5}{8}\right) - \frac{1}{8} + n = 1$

$-\frac{6}{8} + n = 1; n = 1 + \frac{6}{8}$

$n = 1\frac{6}{8} = 1\frac{3}{4}$

11. $x + \left(\frac{1}{5} - \frac{4}{5}\right) = -2$

12. $9\frac{2}{7} - 12 = -3\frac{1}{3} + 2\frac{12}{21} + x$

13. $-12\frac{4}{5} + w - \left(-2\frac{7}{15}\right) = 5\frac{3}{10} - 8\frac{2}{3}$

Solve. Then use substitution and the original equation to check.
(*Hint:* Combine numerical terms, then write a related sentence.)

14. $\frac{1}{2} - x = \frac{4}{7}$

$\frac{7}{14} - \frac{8}{14} = x;\ x = -\frac{1}{14}$

Check: $\frac{1}{2} - \left(-\frac{1}{14}\right) = \frac{4}{7};\ \frac{4}{7} = \frac{4}{7}$ True

15. $7\frac{3}{8} - r = -5\frac{3}{4}$

16. $12 = -8\frac{1}{5} - n$

17. $-5 - k = \frac{3}{10} - \frac{1}{3} + \frac{4}{5}$

18. $-3\frac{1}{5} + \frac{9}{10} = 1\frac{3}{5} - p$

Problem Solving

19. Kylie put her kitty inside of a cat carrier and then put it on the scale. The combined weight was $15\frac{1}{4}$ pounds. The cat carrier alone weighs $4\frac{5}{8}$ pounds. What is the cat's weight? How much greater than the cat carrier is the weight of the cat? Let c = cat's weight.

20. Hiroki ran a total of 12 miles over a four-day period. He ran $2\frac{1}{4}$ miles the first day, $3\frac{1}{2}$ miles the second day, and $4\frac{3}{8}$ miles the third day. On which day did he run the least? Let m = miles Hiroki ran the fourth day.

21. While working at the deli, Alice placed some cheese on a scale. She removed some cheese, leaving $1\frac{3}{4}$ pounds on the scale, then removed $\frac{5}{8}$ pound. If she has removed a total of 1 pound of cheese, how much cheese did she originally place on the scale?

22. Rashid had $24\frac{11}{16}$ feet of cable wire. She cut off a $13\frac{5}{8}$-foot piece to hook up her cable box, then she cut off a $5\frac{1}{4}$-foot piece to connect her cable box to her TV. Is the remaining piece as long as the wire that connects the cable box to the TV?

SPIRAL REVIEW

23. Write in scientific notation. (*Hint:* Use the × symbol when writing scientific notation.)

A. 42,000   **B.** 2,350,000   **C.** 95   **D.** 788,000   **E.** 54,800,000,000

5-15 Multiplication and Division Equations with Fractions

Name _____ Date _____

To solve multiplication equations with fractions, multiply both sides by the reciprocal. To solve division equations with fractions, apply the Multiplication Property of Equality.

> **Remember: Multiplication Property of Equality**
> If $a = b$, then $a \cdot c = b \cdot c$.

Solve: $\dfrac{x}{\left(\frac{5}{6}\right)} = \dfrac{3}{5} \longrightarrow \dfrac{x}{\left(\frac{5}{6}\right)} \cdot \dfrac{5}{6} = \dfrac{3}{5} \cdot \dfrac{5}{6}$

$$x = \dfrac{1}{2}$$

Check: $\dfrac{\frac{1}{2}}{\frac{5}{6}} = \dfrac{3}{5} \longrightarrow \dfrac{1}{2} \div \dfrac{5}{6} \overset{?}{=} \dfrac{3}{5}$

$$\dfrac{1}{2} \cdot \dfrac{6}{5} \overset{?}{=} \dfrac{3}{5}$$

$$\dfrac{3}{5} = \dfrac{3}{5} \quad \text{True}$$

Solve. Use substitution to check.

1. $\dfrac{3}{4}x = 3$

$$\dfrac{4}{3} \cdot \dfrac{3}{4}x = \dfrac{4}{3} \cdot 3$$

$$x = 4$$

Check: $\dfrac{3}{4}\left(\dfrac{4}{1}\right) = 3$; $3 = 3$ True

2. $\dfrac{5}{8}w = 5$

3. $6 = \dfrac{3}{5}z$

4. $-6 = \dfrac{2}{3}y$

5. $4 = \left(-\dfrac{3}{7}\right)s$

6. $\dfrac{3}{7} = -\dfrac{9}{14}d$

7. $-3 = \left(-\dfrac{1}{4}\right)t$

8. $\dfrac{-1}{4}h = \dfrac{-5}{6}$

9. $-\dfrac{3}{8}b = -\dfrac{1}{2}$

Solve. Use substitution to check. (*Hint:* Combine like terms.)

10. $\dfrac{1}{4}w + \dfrac{2}{4}w = 15$

$$\dfrac{3}{4}w = 15$$

$$\dfrac{3}{4} \cdot \dfrac{4}{3} \cdot w = \dfrac{15}{1} \cdot \dfrac{4}{3}; \ w = 20$$

Check: $\dfrac{1}{4}(20) + \dfrac{2}{4}(20) = 15$

$$15 = 15 \text{ True}$$

11. $2 = \dfrac{-5}{9}t + \left(\dfrac{-4}{9}t\right)$

12. $\dfrac{5}{8}x - \dfrac{3}{8}x = 5$

Solve. Use substitution to check.

13. $\dfrac{m}{\frac{3}{4}} = 8$

$\dfrac{m}{\frac{3}{4}} \cdot \dfrac{3}{4} = 8 \cdot \dfrac{3}{4}; \; m = 6$

Check: $\dfrac{6}{\frac{3}{4}} = 8; \; 6 = 8\left(\dfrac{3}{4}\right)$

$6 = 6$ **True**

14. $\dfrac{c}{\frac{2}{3}} = 12$

15. $\dfrac{t}{\frac{-4}{5}} = -15$

16. $-10 = \dfrac{b}{\frac{-3}{4}}$

17. $\dfrac{y}{\frac{3}{4}} = \dfrac{-2}{5}$

18. $\dfrac{z}{\frac{1}{5}} = \dfrac{-1}{2}$

19. $\dfrac{3}{4}d - \dfrac{1}{2}d = \dfrac{2}{3}$

20. $\dfrac{4}{5}s - \left(-\dfrac{1}{3}\right)s = \dfrac{2}{45}$

21. $-5\dfrac{1}{7}e - \left(-5\dfrac{2}{5}\right)e = -\dfrac{1}{2}$

Write a related sentence to solve. Then use the original equation to check your solution.

22. $\dfrac{\frac{2}{3}}{x} = \dfrac{3}{5}$

$\dfrac{2}{3} = \dfrac{3}{5}x; \; \dfrac{5}{3} \cdot \dfrac{2}{3} = \dfrac{\overset{1}{\cancel{5}}}{3} \cdot \dfrac{\overset{1}{\cancel{3}}}{\cancel{5}}x; \; x = \dfrac{10}{9} = 1\dfrac{1}{9}$

Check: $\dfrac{\frac{2}{3}}{1\frac{1}{9}} = \dfrac{3}{5}; \; \dfrac{\overset{1}{\cancel{2}}}{3} \cdot \dfrac{9}{10} = \dfrac{3}{5}$

$\dfrac{3}{5} = \dfrac{3}{5}$ **True**

23. $\dfrac{-\frac{7}{2}}{u} = 6$

24. $\dfrac{5}{4} = \dfrac{\frac{-9}{8}}{w}$

Solve. Check to justify your answer.

25. Toby is 5 feet tall. This is $\dfrac{4}{5}$ the height of his father. How tall is Toby's father?

26. Shakira cuts plastic tubing into $\dfrac{1}{4}$-inch pieces to make beads. If she needs 864 beads, how many yards of plastic tubing does she need to buy? (36 inches = 1 yard)

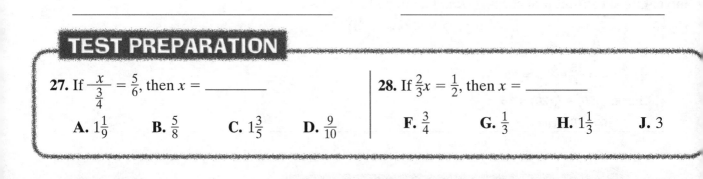

TEST PREPARATION

27. If $\dfrac{x}{\frac{3}{4}} = \dfrac{5}{6}$, then $x =$ _____

   A. $1\dfrac{1}{9}$ **B.** $\dfrac{5}{8}$ **C.** $1\dfrac{3}{5}$ **D.** $\dfrac{9}{10}$

28. If $\dfrac{2}{3}x = \dfrac{1}{2}$, then $x =$ _____

   F. $\dfrac{3}{4}$ **G.** $\dfrac{1}{3}$ **H.** $1\dfrac{1}{3}$ **J.** 3

5-16 Solve Two-Step Equations with Fractions

Name _____   Date _____

To solve a two-step equation with fractions, solve as with integers. First apply the Addition or Subtraction Property of Equality to isolate the term with the variable. Then apply the Multiplication or Division Property of Equality to isolate the variable.

Solve: $\frac{1}{2}p - 16\frac{1}{2} = 15$

$\frac{1}{2}p - 16\frac{1}{2} + 16\frac{1}{2} = 15 + 16\frac{1}{2}$

$\frac{1}{2}p = 31\frac{1}{2}$

$\left(\frac{1}{2}\right)\left(\frac{2}{1}\right)p = \frac{63}{2}\left(\frac{2}{1}\right)$

$p = \frac{63}{1} = 63$

Check: Use substitution.

$\frac{1}{2}(63) - 16\frac{1}{2} \overset{?}{=} 15$

$31\frac{1}{2} - 16\frac{1}{2} \overset{?}{=} 15$

$15 = 15$ True

Translate and write a two-step equation.

1. Twice n diminished by $8\frac{3}{4}$ is 16.

$$2n - 8\frac{3}{4} = 16$$

2. 1 is $\frac{1}{5}$ more than 7 multiplied by x.

_____

3. 26 is 4 less than $\frac{4}{7}$ times a number, k.

_____

4. $\frac{9}{10}$ increased by w times 6 is equal to $-\frac{9}{10}$.

_____

5. Half m increased by $7\frac{1}{2}$ is 14.

_____

6. 43 is 11 less than $\frac{5}{8}$ times a number p.

_____

Solve. Use substitution to check.

7. $\frac{1}{2}m + 12 = 16$

$\frac{1}{2}m = 4;\ m = 8$

Check: $\frac{1}{2}(8) + 12 = 16;\ 16 = 16$ True

8. $1\frac{2}{5}b + 3\frac{1}{2} = 31\frac{1}{2}$

_____

9. $\frac{1}{48}g - (-3) = -1\frac{1}{4}$

_____

10. $-1\frac{1}{4}z - \frac{1}{6} = 2\frac{1}{3}$

_____

11. $-4 = -\frac{3}{10}t + \left(-2\frac{4}{7}\right)$

_____

12. $-15\frac{4}{5} = -3\frac{3}{5}y + \left(-3\frac{2}{10}\right)$

_____

13. $-2\frac{2}{7} = \frac{2}{3}v - \left(-\frac{5}{7}\right)$

_____

14. $\dfrac{k}{1\frac{1}{4}} + 8 = 28$

_____

15. $1\frac{1}{2} = 2\frac{1}{4}h + \left(-\frac{3}{4}\right)$

_____

Solve. Check to justify your answer.

16. $59 = \dfrac{d}{2\frac{1}{4}} - (-17)$

$42 = \dfrac{d}{2\frac{1}{4}};\ d = 94\frac{1}{2}$

Check: $59 = \dfrac{94\frac{1}{2}}{2\frac{1}{4}} - (-17)$

$59 = 42 + 17;\ 59 = 59$ True

17. $-4 = \dfrac{m}{8} - 2\frac{1}{2}$

18. $\dfrac{1}{x} - 8\frac{1}{6} = -2\frac{1}{12}$

Combine like terms, then solve. Check to justify your answer.

19. $-5s + 1\frac{1}{4} + 3s = -5$

$-2s + 1\frac{1}{4} = -5;\ s = 3\frac{1}{8}$

Check: $-5\left(3\frac{1}{8}\right) + 1\frac{1}{4} + 3\left(3\frac{1}{8}\right) = -5;\ -5 = -5$ True

20. $-4 = \dfrac{m}{8} - 2\frac{1}{2} - \dfrac{0}{4}$

21. $4 = \dfrac{h}{3} - 1\frac{1}{4} + \dfrac{2}{3}$

22. $-3q + \dfrac{1}{8} - 5q = \dfrac{7}{8}$

Problem Solving

23. Henry made 39 birdhouses. Fifteen will remain unpainted. He wants to paint the rest. On Saturday he painted $\frac{1}{3}$ of the birdhouses. How many birdhouses, k, are left to be painted?

24. Seventy-eight students are in a chamber orchestra. Thirty-two members play wind instruments. Half of the other members play percussion instruments. About what fraction of the students play a percussion instrument?

MENTAL MATH

Visualize each equation rewritten as an addition equation. Then write the number you would add to each side, and what number you would multiply on both sides to isolate the variable. (*Hint:* Think about opposites, the Subtraction Principle, and multiplicative inverses.)

25. $8 = \frac{1}{3}f - 7$ add _____ to both sides, then multiply _____ on both sides

26. $-\frac{1}{5}a - 21 = 29$ add _____ to both sides, then multiply _____ on both sides

27. $\dfrac{g}{\frac{1}{5}} + 9 = 49$ add _____ to both sides, then multiply _____ on both sides

5-17 Rename Customary Units of Measure

Name _____ Date _____

To rename larger units as smaller units, *multiply*.
To rename smaller units as larger units, *divide*.

How many yards are in $2\frac{1}{2}$ miles?

Think: _?_ yd = $2\frac{1}{2}$ mi or $2\frac{1}{2}$ mi = _?_ yd
      and 1 mi = 1760 yd or 1760 yd = 1 mi

Think: Know miles, want to know yards.
      Rename larger units as smaller units. Multiply.

$2\frac{1}{2}$ mi • 1760 yd = _?_ yd

$\frac{5}{\overset{2}{\underset{1}{\cancel{2}}}} • \frac{\overset{880}{\cancel{1760}}}{1} = 4400$

So $2\frac{1}{2}$ miles = 4400 yards.

Customary Units of Length
1 foot (ft) = 12 inches (in.)
1 yard (yd) = 3 ft or 36 in.
1 mile (mi) = 5280 ft or 1760 yd

Customary Units of Capacity
1 cup (c) = 8 fluid ounces (fl oz)
1 pint (pt) = 2 c
1 quart (qt) = 2 pt
1 gallon (gal) = 4 qt

Customary Units of Weight
1 pound (lb) = 16 ounces (oz)
1 ton (T) = 2000 lb

Rename each unit of measure.

1. 22 fl oz = ___$2\frac{3}{4}$___ c

   $22 \div 8 = 2\frac{3}{4}$

2. 10 pt = _____ qt

3. 10 qt = _____ gal

4. 18 qt = _____ gal

5. $1\frac{3}{8}$ gal = _____ qt

6. $10\frac{1}{2}$ qt = _____ gal

7. 30 in. = _____ ft

8. $6\frac{3}{8}$ yd = _____ in.

9. $15\frac{2}{3}$ yd = _____ in.

10. 1320 ft = _____ mi

11. 4400 yd = _____ mi

12. $4\frac{5}{6}$ mi = _____ ft

13. 48 oz = _____ lb

14. $\frac{1}{2}$ lb = _____ oz

15. $3\frac{3}{8}$ T = _____ lb

16. 11,500 lb = _____ T

Rename each unit of measure. (*Hint:* Rename the units two or more times to find the answer.)

17. 80 c = ___20___ qt

    $80 \div 2 = 40$ pt
    $40 \div 2 = 20$ qt

18. 1 pt = _____ fl oz

19. 17 pt = _____ gal

20. $\frac{3}{4}$ pt = _____ gal

21. 63 c = _____ qt

22. 6 mi = _____ in.

23. 19,008 in. = _____ mi

24. 1 qt = _____ fl oz

25. 1 gal = _____ fl oz

Compare. Write <, =, or >. (*Hint:* Rename one measure to compare like units of measure.)

26. $\frac{1}{4}$ mi __<__ 1500 ft

$\frac{1}{4}$ • 5280 = 1320 ft

27. $12\frac{1}{3}$ yd _____ 37 ft

28. $\frac{3}{4}$ ft _____ 9 in.

29. $\frac{1}{48}$ mi _____ 1320 ft

30. $\frac{1}{3}$ mi _____ $586\frac{2}{3}$ yd

31. $\frac{2}{9}$ yd _____ 8 in.

32. 18 pt _____ 8 qt

33. 202 fl oz _____ 100 c

34. $3\frac{1}{2}$ gal _____ 224 qt

35. 156 qt _____ 56 gal

36. $\frac{1}{8}$ T _____ 600 lb

37. $8\frac{1}{2}$ lb _____ 140 oz

Compute. Write each unit of measure in lowest terms. (*Hint:* Line up the units and rename as needed.)

38. (3 qt 1 pt) + (9 gal 2 qt 1 pt)

9 gal 5 qt 2 pt = 9 gal 6 qt = 10 gal 2 qt

39. (18 gal 3 qt 1 pt) + (7 gal 15 pt)

40. (2 yd 1 ft 30 in.) ÷ 6

41. (5 mi 1000 yards) • 8

42. (5 c 11 fl oz) + (7 qt 3 c 2 fl oz)

43. (9 ft 48 in.) • 2

Solve. Show your work.

44. Biology A male Asian elephant can weigh as much as 11,000 pounds. How many tons is this?

45. Architecture The CN Tower in Toronto, Canada, is 1815 feet tall. How many miles is this?

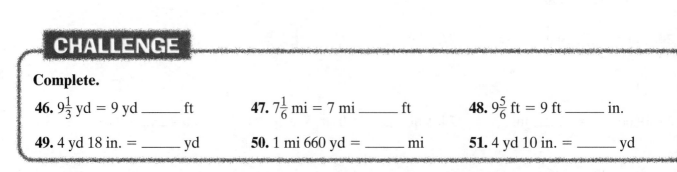

CHALLENGE

Complete.

46. $9\frac{1}{3}$ yd = 9 yd _____ ft

47. $7\frac{1}{6}$ mi = 7 mi _____ ft

48. $9\frac{5}{6}$ ft = 9 ft _____ in.

49. 4 yd 18 in. = _____ yd

50. 1 mi 660 yd = _____ mi

51. 4 yd 10 in. = _____ yd

5-18 Problem-Solving Strategy:
Make a Drawing

Read ▸ Plan ▸ Solve ▸ Check

Name _____ Date _____

Solve by using the strategy Make a Drawing.

1. After making a batch of muffins, Claire brought a third of the batch to school. While she was at school, her brother and his friends ate half of the muffins Claire had left at home. What part of the original batch did Claire find when she got home?

   _____

2. Is it possible to place 60 quarters in 6 stacks so that four stacks are the same height and two are twice as high as any one of those four?

   _____

3. A bag holds 9 marbles. Exactly 7 of them are red. If you are permitted to add 3 marbles at a time—1 red and 2 white—will there ever be a time in which exactly half the marbles in the bag will be red?

   _____

4. A 60-inch wire is cut in half. One of the halves is cut into thirds, and the other half is cut into fourths. One of those thirds and one of those fourths are then used in an electrical connection. Together, how long are the two pieces that were used in the connection?

   _____

5. The top of the chimney on Arnie's house is 8 feet lower than the chimney on Bob's house. But Bob's chimney is twice as tall as Chuck's. Arnie's chimney reaches 32 feet above ground. How high are the tops of Bob's and Chuck's chimneys?

   _____

6. A hot air balloon rises 80 feet in the first minute. Every minute after this it rises 8 more feet than it had risen during the previous minute. How high will the balloon be after 5 minutes?

7. At exactly 12:00 noon, two cars pass each other, heading in opposite directions on parallel roads. One is going 60 mph; the other is going 45 mph. At what time will the cars be 140 miles apart?

8. The chief of police wants to protect an ancient Roman column at a museum. He points to a spot on the ground 46 feet from the column and says, "I want officers placed every 50 feet, forming a circle out to here!" He, of course, means they should be placed in a circle around the monument. Walking the circle would cover a length of about 290 feet (the circle's circumference; keep in mind that the 46-foot distance to its center is the circle's radius). How many police officers would be required?

9. To protect a dignitary arriving by train, the mayor points along the edge of the train platform and tells the chief of police, "Be sure there are police officers no more than 25 feet from each end of the platform." The platform is 200 feet long. If each police officer is responsible for an equal amount of space, what is the least number of police officers required?

10. Two crews begin laying the rails of parallel railroad tracks at the same starting position. The crew members setting the left rail have older equipment that allows them to lay the rail in 18-foot sections. The crew members setting the right rail have newer equipment that allows them to set 28-foot sections. After how many feet will the end of an 18-foot section first align with the end of a 28-foot section?

Enrichment:

Different Ways to Find the GCF

Use the Division method to find the GCF of 412 and 224.

$412 \div 224 = 1R188$ ← Divide the greater number by the lesser number.

$224 \div 188 = 1R36$ ← Divide the divisor by the remainder. If the remainder is not 0, repeat this process.

$188 \div 36 = 5R8$

$36 \div 8 = 4R4$

$8 \div 4 = 2R0$ ← If the remainder is 0, then the last divisor is the GCF.

So the GCF is 4.

Use the Subtraction method to find the GCF of 72 and 120.

$120 - 72 = 48$ ← Subtract the lesser number from the greater number.

$72 - 48 = 24$ ← Repeat this process with the smaller two of the three numbers in the previous step.

$48 - 24 = 24$ ← When two of the numbers are the same, that number is the GCF.

So the GCF is 24.

Use the Division Method to find the GCF of these pairs of numbers.

1. 14, 26 **2.** 18, 81 **3.** 44, 121 **4.** 144, 60 **5.** 35, 84 **6.** 48, 76

$26 \div 14 = 1R12$
$14 \div 12 = 1R2$
$12 \div 2 = 6R0$
The GCF is 2.

Use the Subtraction Method to find the GCF of these pairs of numbers.

7. 12, 28 **8.** 18, 45 **9.** 24, 30 **10.** 42, 28 **11.** 30, 75 **12.** 36, 90

$28 - 12 = 16$
$16 - 12 = 4$
$12 - 4 = 8$
$8 - 4 = 4$
The GCF is 4.

Problem Solving

13. Alberta is buying square tiles for the floor of her office. The dimensions of the room are 72 inches by 88 inches. She wants the side length of the tile to be a whole number of inches, and she does not want to cut any tiles. What is the largest square tile that she can use?

TEST PREPARATION

14. For which pair of numbers is the GCF 16?

A. 432, 504 **B.** 224, 280 **C.** 560, 576 **D.** 264, 440

Name _____ Date _____

Chapter 5 Vocabulary

complex fraction	improper fraction	prime factorization
composite number	Inverse Property of Multiplication	prime number
Density Property	least common denominator (LCD)	reciprocal
equivalent fractions	least common multiple (LCM)	relatively prime
factor tree	mixed number	simplest form
greatest common factor (GCF)	Multiplicative Property of −1	

From the vocabulary list above, choose the term(s) that best complete each sentence. Write the term(s) in the space(s) provided.

1. The expression $2^2 \cdot 3 \cdot 5$ is the _____ of 60.

2. The _____ states that an infinite number of rational numbers can be found between any two rational numbers.

3. You can find the _____ or the _____ of two or more numbers by listing the multiples of the numbers and choosing the least number that appears on each list.

4. The _____ of a number is its multiplicative inverse.

5. A fraction is in _____ when the only common factor of the numerator and denominator is 1.

6. A number whose only factors are itself and one is a _____.

7. A _____ is a fractional number with an integer part and a fraction part.

8. In an _____ the numerator is greater than the denominator.

9. $a(-1) = -(a)$ represents the _____.

Choose two terms from the list that you did not use in Questions 1–9. For each term, write a definition in your own words and give an example.

10. _____

_____

_____

_____

_____

Test Prep: Short Answer Questions
Strategy: Show All Your Work

Name _____ Date _____

<table>
<tr><td>

When answering short answer questions, you should *explain your thinking* about how you solve the problem.

To solve the problem, try using these strategies:

- Reread the item.
- Use the Test-Prep Strategy.
- Apply appropriate rules, definitions, properties, or strategies.
- Analyze your answers.

</td><td>

Sample Test Item

What is the prime factorization of 180 written in exponential form?

The prime factorization of a number is that number written as the product of its prime factors. Use a tree diagram to write the factors of 180.

180

60   3

20   3

4   5

2   2

$180 = 2 \cdot 2 \cdot 5 \cdot 3 \cdot 3 = 2^2 \cdot 3^2 \cdot 5$

Answer: $2^2 \cdot 3^2 \cdot 5$

</td></tr>
</table>

Solve. *TIP: Use another solution method to check your answers.*

1. What is the least common multiple of 6, 12, and 20?

Show all your work.

Answer _____

2. Simplify: $8\left(\frac{1}{2} - \frac{3}{4}\right)^2$

Show all your work.

Answer _____

---

3. Rhu is $62\frac{3}{8}$ in., Juan is 5 ft $2\frac{1}{3}$ in., and Tim is 5 ft $\frac{29}{12}$ in. Write their names in order of height from *tallest* to *shortest*.

Show all your work.

Answer _____

4. Mrs. Latte prepares 3 gallons of lemonade. How many cups of lemonade does she make?

Show all your work.

Answer _____

5. The art teacher needs to order 4 ounces of clay for each student in the ceramics class. There are 26 students in the class. How many *pounds* of clay need to be ordered?

Show all your work.

Answer _____

6. Ramón's height is two thirds of his father's height. If Ramón is $4\frac{1}{9}$ feet, what is his father's height in *feet and inches*?

Show all your work.

Answer _____

7. What is the greatest common factor of 108, 81, 162 and 216?

Show all your work.

Answer _____

8. Rhianna used 14 quarts, 2 pints, and 6 fluid ounces of juice at a party, and has $15\frac{1}{8}$ pints left. How many *quarts* of juice did she have before the party?

Show all your work.

Answer _____

9. This aquarium contains 4 gallons of water.

Estimate the amount of water in the aquarium when it is full.

Show all your work.

Estimation _____

10. Solve the equation: $10m + 2\frac{1}{5} = -\frac{3}{10}$

Show all your work.

Answer _____

Practice Chapter 5 Test

Name _____ Date _____

1. Write the prime factorization of 260 in exponential form. _____

2. Write $\frac{32}{72}$ in simplest form. _____

3. Find the greatest common factor (GCF) of 75 and 100. _____

4. Find the least common multiple (LCM) of 75 and 100. _____

5. Find the least common denominator (LCD) of $\frac{2}{3}, \frac{5}{8}, \frac{1}{6}$. _____

Tell whether the fraction is close to $-1, \frac{-1}{2}, 0, \frac{1}{2}$, or 1.

6. $\frac{-11}{25}$

7. $-\frac{95}{103}$

8. $\frac{9}{77}$

_____ _____ _____

9. $\frac{11}{15}$

10. $\frac{7}{13}$

11. $\frac{1}{8}$

_____ _____ _____

Compare. Write <, = or >.

12. $3\frac{2}{5}$ ___ $\frac{34}{10}$

13. $\frac{-3}{7}$ ___ -0.4

14. $6\frac{5}{8}$ ___ $6\frac{7}{12}$

15. Order $-4\frac{7}{12}, -4\frac{5}{8}, -4.6$ from least to greatest. _____

Simplify. Express your answer in lowest terms.

16. $\frac{-3}{4} + \frac{1}{6}$

17. $\frac{3}{8} - \frac{7}{10}$

18. $\frac{-5}{9} - \left(-\frac{8}{15}\right)$

_____ _____ _____

19. $2\frac{5}{6} - 1\frac{3}{4}$

20. $-4\frac{4}{5} + 1\frac{2}{3}$

21. $-10\frac{1}{2} - 7\frac{7}{10}$

_____ _____ _____

22. $-4\frac{1}{3} \cdot 2\frac{3}{5}$

23. $8\frac{1}{2} \div 2\frac{1}{8}$

24. $\dfrac{9\frac{5}{9}}{3\frac{2}{3}}$

_____ _____ _____

25. $\left(\frac{-1}{2}\right)^5 \cdot 0.2^2$

26. $\dfrac{\frac{-4}{5} + \frac{1}{3}}{\frac{-1}{3} - \frac{0}{5}}$

27. $\dfrac{6.75 - (76.32 - 10^2)(0.5)}{3.3 - 0.8 \cdot 8 + 4.1}$

_____ _____ _____

Evaluate when $a = \frac{-5}{6}$, $b = \frac{-3}{8}$, and $c = \frac{4}{15}$.

28. $a \cdot b$

29. bc

30. $a \div c$

What number makes each sentence true? Name the property used.

31. $9\frac{1}{4} + a = 9\frac{1}{4}$

32. $-3\left(\frac{2}{3} + \frac{3}{8}\right) = -3y + (-3)\frac{3}{8}$

33. $x \cdot \left(\frac{-1}{10}\right) = 1$

Rename each unit of measure.

34. $2\frac{3}{8}$ mi = _____ ft

35. 26 qt = _____ gal

36. $\frac{1}{20}$ T = _____ lb

37. 85 c = _____ pt

38. $1\frac{2}{3}$ yd = _____ ft

39. $\frac{1}{8}$ oz = _____ lb

Solve. Check to verify your answer.

40. $x + 3\frac{1}{7} + 1\frac{2}{7} = 2\frac{1}{7}$

41. $1\frac{3}{4} = 5v - 4v - \frac{3}{8}$

42. $\frac{5}{12} = \frac{-2}{3}c$

43. $\dfrac{y}{\frac{1}{2}} - 4 = \frac{3}{4}$

44. $\frac{6}{7}b + 3 = 3\frac{3}{8}$

Tell About It

Explain how you solve each problem. Show all your work.

45. Government In 2007, there were 71 female representatives in the U.S. House of Representatives. This is 20 fewer than $\frac{1}{4}$ the number of male representatives. How many male representatives were in the U.S. House of Representatives?

46. Erin owns 48 movies on DVD. Three eighths of the movies are comedies, $\frac{1}{3}$ are dramas, $\frac{1}{4}$ are action adventure, and the rest are science fiction. What part of her movie collection is science fiction?

Cumulative Review: Chapters 1–5

Name _____ Date _____

Circle the best answer.

1. If $\frac{-3}{5} \bullet a = 1$, what is the value of a?

    A. 1   **B.** $\frac{-3}{5}$

    C. 0   **D.** $\frac{-5}{3}$

2. Which is *not* a rational number?

    F. $0.\overline{25}$

    G. $\frac{2\pi}{\pi}$

    H. $0.2020020002\ldots$

    J. $\frac{237}{301}$

3. Simplify.

10^{-5}

    A. $-100,000$ **B.** $-10,000$

    C. $\frac{1}{10,000}$ **D.** 0.00001

4. Which expression is equivalent to the expression below?

$3(a - b^2) + 5ab^2 - a$

    F. $5ab^2 - 3b^2 + 2a$ **G.** $5ab^2 - a$
    H. $8ab^2 - a$ **J.** $5ab^2 + 3b^2$

5. Divide.

$\frac{3}{8} \div \frac{4}{9}$

    A. $\frac{1}{6}$ **B.** $\frac{27}{32}$

    C. $\frac{7}{17}$ **D.** $\frac{59}{72}$

6. If $-\left(\frac{x}{16}\right) = 4$, what is the value of x?

    F. -64
    G. -4
    H. 4
    J. 64

7. Find the solution set for $-\frac{2}{3}x > 2$ if the replacement set is $R = \{-9, -6, -3, 0, 3, 6, 9\}$.

    A. $S = \{-9, -6, -3\}$
    B. $S = \{-9, -6\}$
    C. $S = \{3, 6, 9\}$
    D. $S = \{6, 9\}$

8. Even if Matt scores 5 more points, he still will not score as many points as Carlos. If Matt scores m points and Carlos scores c points, which statement represents this situation?

    F. $c + 5 > m$ **G.** $c + 5 < m$
    H. $m + 5 > c$ **J.** $m + 5 < c$

9. Divide.

$0.063 \div 0.7$

    A. 0.009 **B.** 0.9
    C. 0.09 **D.** 9

10. Which is the LCD of $\frac{19}{28}, \frac{7}{12}, \frac{3}{4}$?

    F. 4   **G.** 28
    H. 56   **J.** 84

11. The graph below is the solution to which inequality?

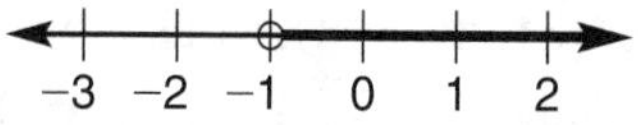

    A. $-2x + 3 < 5$ **B.** $-2x > 2$
    C. $3x + 3 \geq 0$ **D.** $7x + 5 \leq 2$

12. The formula for the area of a triangle is $A = \frac{1}{2}bh$. If $A = 12$ and $b = 4$, what is the value of h?

    F. $\frac{2}{3}$ **G.** 3

    H. 6   **J.** 24

13. Which point is in Quadrant IV of the coordinate plane?

A. $(-2, 6)$ **B.** $(4, 0)$
C. $(6, -2)$ **D.** $(-2, -6)$

14. Which expression represents the square of the sum of a number and 4?

F. $x^2 + 4$ **G.** $x + 4^2$
H. $(x + 4)^2$ **J.** $4x^2$

15. In Australian football, 18 players from each team play at once. This is 2 fewer than 5 times the number of players from a polo team that play at once. Which equation represents this?

A. $18 - 2 = 5p$
B. $18 = 2p - 5$
C. $5 \cdot 18 = p - 2$
D. $18 = 5p - 2$

16. Which is an example of the Inverse Property of Addition?

F. $-5 + 0 = -5$ **G.** $0 = -5 + 5$

H. $0 - 5 = -5$ **J.** $-5 \cdot \frac{-1}{5} = 1$

17. $\frac{3}{4}$ gal = _____ pt

A. $1\frac{1}{2}$ **B.** 3

C. 6 **D.** 12

18. Simplify.

$$16 + (-2)^3 \cdot 3^0(3) - 6 \div (-1)$$

F. -18 **G.** -2
H. 30 **J.** 46

19. 0.38 m = _____ mm

A. 3.8 **B.** 38
C. 380 **D.** 3800

20. If $-1\frac{3}{5}x = 4\frac{7}{10}$, what is the value of x?

F. $-7\frac{13}{25}$

G. $-2\frac{15}{16}$

H. $6\frac{3}{10}$

J. $\frac{-16}{47}$

21. Which set is closed under subtraction?

A. positive integers
B. negative integers
C. $\{-2, 0, 2\}$
D. even integers

22. Which statement is never true?

F. $|x| \geq 0$ **G.** $|x| > x$

H. $|x| = -(x)$ **J.** $|x| < -5$

Tell About It

Explain how you solve each problem. Show all your work.

23. Last week, Frank worked as a waiter for $6\frac{1}{4}$ hours, earning $9.80 per hour. He also earned $14.50 per hour delivering packages for $7\frac{1}{2}$ hours. How much money did he earn last week?

24. Akila has 172 stamps in her collection. This is 8 fewer than $\frac{5}{6}$ the number of stamps Garth has. How many stamps does Garth have?

6-1 Ratio

Name _____ Date _____

You can write a ratio in *different forms*.

Word Form a to b	**Ratio Form** $a:b$	**Fraction Form** $\frac{a}{b}, b \neq 0$
48 to 88	48 : 88	$\frac{48}{88}$

To write *equivalent ratios*, multiply or divide both terms of the ratio by the same nonzero number.

Equivalent ratios

$$\frac{48 \cdot 2}{88 \cdot 2} = \frac{96}{176} \text{ and } \frac{48 \div 4}{88 \div 4} = \frac{12}{22}$$

Is $\frac{1}{2} : \frac{5}{4}$ equivalent to $0.2 : 0.5$?

To determine if two ratios are *equivalent*, express each ratio in simplest form.

Remember: A ratio is in simplest form if its terms are relatively prime.

$$\frac{1}{2} : \frac{5}{4} \longrightarrow \frac{1}{2} \div \frac{5}{4} = \frac{1}{2} \cdot \frac{\overset{2}{\cancel{4}}}{5} = \frac{2}{5} = 2 : 5 \qquad 0.2 : 0.5 = 0.2(10) : 0.5(10) = 2 : 5$$

So both ratios are equivalent.

Write equivalent ratios in different forms.

1. 4 to 7

$4 : 7; \frac{4}{7}$

2. 54 to 81

$54 : 81, \frac{54}{81}$

3. 0 to 101

$0 : 101, \frac{0}{101}$

4. 13.5 to 43.8

$135 : 43.8, \frac{135}{438}$

Compare the data in the table as ratios in fraction form. Do not simplify.

5. Number of dogs to number of birds treated

$\frac{53}{11}$

6. Number of reptiles to number of dogs and cats treated

$4 : 115$

$\frac{53}{+62} \Big/ {}_{5}$

7. Number of dogs and birds to number of cats treated

$64 : 62$

$\frac{53}{+11} \Big/ 64$

Treatment Log (January 15–22)	
Kind of Animal	**Number Treated**
Dog	53
Cat	62
Bird	11
Reptile	4
Other small mammals	11

Write three equivalent ratios for each ratio given.

8. $\frac{0}{15}$

$\frac{0}{5}, \frac{0}{75}, \frac{0}{300}$

9. $\frac{2}{7}$

$\frac{2}{7}, 2 \cdot 7, 2 \cdot 7$

10. 1.5 to 3.5

$\frac{15}{35}, 1.5 \text{ to } 35$

$15 : 35$

11. 6.25 to 1.25

$\frac{625}{125}, 6.25 \cdot 1.25$

$6.25 : 1.25$

12. $3 : 3\frac{1}{2}$

$3 : 3.5$

$3 \text{ to } 35$

$\frac{3}{3.5}$

13. $1\frac{2}{3} : \frac{5}{4}$

$1\frac{2}{3} : \frac{5}{4}$

$\frac{1\frac{2}{3}}{\frac{5}{4}}$

Write each ratio in simplest form.

14. 75 to 100

     3 to 4

15. 4 to 40

     1:16

16. 0 : 1001

     0:0

17. 8 : 6

     4:3

18. 64 : 12

     16:3

19. $\frac{64}{512}$

     34:256

     17:128

20. $\frac{3.9}{1.3}$

     3:1

21. $\frac{52.5}{14}$

     26.25:7

Compare the ratios. Write <, =, or >.

22. $\frac{0.5}{20}$ <   0.04

   $\frac{2.5}{100}$ < $\frac{4}{100}$

23. $1\frac{2}{5} : 5$ $\frac{3}{10}$

24. $\frac{21}{0.7}$ 23.2 to $\frac{4}{5}$

    30   23.2

25. 0.33 $\frac{1.7}{5}$

26. $\frac{42}{3.5}$ < 17.8 to $\frac{9}{10}$

27. $2\frac{1}{3} : 6$ $\frac{7}{18}$

    $\frac{7:6}{3}$

Problem Solving

28. A recipe for fruit punch calls for mixing 64 fluid ounces of cranberry juice with 128 fluid ounces of orange juice. How much cranberry juice would you need if you had 256 fluid ounces of orange juice?

$\frac{64}{128} = \frac{2 \cdot 64}{2 \cdot 128} = \frac{128}{256}$; **You would need 128 fl oz of cranberry juice.**

29. Sports In the 2004 Summer Olympics in Athens, France won 11 gold medals, 9 silver medals, and 13 bronze medals. What is the ratio of gold medals to total medals that France won? Simplify the ratio.

30. There are 20 girls in a class, and the ratio of boys to girls is 3 to 5.

   a. What is the total number of students in the class?

   b. If four boys and four girls are moved to another class, does the ratio of boys to girls change? Explain.

TEST PREPARATION

31. Which ratio is *not* equivalent to 8 to 10?

   A. 8 : 10   **C.** $\frac{4}{5}$

   B. 4 : 5   **D.** $\frac{5}{4}$

32. Which ratio represents 35 : 75 in simplest form?

   F. $\frac{3}{7}$ **H.** $\frac{5}{7}$

   G. $\frac{7}{15}$ **J.** $\frac{1}{3}$

6-2 Unit Rate and Unit Cost

Name _____ Date _____

A *rate* is a special kind of ratio that compares *two unlike quantities*. The word *per* can be used to describe rates. A *unit rate* is a ratio that compares an amount, *x*, to 1 unit: $\frac{x}{1}$. A *unit cost*, or *unit price*, is the price per unit of an item.

To find a unit rate or a unit cost:

Given Rate	Method 1: Divide	Method 2: Simplify	
A train travels 450 miles in 6 hours.	$450 \div 6 = 75$	$\frac{450 \div 6}{6 \div 6} = \frac{75}{1}$	**Unit Rate** The train travels 75 miles per hour, or $\frac{75\ miles}{1\ hour}$.
A store charges $15.00 for a pack of 6 mugs.	$15.00 \div 6 = 2.50$	$\frac{15.00 \div 6}{6 \div 6} = \frac{2.50}{1}$	**Unit Cost** It costs $2.50 per mug, or $\frac{\$2.50}{1\ mug}$.

Write each rate in two ways.

1. A plane travels 912 miles in 1.75 hours.

521.1/hr

2. Ms. Novak types 205 words in one minute.

205/min

Express each ratio as a unit rate.   (9/4) - 2347654

3. A cheetah runs 15 miles in 15 minutes.

$\frac{15}{15}$ = 1 mile per minute

4. Pedro drives 1350 miles in 3 days.

450

5. Avi uses 60 minutes to answer 75 questions.

1.25.8/question

6. A plane flies 2275 miles in 3.5 hours.

650/hr

The following chart lists items Mr. Raskalnikov bought for a picnic. Find the unit cost of each item. Round to the nearest hundredth, if necessary.

Item	Quantity (by number or weight)	Total Price
Apples	3.5 pounds	$4.90
Paper plates	150 plates	$4.50
Potato salad	60 ounces	$12.57
Hot dog buns	50	$17.50
Hot dogs	64	$26.24
Cookies	125	$11.25

7. cost per paper plate

$$\frac{\$4.50}{150\ plates} = \frac{4.5 \div 150}{150 \div 150} = \frac{0.03}{1}$$

Plates are $0.03 each.

8. cost per cookie

$.9/10

9. price of apples per pound $1.4/lb

$1.4/lb

10. price of potato salad per ounce

$.20 oz

To find the *best buy* or *better buy,* compare unit costs to find the least unit cost. Circle the better buy. Show your work. (*Hint:* 1 pound = 16 ounces)

11. 8 lbs of potatoes for $4 or (192 oz for $3)?

$$\frac{\$4}{8} = \$0.50/\text{lb} > \frac{\$3}{192 \div 16} = \$0.25/\text{lb}$$

12. 10 lbs of ice for $9.99 or 152 oz for $7.25?

$$\frac{16}{160}$$

13. 8 oz of cream cheese for $1.98 or 1 pound for 3.75?

14. 2.5 lbs of apples for $3.25 or 35 oz for $3.50?

Density is the ratio of the mass of substance to the volume of the same substance. It is calculated using the formula, $Density = \frac{mass}{volume}$

Write the density of each substance in decimal form.

	Substance	Mass (g)	Volume (cm³)	Density (g/cm³)
15.	Gold	19	1	19
16.	Water	14	14	1
17.	Ethanol	39	50	.78
18.	Salt (sodium chloride)	54	25	2.16

Problem Solving

19. A café sells drinks in 3 sizes: small, medium, and large. The small cup costs $0.89 and holds 9 ounces. The medium cup costs $1.29 and holds 12 ounces. The large costs $1.69 and holds 22 ounces. Which size cup is the best buy?

20. Lisle and Linda walk in opposite directions from the same point. Lisle walks 0.8 kilometers every 10 minutes, and Linda walks 2.8 kilometers every 30 minutes. How far apart are they after 1 hour?

MENTAL MATH

Write each ratio as a unit rate.

21. 300 calories burned in $\frac{1}{3}$ hour

22. $4.80 for 2 loaves of bread

23. 500 miles in 25 hours

24. $3.25 for $\frac{1}{2}$ pound of watermelon

6-3 Write and Solve Proportions

Name _____ Date _____

A proportion is an *equation* stating that two ratios are equivalent.

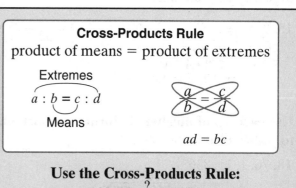
- To determine if $\frac{132}{11} = \frac{84}{7}$ forms a proportion, you can compare simplified ratios, or use the Cross-Products Rule.

Use the Cross-Products Rule:
$$132 \cdot 7 \overset{?}{=} 11 \cdot 84$$
$$924 = 924$$

- To find the missing term in the proportion $\frac{x}{50} = \frac{20}{250}$, you can use cross products, or use proportional reasoning and mental math.

Use proportional reasoning:
$$\frac{x}{50} = \frac{20}{250} \longleftarrow \textit{Think: } 50 \cdot 5 = 250.$$
What number times 5 is 20?
$$x = 4$$

Does each pair of ratios form a proportion? Use cross products, simplification, or proportional reasoning.

1. $8 : 15 \overset{?}{=} 20 : 45$

$15 \cdot 20 \overset{?}{=} 8 \cdot 45$
$300 \neq 360;$
no

2. $1 : 8 \overset{?}{=} 3 : 14$

$8 \cdot 3 = 1 \cdot 14$
$24 \neq 14$
no

3. $\frac{4}{5} \overset{?}{=} \frac{12}{15}$

$60 = 60$
yes

4. $\frac{63}{28} \overset{?}{=} \frac{9}{4}$

$252 = 252$
yes

5. $\frac{9}{16} \overset{?}{=} \frac{3}{4}$

$48 \neq 36$
no

6. $\frac{4}{15} \overset{?}{=} \frac{3}{7}$

$45 \neq 28$
no

7. $\frac{1}{2} \overset{?}{=} \frac{17}{34}$

$34 = 34$
yes

8. $\frac{12}{28} \overset{?}{=} \frac{11}{25}$

$308 \neq 300$
no

Find the missing term in each proportion. Then check your work to justify your answer.

9. $\frac{5}{y} = \frac{25}{10}$

$5 \cdot 5 = 25; \ y \cdot 5 = 10$
$y = 2$
Check: $5 \cdot 10 \overset{?}{=} 2 \cdot 25$
$50 = 50$ **True**

10. $\frac{n}{32} = \frac{3}{8}$

$\frac{96}{8}$
$n = 12$

11. $\frac{4}{p} = \frac{14}{28}$

$\frac{112}{14}$
$p = 8$

12. $\frac{7}{10} = \frac{z}{8}$

$\frac{56}{10}$
$z = 5.6$

13. $\frac{100}{50} = \frac{s}{45}$

$\frac{4500}{50}$
$s = 90$

14. $\frac{6.8}{17} = \frac{2}{k}$

$\frac{34}{68}$
$k = 5$

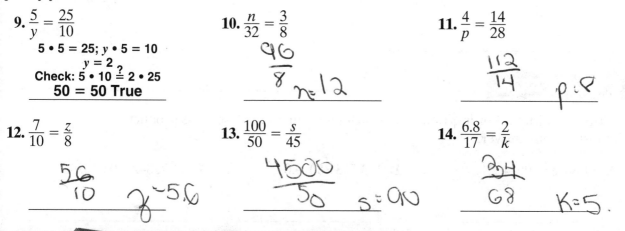

Find the missing terms in each proportion. Then check your work to justify your answer.

15. $\frac{2}{3} = \frac{x}{15} = \frac{8}{y}$

$3 \cdot 5 = 15, 2 \cdot 5 = x = 10$
$2 \cdot 4 = 8, 3 \cdot 4 = y = 12$
$x = 10, y = 12$

16. $\frac{r}{32} = \frac{5}{8} = \frac{30}{t}$

17. $\frac{52}{a} = \frac{10}{20} = \frac{b}{350}$

Use each set of numbers to form a proportion. Use cross products to justify your answer.

18. 76, 1, 11, 836

$\frac{836}{11} = \frac{76}{1}$
$836 = 836$

19. 144, 252, 35, 20

20. 14, 27, 21, 18

21. 48, 16, 36, 12

Solve. Check to justify your answer.

22. Jayita's snack mix contains peanuts and pecans in a ratio of 8 to 3. How many grams of pecans are in the mix if it contains 584 grams of peanuts?

23. The dose of a certain medication is 2 milligrams for every 80 pounds of body weight. How many milligrams of this medication are required for a person weighing 200 pounds?

24. A woodcut artist makes calendars by hand. In one workday, he can make approximately 4 calendars.

a. If he works for nine weeks (working five days per week), how many calendars can he produce?

b. The woodcut artist charges $22 per calendar and sells about seven of every eight calendars he produces. About how much money can he expect to make in nine weeks?

CHALLENGE

25. Write two different proportions using each set of numbers. Use cross products to justify your answer.

A. $1.80, $1.20, 14, 21

B. 1, 3.5, 31.50, 9.0

C. 11.7, 8424, 0.02, 14.4

6-4 Direct Proportion

Name _____ Date _____

A direct proportion is a proportional relationship where an increase or decrease in one quantity causes the *same kind of change* in the other quantity.

Melissa bought some photo frames that were priced at four frames for $15. She bought 12 frames. How much money did she pay? Let c = cost of frames.

To solve, use the Cross-Products Rule.

$$\frac{4}{15} = \frac{12}{c}$$

$4c = 12(15)$
$4c = 180$
$c = 45$

Remember: You can set up direct proportions by comparing unlike units in each ratio, or like units in each ratio.

like units ⟶ $\dfrac{\text{frames}}{\text{frames}} = \dfrac{\text{cost}}{\text{cost}}$ ⟶ $\dfrac{4}{12} = \dfrac{15}{c}$

unlike units ⟶ $\dfrac{\text{frames}}{\text{cost}} = \dfrac{\text{frames}}{\text{cost}}$ ⟶ $\dfrac{12}{c} = \dfrac{4}{15}$

So the cost is $45 for 12 frames.

Check: Use substitution. $12(15) = 4(45)$
$180 = 180$ True

Write each proportion two ways: as ratios with unlike units and ratios with like units.

1. $6.50 for 1-hour parking is the same as $26.00 for 4-hour parking.

$$\frac{\$6.50}{1 \text{ hour}} = \frac{\$26}{4 \text{ hours}} \; ; \; \frac{\$6.50}{\$26} = \frac{1 \text{ hour}}{4 \text{ hours}}$$

2. 4 lb of bananas for $2.76 is the same as 1 lb of bananas for $.69.

$$\frac{4}{\$2.76} = \frac{1}{\$.69} \; ; \; \frac{4}{1} = \frac{\$2.76}{\$.69}$$

3. Keisha and Katie ran at the same speed. Keisha ran 3 miles in 21 minutes. Katie ran 2 miles in 14 minutes.

$$\frac{3}{21} = \frac{2}{14} \; ; \; \frac{3}{2} = \frac{21}{14}$$

4. Brad and Amy typed at the same speed. Brad typed 292 words in 5 minutes. Amy typed 146 words in 2 minutes.

$$\frac{292}{5} = \frac{146}{2} \; ; \; \frac{292}{146} = \frac{5}{2}$$

For each pair of triangles, write a proportion that shows that the ratios of the base, *b*, to the height, *h*, are the same. Use the Cross-Products Rule to check.

5.

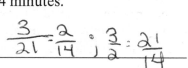

40 m   24 m   60 m   36 m

$$\frac{60}{36} = \frac{40}{24} \quad 1440 = 1440$$

6.

5 cm   7.5 cm   12 cm   18 cm

$$\frac{12}{18} = \frac{5}{7.5} \quad 90 = 90$$

Average speed is the unit rate in a proportion involving distance and time. Write a proportion to find the missing average speed.

7. At what average speed can a locust fly if it can travel 46 meters in 5 seconds?

$$\frac{m}{s}; \frac{r}{1} = \frac{46}{5}; r = 9.2$$

A locust can fly at a rate of 9.2 m/s.

8. A ghost crab ran 15 meters in 9 seconds. What was its average speed?

$$\frac{m}{s} \frac{r}{1} \frac{15}{9}$$

$$r = 1.7 \, m/s$$

9. At what average speed does Adele ride her bicycle, if she rides 28 miles in 3.5 hours?

$$\frac{m}{h} \frac{r}{1} \frac{28}{3.5}$$

$$r = 8 \, m/h$$

10. Stephanie ran 2.25 miles in 12 minutes. What was her average speed in miles per hour? (1 hour = 60 minutes)

$$\frac{m}{m} \frac{r}{1} = \frac{2.25}{12}$$

$$r = .19 \, m/m$$

The graph of a rate is a straight line. Write each exercise as a rate. Then express the rate as an ordered pair. Plot the coordinates on the graph.

11. $15 for 1 T-shirt

1 : 15 (1, 15)

12. $30 for 2 T-shirts

13. $45 for 3 T-shirts

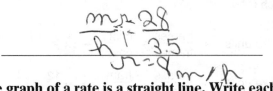

Cost per T-shirt: $60, $45, $30, $15

0 1 2 3 4

T-shirts

Problem Solving

14. The first Russian space satellite was called Sputnik. It orbited Earth at a speed of 29,000 kilometers per hour. How many hectometers did it travel in one day?

15. Jorge took a speed reading class last Saturday from 9 A.M. to 4 P.M. He learned that he could speed read 330 pages of a novel in one hour with good comprehension. How many pages does he speed read in 225 minutes?

WRITE ABOUT IT

16. Nina wants to know if this is a proportion: $\frac{30 \text{ in.}}{20 \text{ min}} = \frac{2.5 \text{ ft}}{\frac{1}{3}\text{h}}$. Explain how she can find out.

6-5 Proportion by Parts

Name _____ Date _____

There are 28 guests at a banquet. For every 9 salads Amy serves,
Thom serves 5. How many salads will each person serve?

Find the ratio. Amy to Thom is 9 : 5.
Then find an equivalent ratio whose terms have a sum that is equal
to the total. You can use a model, a table, or a proportion.

Method 1 Use a Model

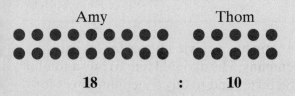

Amy   Thom

        18   :   10

Check: Write an equation and combine like
terms. Then find the value of the parts.

Let s = number of salads per server.

Method 2 Make a Table

Amy	9	18
Thom	5	10
Total	14	28

Amy + Thom = Total number
$$9s \;+\; 5s \;=\; 28$$

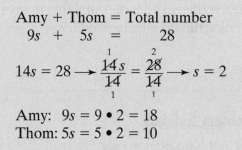

$$14s = 28 \longrightarrow \frac{\overset{1}{14}s}{\underset{1}{14}} = \frac{\overset{2}{28}}{\underset{1}{14}} \longrightarrow s = 2$$

Amy: $9s = 9 \cdot 2 = 18$
Thom: $5s = 5 \cdot 2 = 10$

So Amy serves 18 salads, and Thom serves 10 salads.

Use a separate sheet of paper to draw a model or make a table to solve.

1. Patrick's painting job requires 2 cans of red
   paint for every 3 cans of white paint. A total
   of 20 cans of paint are needed. How many
   cans of each color does Patrick need?

   Red   White

   ●● ●●● or

Red	2	4	6	8
White	3	6	9	12
Total	5	10	15	20

   Patrick needs 8 cans of red paint and
   12 cans of white paint.
   _____

2. Arlene makes a necklace using 14 purple
   beads for every 6 silver beads. The necklace
   contains 80 beads. How many of each color
   bead are in the necklace?

   _____

3. Toby buys 40 pairs of socks in packs of
   5 pairs of white socks and 3 pairs of black
   socks. How many pairs of each color does
   he buy?

4. Maribel's herd of 64 steers has 11 brown-
   and-white steers for every 5 black-and-
   white steers. How many of each color
   does she own?

_____   _____

Solve using proportions.

5. Suzanne owns a farm. For every 7 acres of soybeans she plants, she plants 10 acres of corn. She plants 1020 acres in all. How many acres, c, of each crop does she plant?

$$\frac{10}{10 + 7 = 17} = \frac{c}{1020} \longrightarrow 1020 \cdot 10 = 17c$$

$$\frac{\overset{6}{\cancel{10,200}}}{\underset{1}{\cancel{17}}} = \frac{\overset{1}{\cancel{17c}}}{\underset{1}{\cancel{17}}}; \ c = 600; \ 1020 - 600 = 420$$

Suzanne plants 420 acres of soybeans and 600 acres of corn.

6. Brandon and Marta are mowing a lawn. For every 4 square feet that Brandon mows, Marta mows 9 square feet. The lawn is 5200 square feet. How much lawn does each person mow?

7. Nate is tiling a floor with a pattern that requires 16 white tiles for every 9 blue tiles. The floor has an area of 600 square feet, and each tile is 1 square foot. How many of each color tile does Nate need?

8. Jeremy buys moving boxes for his dad's company. His dad told him to buy a total of 288 boxes and to buy 5 medium boxes for every 7 large boxes. How many of each size box should he buy?

Problem Solving

9. Chef Kim plans to serve a fruit plate to each of 336 diners at a banquet. Each plate will contain 6 slices of kiwi fruit, 3 pieces of mango, and 5 strawberries. If a mango yields 5 pieces and a kiwi fruit yields 8 slices, how many fruits are needed?

10. Diego works at a toy store. His boss tells him to order 420 stuffed bears and toy cars. He must order 4 stuffed bears for every 3 toy cars.

    a. If he must order 9 large stuffed bears for every 7 small stuffed bears, how many of each stuffed bear should he order?

    b. If Diego must order 7 toy racecars for every 3 toy trucks, how many of each toy car should he order?

CRITICAL THINKING

11. A rancher owns 180 goats. For every 7 brown goats, there are 3 black goats and 5 white goats. How many of each color goat does he own? Explain how you found your answer.

6-6 Scale Drawings and Models

Name _____ Date _____

To find the actual distance between two cities on a map, use the map scale and the map distance. Then write and solve a proportion.

Map scale: 1 inch = 50 miles
Map distance: 2.5 inches

$\dfrac{\text{scale measure} \longrightarrow}{\text{actual measure} \longrightarrow}$ $\dfrac{1 \text{ in.}}{50 \text{ mi}} = \dfrac{2.5 \text{ in.}}{d \text{ mi}}$

$1 \cdot d = 2.5 \cdot 50$
$d = 125$

The actual distance is 125 miles.

A *scale model* is a three-dimensional model that accurately represents a real object.

The *scale factor* is a ratio that tells how much larger or smaller the scale model is than the object it represents. The terms of the scale factor are expressed in like units.

$$\text{scale factor} = \dfrac{\text{scale model}}{\text{actual object}}$$

Solve the proportion.

1. $\dfrac{2}{t} = \dfrac{18}{63}$

$18t = 2(63); \; t = 7$

2. $\dfrac{10}{3} = \dfrac{r}{24}$

3. $\dfrac{1}{60} = \dfrac{3}{b}$

4. $\dfrac{18}{x} = \dfrac{6}{90}$

5. $\dfrac{a}{0.2} = \dfrac{5}{2}$

6. $\dfrac{1}{0.8} = \dfrac{4}{m}$

Use an inch ruler to measure each distance on the blueprint. Then write a proportion using the scale to find each actual distance. *Scale:* 1 in. = 12 ft

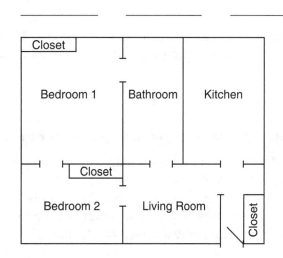

7. Width of the kitchen

1 in.; $\dfrac{1 \text{ in.}}{12 \text{ ft}} = \dfrac{1 \text{ in.}}{d \text{ ft}}$, $d = 12$

The kitchen is 12 ft wide.

8. Width of the entire apartment

_____

9. Width of the entry closet

_____

10. Length of bedroom 1

_____

The scale factor used in a set of drawings of a classroom is $\dfrac{1}{6}$.

Find the dimensions in the scale drawings of each classroom object.

11. A picture window that has a length of 96 inches

12. A chalkboard that has a length of 60 inches

13. A student desk that has a length of 24 inches and a width of 18 inches

_____

Complete the chart.

Object	Scale Model Length	Actual Object Length	Scale Factor of Model	Is the model an enlargement or a reduction of the original?
Car	4 in.	196 in.	**14.**	**15.**
Airplane	4.5 in.	1800 in.	**16.**	**17.**
Amoeba	40 mm	0.4 mm	**18.**	**19.**
Ant	36 mm	8 mm	**20.**	**21.**

Use separate sheets of centimeter graph paper for each item.

22. Draw a net for a rectangular prism. Then cut out, fold, and tape the net you drew. Label it: *Original Prism Model.*

23. Draw a net for the scale model of the rectangular prism that you made in exercise 22. Use a scale factor of $\frac{3}{1}$, or 3. Then cut out, fold, and tape the net you drew. Label it: *Scale Model Prism.*

24. Is the scale model you made in exercise 23 an enlargement or a reduction of the prism you made in exercise 22?

_____

Write and solve a proportion, then answer each question.

25. Mark's job is to draw a map with a scale of 1 centimeter = 10 kilometers. An actual distance of a stretch of highway is 78 kilometers. What is the length of the line segment he needs to draw on the map?

26. Ted knows the actual distance between two cities is 150 miles. His map shows a distance of 2 inches between these cities. What is the scale used on his map?

_____   _____

SPIRAL REVIEW

Solve each equation.

27. $\frac{x}{2} + 4 = \frac{3}{7}$

28. $\frac{3}{4}y - 5 = \frac{11}{2}$

29. $\frac{3}{y} - \frac{7}{10} = -\frac{6}{5}$

_____   _____   _____

6-7 Similarity

Name _____ Date _____

Rectangle *FGHJ* is similar to rectangle *LMNO*. Find the missing length $\overline{MN}$.

To find missing lengths of similar figures, use ratios of corresponding parts to write and solve proportions.

$$\frac{FG}{LM} = \frac{GH}{MN} \longrightarrow \frac{6 \text{ cm}}{3 \text{ cm}} = \frac{8 \text{ cm}}{x \text{ cm}}$$

$$6x = 3 \cdot 8$$

$$\frac{6x}{6} = \frac{24}{6}$$

$$x = 4$$

$\overline{MN} = 4$ centimeters

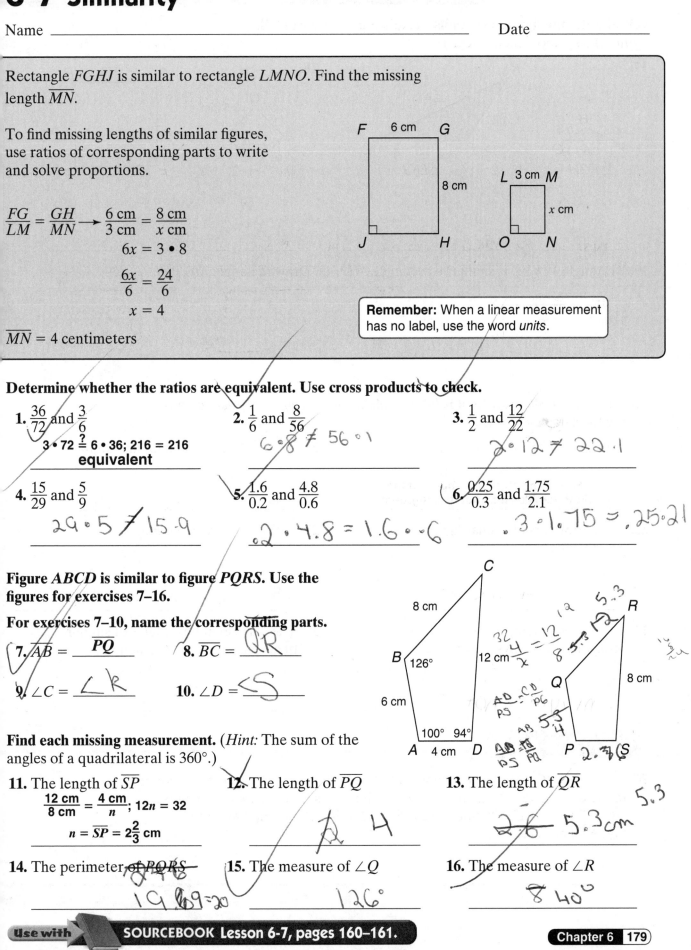

Remember: When a linear measurement has no label, use the word *units*.

Determine whether the ratios are equivalent. Use cross products to check.

1. $\frac{36}{72}$ and $\frac{3}{6}$

$3 \cdot 72 \overset{?}{=} 6 \cdot 36$; $216 = 216$
equivalent

2. $\frac{1}{6}$ and $\frac{8}{56}$

$6 \cdot 8 \neq 56 \cdot 1$

3. $\frac{1}{2}$ and $\frac{12}{22}$

$2 \cdot 12 \neq 22 \cdot 1$

4. $\frac{15}{29}$ and $\frac{5}{9}$

$29 \cdot 5 \neq 15 \cdot 9$

5. $\frac{1.6}{0.2}$ and $\frac{4.8}{0.6}$

$.2 \cdot 4.8 = 1.6 \cdot .6$

6. $\frac{0.25}{0.3}$ and $\frac{1.75}{2.1}$

$.3 \cdot 1.75 = .25 \cdot 21$

Figure *ABCD* is similar to figure *PQRS*. Use the figures for exercises 7–16.

For exercises 7–10, name the corresponding parts.

7. $\overline{AB} = $ __$\overline{PQ}$__

8. $\overline{BC} = $ __$\overline{QR}$__

9. $\angle C = $ __$\angle R$__

10. $\angle D = $ __$\angle S$__

Find each missing measurement. (*Hint:* The sum of the angles of a quadrilateral is 360°.)

11. The length of $\overline{SP}$

$\frac{12 \text{ cm}}{8 \text{ cm}} = \frac{4 \text{ cm}}{n}$; $12n = 32$

$n = \overline{SP} = 2\frac{2}{3}$ cm

12. The length of $\overline{PQ}$

$2 \ 4$

13. The length of $\overline{QR}$

$2.6 \ 5.3$cm

14. The perimeter of *PQRS*

$19.69 = 20$

15. The measure of $\angle Q$

$126°$

16. The measure of $\angle R$

$8 \ 40°$

Tell whether the figures are similar. Explain how you can tell.
(*Hint:* The symbol ′ means feet.)

17.

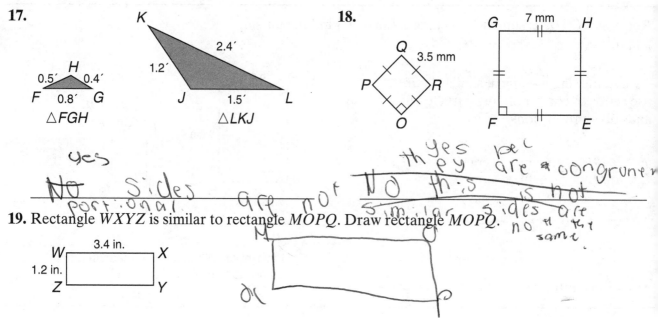

△FGH   △LKJ

18.

yes
~~No Sides~~ ~~are not~~
~~portional~~

th *yes* per
ey are *congruent*
~~No th:s~~ ~~is not~~
~~similar~~ sides are
~~not~~ the
same

19. Rectangle *WXYZ* is similar to rectangle *MOPQ*. Draw rectangle *MOPQ*.

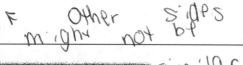

True or false? If the statement is false, explain why. (*Hint: Congruent* means
exactly the same measure.)

20. All right triangles are similar.

False; The other two angles of the
right triangles may not be congruent.

21. All equilateral triangles are similar.

Trues

22. The perimeters of similar figures are
proportional.

true

23. All rectangles are similar.

Falses   hot
all angles art
congruen4

24. The corresponding sides of similar
hexagons are always congruent.

F Other sides
might not bt
similar

25. The corresponding angles of similar
quadrilaterals are congruent.

Trut

MENTAL MATH

26. Triangle *ABC* is similar to triangle *DEF*, and the vertices are corresponding
in the order given. You know the following measurements: $\overline{AB}$ = 6 units,
$\overline{BC}$ = 7 units, $\overline{AC}$ = 8 units, and $\overline{DE}$ = 12 units. Use mental math to
find $\overline{EF}$ and $\overline{DF}$.

6-8 Indirect Measurement

Name _____   Date _____

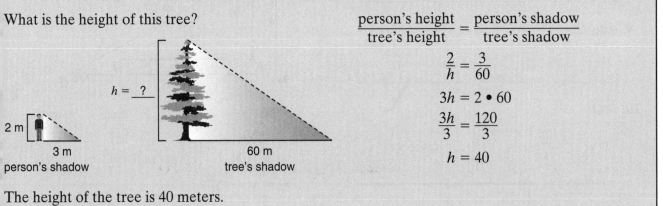

To find the *indirect measurement* of a distance, height, or length that is difficult to measure directly, use a proportion based on similar triangles.

What is the height of this tree?

$$\frac{\text{person's height}}{\text{tree's height}} = \frac{\text{person's shadow}}{\text{tree's shadow}}$$

$h = $?

2 m

3 m
person's shadow

60 m
tree's shadow

$$\frac{2}{h} = \frac{3}{60}$$
$$3h = 2 \bullet 60$$
$$\frac{3h}{3} = \frac{120}{3}$$
$$h = 40$$

The height of the tree is 40 meters.

Use the shadow lengths measured at the same time to find each height. Draw a picture to help.

1. flagpole shadow: 55 feet
boy's shadow: 5 feet
boy's height: 4 feet
How tall is the flagpole?

$\frac{4}{x} = \frac{5}{55}$, $5x = 220$; $x = 44$
The flagpole is 44 ft tall.

2. mailbox shadow: 4 feet
lamppost shadow: 26 feet
mailbox height: 3.5 feet
How tall is the lamppost?

$\frac{4}{x} = \frac{26}{3.5}$

.54 ft

3. kangaroo's shadow: 1.5 meters
giraffe: 5.76 meters tall
giraffe's shadow: 4.8 meters
How tall is the kangaroo?

$\frac{1.5}{x} = \frac{5.76}{4.8}$

$x = 1.25$

Solve. Show your work.

4. A 12-foot tall tree casts a 6 foot shadow. A flagpole 9 feet tall also casts a shadow. How long is the shadow cast by the flagpole?

4.5

$\frac{12}{6} = \frac{9}{x}$ 54

5. How long is the shadow cast by a building $68\frac{1}{2}$ meters tall? A lamppost 3 meters tall casts a shadow 6 meters long.

$\frac{68.5}{x} = \frac{3}{6}$

137

The pair of triangles below is similar. Set up a proportion and find each missing length.

6. $\overline{AF}$

35

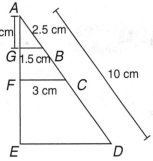

A

2 cm   2.5 cm

G 1.5 cm *B*

10 cm

F   3 cm   *C*

E   *D*

7. $\overline{ED}$

5

Each pair of triangles is similar. Set up a proportion and find each missing length.

8. side *FH*

_____

9. side *JK*

_____

10. $\overline{MO}$

_____

11. $\overline{OP}$

_____

12. side *CE*

_____

13. side *AB*

_____

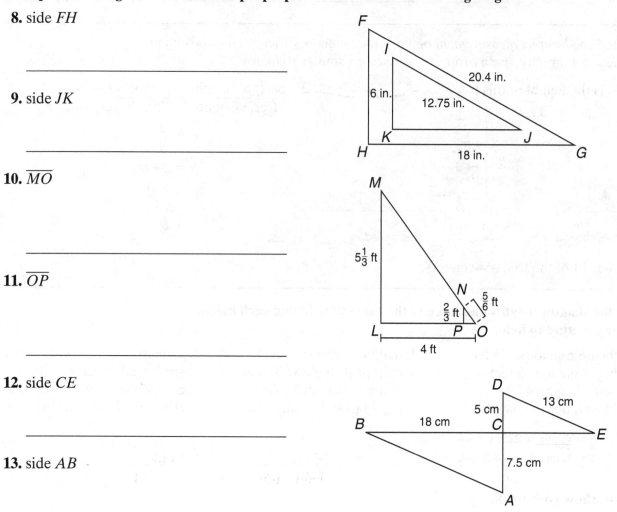

Problem Solving

14. Two boats, Misty and Surfer, leave the same dock and travel north. After one hour, Misty has traveled 20 miles and Surfer has traveled 32 miles. Then each boat stops and sails east. How far has Surfer traveled when Misty has traveled 15 miles east?

_____

WRITE ABOUT IT

15. Ray would like to enlarge a 5-inch by 7-inch photograph so that it measures 8 inches by 10 inches. Will the original photo and the enlargement be similar figures? Explain.

_____

_____

6-9 Inverse Proportion

Name _____ Date _____

An inverse proportion is a relationship such that an increase or decrease in one quantity causes the *opposite* kind of change in the other quantity.

When Casey drives at 40 miles per hour it takes her $\frac{3}{4}$ hour to get to work. If she drives 60 miles per hour, how much time, t, will the same drive take?

To solve, first write a proportion. Then apply the Cross-Products Rule.

$$\textbf{Solve: } \frac{40}{60} = \frac{t}{\frac{3}{4}}$$

$$40 \cdot \frac{3}{4} = 60t$$

$$30 = 60t$$

$$\frac{30}{60} = \frac{60t}{60}$$

$$\frac{1}{2} = t$$

So it will take Casey $\frac{1}{2}$ hour if she drives 60 miles per hour.

Remember: You can set up indirect proportions by comparing unlike units in each ratio, or like units in each ratio.

$$\textit{like units} \longrightarrow \frac{\text{less speed}}{\text{more speed}} = \frac{\text{more time}}{\text{less time}}$$

$$\textit{unlike units} \longrightarrow \frac{\text{less speed}}{\text{more time}} = \frac{\text{more speed}}{\text{less time}}$$

$$\textbf{Check: } \frac{40}{60} \overset{?}{=} \frac{\frac{1}{2}}{\frac{3}{4}}$$

$$40 \cdot \frac{3}{4} \overset{?}{=} 60 \cdot \frac{1}{2}$$

$$30 = 30 \text{ True}$$

Write an inverse proportion in like units and with unlike units. Then solve.

1. It takes Ms. Linden 45 minutes to shovel her driveway. If her two teenage children help her, about how long would it take the three of them to shovel the driveway?

_____

Solve each work problem. Use inverse proportions. (*Hint:* Assume that everybody works at the same speed.)

2. It takes two boys six hours to paint one side of a fence. How long will it take if six boys paint the other side of the fence?

3. It takes 14 girls 0.8 hours, or 48 minutes, to deliver the daily newspapers in their neighborhood. How long will it take if 4 girls deliver the newspapers?

_____ _____

4. Explain why problems 2 and 3 represent inverse proportions.

_____

Solve each change-of-rate problem. Use inverse proportions.

5. When Carl drives at a speed of 40 miles per hour, his trip to work takes 40 minutes. If Carl drives at a speed of 50 miles per hour, how long would his trip take?

6. When Theresa walks at a pace of 88 steps per minute, it takes her 90 minutes to walk the trail. If she alters her pace to 33 steps per minute, how long will it take her to walk the trail?

$$\frac{40 \text{ mph}}{50 \text{ mph}} = \frac{40 \text{ min}}{m} \longrightarrow \frac{40}{50} = \frac{m}{40}; \ 40(40) = 50m; \ m = 32$$

His trip would take 32 minutes.

7. Explain why problems 8 and 9 represent inverse proportions.

_____

Determine if each proportion is a direct proportion or an inverse proportion. (*Hint:* A relationship is a direct proportion when both quantities change in the *same way*.)

8. $\dfrac{\text{fewer workers}}{\text{job takes more time}} = \dfrac{\text{more workers}}{\text{job takes less time}}$

9. $\dfrac{\text{work less time}}{\text{work more time}} = \dfrac{\text{earn less money}}{\text{earn more money}}$

_____

Solve. Explain why the proportion is direct or inverse.

10. It takes two students nine minutes to sweep the gymnasium floor. How long would it take six students to sweep the gymnasium floor?

11. A grasshopper jumps a total distance of 18 meters in six seconds. At this rate, how far would it jump in 27 seconds?

_____

CHALLENGE

12. Four cats catch a total of 56 mice in two hours. How many cats are needed to catch 56 mice in $\frac{3}{4}$ hour? (*Hint:* Let cats be represented by whole numbers.)

_____

6-10 Dimensional Analysis

Name _____ Date _____

Convert: 1.7 mi/h ≈ __?__ ft/s.

Given: $\dfrac{\text{miles}}{\text{hour}}$ Want: $\dfrac{\text{feet}}{\text{second}}$

Use 5280 ft = 1 mi; 1 h = 60 min; 1 min = 60 s

1.7 mi/h = $\dfrac{1.7 \text{ mi}}{1 \text{ h}} \cdot \dfrac{5280 \text{ ft}}{1 \text{ mi}} \cdot \dfrac{1 \text{ h}}{60 \text{ min}} \cdot \dfrac{1 \text{ min}}{60 \text{ s}}$

$\dfrac{8976 \text{ ft}}{3600 \text{ s}} = 8976 \div 3600 = 2.493\ldots \approx 2.5 \text{ ft/s}$

So 1.7 mi/h ≈ 2.5 ft/s.

To use dimensional analysis:
- Analyze the given information, and determine the conversion factors—the unit ratios—needed to convert the units. These ratios may be inverted.
- Then multiply the units of measure. Simplify the units and the unit labels. Approximate the answer as needed.

Use dimensional analysis to make each conversion of customary units. Use the chart to help.

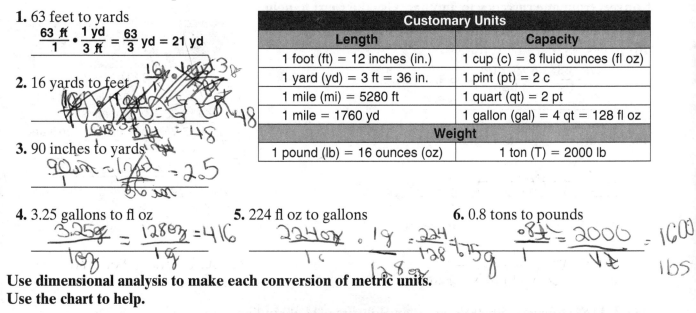

1. 63 feet to yards

$\dfrac{63 \text{ ft}}{1} \cdot \dfrac{1 \text{ yd}}{3 \text{ ft}} = \dfrac{63}{3}$ yd = 21 yd

Customary Units	
Length	**Capacity**
1 foot (ft) = 12 inches (in.)	1 cup (c) = 8 fluid ounces (fl oz)
1 yard (yd) = 3 ft = 36 in.	1 pint (pt) = 2 c
1 mile (mi) = 5280 ft	1 quart (qt) = 2 pt
1 mile = 1760 yd	1 gallon (gal) = 4 qt = 128 fl oz
Weight	
1 pound (lb) = 16 ounces (oz)	1 ton (T) = 2000 lb

2. 16 yards to feet

3. 90 inches to yards

4. 3.25 gallons to fl oz

5. 224 fl oz to gallons

6. 0.8 tons to pounds

Use dimensional analysis to make each conversion of metric units. Use the chart to help.

7. 56 millimeters to centimeters

$\dfrac{56 \text{ mm}}{1} \cdot \dfrac{1 \text{ cm}}{10 \text{ mm}} = \dfrac{56}{10}$ cm = 5.6 cm

Metric Units	
Length	**Capacity**
1000 meters (m) = 1 kilometer (km)	1000 liters (L) = 1 kiloliter (kL)
100 centimeters (cm) = 1 m	1000 milliliters (mL) = 1 L
1000 millimeters (mm) = 1 m	**Mass**
10 mm = 1 cm	1000 grams (g) = 1 kilogram (kg)
100 cm = 1 m	1000 milligrams (mg) = 100 centigrams = 1 g

8. 9.37 kilometers to meters

9. 65 kiloliters to liters

10. 14,670 milliliters to liters

11. 850 grams to kilograms

12. 10,347 centigrams to kilograms

Use dimensional analysis to convert two units of measure. Use the charts on page 185. If necessary, round decimals to the nearest hundredth.

13. Driving speed
60 mi/h to ft/min

$$\frac{60 \text{ mi}}{1 \text{ h}} \cdot \frac{5280 \text{ ft}}{1 \text{ mi}} \cdot \frac{1 \text{ h}}{60 \text{ min}}$$

$$\frac{(60)5280 \text{ ft}}{60 \text{ min}} = 5280 \text{ ft/min}$$

14. Road surface material
6 T/mi to lb/ft

[handwritten] $\frac{6 T}{1 mi} \cdot \frac{2000 lb}{1 T} \cdot \frac{1 mi}{5280} = 2.27 lbs/ft$

15. Chemical compound
2 L/kg to mL/g

[handwritten] $\frac{2L}{1 kg} \cdot \frac{2000 kg}{1 L} \cdot \frac{1 kg}{100} = 4 mL/g$

Use dimensional analysis to determine the unit price.
Round to the nearest penny.

16. 12 oz for $3.45.
Find the price per pound.

$$\frac{\$3.45}{12 \text{ oz}} \cdot \frac{16 \text{ oz}}{1 \text{ lb}} = \$4.60/\text{lb}$$

17. 1 liter for $0.96
Find the price per kiloliter.

[handwritten] $\frac{\$.96}{1L} \cdot \frac{1000}{1L} = \$960$

18. 7.5 lb for $25.00.
Find the price per ounce.

[handwritten] $\frac{\$25}{7.5 lb} = \frac{16 oz}{1 \cdot 16 g} = \$3. $

Convert from one currency to another. Use the chart to help.
(*Hint:* Round to the nearest whole number.)

19. 75 U.S. Dollars ≈ _?_ Euros

$$\frac{75 \text{ USD}}{1} \cdot \frac{0.745 \text{ EUR}}{1 \text{ USD}} = 55.875 \text{ EUR}$$

$$\approx 56 \text{ EUR}$$

Foreign Currency Exchange Rates As of April 2007 $1.00 (U.S. Dollar, USD) =
0.745 EUR (Euro)
1.151 CAD (Canadian Dollars)
118.66 JPY (Japanese Yen)
2144.6 VEB (Venezuelan Bolivars)
45.3 INR (Indian Rupees)
7.131 ZAR (South African Rands)

Note: Currency exchange rates vary over time.

20. 75 Euros ≈ _?_ U.S. Dollars

[handwritten] $98.54

21. 500 U.S. Dollars ≈ _?_ Japanese Yen

[handwritten] 51,824 Japanese Yen

22. _?_ South African Rands ≈ 245 U.S. Dollars

[handwritten] 3,851 South African Rands

23. _?_ U.S. Dollars ≈ 5,000 Venezuelan Bolivars

[handwritten] $501

24. 90 Indian Rupees ≈ _?_ U.S. Dollars

[handwritten] $1

CRITICAL THINKING

25. How many Euros would you get if you exchange 5000 Japanese Yen? Explain how you found your answer. Round to the nearest whole number.

6-11 Problem-Solving Strategy:
Solve a Simpler Problem

Read ▸ **Plan** ▸ **Solve** ▸ **Check**

Name _____ Date _____

Solve by using the strategy Solve a Simpler Problem.

1. Find the product $\frac{1}{3} \cdot \frac{2}{5} \cdot \frac{3}{7} \cdot 25 \cdot 11 \cdot 9 \cdot 14$ without a calculator.

_____

2. Find the product $\left(1 - \frac{1}{3}\right)\left(1 - \frac{1}{4}\right)\left(1 - \frac{1}{5}\right)\left(1 - \frac{1}{6}\right)\left(1 - \frac{1}{7}\right)\left(1 - \frac{1}{8}\right)$ without a calculator.

_____

3. Suppose the corresponding sides of the right triangles shown below are the same distance (*a* in the figure) apart. What is that distance?

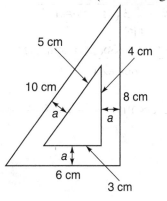

_____

4. Ned has a coupon for one fourth off the cost of any item. Today all items are on sale for one third off. Does it matter whether the store applies the sale first or the coupon first? Explain.

_____

5. Here is a tally of the points Trina scored over the course
of two basketball games:
2, 2, 1, 2, 3, 2, 2, 2, 1, 1, 1, 2, 2, 2, 2, 3,
1, 2, 2, 2, 2, 2, 1, 2, 2, 1, 1, 3, 2, 2, 2.
How many total points are represented here?

6. What is the perimeter of the polygon shown at the right?

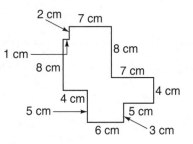

7. Compare the sums $0.\overline{3} + 0.\overline{6}$ and $\frac{1}{3} + \frac{2}{3}$. Are they equal? Explain.

8. If A is an amount in dollars, which is larger: half of one-third
of one-fourth of A or one-fourth of one-half of one-third of A?

9. If number values are assigned to letters (that is, A = 1, B = 2,
C = 3, D = 4, ..., Z = 26), which word has values with a
greater sum: PROBLEM or PRODUCT?

Enrichment:
Bicycle-Gear Math

Name _____   Date _____

What is the gear ratio of a 10-speed bicycle that has a front sprocket with 36 teeth and a back sprocket with 20 teeth?

$$\text{gear ratio} = \frac{\text{front teeth}}{\text{rear teeth}} = \frac{36}{20} = 1.8$$

If a 10-speed bicycle with a gear ratio of 1.8 has 35-inch diameter wheels, how far will it travel with each pedal stroke?

The circumference of the wheel is 35π or about 110 inches. Because the gear ratio is 1.8, the bicycle would travel about $1.8 \cdot 110$ inches, or approximately 198 inches with one pedal stroke.

Complete the table for this 10-speed bicycle with 24-inch diameter wheels.

	Front Teeth	Rear Teeth	Gear Ratio	Distance for 1 Pedal Stroke (to nearest inch)
1.	36	10		
2.	36	14		
3.	36	20		
4.	36	24		
5.	36	28		
6.	42	10		

Problem Solving

7. Using one gear on her 10-speed bicycle, Lucy pedaled 520 times on her way to school. If the gear had 40 teeth on the front sprocket, 22 teeth on her rear sprocket, and if Lucy has 26-inch diameter wheels, approximately how many feet did she pedal her bike? (Round to the nearest hundred feet.)

_____

WRITE ABOUT IT

8. The use of gears helps a person or machine use energy to complete a task efficiently. Research a machine with gears that affects your daily life. Summarize the way gears are used by the machine.

_____

Vocabulary Development

Name _____ Date _____

Chapter 6 Vocabulary

conversion factor	equivalent ratios	rate	scale model
corresponding angles	exchange rate	ratio	similar figures
corresponding sides	indirect measurement	scale	terms
dimensional analysis	inverse proportion	scale drawing	unit cost
direct proportion	proportion	scale factor	unit rate

From the vocabulary list above, choose the term(s) that best completes each sentence. Write the term(s) in the space(s) provided. (*Hint:* Use the terms above only once.)

1. A _____ is an equation stating that two _____ are equivalent.

2. 1 quart = 2 pints may be called a _____.

3. You can use _____ to find the speed in miles per hour when you know the speed in feet per hour.

4. An _____ can be used to convert from US Dollars to Euros.

5. You can use _____ to find the height of an object that would be difficult to measure directly, such as a tree.

6. An example of a _____ is $10.50 for one ticket; and 54 miles per hour is an example of a _____.

7. The sides of _____ are always proportional.

8. If the distance between two cities is 10 miles, but a map represents the distance using 2 inches, the _____ is 1 inch = 5 miles.

9. A sketch is a _____ and a three-dimensional structure is a _____ when the measures are proportional to an actual object.

10. Ratios that have the same value are called _____.

11. If a map has a scale of 1 centimeter : 10 meters, the _____ is 1 : 1000; both terms are expressed using the same units.

Tell whether each statement is true or false. Change it to make it true.

12. Two quantities have a direct proportion relationship when an increase or decrease in one quantity causes the opposite kind of change in the other quantity.

13. If two figures are *similar*, all pairs of corresponding angles are congruent and all pairs of corresponding sides are also congruent.

_____   _____

Use after ▶ **SOURCEBOOK Lessons 6-1–6-10, pages 148–167.**

Test Prep: Extended-Response Questions

Strategy: Organize the Information

Name _____ Date _____

Extended-response items may include diagrams. You can *use a diagram* to organize your thinking and to help you understand the information you need to solve a problem.

To find the answer, try using these strategies:
- Reread the item.
- Use the Test-Prep Strategy.
- Apply appropriate rules, definitions, properties, or strategies.
- Analyze your answers.

Solve. *TIP: Budget your time carefully.*

1. Arsenio measured the length of the shadows cast by his 6-foot father and a tree at the same time of day.

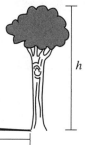

6 ft

13 ft   104 ft

Part A
Write a proportion to find the height of the tree.
Show all your work.

Part B
What is the height of the tree?
Show all your work.

Answer _____

Answer _____

---

2. Use the figures at the right.

Part A
Draw the next figure.

Part B
How many arrows will face right in the seventh figure?
Show all your work.

Figure _____

Answer _____

3. Ms. Vesta made a scale drawing of the floor plan of her boutique.

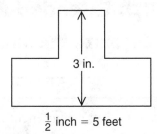

3 in.

$\frac{1}{2}$ inch = 5 feet

Part A

The width of the scale drawing of the boutique is 3 inches. What is the actual width of Ms. Vesta's boutique?

Show all your work.

Part B

Ms. Vesta is building an additional room for the boutique. The actual dimensions of the additional room are 40 feet by 20 feet. What are the dimensions on the scale drawing?

Show all your work.

Answer _____

Answer _____

---

4. To make light brown paint, Hillary mixes 1 part white, 3 parts red, and 2 parts green.

Part A

If Hillary wants to make 1 pint of light brown paint, how many cups of each type of paint does she need?

Show all your work.

Part B

If Hillary has 3 fluid ounces of green paint, how many fluid ounces of each paint will she need to make the light brown paint? How much light brown paint will she make?

Show all your work.

Answer _____

Answer _____

Practice Chapter 6 Test

Name _____ Date _____

Express each ratio in fractional form. Then write your answer in lowest terms.

1. 6 to 10

2. 15 : 21

3. $\dfrac{18}{12}$

4. 5 : 5

_____ _____ _____ _____

Determine which ratio is not equivalent.

5. $\dfrac{90}{150}, \dfrac{21}{35}, \dfrac{45}{75}, \dfrac{6}{12}$

6. $\dfrac{7}{56}, \dfrac{9}{72}, \dfrac{12}{48}, \dfrac{8}{64}$

_____ _____

Compare the ratios. Write <, =, or >.

7. $\dfrac{3.2}{40}$ _____ 0.08

8. $2\dfrac{1}{4}$ _____ $\dfrac{16}{9}$

9. $\dfrac{36}{4.1}$ _____ 7.2 to $\dfrac{1}{3}$

Determine which rate is the better buy. Explain your answer. If necessary, round your answer to the nearest cent.

10. $5 for 4 granola bars or $4 for 3 granola bars

11. $2.98 for 2 batteries or $8.98 for 12 batteries

_____ _____

Determine if each set of ratios is equivalent. Write = or ≠.

12. $\dfrac{1}{4}$ _____ $\dfrac{20}{100}$

13. $\dfrac{2}{7}$ _____ $\dfrac{26}{90}$

14. $\dfrac{72}{45}$ _____ $\dfrac{16}{10}$

15. $\dfrac{64}{49}$ _____ $\dfrac{7}{8}$

Solve each proportion. Check to justify your answer.

16. $\dfrac{2}{3} = \dfrac{x}{15}$

17. $\dfrac{8}{n} = \dfrac{2}{5}$

18. $\dfrac{a}{9} = \dfrac{9}{27}$

19. $\dfrac{36}{12} = \dfrac{18}{b}$

_____ _____ _____ _____

Solve. Explain why each proportion is either a direct proportion or an inverse proportion.

20. Mark makes $60 for every six hour shift he works. How much does he make if he works an eight hour shift?

21. Maria drives at a rate of 60 miles per hour. It takes her 3 hours to get to her aunt's house. How long will it take if she drives at a rate of 50 miles per hour?

_____ _____

Use dimensional analysis to make each conversion. Identify the conversion factor for each.

22. 36 yards to feet

23. 25 quarts to pints

24. 75 pounds to ounces

_____

_____

_____

Write a proportion using the given information to answer each question. Then solve.

25. Carrie scored 10 points for every eight points that Alan scored. If the two scored a total of 90 points, how many points did each person score?

26. Adam and Kate deliver a total of 72 newspapers every morning. For every five newspapers Adam delivers, Kate delivers four. How many papers does each person deliver?

_____

_____

27. Norma builds a $\frac{1}{8}$-scale model of her own house. Her living room measures 12 feet by 28 feet. What are the dimensions of the model's living room?

28. A map shows a scale of 1 centimeter = 40 kilometers. The actual distance of a highway is 116 kilometers. To the nearest tenth of a centimeter, what is the length of that highway on the map?

_____

_____

Complete each statement.

29. The ratio of $\overline{JK}$ to $\overline{NO}$ is _____.

30. The length of $\overline{PO}$ is _____.

31. The measure of $\angle N$ is _____.

32. The measure of $\angle O$ is _____.

Triangles *JKL* and *NOP* are similar.

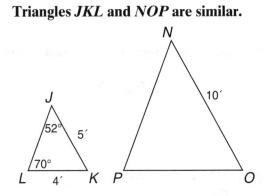

Tell About It

Explain how you solve the problem. Show all your work.

33. A person who is 6 feet tall casts a shadow that is 3.5 feet long. A nearby tree casts a shadow that is 22.75 feet long. What is the height of the tree?

_____

Cumulative Review: Chapters 1–6

Name _____ Date _____

Circle the best answer.

1. Divide.

$\frac{3}{7} \div \frac{14}{27}$

    A. $\frac{98}{81}$

    B. $\frac{81}{98}$

    C. $\frac{1}{2}$

    D. $\frac{2}{9}$

2. Simplify.

$|8| + |-9| - |-12|$

    F. −13   **G.** 5

    H. 11   **J.** 29

3. Evaluate.

4^{-3}

    A. −12   **B.** $\frac{1}{64}$

    C. $\frac{1}{4}$ **D.** 64

4. An ordered pair has a negative coordinate followed by a positive coordinate. In which quadrant does the point lie?

    F. I   **G.** II

    H. III   **J.** IV

5. What is the solution of $8x - 13 = 19$?

    A. $x = \frac{3}{4}$ **B.** $x = 4$

    C. $x = 32$ **D.** $x = 40$

6. Noah read 20 pages of his book in 30 minutes. What was Noah's average reading speed in page(s) per minute?

    F. $\frac{2}{3}$ **G.** $\frac{3}{2}$

    H. 2   **J.** 6

7. Which is the algebraic equation for "ten is four less than half of a number?"

    A. $10 = \frac{1}{2}(n - 4)$

    B. $10 - 4 = \frac{1}{2}n$

    C. $10 = 4 - \frac{1}{2}n$

    D. $10 = \frac{1}{2}n - 4$

8. Solve.

$-3x \le -12$

    F. $x \le 4$ **G.** $x \ge -4$

    H. $x \ge 4$ **J.** $x \ge -10$

9. If $3\frac{1}{2}x = -3\frac{4}{7}$, what is the value of x?

    A. $-12\frac{1}{2}$ **B.** $-1\frac{1}{49}$

    C. $1\frac{1}{49}$ **D.** $12\frac{1}{2}$

10. Which algebraic sentence represents the statement, "four times a number divided by 5 is less than or equal to 9"?

    F. $\frac{4n}{5} < 9$ **G.** $\frac{n + 4}{5} \le 9$

    H. $\frac{4n}{5} \le 9$ **J.** $\frac{4n}{5} \ge 9$

11. Simplify.

$6 - (3 + 2 \bullet 5) + (-3)^2$

    A. −15   **B.** 2

    C. 28   **D.** 34

12. The sum of two integers is 5. Their product is −6. What are the integers?

    F. −1, 6   **G.** 2, 3

    H. 1, −6   **J.** 2, −3

13. A rectangular container has a capacity of 140 cubic inches. The width is 7 inches, and the height is 2 inches. What is the length of the container?

A. 10 in. **B.** 14 in.
C. 20 in. **D.** 70 in.

14. Rewrite 1,907,000 using scientific notation.

F. 1.907×10^5
G. 19.07×10^6
H. 0.1907×10^7
J. 1.907×10^6

15. Use rounding to estimate the sum.

$0.98 + 0.8 + 7.49$

A. 7 **B.** 8
C. 9 **D.** 10

16. Write the prime factorization of 120.

F. $2^3 \cdot 3 \cdot 5$ **G.** $2^3 \cdot 15$
H. $2^2 \cdot 3^2 \cdot 5$ **J.** $2 \cdot 3 \cdot 5$

17. A park has a length of 50 meters. The length of the park is less than or equal to twice the width. Which inequality could be used to find the width of the park?

A. $50 \leq 2w$
B. $50 \leq 2\ell$
C. $2w \leq 50$
D. $2w - \ell \leq 50$

18. Simplify.

$$[-2.3 + (-8.9)] \div (-3.2)$$

F. 0.35 **G.** 3.5
H. −3.5 **J.** −0.35

19. Which is a solution of $4x - 14x > -5$?

A. $x < \dfrac{1}{2}$

B. $x > -\dfrac{1}{2}$

C. $x < 1$

D. $x > \dfrac{1}{2}$

20. Which ratio is *not* equivalent to $\dfrac{3}{4}$?

F. $\dfrac{9}{12}$ **G.** $\dfrac{1.5}{2}$

H. $\dfrac{36}{48}$ **J.** $\dfrac{21}{24}$

21. Which is the missing term in the proportion $\dfrac{2}{7} = \dfrac{x}{63}$?

A. 9 **B.** 18
C. 126 **D.** 220.5

22. Triangle *ABC* is similar to triangle *DEF*. Angle *A* measures 70°, angle *B* measures 50°, and angle *C* measures 60°. What is the measure of angle *E*?

F. 70°
G. 50°
H. 60°
J. 180°

Tell About It

Explain how you solve each problem. Show all your work.

23. Jess jogs at a rate of 6 miles per hour. The next time she jogs she increases her speed to a rate of 7 miles per hour. How long will it take her to jog 6 miles?

24. The Statue of Liberty is about 152 feet tall. An artist creates a model of the Statue of Liberty using a scale factor of $\dfrac{1}{32}$. How tall is the artist's model?

7-1 Percents

Name _____   Date _____

A *percent* (%) is a ratio or comparison of a quantity to 100. $\dfrac{part}{whole} = \dfrac{n}{100} = n\%$

To rename a fraction as a percent, find an equivalent fraction with a denominator of 100.

When the second term of a ratio is 10:

$$\frac{3}{10} = \frac{3 \cdot 10}{10 \cdot 10} = \frac{30}{100} = 30\%$$

Think
10 • 10 = 100

When the second term of a ratio is 1000:

$$\frac{25}{1000} = \frac{25 \div 10}{1000 \div 10} = \frac{2.5}{100} = 2.5\%$$

Think
1000 ÷ 10 = 100

When the second term of a ratio is a factor of 100:

$$\frac{9}{20} = \frac{9 \cdot 5}{20 \cdot 5} = \frac{45}{100} = 45\%$$

Think
20 • 5 = 100

Find the percent that names the shaded part of each figure.

1.

$$\frac{2}{10} = \frac{2 \cdot 10}{10 \cdot 10} = \frac{20}{100}$$

20%

2.

3.

Rename each ratio as a percent.

4. 1 : 10

$$\frac{1}{10} = \frac{1 \cdot 10}{10 \cdot 10} = \frac{10}{100}$$

10%

5. 4 : 10

40%

6. 12 : 10

120%

7. 87 : 10

870%

8. $\dfrac{0.1}{10}$

1%

9. $\dfrac{0.9}{10}$

9%

10. $\dfrac{1.5}{10}$

15%

11. $\dfrac{9.2}{10}$

92%

12. 30 : 1000

3%
30000

13. 80 : 1000

8%
80000

14. 32 : 1000

3.2%
3200

15. 86 to 1000

8.6%

Rename each ratio as a percent.

16. 3 : 5

$$\frac{3}{5} = \frac{3 \cdot 20}{5 \cdot 20} = \frac{60}{100}$$

60%

17. 1 : 4 $\frac{1}{4} = .25 \cdot \frac{25}{100}$

25%

18. 3 : 2

$\frac{3}{2} = 150\%$

19. 9 : 5

$\frac{9}{5} \cdot 20 = 180\%$

20. 3 to 50

$\frac{3 \cdot 2}{50 \cdot 2} = 6\%$

21. 4 to 25

$\frac{4 \cdot 4}{25 \cdot 4} = 16\%$

22. 17 to 25

$\frac{17}{15} = 68\%$

23. 14 to 20

$\frac{14}{20} = 70\%$

24. $\frac{1.2}{5}$

$\frac{1.2}{5} = 24\%$

25. $\frac{3.4}{4}$

$\frac{3.4}{4} \cdot \frac{25}{25} = 85\%$

26. $\frac{6.3}{20}$

$\frac{6.3}{20} \cdot \frac{5}{5} = 31.5\%$

27. $\frac{8.5}{25}$

$\frac{8.5}{25} \cdot \frac{4}{4} = 34\%$

Problem Solving

28. A theater company sells 43 of the 50 seats available in their performance space. What percent of the seats have not been sold?

$$\frac{7}{50} = \frac{7 \cdot 2}{50 \cdot 2} = \frac{14}{100} = 14\%$$

14% of the seats have not been sold

29. Your friend has a bag of 20 marbles. Seven are blue, four are red, two are green, and three are yellow. If the rest are white, what percent of the marbles are white?

30. One hundred people in a supermarket survey were asked what kind of pet they own. Forty-seven people surveyed have only cats, thirty-three have only dogs and seven have only an "other" kind of pet. If no one surveyed has more than one kind of pet, what percent of the people surveyed do not own a pet?

31. Out of 1000 teens surveyed about next summer vacation, 362 said they will stay at home, 218 will go to summer camp, and 195 will go on a family vacation. What percent of students do not fit into the three categories?

SPIRAL REVIEW

Round to the nearest tenth.

32. 5.976

33. 0.0931

Round to the nearest hundredth.

34. 11.1237

35. 1000.0452

Divide.

36. 1100 ÷ 100

37. 214.7 ÷ 10

38. 3752 ÷ 1000

39. 1890 ÷ 100

7-2 Fractions, Decimals, Percents

Name _____ Date _____

You can rename a percent as a decimal or as a fraction.

Write a percent as a decimal.

Remove the % symbol and move the decimal point *two places to the left*.

$$60\% \longrightarrow 0.60$$

Write a percent as a fraction.

$60\% = \dfrac{60}{100}$ ← Write as a fraction with a denominator of 100.

$= \dfrac{60 \div 20}{100 \div 20}$ ← Divide both terms by the GCF.

$= \dfrac{3}{5}$

Write a decimal as a percent.

Rename as a fraction in hundredths.

$0.1 = \dfrac{1}{10} = \dfrac{1 \cdot 10}{10 \cdot 10} = \dfrac{10}{100} = 10\%$

Move the decimal *two places to the right*. Then insert the % symbol.

$0.1 \longrightarrow 10.0 \longrightarrow 10\%$

Write a fraction as a percent.

Method 1

$\dfrac{3}{8} = 3 \div 8 = 0.375$ ← Rename as a decimal.

$0.375 \longrightarrow 37.5\%$ ← Write as a percent.

Method 2

$\dfrac{3}{8} = \dfrac{x}{100}$ ← Use a proportion.

$8x = 300$ ← Cross multiply.

$\dfrac{8x}{8} = \dfrac{300}{8}$ ← Divide both sides by 8.

$x = 37.5 \longrightarrow \dfrac{3}{8} = 37.5\%$

Write each fraction or decimal as a percent.

1. 0.19
   0.19(100%)
   19%

2. 0.56 56%

3. 0.06 6%

4. 0.01 1%

5. 0.125 12.5%

6. 0.717 71.7%

7. $\dfrac{9}{20}$ 45%

8. $\dfrac{24}{25}$ 96%

9. $\dfrac{7}{8}$ 87.5%

10. $\dfrac{9}{16}$ 56.25%

11. $\dfrac{0.12}{0.20}$ 60%

12. $\dfrac{0.02}{0.1}$ 20%

Write each percent as a decimal.

13. 39%
    39 ÷ 100
    0.39

14. 6% $.06$

15. 31.8% $.318$

16. 8.5% $.085$

17. $14\frac{3}{4}\%$ $.1475$

18. $1\frac{1}{2}\%$ $.015$

Write each percent as a fraction in simplest form.

19. 55%
    $\dfrac{55}{100} = \dfrac{55 \div 5}{100 \div 5}$
    $\dfrac{11}{20}$

20. 62% $\dfrac{62}{100}$ $\dfrac{31}{50}$

21. 12% $\dfrac{12}{100}$ $\dfrac{6}{50}$

22. 42% $\dfrac{42}{100}$ $\dfrac{21}{50}$

23. 17.5% $\dfrac{17.5}{100}$

24. $6\frac{2}{3}\%$

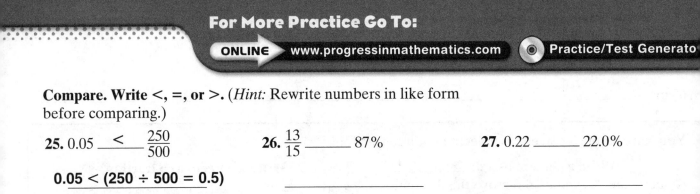
Compare. Write <, =, or >. (*Hint:* Rewrite numbers in like form before comparing.)

25. 0.05 __<__ $\dfrac{250}{500}$

$\underline{0.05 < (250 \div 500 = 0.5)}$

26. $\dfrac{13}{15}$ _____ 87%

27. 0.22 _____ 22.0%

Match the labeled points on the number line with each percent, decimal, or fraction.

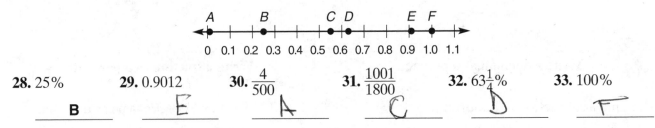

28. 25%

__B__

29. 0.9012

E

30. $\dfrac{4}{500}$

A

31. $\dfrac{1001}{1800}$

C

32. $63\frac{1}{4}\%$

D

33. 100%

F

Order from least to greatest. (*Hint:* Rewrite numbers in like form, then compare.)

34. $\dfrac{102}{1000}, 0.120, 1.40, 0.14\%$ and 10%

.102, .120, 1.40, .14, .0014, .1

.0014, .14%, 10%, $\dfrac{102}{1000}$, 0.120,

1.40

35. $24\%, \dfrac{0.1}{0.5}, \dfrac{19}{20}, 95\%$, and 0.950

.24, .2, .95, .95, .950

1.40 $\dfrac{.1}{.5}$, 24%, $\dfrac{19}{20}$, 95%, 0.9

Solve. Check to justify your answer.

36. The girls' soccer team won 78.6% of its matches this season. The boys' team won 0.77 of its matches, and the co-ed team won 18 of the 24 matches it played. Which team had the best season record?

37. Of the pairs of jeans sold at the Jeans Store, 45% are blue, 0.2 are black, and $\dfrac{1}{8}$ are white; and the rest are other colors. What percent of the jeans are neither blue, black, nor white?

WRITE ABOUT IT

38. Explain how to order $\dfrac{16}{250}, 6.5\%$, and 0.062 from least to greatest as fractions in thousandths.

_____

_____

_____

7-3 Percents Greater Than 100%/Less Than 1%

Name _____ Date _____

To rename a percent as a *decimal*:

Greater than 100%
110% → 1.10. → 1.1

Less than 1%
0.1% → 0.00.1 → 0.001

To rename a decimal as a *percent*:

Greater than 100%
2.1 → 2.10 → 210%

Less than 1%
0.002 → 0.00.2 → 0.2%

Think
Reverse the steps for writing a percent as a decimal.

To rename a percent as a *fraction*:

Greater than 100%
$120\% = \frac{120}{100} = \frac{120 \div 20}{100 \div 20} = \frac{6}{5}$

Less than 1%
$0.2\% = \frac{0.2}{100} = \frac{0.2 \cdot 5}{100 \cdot 5} = \frac{1}{500}$

To rename a fraction as a *percent*:

Greater than 100%
$\frac{3}{2} = 3 \div 2 = 1.5 \rightarrow 1.50. \rightarrow 150\%$

Less than 1%
$\frac{2}{500} = 2 \div 500 = 0.004 \rightarrow 0.00.4 \rightarrow 0.4\%$

To rename *a part of a percent* as a fraction:

Divide by 100 $\left(\text{or multiply by } \frac{1}{100}\right)$.

$\frac{1}{2}\% = \frac{1}{2} \cdot \frac{1}{100} = \frac{1}{200}$

Write each decimal as a percent.

1. 4.5
4.5(100%)
450%

2. 6.8

3. 9

4. 2

5. 3.33

6. 7.21

7. 0.003

8. 0.007

9. 0.0021

10. 0.0064

11. 0.0001

12. 0.0005

13. 0.00020

14. 0.00110

15. 0.03760

Write each fraction as a percent in decimal form.

16. $\frac{6}{1}$
6 ÷ 1 = 6
600%

17. $\frac{10}{1}$

18. $\frac{7}{2}$

19. $\frac{6}{5}$

20. $\frac{110}{40}$

21. $\frac{325}{50}$

22. $\frac{3}{400}$

23. $\frac{7}{800}$

24. $\frac{1}{2500}$

25. $\frac{9}{2000}$

26. $\frac{17}{3400}$

27. $\frac{41}{5000}$

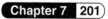

Write each percent as a decimal.

28. 104%

$$104 \div 100$$
$$\underline{\mathbf{1.04}}$$

29. 658%

30. 0.8%

31. 0.7%

32. 0.42%

33. 0.57%

34. 622.2%

35. 671.3%

Write each percent as a fraction or mixed number in simplest form.
(*Hint:* You can rename percents as mixed numbers by breaking them into parts.)

36. 130%

$$100\% + 30\%$$
$$1 + \frac{30}{100} = 1\frac{3}{10}$$

37. 184%

38. 0.4%

39. 0.9%

40. $\frac{1}{4}$%

41. $\frac{7}{10}$%

42. $\frac{2}{3}$%

43. $\frac{4}{5}$%

(*Hint:* Rename fractions greater than 1 as improper fractions.)

44. $8\frac{1}{6}$%

45. $31\frac{1}{4}$%

46. $410\frac{3}{7}$%

47. $680\frac{3}{9}$%

Solve. Check to justify your answer.

48. The number of students who won scholarships this year is 340% of the number of students who won in 1954. Express this percent as a fraction.

49. One and one-fifth times the number of students who tried out last year for the baseball team tried out this year. Express this number as a percent.

WRITE ABOUT IT

50. How can you tell which fractions represent a number that is less than 1% without doing any computation?

$$\frac{0.02}{5}, \frac{0.2}{5}, \frac{2}{5}, \frac{2}{50}, \frac{2}{500}$$

7-4 Find a Percentage of a Number

Name _____ Date _____

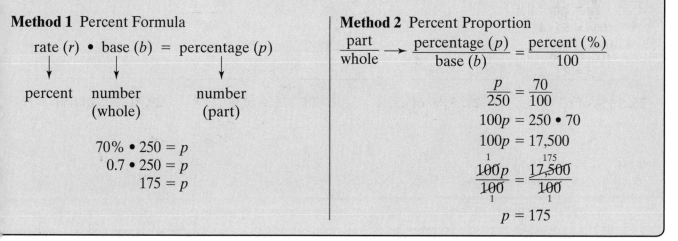

What is 70% of 250?

Method 1 Percent Formula

rate (r) • base (b) = percentage (p)

↓ ↓ ↓

percent   number   number
          (whole)   (part)

70% • 250 = p
0.7 • 250 = p
175 = p

Method 2 Percent Proportion

$\dfrac{part}{whole}$ → $\dfrac{percentage\ (p)}{base\ (b)} = \dfrac{percent\ (\%)}{100}$

$\dfrac{p}{250} = \dfrac{70}{100}$

$100p = 250 • 70$
$100p = 17,500$

$\dfrac{100p}{100} = \dfrac{17,500}{100}$

$p = 175$

Write each percent as a decimal. Then use the percent formula to find each percentage.

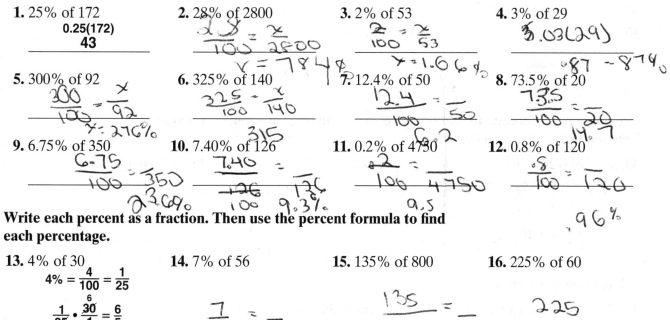

1. 25% of 172
0.25(172)
43

2. 28% of 2800
$\dfrac{28}{100} = \dfrac{x}{2800}$
$x = 784$

3. 2% of 53
$\dfrac{2}{100} = \dfrac{x}{53}$
$x = 1.66$ %

4. 3% of 29
3 .03(29)
.87 ~ .874

5. 300% of 92
$\dfrac{300}{100} = \dfrac{x}{92}$
$x = 276$%

6. 325% of 140
$\dfrac{325}{100} = \dfrac{x}{140}$
315

7. 12.4% of 50
$\dfrac{12.4}{100} = \dfrac{x}{50}$
6.2

8. 73.5% of 20
$\dfrac{73.5}{100} = \dfrac{x}{20}$
14.7

9. 6.75% of 350
$\dfrac{6.75}{100} = \dfrac{x}{350}$
23.69%

10. 7.40% of 126
$\dfrac{7.40}{126} = \dfrac{x}{126}$
9.3%

11. 0.2% of 4750
$\dfrac{.2}{100} = \dfrac{x}{4750}$
9.5

12. 0.8% of 120
$\dfrac{.8}{100} = \dfrac{x}{120}$
.96%

Write each percent as a fraction. Then use the percent formula to find each percentage.

13. 4% of 30
$4\% = \dfrac{4}{100} = \dfrac{1}{25}$
$\dfrac{1}{25} • \dfrac{\overset{6}{30}}{1} = \dfrac{6}{5}$
$\dfrac{6}{5} = 1\dfrac{1}{5}$

14. 7% of 56
$\dfrac{7}{100} = \dfrac{x}{56}$
3.9%

15. 135% of 800
$\dfrac{135}{100} = \dfrac{x}{800}$
1080%

16. 225% of 60
$\dfrac{225}{100} = \dfrac{x}{60}$
135

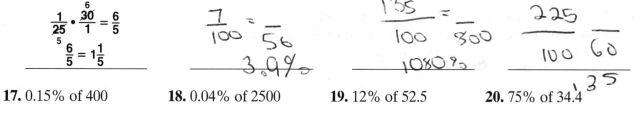

17. 0.15% of 400
$\dfrac{.15}{100} = \dfrac{x}{400}$
.6

18. 0.04% of 2500
$\dfrac{.04}{100} = \dfrac{x}{2500}$
1

19. 12% of 52.5
$\dfrac{12}{100} = \dfrac{x}{525}$
6.3

20. 75% of 34.4
$\dfrac{75}{100} = \dfrac{x}{34.4}$
25.8

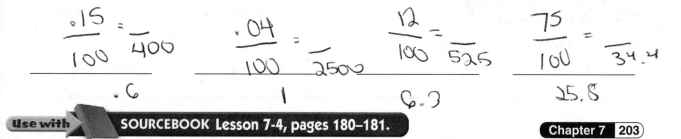

Use a percent proportion to find each percentage. (*Hint:* Rename mixed number percents as fractions greater than 1.)

21. 4% of 50

$$\frac{p}{50} = \frac{4}{100}$$
$$100p = 50 \cdot 4$$
$$\frac{100p}{100} = \frac{200}{100}$$
$$p = 2$$

22. 5% of 74

3.4

23. 18% of 130

$$\frac{18}{100} = \overline{130}$$
23.4

24. 51% of 650

$$\frac{51}{100} = \overline{650}$$
331.50

25. 6.75% of $720

26. $1\frac{1}{7}$% of 63

27. $5\frac{1}{3}$% of 45

28. $33\frac{1}{3}$% of 90

29. $10\frac{2}{11}$% of 660

Use the percent formula to find the number of degrees in a section of a circle. (*Hint:* A circle measures 360°.)

30. 90% of a circle

0.9 • 360°
324°

31. 55% of a circle

32. 12.5% of a circle

Use the percent formula to find the percent of a number in scientific notation. Rename the percent as a fraction.

33. 50% of 6.24×10^8

$$\frac{50}{100} = \frac{1}{2}; \frac{1}{2} \cdot 6.24 \times 10^8$$
$$\frac{6.24}{2} \times 10^8$$
$$3.12 \times 10^8$$

34. 6% of 9.1×10^{32}

35. 70% of 4.5×10^{21}

Solve. Show your work.

36. Gail conducted a survey. Twenty percent of 200 girls and 40% of 100 boys surveyed use the town pool on weekends. Do more girls or boys use the pool on weekends?

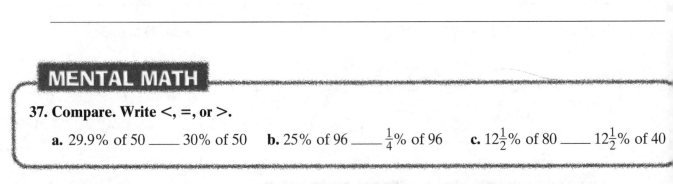

MENTAL MATH

37. Compare. Write <, =, or >.

   a. 29.9% of 50 _____ 30% of 50   **b.** 25% of 96 _____ $\frac{1}{4}$% of 96   **c.** $12\frac{1}{2}$% of 80 _____ $12\frac{1}{2}$% of 40

7-5 Find a Percent

Name _____ Date _____

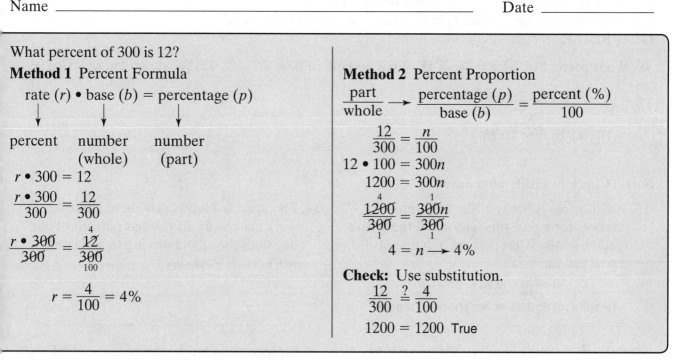

What percent of 300 is 12?

Method 1 Percent Formula

rate (r) • base (b) = percentage (p)

percent   number (whole)   number (part)

$r \cdot 300 = 12$

$\dfrac{r \cdot 300}{300} = \dfrac{12}{300}$

$\dfrac{r \cdot \cancel{300}}{\cancel{300}} = \dfrac{\cancel{12}^{4}}{\cancel{300}_{100}}$

$r = \dfrac{4}{100} = 4\%$

Method 2 Percent Proportion

$\dfrac{\text{part}}{\text{whole}} \longrightarrow \dfrac{\text{percentage }(p)}{\text{base }(b)} = \dfrac{\text{percent }(\%)}{100}$

$\dfrac{12}{300} = \dfrac{n}{100}$

$12 \cdot 100 = 300n$

$1200 = 300n$

$\dfrac{\cancel{1200}^{4}}{\cancel{300}_{1}} = \dfrac{\cancel{300}^{1} n}{\cancel{300}_{1}}$

$4 = n \longrightarrow 4\%$

Check: Use substitution.

$\dfrac{12}{300} \overset{?}{=} \dfrac{4}{100}$

$1200 = 1200$ True

Use the percent formula to find each percent.

1. What percent of 30 is 6?

$\dfrac{r}{100} \cdot 30 = 6; \; 0.30r = 6;$

$\dfrac{0.3r}{0.3} = \dfrac{6}{0.3}; \; r = 20; \; \mathbf{20\%}$

2. What percent of 20 is 8?

$\dfrac{8}{100 \quad 20}$

40%

3. What percent of 66 is 99?

$\dfrac{99}{100 \quad 66}$

150%

4. 420 is what percent of 120?

$\dfrac{420}{100 \quad 120}$

350%

5. 2.5 is what percent of 5?

$\dfrac{2.5}{100 \quad 5}$

50%

6. 3.9 is what percent of 13?

$\dfrac{3.9}{100 \quad 13}$

30%

Use the percent proportion and the circle graph to answer exercises 7–9.

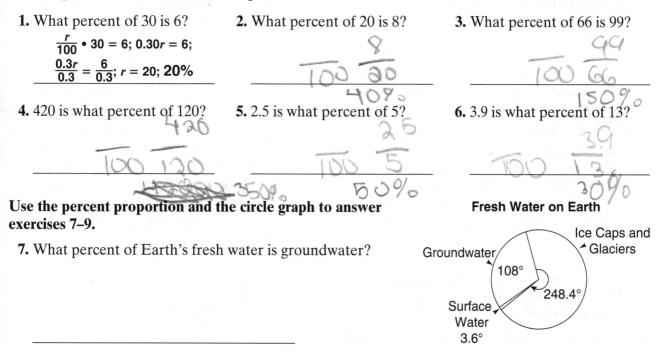

Fresh Water on Earth

Groundwater — 108°
Ice Caps and Glaciers — 248.4°
Surface Water — 3.6°

7. What percent of Earth's fresh water is groundwater?

_____

8. What percent of Earth's fresh water is in ice caps and glaciers?

_____

9. What percent of the Earth's fresh water is on its surface?

_____

Use the percent proportion to solve for the percent. Write the
percent in fraction and decimal form. If necessary, round to tenths.
(*Hint:* Rewrite fractions in decimal form.)

10. What percent of 1.2 is 0.2? **11.** What percent of 20 is $\frac{1}{2}$? **12.** What percent of 80 is $2\frac{1}{2}$?

$\frac{0.2}{1.2} = \frac{n}{100}$; $20 = 1.2n$; $\frac{20}{1.2} = \frac{\overset{1}{\cancel{1.2}}n}{\underset{1}{\cancel{1.2}}}$

$n = 16\frac{2}{3}\%$; $16.\overline{6} \approx 16.7\%$

Solve. Check to justify your answer.

13. Amanda plays hockey. She attempted
25 shots for a goal this season. Of these, she
made 6 goals. What percent of her shots for
a goal did she make?

$$r = \frac{6}{25} = 0.24 = 24\%$$

Amanda made 24% of her shots for a goal.

14. Lisa spends 3 hours driving to and from
work each work day. What percent of her
day does she spend driving to and from
work, each work day?

15. Carmen's gross wages are $240, but 30% of
her wages are withheld for taxes. How much
money is withheld for taxes?

16. Biology The human body is about 18.5%
carbon. Manuel weighs 150 pounds.
About how many pounds of carbon are
in Manuel's body?

Problem Solving

17. Sanjay and Vanden practiced soccer penalty
kicks. Sanjay made 15 of 40 attempts and
Vanden made 12 of 35 attempts. Who made
a fewer percent of penalty kicks? How
much fewer? Round each percent to the
nearest tenth.

18. Justin and his sister Stephanie are discussing
the results of their recent mathematics
quizzes. Justin earned 63 out of 75 points,
and Stephanie earned 63 out of 70 points.
Who earned a higher percent score? How
much higher?

CHALLENGE

19. A forested research site contains three dominant types of trees: maple,
oak, and ash. There are 268 maple trees, 204 oak trees, and 148 ash trees.
What percent of each type of dominant tree is on the site? Round your
answer to the nearest percent. Explain how you found your answer.

7-6 Find the Original Number or the Base

Name _____ Date _____

Solve: 25% of what number is 8?

Method 1 Percent Formula

$$\text{rate } (r) \cdot \text{base } (b) = \text{percentage } (p)$$

percent   number   number
(whole)   (part)

$$25\% \cdot b = 8$$
$$0.25b = 8$$
$$\frac{0.25b}{0.25} = \frac{8}{0.25}$$
$$b = 32$$

Method 2 Proportion

$$\frac{\text{part}}{\text{whole}} \rightarrow \frac{\text{percentage } (p)}{\text{base } (b)} = \frac{\text{percent } (\%)}{100}$$

$$\frac{8}{b} = \frac{25}{100}$$
$$25b = 8 \cdot 100$$
$$25b = 800$$
$$25b \div 25 = 800 \div 25$$
$$b = 32$$

Use the percent formula to solve for the original number.

1. 20% of what number is 7?

20% • b = 7
0.20b = 7
0.2b ÷ 0.2 = 7 ÷ 0.2
b = 35

2. 70% of what number is 63?

$$\frac{70}{100} \quad \frac{63}{}$$

3. 150% of what number is 120?

$$\frac{150}{100} \quad \frac{120}{}$$

4. 250% of what number is 190?

$$\frac{250}{100} \quad \frac{190}{}$$
76%

5. 662 is 33.1% of what number?

90%
$$\frac{33.1}{100} \quad \frac{662}{}$$
2000

6. 500 is 62.5% of what number?

80%
$$\frac{62.5}{100} \quad \frac{500}{}$$
800

Use a percent proportion to solve for the original number.

7. 6.0% of what number is 4.2?

$$\frac{4.2}{n} = \frac{6.0}{100}; \ 6n = 4.2 \cdot 100$$
6n = 420; 6n ÷ 6 = 420 ÷ 6
n = 70

8. 5.4% of what number is 16.2?

$$\frac{5.4}{100} = \frac{16.2}{x}$$
300

9. 14 is $\frac{1}{2}$% of what number?

$$\frac{.5}{100} = \frac{14}{x}$$
2800

10. 24 is $\frac{3}{4}$% of what number?

$$\frac{.75}{100} = \frac{24}{x}$$
3200

11. 0.7% of what number is 49?

$$\frac{.7}{100} = \frac{49}{y}$$
7000

12. 6.25% of what number is 0.9?

$$\frac{6.25}{100} = \frac{.9}{x}$$
144

13. 12 is 0.5% of what number?

$$\frac{.5}{100} = \frac{12}{x}$$
2400

14. 325 is $\frac{1}{4}$% of what number?

$$\frac{.25}{100} = \frac{325}{x}$$
130,000

15. 0.25 is 7.5% of what number?

$$\frac{7.5}{100} = \frac{.25}{x}$$
333.3

Use the percent proportion to solve for the rate, base, or percentage.

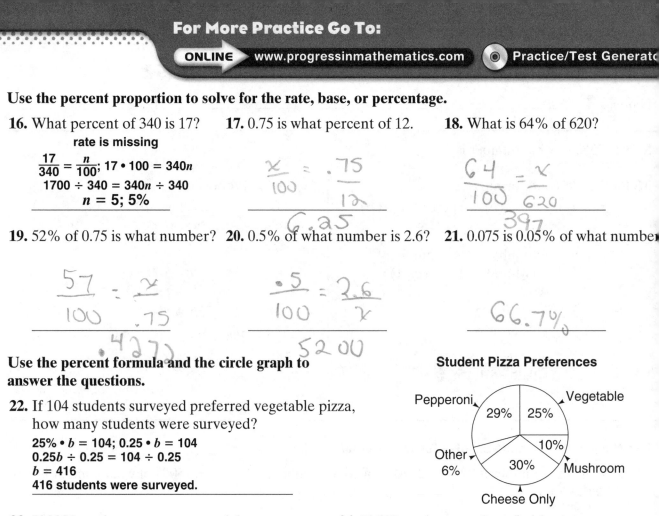

16. What percent of 340 is 17?

rate is missing

$\frac{17}{340} = \frac{n}{100}$; $17 \cdot 100 = 340n$

$1700 \div 340 = 340n \div 340$

$n = 5$; 5%

17. 0.75 is what percent of 12.

$\frac{x}{100} = \frac{.75}{12}$

6.25

18. What is 64% of 620?

$\frac{64}{100} = \frac{x}{620}$

397

19. 52% of 0.75 is what number?

$\frac{57}{100} = \frac{x}{.75}$

.4275

20. 0.5% of what number is 2.6?

$\frac{.5}{100} = \frac{2.6}{x}$

5200

21. 0.075 is 0.05% of what number

66.7%

Use the percent formula and the circle graph to answer the questions.

22. If 104 students surveyed preferred vegetable pizza, how many students were surveyed?

25% • b = 104; 0.25 • b = 104

0.25b ÷ 0.25 = 104 ÷ 0.25

b = 416

416 students were surveyed.

Student Pizza Preferences

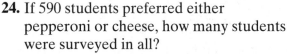

Pepperoni 29% Vegetable 25%

10%

Other 6% 30% Mushroom

Cheese Only

23. If 2000 students were surveyed, how many students answered "Other"?

24. If 590 students preferred either pepperoni or cheese, how many students were surveyed in all?

Problem Solving

25. North High School's basketball team scored 850 points this season. This is $8\frac{1}{2}$% of the total points scored in the league. How many points scored in the league were not scored by North High School?

26. A fire department received 71 false alarms out of 639 alarms. What percent of the alarms received were *not* false? If needed, round to the nearest percent.

CHALLENGE

27. Joyce's age is 25% of Marta's age. Marta's age is 50% of Cesar's age. If Joyce is 11, what percent of Cesar's age is Joyce's age?

7-7 Estimate with Percents

Name _____ Date _____

Use compatible numbers to estimate with percents.

Estimate: 47% of 1802

$$rb = p$$
$$47\% \bullet 1802 = p$$

Think

$47\% \approx 50\% = \frac{1}{2};\ 1802 \approx 1800$

$$\frac{1}{2} \bullet 1800 = p$$

$$900 = p$$

So 47% of 1802 is about 900.

Using benchmark percents can help you accurately estimate with mental math.

Estimate: 4% of 48

Think

$48 \approx 50$ and $4\% = 4 \bullet 1\%$

1% of $50 = 0.01 \bullet 50 = \textbf{0.5}$
4% of $50 = \quad 4 \bullet \textbf{0.5} = 2$

So 4% of 48 is about 2.

Complete the chart.

Fraction	$\frac{1}{10}$	$\frac{1}{8}$	$\frac{1}{5}$	$\frac{1}{4}$	$\frac{1}{3}$	$\frac{1}{2}$	$\frac{2}{3}$	$\frac{3}{4}$
1. Percent	___	___	___	___	___	___	___	___
2. Decimal	___	___	___	___	___	___	___	___

Estimate. Use compatible numbers and benchmark fractions.

3. 53% of 603

$53\% \approx 50\% = \frac{1}{2}$
$603 \approx 600$
$p \approx \frac{1}{2} \bullet 600$
$\underline{p \approx 300}$

4. 31% of 90

5. 48% of $5.20

6. 66% of $2.90

7. 73.6% of 106

8. 12.7% of 71

9. $62\frac{1}{2}\%$ of 308

10. $31\frac{3}{4}\%$ of 150

Estimate. Use the benchmark percents 1% and 10%.

11. 10% of 44

$44 \approx 40$
10% of $40 = 0.1 \bullet 40 = 4$
$\quad$ **about 4**

12. 40% of 49

13. 2% of 81

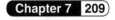

Estimate. Use the benchmark percents 1% and 10%.

14. 4% of 600

_____

15. 15% of 73

_____

16. 15% of 92

_____

17. 71% of 123

_____

18. 71% of 32

_____

19. 38% of 190

_____

Estimate the rate or percent.

20. 30 is about what percent of 79?

$$r \approx \frac{30}{80} = \frac{3}{8} = 37.5\%$$

_____

21. 6 is about what percent of 13?

_____

22. 23.9 is about 46.1% of what number?

_____

23. 9.9 is about 11% of what number?

_____

24. About 21.6% of what number is $20?

_____

25. About 77.2% of what number is $15?

_____

Use visual benchmarks to estimate the percent of each figure that is shaded.

26.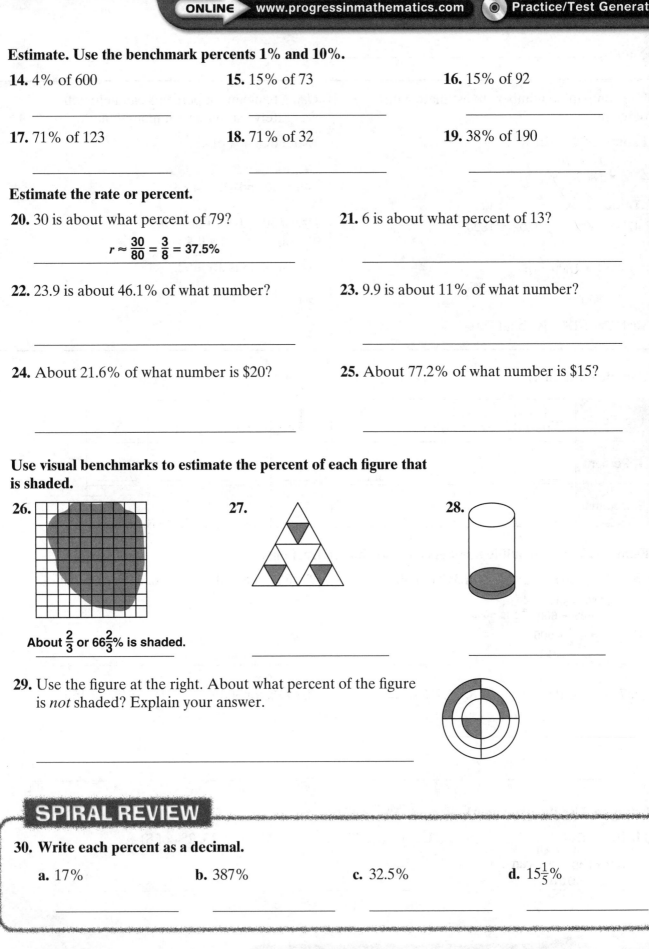

About $\frac{2}{3}$ or $66\frac{2}{3}\%$ is shaded.

27.

_____

28.

_____

29. Use the figure at the right. About what percent of the figure is *not* shaded? Explain your answer.

_____

SPIRAL REVIEW

30. Write each percent as a decimal.

    a. 17%

    b. 387%

    c. 32.5%

    d. $15\frac{1}{5}\%$

_____ _____ _____ _____

7-8 Percent Increase

Name _____ Date _____

Ana starts her sticker collection with 20 stickers. After 1 year she has 150 stickers. What is the *percent increase* in the number of her stickers?

To find the percent increase:

Method 1 Write an Equation.

$150 - 20 = \mathbf{130}$ ← The amount of increase.

Let R_I = percent increase

$$R_I = \frac{\text{amount of increase}}{\text{original amount}}$$

$$R_I = \frac{150 - 20}{20}$$

$$= \frac{130}{20}$$

$$= 6.5$$

$$= 650\%$$

Method 2 Write and Solve a Proportion.

$$\frac{\text{amount of increase}}{\text{original amount}} = \frac{\text{percent increase (\%)}}{100}$$

$$\frac{130}{20} \diagup \frac{n}{100}$$

$$20n = 130 \cdot 100$$

$$\frac{20n}{20} = \frac{13,000}{20}$$

$$n = 650$$

$$n = 650\%$$

So the percent increase is 650%.

To *find the amount of profit* from the sale of an item:

- equation: profit (P) = cost $(C) \cdot$ percent of profit (%)
- proportion: $\dfrac{\text{profit }(P)}{\text{cost }(C)} = \dfrac{\text{percent profit (\%)}}{100}$

To *find the selling price:*

- selling price (SP) = profit (P) + cost (C)

Find the percent increase. If necessary, round to the nearest tenth of a percent.

1. from 8 to 12

$R_I = \dfrac{12 - 8}{8} = \dfrac{4}{8} = 0.5$

The percent increase is 50%.

2. from 32 to 36

$\dfrac{4}{32} = \dfrac{4}{32} = .125$

$= 12.5\%$

3. from 15 to 22

$\dfrac{7}{15} = .46$

$= 46\%$

4. from 17 to 28

$\dfrac{11}{17} = .647$

65%

5. from 20 to 85

$\dfrac{65}{20} = 3.25$

325%

$= 325\%$

6. from 0.1 to 0.55

$\dfrac{.45}{.1} = 4.5$

$450\% \; 4.5$

7. from 0.65 to 0.7

$\dfrac{.05}{.62} = .07$

$= 7\%$

8. from 2.2 to 8

$\dfrac{5.8}{2.2} = 2.63\%$

9. from 3.5 to 12.5

$\dfrac{9}{3.5} = 2.57\%$

Find the profit. If necessary, round to the nearest cent.

10. Cost: $50
Percent of profit: 16%

$P = 16\% \cdot \$50, \; P = 0.16 \cdot \$50$

$P = \$8$

profit: $8

11. Cost: $46.58
Percent of profit: 20%

$9.31

12. Cost: $10.50
Percent of profit: 35%

$3.67

Find the profit. If necessary, round to the nearest cent.

13. Cost: $12.10
Percent of profit: 40%

_____

14. Cost: $125.50
Percent of profit: 8.5%

_____

15. Cost: $34.26
Percent of profit: 10.6%

_____

Find the selling price of each item.

16. A pair of jeans costs $20 and sells at a profit of 30%.

$$P = \$20 \cdot 0.30 = \$6$$
$$SP = \$20 + \$6 = \$26$$
The selling price is $26.

_____

17. A CD costs $10 and sells at a profit of 20%

_____

18. A stereo costs $200 and sells at a profit of 25%.

_____

19. A ring costs $50 and sells at a profit of 200%.

_____

20. A drum set costs $375 and sells at a profit of 30%.

_____

21. A flatscreen TV costs $1280 and sells at a profit of 125%.

_____

Problem Solving

22. A guitar dealer buys an acoustic guitar for $300 and sells it at a profit of 15%. She buys an electric guitar for $525 and sells it at a profit of 10%. Which guitar generates the greater profit for the guitar dealer?

_____

23. A beverage company is changing its juice package size. Currently, there are 8 ounces of juice in each package. The new package will contain 12 ounces. What percent more juice will be in the new package?

_____

TEST PREPARATION

24. An amount increases from 40 to 50. What is the percent increase?

A. $\frac{1}{5}$%   **C.** $\frac{1}{4}$%

B. 20%   **D.** 25%

25. A car dealer buys a used car for $3200. The dealer sells the car at a 24% profit. For how much does the car dealer sell the car?

F. $668   **H.** $66,800

G. $3968   **J.** $70,000

7-9 Percent Decrease

Name _____ Date _____

The average rainfall in a town is 4.43 inches in January and 3.02 inches in June. What is the *percent decrease* in the average rainfall from January to June? To find the percent decrease:

Method 1 Write an Equation.

Let R_D = percent decrease

$$R_D = \frac{\text{amount of decrease}}{\text{original amount}}$$

$$R_D = \frac{4.43 - 3.02}{4.43}$$

$$= \frac{1.41}{4.43}$$

$$= 0.31828\ldots \approx 31.8\%$$

Method 2 Write and Solve a proportion.

$$\frac{\text{amount of decrease}}{\text{original amount}} = \frac{n}{100}$$

$$\frac{1.41}{4.43} \diagdown \frac{n}{100}$$

$$4.43n = 141$$

$$\frac{4.43n}{4.43} = \frac{141}{4.43}$$

$$n = 31.828\ldots \approx 31.8\%$$

So the percent decrease is about 31.8%.

To *find the loss* when an item is sold for less than the cost:

- equation: loss (L) = cost (C) • percent of loss (%)
- proportion: $\dfrac{\text{loss } (L)}{\text{cost } (C)} = \dfrac{\text{percent loss } (\%)}{100}$

To *find the selling price* when an item is sold at a loss:

- selling price (SP) = cost (C) − loss (L)

Find the percent decrease. If necessary, round to the nearest tenth of a percent.

1. from 20 to 18

$$R_D = \frac{20 - 18}{20} = \frac{2}{20} = 0.1$$
The percent decrease is 10%.

2. from 70 to 28

$$\frac{52}{70} = .742$$
$$74.2\%$$

3. from 48 to 30

$$\frac{18}{48} = .375$$
$$37.5\%$$

4. from 39 to 28

$$\frac{11}{39} = .28$$
$$.28\%$$

5. from 83 to 35

$$\frac{48}{83} = .57\rho$$
$$58\%$$

6. from 13 to 7.4

$$\frac{5.6}{13} = 43\%$$

7. from 5.6 to 4.2

$$\frac{1.4}{5.6} = 25\%$$

8. from 11.2 to 1.68

$$\frac{9.52}{11.2} = 85\%$$

9. from 0.75 to 0.3

$$\frac{.45}{.75} = 60\%$$

10. from 9.8 to 4.4

$$\frac{5.4}{9.8} = 55\%$$

11. from 6.5 to 3.1

$$\frac{3.4}{6.5} = 52\%$$

12. from 8.2 to 2.3

$$\frac{5.9}{8.2} = 72\%$$

Find the loss. If necessary, round to the nearest cent.

13. Cost: $1200
Percent of loss: 32%
L = $1200 • 32%
L = 1200 • 0.32; L = 384
The loss is $384.

14. Cost: $124
Percent of loss: 10%

15. Cost: $29.30
Percent of loss: 8.4%

16. Cost: $224.25
Percent of loss: 9.2%

17. Cost: $30
Percent of loss: 63.2%

18. Cost: $524.20
Percent of loss: 19.2%

Find the selling price of each item.

19. a stuffed animal costs $5
and sells at a loss of 30%
SP = $5 − (30% of $5); SP = 5 − 1.5 = 3.5
The selling price is $3.50.

20. a T-shirt costs $9
and sells at a loss of 50%

21. a DVD costs $12
and sells at a loss of 60%

22. an MP3 player costs $54
and sells at a loss of 9%

23. a bicycle costs $428
and sells at a loss of 20%

24. a soccer ball costs $8
and sells at a loss of 25.4%

Solve. If necessary, round to the nearest tenth.

25. A runner ran one mile in 11 minutes. A year
later, she ran one mile in 8 minutes. What is
the percent decrease in her running time?

26. A family bought a refrigerator for $1240,
then sold it at a 65% loss. For how much did
they sell the refrigerator?

CRITICAL THINKING

27. A family buys a truck for $8500. The truck loses 18% of its value
in the first year and 15% of its value in the second year. How
much is the truck worth at the end of the second year? Explain
your answers. If necessary, round to the nearest cent.

7-10 Sales Tax and Tips

Name _____ Date _____

A shirt is marked $14. The sales tax is 7%. How much will the shirt cost after sales tax? If necessary, round to the nearest cent.

To find the *amount of sales tax*:

Method 1 Write an Equation

sales Tax (T) = sales Tax Rate • marked Price

$$T = 7\% \cdot \$14$$
$$T = 0.07 \cdot 14$$
$$T = 0.98 \longrightarrow \$0.98$$

So the sales tax is $0.98.

Method 2 Write and Solve a Proportion

$$\frac{\text{sales Tax }(T)}{\text{marked Price }(MP)} = \frac{\text{sales Tax Rate }(\%)}{100}$$

$$\frac{T}{\$14} \diagdown \frac{7}{100}$$

$$100T = 7 \cdot 14$$
$$\frac{100T}{100} = \frac{98}{100}$$
$$T = \$0.98$$

Use the formula to calculate the *total cost*:

marked price	+	amount of sales tax	=	total cost
↓		↓		↓
$14	+	$0.98	=	**$14.98**

So the total cost of the shirt is $14.98.

Find the amount of sales tax and total cost. If necessary, round to the nearest cent.

1. A plane ticket costs $443. The sales tax is 8%.

$T = 8\% \cdot \$443$
$T = 0.08 \cdot 443 = \$35.44$
$TC = \$443 + \$35.44 = \$478.44$

2. A skateboard costs $40.00. The sales tax is 4%.

3. Marked price: $48 Sales tax: 6%

4. A DVR costs $94. The sales tax is 7%.

5. Marked price: $536 Sales tax: 7.5%

6. Marked price: $143 Sales tax: 6.5%

7. Marked price: $56 Sales tax: $5\frac{1}{2}\%$

8. Marked price: $81.60 Sales tax: 3.5%

9. Marked price: $197.30 Sales tax: $6\frac{3}{4}\%$

10. Marked price: $94 Sales tax: $7\frac{1}{2}\%$

11. Marked price: $12.75 Sales tax: 4.5%

12. Marked price: $25.50 Sales tax: $5\frac{1}{2}\%$

Use the table below to find the amount of sales tax and total cost.

13. a CD that costs $12.97

_TC_ = **$12.97 + $0.91 = $13.88**

14. a calculator marked $13.45

_____

15. two shirts marked $13.25 each

_____

Marked Price	7% Sales Tax
$12.93 – $13.07	$0.91
13.08 – 13.21	0.92
13.22 – 13.35	0.93
13.36 – 13.49	0.94
13.50 – 13.64	0.95
13.65 – 13.78	0.96

Find the tip. Round and use mental math.

16. 10% of $16.85   **17.** 20% of $63.15   **18.** 5% of $16.40   **19.** 15% of $5.80

$16.85 ≈ $17
10% of $17 = $1.70; $1.70 _____   _____   _____

Find the tip and total cost. (_Hint:_ Use rounding and mental math to calculate the tip.)

20. a 5% tip for a $30 taxi cab ride
Tip: 10% of $30 = $3
½ of $3 = $1.50
_TC_ = $30 + $1.50 = $31.50

21. a 20% tip on a $62.39 dinner

62.39
1.20

$74.8

22. a 15% tip on a $25 haircut

25
× 1.15

$28.75

Problem Solving

If necessary, round to the nearest cent.

23. You order a $3 soup and an $8 sandwich at a restaurant. The sales tax is 6%. You leave a 20% tip based on the cost of the food before the tax is added. How much is the total cost of the meal?

24. A movie rental costs $4.75. The sales tax is $7\frac{1}{2}$%. Vinee has $15 to spend on movie rentals. How many movies can she rent?

_____   _____

WRITE ABOUT IT

25. Write two word problems, one about finding sales tax and total cost, the other about finding a tip and total cost.

_____

_____

_____

7-11 Discount and Markup

Name _____   Date _____

A pair of $45 sneakers is on sale at a discount rate of 30%. What is the sale price of the sneakers?

To find the *amount of discount*:
Write and Solve an Equation.

discount (D) = discount rate • list price
$$D = 30\% \bullet \$45$$
$$D = 0.3 \bullet \$45$$
$$D = \$13.50$$

To calculate the *sale price*:

list price	−	amount of discount	=	sale price
↓		↓		↓
$45	−	$13.50	=	**$31.50**

So the sale price of the sneakers is $31.50.

A board game is bought for $21.50. The retailer sells the game for $26.88. What is the markup rate for the board game?

To find the amount of markup:
Use the Markup Formula.

$$\text{markup rate } (R) = \frac{\text{amount of markup}}{\text{wholesale price}}$$

$$R = \frac{26.88 - 21.50}{21.50}$$
$$= \frac{5.38}{21.50}$$
$$= 0.25023\ldots$$
$$\approx 0.25 \longrightarrow 25\%$$

So the markup rate is about 25%.

> **Remember:** You can also use a proportion to solve discount problems.
> $$\frac{\text{discount } (D)}{\text{list price } (LP)} = \frac{\text{discount rate (\%)}}{100}$$

Find the amount of discount and the sale price to the nearest cent.

1. List price: $28; Discount rate: 25%
$D = 25\% \bullet \$28; D = 0.25 \bullet \$28 = \$7$
sale price: $28 − $7 = $21
The discount is $7; sale price is $21.

2. List price: $20; Discount rate: 12%

_____

3. List price: $6.40; Discount rate: 15%

4. List price: $4.50; Discount rate: 24%

_____   _____

Find the discount rate. (*Hint:* Percents can be written as mixed numbers or approximate decimals.)

5. List price: $600; Sale price: $480
$R = \frac{600 - 480}{600}; R = \frac{120}{600}$
$R = 0.2 = 20\%$
The discount rate is 20%.

6. List price: $528; Sale price: $462

_____

7. List price: $3.99; Sale price: $2.80

8. List price: $41.93; Sale price: $35.94

_____   _____

Find the markup rate. If necessary, round to the nearest tenth of a percent.

9. Wholesale price: $20; List price: $28

$R = \dfrac{28 - 20}{20} = \dfrac{8}{20}; R = 0.4 = 40\%$

The markup rate is 40%.

10. Wholesale price: $60; List price: $75

_____

11. Wholesale price: $29.40; List price: $31.50

_____

12. Wholesale price: $62.55; List price: $76.45

_____

Solve. Show your work.

13. A beach pass costs $150 for the season. The town offers a $33\frac{1}{3}\%$ discount on passes purchased before June 1. What will a beach pass cost if purchased before June 1?

_____

14. Jessica bought a tote bag that usually sells for $14.95 at a 5% discount. How much money did she save buying the tote bag?

_____

15. A binder normally costs $8.99. Use this information to answer the questions below.

a. A store marks the binder down by 30%. A week later the price is reduced by another 20%. What is the sale price of the binder after the second reduction?

b. Would the price of the binder after the two markdowns be the same if the store had reduced the original price one time by 50%? Explain your answer.

_____

CRITICAL THINKING

16. You can use the following formula to find the discount or markup rate for each pair of prices in the chart below:

$$\text{percent of change} = \frac{\text{new amount} - \text{original amount}}{\text{original amount}}$$

Original Price	$40	$6	$230	$22.50
New Price	$50	$5.10	$161	$13.50
Percent of Change	a. _____	b. _____	c. _____	d. _____

What does a negative percent of change represent?
What does a positive percent of change represent?

_____

_____

7-12 Commission

Name _____ Date _____

Lloyd earns 5% *commission* on a $1140 sale.
How much money did Lloyd earn?

To find Lloyd's commission dollar amount:

Method 1 Write and Solve an Equation.

commission = commission rate • total sales

$$C = 5\% \cdot \$1140$$
$$C = 0.05 \cdot \$1140$$
$$C = \$57$$

So Lloyd earns a commission of $57.

Method 2 Write and Solve a Proportion.

$$\frac{\text{commission } (C)}{\text{total sales } (TS)} = \frac{\text{commission rate } (\%)}{100}$$

$$\frac{n}{1140} \diagdown \frac{5}{100}$$

$$1140 \cdot 5 = 100n$$

$$\frac{5700}{100} = \frac{100n}{100}$$

$$57 = n$$

Find the commission. If necessary, round to the nearest cent.

1. 5% commission rate on $12,000 in sales

$$C = 0.05 \cdot \$12,000$$
$$C = \$600$$

2. 8% commission rate on $175,000 in sales

14000

3. 11% commission rate on $245 in sales

$26.95

4. 15% commission rate on $3600 in sales

540

5. 9.6% commission rate on $17,500 in sales

6. 8.3% commission rate on $24,595 in sales

Find the commission rate.

7. $370 earned on $7400 in sales

$$R = \frac{\$370}{\$7400}$$
$$R = 0.05 = 5\%$$

8. $5250 earned on $175,000 in sales

9. $61.25 earned on $875 in sales

10. $198.60 earned on $1655 in sales

11. $407.40 earned on $5820 in sales

12. $14.72 earned on $460 in sales

13. $919.05 earned on $13,925 in sales

14. $4396.50 earned on $97,700 in sales

Find the total sales.

15. $26 earned with 4% commission rate

$TS = \frac{\$26}{4\%}$; $TS = \frac{\$26}{0.04}$

$TS = \$650$

16. $85 earned with 2% commission rate

17. $960 earned with 3% commission rate

18. $3950 earned with 5% commission rate

19. $285 earned with 3.8% commission rate

20. $104 earned with 2.6% commission rate

21. $245.30 earned with 4.4% commission rate

22. $5944.72 earned with 7.6% commission rate

Determine which results in a greater commission.

23. 4% commission rate on $4999 in sales
or 5% commission rate on $4005 in sales

24. 6% commission rate on $15,500 in sales
or 5% commission rate on $19,200 in sales

Problem Solving

25. Marcy and Jill sell insurance policies. They each earn a commission rate of 4% on their sales. One week, Marcy sells $1650 in insurance. The same week, Jill sells $1495 in insurance. How much more commission does Marcy earn for the week?

26. Mr. Li and Ms. Brown both sell used cars. Mr. Li sells a car for $9950 and earns $447.75 commission. Ms. Brown sells a car for $10,300 and earns $453.20 commission. Who earns a greater commission rate?

SPIRAL REVIEW

Use the benchmark percents 1% and 10% to estimate.

27. 4% of 111

28. 70% of 52

29. 15% of 33

7-13 Simple Interest

Name _____   Date _____

Matt borrows $2000 from the bank at 9.5% interest per year. Find the
amount of interest and the total amount Matt will pay in 2 years.

- Write and Solve the Interest Formula

  $I = prt$

  $I = \$2000 \cdot 9.5\% \cdot 2$

  $I = \$2000 \cdot 0.95 \cdot 2$

  $I = \$380$

Interest Formula
Interest = principal • rate of interest • time
$I = prt$
To *find the annual rate of interest*, or *the amount of time*, substitute the known values into the interest formula. Then solve for the unknown.

- Then add to find the total.

  interest + principal = total amount due

  $\$380$ + $\$2000$ = $\$2380$

  Matt will pay a total of $2380.

Find the simple interest and the total amount earned.
(*Remember:* 1 year = 12 months.)

1. $500 at 5% for 4 years
$I = 500 \cdot 0.05 \cdot 4 = \$100$
Total: $500 + $100 = $600
The simple interest is $100; total earned $600.

2. $1100 at 4% for 12 years

$1100(.04)12$
$= 528$
$1100 + 528 = 1628$

3. $1400 at 2.8% for 5 years

$1400(.028)(5)$
196
$1400 + 196 \quad 596$

4. $380 at 12.5% for 9 years

$380(.125)9$
$\$427.50 \qquad 427.50$
$380 + 12.5 \qquad = 807.5$
$= 807.5$

5. $860 at 6% for 6 months

$860 \cdot .06 \cdot 6 = 308.60$
$860 + 308.60 = 1188.60$

6. $1620 at 8% for 3 months

$1620 \cdot .08 \cdot 3 = 388.8$
$1620 + 388.8 = 2008.8$

Find the interest rate per year, *r*. Use the simple interest formula.
(*Remember:* 1 year = 12 months)

7. $1800 for 2 years, $144 interest

$144 = $1800 • *r* • 2; $144 = $3600*r*
$\dfrac{144}{3600} = \dfrac{3600r}{3600}; r = 0.04 = 4\%$
The interest rate is 4%.

8. $700 for 6 years, $252 interest

$\$252 = 700 r \cdot 6$
$\dfrac{252}{4200} = \dfrac{4200 r}{4200}$
6%

9. $1695 for 5 years, $694.95 interest

$694.95 = 1695 r \cdot 5$
$\dfrac{8475}{8475} \qquad \dfrac{8475 r}{8475}$
8.2%

10. $3275 for 10 years, $3569.75 interest

$10\,9\%$

11. $1240 for $7\frac{1}{2}$ years, $46.50 interest

5%

12. $2350 for 1 year 9 months, $378.35 interest

8%

Find the *time*, *t*. Use the simple interest formula. Express time as years.
(*Remember*: 1 year = 12 months.)

13. $900 at 9.0%, $243 interest
$9\% = 0.09$; $243 = \$900 \cdot 0.09 \cdot t$
$243 = \$81 \cdot t$; $\dfrac{\$243}{\$81} = \dfrac{\$81t}{\$81}$; $3 = t$
The time is 3 years.

14. $2020 at 7.6%, $2302.80 interest

16 years

15. $670 at 5%, $16.75 interest

5 years

16. $1880 at 10%, $141 interest

.75 years

17. $1690 at 4.4%, $464.75 interest

6¼ years

18. $430 at 8.8%, $321.64 interest

8½ years

Complete the table. Use a separate piece of paper to show your work.

	Principal	Annual Interest Rate	Time	Interest
19.	$950	14%	_____	$1197
20.	_____	5.6%	4 years	$145.60
21.	$700,000	_____	5 years 6 months	$269,500
22.	$2100	23.8%	1 year 3 months	_____

Problem Solving

23. Mr. Bell borrows $5000 from a bank that charges 8.5% interest per year. How much more will Mr. Bell have to pay in interest each year if he chooses to pay the loan in three years as opposed to two years?

24. Julia takes out a loan for $1200 from a bank that charges 5.4% simple interest per year. If the total amount she repays is $1297.20, for how long did she borrow the money?

WRITE ABOUT IT

25. Using graph paper, plot the given points and predict the interest earned after 10 years. Explain.

Time (years)	1	2	3	4	5
Balance	$1045.50	$1093.10	$1142.80	$1194.80	$1249.20

7-14 Compound Interest

Name _____   Date _____

Mrs. Chen deposits $800 into a savings account with an annual interest rate of 6%, compounded quarterly for 2 years.

> annually = once per year
> semi-annually = twice per year
> quarterly = four times per year

To *find the balance* and *interest earned,* use a compound interest table.

- Find the interest rate per period.
  Number of interest periods: 2 years • **4** periods per year = **8** periods
  Annual interest rate: 6%
  Quarterly interest rate: 6% ÷ **4** = **1.5%**

- Find the factor. Use the table below. Look across the **8th** period row and down the **1.5%** interest rate column to find the factor.   **1.1265**

- Multiply the deposit by the factor to find the balance. $800 • 1.1265 = **$901.20**

- Subtract the principal from the balance to find the interest earned. $901.20 − $800 = **$101.20**

After 2 years, the interest earned will be $101.20. The account balance will be $901.20.

Compound Interest Table

Number of Periods	1.25%	1.5%	1.75%	2%	2.25%	2.5%
1	1.0125	1.0150	1.0175	1.0200	1.0225	1.0250
2	1.0252	1.0302	1.0353	1.0404	1.0455	1.0506
3	1.0380	1.0457	1.0534	1.0612	1.0690	1.0769
4	1.0509	1.0614	1.0719	1.0824	1.0931	1.1038
5	1.0641	1.0773	1.0906	1.1041	1.1177	1.1314
6	1.0774	1.0934	1.1097	1.1262	1.1428	1.1597
7	1.0909	1.1098	1.1291	1.1487	1.1685	1.1887
8	1.1045	1.1265	1.1489	1.1717	1.1948	1.2184
9	1.1183	1.1434	1.1690	1.1951	1.2217	1.2489
10	1.1323	1.1605	1.1894	1.2190	1.2492	1.2801

Find the number of interest periods for each amount of time.
(*Hint:* 1 year = 12 months)

1. compounded annually, for 8 years

    1 period • 8 years = 8 periods

2. compounded annually, for 15 years

3. compounded semi-annually, for 4.5 years

4. compounded semi-annually, for 7.5 years

5. compounded quarterly, for 6 years

6. compounded quarterly, for 11 years

7. compounded semi-annually, for 6 months

8. compounded quarterly, for 27 months

Use the Compound Interest table on page 223 to find the amount of interest earned. If necessary, round to the nearest cent.
(*Hint: APR* is annual percent rate.)

9. $8000 at 4% annual rate, compounded semi-annually, for 3 years
$8000 • 1.1262 = $9009.60
$9009.60 − $8000
interest earned: $1009.60

10. $6300 at 5% annual rate, compounded semi-annually, for 2 years

11. $600 at 6% annual rate, compounded quarterly, for 2 years

12. $1900 at 9% annual rate, compounded quarterly, for 3 months

13. $2200 at 4.5% annual rate, compounded semi-annually, for 18 months

14. $1460 at 3.5% APR, compounded semi-annually, for 42 months

15. $9876 at 5% APR, compounded quarterly, for 24 months

16. $3500 at 10% APR, compounded quarterly, for 15 months

17. $4690 at 6% APR, compounded quarterly, for 21 months

Solve. Check to justify your answer.

18. A savings account earns an annual interest rate of 6%, compounded quarterly. Harold deposits $750 into the account. How much interest will Harold earn in 21 months?

19. Save-here Bank pays 5% annual interest compounded semi-annually. Earn-lots Bank pays 5% annual interest compounded quarterly. Caleb wants to invest $2000 for 18 months. Which Bank pays more interest? How much more?

WRITE ABOUT IT

Use the Compound Interest table on page 223 to answer this problem.

20. An account earns an annual rate of 4.5%. Interest is compounded semi-annually. Evan deposits $1000 into the account. Complete a table showing the balance in the account for the first five years. Predict the account balance after 10 years. Explain your answer.

7-15 Problem-Solving Strategy:
Reason Logically

Read   Plan   Solve   Check

Name _____   Date _____

Solve by using the strategy Reason Logically.

1. An enlarged version of the checkerboard pattern seen at the right is on the floor of a classroom. A boy is on each grey square, and a girl is on each white square. Can the students be rearranged so that the girls occupy the grey squares and the boys occupy the white squares? If so, explain how.

_____

2. Three 3s and three 5s are arranged in every possible way to form six-digit whole numbers (for example, 353,535 and 553,335). How many of these six-digit numbers are prime?

_____

3. Can the 34 squares of the truncated checkerboard seen here be exactly covered with 17 of these two-square tiles: ▨▨ ? Explain.

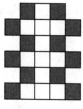

_____

4. In the number 1_,6_3,000,000,000,000,091, the two missing numbers are the *same*. If this large number is evenly divisible by 9, what digit is missing in those two places?

_____

5. Square tiles on the floor of the center of a classroom are shown at the right. A boy stands on each grey square, and a girl stands on each white square. Is it possible for the students to be rearranged so that each girls stands on a grey square and each boy stands on a white square? Explain.

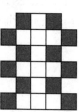

_____

6. In how many ways can you form multiple stacks of equal heights using 36 identical cubes? (You must use all the cubes.)

7. There are 10 marbles in a hat. 7 are white, and 3 are black. Thus, they are 70% white. You may add 4 marbles at a time, and they can be any combination of white and black. Is it possible to add marbles so that 40% of the marbles in the hat are white?

8. Malcolm lives near a subway station where the A and B trains alternately arrive. The time between consecutive A trains is the same as the time between consecutive B trains. Only the A train goes to the library, and only the B train goes to the museum. One summer, Malcolm decides to arrive at the station at random times and to take the first train that arrives. He thought that he would go to the library and the museum the same number of times, but he soon discovers that he visits the library three times as often as the museum. How can this be?

9. Four art teachers travel separately to four different craft stores to purchase bags of beads for a certain project. The first found bags of 40 beads, the second found bags of 55, the third found bags of 60, and the fourth found bags of 80. If they agree to buy the *same* number of beads, what is the *smallest* number of beads each should get at their respective stores? (They may not rip the bags open!)

10. Can the 34 grey squares of this 6-by-6 arrangement of 36 squares be covered exactly with 17 of these two-square tiles 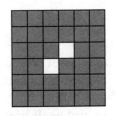? Explain.

Enrichment:
Successive Discounts and Increases

Name _____ Date _____

Last week, a store offered a 30% discount on all items. This week the store is giving an *additional* 30% discount. What is the single discount equivalent of the store's combined discounts over these two weeks?

• The original price of an item is x. If you save 30%, then you pay 70%, which is $0.7x$.
• Applying the second discount, you save an additional 30% of $0.7x$. So you pay 70% of $0.7x$, which is $0.49x$.
• The final price is $0.49x$, or 49% of the original price. So the store is giving an overall discount of 51%.

Complete the chart below to find the single discount equivalent to each set of successive discounts. Round your answer to the nearest hundredth of a percent.

Problem	1st Discount	2nd Discount	Single Discount Equivalent
1.	15%	30%	
2.	10%	5%	
3.	12.5%	50%	

Complete the chart below to find the single increase equivalent to each set of successive increases. Round your answer to the nearest hundredth.

Problem	1st Increase	2nd Increase	3rd Increase	Single Increase Equivalent
4.	6.5%	11.1%	9.2%	
5.	12.3%	25%	20.64%	
6.	50%	75.75%	75.2%	

Problem Solving

7. Derek bought a fruit bar from the school snack store at an increase of 638.3% over what the school paid. The school bought the fruit bar from a retail store at an increase of 75% over the distributor's price. What is the single increase equivalent of the distributor's price?

_____

SPIRAL REVIEW

8. Luis bought a comic book for $0.85. Then he sold it to his brother for $2.15. What was the percent increase?

_____

Name _____ Date _____

Chapter 7 Vocabulary

balance	interest	percent formula	sales tax
base	list price	percent increase	sales tax rate
commission	marked price	percent proportion	selling price
commission rate	markup	percentage	simple interest
compound interest	markup rate	principal	total cost
cost	percent (%)	profit	total sale
discount	percent change	rate of interest	wholesale price
discount rate	percent decrease	sale price	

From the vocabulary list above, choose the term(s) that best complete each sentence. Write the term(s) in the space(s) provided.

1. _____ is an amount of money a salesperson earns based on goods or services sold.

2. A _____ is a ratio of a number to 100.

3. An amount of money invested or borrowed is the _____.

4. A _____ is a dollar amount by which the regular price of an item is reduced.

5. The amount of money added to the marked price by a state or local government is the _____.

6. The percent that a price is lowered is called the _____.

7. The percent that a person pays on a credit card balance is called the _____.

8. The percent that a realtor receives from closing a sale on a house is the _____.

9. The cost of an item is $80 and the selling price is $100. The _____ is 25%.

Choose two terms from the list that you did not use in Questions 1–9. For each term, write a definition in your own words and give an example.

10. _____

_____

_____

 **Use after** SOURCEBOOK **Lessons 7-1–7-14, pages 174–201.**

Test Prep: Extended-Response Questions
Strategy: Answer All Parts

Name _____ Date _____

Sometimes a problem may require several steps to solve. *Show or describe the steps* to help organize your thoughts. Think about how to order your steps to build a solution to the problem.

To solve the problem, try using these strategies:
- Reread the item.
- Use the Test-Prep Strategy.
- Apply appropriate rules, definitions, properties, or strategies.
- Analyze your answers.

Solve. *TIP: If you have time, go back to problems you skipped.*

1. Samuel works at a furniture store. Before his raise, he received a weekly base salary of $350. Last month he got a 4% raise. Samuel also earns a commission of 12% on his total sales each week.

   Part A
   What is Samuel's new weekly base salary after his raise?
   Show all your work.

   Part B
   This week Samuel had sales that totaled $7860. What is Samuel's total salary this week?
   Show all your work.

   Answer _____

   Answer _____

2. Tricia is considering two different simple annual interest loans.

   | Loan A: $800 at 8.75% for 2 years |
   | Loan B: $800 at 7.25% for 3 years |

   Part A
   Which loan has the *greater* interest payment?
   Show all your work.

   Part B
   What is the difference in interest payment amounts between Loan A and Loan B?
   Show all your work.

   Answer _____

   Part C
   If Tricia chooses Loan B, how much will she have to pay in all?
   Show your work.

   Answer _____

   Answer _____

3. A store manager buys shirts at a wholesale price of $12 and marks them up 60%. After two months, the shirts are sold on sale for 30% off the retail price.

Part A
What was the original retail price of the shirts?
Show all your work.

Answer _____

Part B
What is the sale price of the shirts?
Show all your work.

Answer _____

Part C
Does the store make a profit by selling the shirts at the sale price?
Explain your answer.

Answer _____
_____

4. A gift shop sells boxes of candles. A box of 12 candles costs $21.36. The cost per candle is the same in every box.

Part A
What is the unit price of each candle?
Show all your work.

Answer _____

Part B
What is the price of 5 candles?
Show all your work.

Answer _____

5. A young tree that is 24 inches tall grows at a constant rate of $\frac{2}{3}$ inch per week.

Part A
How long will it take for the tree to become 30 inches tall?
Show all your work.

Part B
How many feet tall will the tree be in 6 weeks?
Show all your work.

Answer _____

Answer _____

Practice Chapter 7 Test

Name _____ Date _____

Write each as a percent.

1. 75 to 100   **2.** 620 : 1000   **3.** $\dfrac{35}{250}$ **4.** 0.86   **5.** 0.379   **6.** 1.021

75%   *62%*   *14%*   *86%*   *37.9%*   *1.021%*

Write each percent as a decimal and as a fraction in simplest form.

7. 5%   **8.** 115%   **9.** 72.5%

Compare. Write <, =, or >.

10. 53% _____ $\dfrac{13}{25}$ **11.** 0.0058 _____ 5.8%   **12.** 156% _____ $1\dfrac{35}{63}$

Solve. If necessary, round to the tenths place.

13. What is 63% of 125?   **14.** 78% of 62 is what number?   **15.** 23% of what number is 115?

16. 1155 is 110% of what number? **17.** What percent of 610 is 457.5? **18.** 650 is what percent of 195.

Estimate.

19. About how much is 72% of 126?   **20.** About what percent of 794 is 207?   **21.** 28.2 is about 18% of what number?

Use visual benchmarks to estimate the percent that is shaded.

22.

23.

24.

Find the percent increase or decrease.

25. from 20 to 35   **26.** from 1450 to 957

Find the profit or loss to the nearest cent.

27. Cost: $160
Percent loss: 12%

28. Cost: $45.75
Percent profit: 80.5%

Find the sales tax or tip and the total cost to the nearest cent.

29. $39.99 video game with 4.5% sales tax

30. $52.75 meal with a 15% tip

Find the discount rate or markup rate.

31. $24 table price increased to $25.44

32. $110 jacket on sale for $82.50

Find the commission, the commission rate, or the total sales.

33. $14,750 total sales,
6% commission rate
What is the commission?

34. $365 total sales,
$14.60 commission
What is the commission rate?

35. 12.5% commission rate,
$27,600 commission
What are the total sales?

Solve. Use *I = prt*.

36. $2000 at an annual
rate of 7%, for 3 months
What is the interest?

37. $650 borrowed, for 10 years,
$390 in interest
What is the annual interest rate?

38. $9300 loan at 4.5% per year,
$2092.50 in interest
How many years is the loan.

Tell About It

Explain how you solve the problem. Show all your work.

39. Grace had $7450 in sales last month and earned 5.2% commission. Abby had $8200 in sales last month and earned 4.8% commission. Who earned more commission? How much more?

Cumulative Review: Chapters 1–7

Name _____   Date _____

Circle the best answer.

1. Evaluate the expression when $x = -4$.

$x^2 \cdot (x^{-2})$

A. -16 B. -1
C. 1 D. 1

2. Simplify.

$8x^3y - 4x^2y + 6x^3y + 4x^2y - 2xy^2$

F. $14x^3y - 2xy^2$
G. $14x^3y - 2x^2y$
H. $14x^2y - 2xy^2$
J. $14x^3y - 8x^2y - 2xy^2$

3. Simplify: $15 - \dfrac{15 - (-5)^2}{-2}$

A. 5 B. 10
C. 15 D. 20

4. What is the greatest common factor of 72, 144, and 240?

F. 6 G. 24
H. 144 J. 720

5. What is the missing term in the proportion $\dfrac{18}{114} = \dfrac{3}{x}$?

A. $x = 19$ B. $x = 38$
C. $x = 342$ D. $x = 684$

6. Brandi buys 1 dozen ears of corn for $6.96. Johanna buys $1\frac{1}{2}$ dozen ears of corn at the same price per ear as Brandi. How much does Johanna pay in total for her corn?

F. $0.58   G. $4.64
H. $10.44   J. $15.66

7. Which statement is true?

A. $60 \text{ cL} = 600 \text{ dL}$
B. $60 \text{ kL} = 0.06 \text{ L}$
C. $60 \text{ dL} = 6000 \text{ mL}$
D. $60 \text{ hL} = 6000 \text{ dL}$

8. What is $3.04 \cdot 10^{-6}$ written in standard form?

F. 0.000000304 G. 0.00000304
H. $\dfrac{1}{3,040,000}$ J. $\dfrac{1}{304,000,000}$

9. Marcus deposits $1300 into an account that earns 4% simple annual interest. What is the balance in his account after 21 months?

A. $91   B. $1352
C. $1391   D. $2210

10. Solve: $12 - 3y = 15$

F. $y = -9$ G. $y = -1$
H. $y = 1$ J. $y = 9$

11. In an English class, there are 15 girls and 9 boys. What percent of the class is made up of girls?

A. 37.5% B. 60%
C. 62.5% D. 167%

12. Which inequality is represented by the graph?

-3 -2 -1   0   1   2   3

F. $x \le -1.50$ G. $x \le -0.5$
H. $x < -1.50$ J. $x < -0.5$

13. Rick needs 5 pieces of poster board that are each $3\frac{1}{3}$ feet long. How many yards of poster board does he need?

A. $1\frac{1}{9}$ yards   B. $5\frac{5}{9}$ yards
C. $16\frac{2}{3}$ yards   D. 50 yards

14. Simplify: $3^2 - (-2)^4$

F. -7
G. -1
H. 14
J. 25

15. Which is equivalent to $(-2)^2(-2)^3$?

   A. $(-2)^6$ **B.** $(-2)^5$

   C. $(2)^5$ **D.** $(4)^5$

16. What percent of 800 is 1400?

   F. $1\frac{3}{4}\%$ **G.** $57\frac{1}{7}\%$

   H. 75% **J.** 175%

17. A map has a scale of 2 cm = 15 km. The distance between two cities is 240 km. What is the distance between the cities on the map?

   A. 8 cm   **B.** 16 cm

   C. 32 cm   **D.** 120 cm

18. How many pints are in $5\frac{3}{4}$ gallons?

   F. 184 pt   **G.** 92 pt

   H. 46 pt   **J.** 19 pt

19. Which point lies in quadrant III?

   A. $(-3, -7)$ **B.** $(0, -2)$

   C. $(6, -8)$ **D.** $(-5, 1)$

20. Solve: $4.5x + 6.75 = 13.95$

   F. $x = -4.6$

   G. $x = -1.6$

   H. $x = 1.6$

   J. $x = 4.6$

21. Solve: $3x - 2x + 9 \geq 16$

   A. $x \leq -7$ **B.** $x \leq 7$

   C. $x \geq 7$ **D.** $x \geq 25$

22. Pete buys $2\frac{3}{4}$ pounds of apples at $1.49 per pound. About how much did Pete spend?

   F. $1.80   **G.** $1.85

   H. $4.05   **J.** $4.10

23. Carl goes to a restaurant and leaves a 19% tip on the cost of his meal. The cost of the meal was $45. How much tip did Carl leave?

   A. $8.50   **B.** $0.85

   C. $8.55   **D.** $9.00

24. Three less than twice a number is more than 128. Which inequality represents this situation?

   F. $3 - 2x > 128$ **G.** $3 < 2x + 128$

   H. $2x - 3 < 128$ **J.** $2x - 3 > 128$

25. Simplify: $(-12) + 7 - (-12) + 18$

   A. 1   **B.** 13

   C. 25   **D.** 35

26. Under the late afternoon sun, a lamppost casts a 30.6 foot shadow. Nearby, a 5.5-foot tall person casts a shadow 17 feet long. What is the height of the lamppost?

   F. 4.4 feet   **G.** 9.9 feet

   H. 13.6 feet   **J.** 22.5 feet

Tell About It

Explain how you solve each problem. Show all your work.

27. Brian buys a shirt that originally costs $22. All shirts are 25% off. When he pays at the register, that cashier adds 6% sales tax to the sale price. How much does Brian pay for the shirt?

_____

28. Mrs. Peterson sold a new refrigerator for $780 and earned a commission rate of 5.5%. Ms. Robbins sold a dishwasher for $650 and earned a commission rate of 6.5%. Which salesperson earned a greater commission? How much greater?

_____

8-1 Samples and Surveys

Name _____ Date _____

Use the table to predict how many of 8000 teens listen to radio station WROC. Use proportional reasoning.

	Question: What is your favorite radio station?		
Response	Tally	Frequency	Cumulative Frequency
WROC	卌 卌 卌 卌 卌 卌 卌	35	35
WFUN	卌 卌 I	11	46
Other	IIII	4	50

$$\frac{\text{WROC listeners in sample}}{\text{Size of sample}} = \frac{\text{WROC listeners in population}}{\text{Size of population}}$$

$\frac{35}{50} = \frac{n}{8000}$ ← Substitute. Let n = the predicted number of teen listeners.

$35 \cdot 8000 = 50 \cdot n$ ← Cross multiply.

$\frac{280,000}{50} = \frac{50 \cdot n}{50}$ ← Divide both sides by 50 to isolate n.

$5600 = n$ ← Simplify.

So you could predict that 5600 teens in one city listen to WROC.

A *representative sample* has characteristics similar to the entire population. Choose the sample most likely to be representative of the population.

1. To find the most popular exhibit at a museum,

   A. ask several people in the space exhibit.
   B. ask several people as they exit the museum.

2. If a biologist wants to study deer in a state park,

   A. she should tag every tenth deer she sees.
   B. she should tag the first 10 deer she sees.

A *biased question* favors a particular outcome. Select the survey question that is least biased.

3. A math teacher who wants to start an after school club should ask,

   A. Are you interested in a fun way to improve your math skills?
   B. Are you interested in joining an after school math club?

4. To find what people think about a mall being built,

   A. Would you mind the increased traffic a mall would bring to your neighborhood?
   B. Would a mall be a good addition to your neighborhood?

Answer each question. Use the frequency table to write and solve a proportion.

5. Of 240 seventh graders, predict how many use a computer more than 10 hours each week.
   $2 + 11 + 7 = 20; \frac{7}{20} = \frac{n}{240}; n = 84$
   You can predict that 84 seventh graders use a computer more than 10 hours each week.

Question: How many hours do you use a computer each week?	
Less than 5 hours	II
5–10 hours	卌 卌 I
More than 10 hours	卌 II

6. Of 300 seventh graders, predict how many use a computer 5–10 hours each week.

7. Of 360 seventh graders, predict how many use a computer 10 hours or less each week.

_____ _____

Use the proportional reasoning to make a prediction.

8. Of 25 grocery store shoppers, 14 said that their family's favorite breakfast is cereal bars. Predict how many of 500 families at a grocery store would buy cereal bars.

$$\frac{14}{25} = \frac{n}{500}; 7000 = 25n; 280 = n$$
You can predict that 280 families would buy cereal bars.

9. Of 200 radio-controlled cars that were manufactured by one company, 3 were defective. The company manufactures 1000 cars each day. About how many defective cars would you predict are produced each day?

10. Of 80 voters, 42 said they would vote for Anna Montoya for mayor. If 6000 citizens are expected to vote, about how many would you predict will vote for Montoya?

11. Of 12 customers at one restaurant, 10 said that they were very satisfied with the service. Predict the number of satisfied customers if 300 people are at the restaurant.

Solve. Use the frequency table. It shows the results of a survey taken at a factory.

Question: What means of transportation do you use to get to work?			
Response	Tally	Frequency	Cumulative Frequency
Car	⊬⊬ ⊬⊬ ⊬⊬	15	15
Bus	⊬⊬ ⊬⊬ ⊬⊬ ⊬⊬ IIII	24	39
Train	⊬⊬ ⊬⊬	10	49
Bicycle	⊬⊬	5	54
Walk	⊬⊬ I	6	60

12. Predict how many people out of 200 factory workers walk to work.
$$\frac{6}{60} = \frac{n}{200}; 1200 = 60n; 20 = n$$
You can predict that 20 people walk to work.

13. Predict how many bike-rack spaces are needed for 750 warehouse workers.

14. Suppose 450 people work at the factory. Predict how many of them take public transportation.

15. In the survey, of those who use a car, 12 drive alone. The others carpool. Out of 750 employees, predict the number that carpool.

WRITE ABOUT IT

16. How would you survey students in your school to accurately find the most popular subject? Explain.

8-2 Measures of Central Tendency and Range

Name _____ Date _____

Which *measure of central tendency* best describes data in the set?

Noon Temperatures (°F)	
Date	Temperature
Mar. 26	23
Mar. 27	57
Mar. 28	52
Mar. 29	57
Mar. 30	55
Mar. 31	53

- To find the *mean*, add the numbers in a data set and divide this sum by the number of items.

$$\frac{23 + 57 + 52 + 57 + 55 + 53}{6} = \frac{297}{6} = 49.5$$

The mean temperature is 49.5°F.

- To find the *median*, list the numbers in order, and identify the middle number.
  When there are 2 middle numbers, find their mean.

$$23, 52, \mathbf{53}, \mathbf{55}, 57, 57$$
$$\frac{53 + 55}{2} = \frac{108}{2} = \mathbf{54}$$

The median temperature is 54°F.

- To find the *mode*, find the item in the data set that occurs most frequently.

$$23, 52, 53, 55, \mathbf{57}, \mathbf{57}$$

The mode of the temperatures is 57°F.

- To find the *range* of a set of data, find the difference between the greatest and least numbers in the set.

$$57 - 23 = \mathbf{34}$$

The range of temperatures is 34°F.

The median describes this data set most accurately because it is closest to most of the values.

Find the mean, median, mode, and range for each data set. Tell which measure of central tendency best describes the data set. Explain.

1. 85, 90, 75, 85, 95

median: __85__

mean: $\frac{430}{5}$ = 86

mode: __85__

range: __95 − 75 = 20__

The median, mean, or mode could be used.

2. 8.1, 8.7, 8.6, 7.5, 8.8, 8.7

median: _____

mean: _____

mode: _____

range: _____

_____

_____

3. −2, 6, 2, −14

median: _____

mean: _____

mode: _____

range: _____

_____

_____

4. 70.8, 72.1, 71.9, 82.4, 98.1, 85.3

median: _____

mean: _____

mode: _____

range: _____

_____

_____

5. $1\frac{1}{4}$, 1, $10\frac{1}{2}$, 1, $11\frac{1}{4}$

median: _____

mean: _____

mode: _____

range: _____

_____

_____

6. $\frac{1}{8}$, $\frac{1}{2}$, 0.13, 0.5, $\frac{1}{4}$

median: _____

mean: _____

mode: _____

range: _____

_____

_____

Use logical reasoning to solve.

7. Add a number to the following data set that makes the mean 24. 20, 32, 18

$$\frac{20 + 32 + 18 + n}{4} = 24; \frac{70 + n}{4} = \frac{24}{1}$$

$70 + n = 96; n = 26;$ **The number is 26.**

8. Add a whole number to the following data set that makes the median 10. 14, 6, 9, 17, 11,

9. Remove a number from the following data set so the median is 12. 18, 6, 3, 13, 12, 4

10. Remove a number from the following data set so the mean is 20. 25, 23, 12, 10, 20

Problem Solving

11. **Economics** Weekly salaries at the public relations department in a company are $1200, $1000, $900, $2000, and $1500. Suppose a new employee is added and that her salary does not change the median. What is the weekly salary of the new employee?

CRITICAL THINKING

12. How does the magnitude of the value added to a data set affect the mean? Find the mean of each data set. Then find the mean when each fifth number (0, 1, 10, 100, and 1000) is added to each set. (*Hint:* Think of *magnitude* as the number of places in a number.)

	Data Sets	Original Mean	Mean with fifth value: 0	Mean with fifth value: 1	Mean with fifth value: 10	Mean with fifth value: 100	Mean with fifth value: 1000
a.	10, 20, 30, 40	___	___	___	___	___	___
b.	100, 200, 300, 400	___	___	___	___	___	___
c.	1000, 2000, 3000, 4000	___	___	___	___	___	___

8-3 Interpret Data

Name _____ Date _____

Movies	A	B	C	D	E	F
Length (in min)	110	62	108	112	106	108

Compare the measures with and without the outlier, 62.

	With Outlier	Without Outlier
Mean	110 + 62 + 108 + 112 + 106 + 108 = 606 606 ÷ 6 = 101 The mean is 101 minutes.	110 + 108 + 112 + 106 + 108 = 544 544 ÷ 5 = 108.8 The mean is 108.8 minutes.
Median	62, 106, **108**, **108**, 110, 112 The median is 108.	106, 108, **108**, 110, 112 The median is 108.
Mode	The mode is 108.	The mode is 108.
Range	112 − 62 = **50** The range is 50.	112 − 106 = **6** The range is 6.

The outlier decreases the mean by 7.8 minutes and the range by
44 minutes. The median and mode were not changed and provide
the best description of the data with one outlier.

**Identify the outlier in each data set. On a separate sheet of paper find the
mean, median, and mode for the data set, with and without the outlier.**

1. 8, 4, 4, 10, 9, 24, 4, 10

outlier: __24__

mean with outlier: __9.125__

mean without outlier: __7__

median with outlier: __8.5__

median without outlier: __8__

mode with outlier: __4__

mode without outlier: __4__

2. −3, −5, −10, 0, 11, −10, −2, −5

outlier: _____

mean with outlier: _____

mean without outlier: _____

median with outlier: _____

median without outlier: _____

mode with outlier: _____

mode without outlier: _____

3. $4\frac{1}{2}$, 20, 5, $5\frac{1}{4}$, 7, $4\frac{3}{4}$, 6

outlier: _____

mean with outlier: _____

mean without outlier: _____

median with outlier: _____

median without outlier: _____

mode with outlier: _____

mode without outlier: _____

4. outlier: _____

mean with outlier: _____

mean without outlier: _____

median with outlier: _____

median without outlier: _____

mode with outlier: _____

mode without outlier: _____

Annual Rainfall	
Year	Inches
2004	37.8
2005	15.6
2006	40.2
2007	35.4
2008	38.2

Tell whether each statement is *sometimes true, always true*, or *never true*. Explain.

5. Adding an outlier increases the mean of a data set.
Sometimes true; An outlier increases the mean only if it is greater than the other values in the data set.

6. Adding an outlier increases the median of a data set.

_____

7. Adding an outlier changes the mode of a data set.

_____

8. Adding an outlier increases the range of a data set.

_____

Tell what kind of data is needed to make an estimate. Explain, using the mean, median, and mode.

9. You want to decide what price to sell donated T-shirts at a school fundraiser.
Survey the class for the price they would be willing to pay for a T-shirt, and find the mode.

10. A farmer wants to know how much rainfall to expect during July.

_____

11. A restaurant manager wants to advertise a dinner item on the menu that will attract new customers.

_____

12. A hiker needs to estimate how many days it will take to cover 200 miles of a cross-country trail.

_____

Solve. Explain your answer.

13. Theo scored 81, 79, 84, 80, and 81 on 5 math tests. He scored 98 on the next math test. Without computing the mean, median, mode, or range, tell how his latest grade will affect each statistical measure.

14. One weekend a salesperson sold cars for $22,000; $20,000; $8000; $22,000; and $24,000. What is the outlier in this set of data? What effect does the outlier have when interpreting the mean price of the cars sold?

_____

CHALLENGE

15. A bicycle shop owner offers five styles of mountain bikes for $450, $275, $675, $490, and $300. He wants to increase the mean price, but keep the median price and range of prices the same. Suggest a new set of prices for the five styles.

_____

_____

_____

8-4 Choose an Appropriate Graph

Name _____ Date _____

> Different types of graphs present data in different ways.
>
> *Circle Graph:* Shows how a whole is divided into parts. The parts must total 100%.
>
> | *Line Graph:* Uses the location of points to display *changes* that occur in a data set *over time*. | *Bar Graph:* Uses the length or height of bars in relation to a scale of equal intervals to *compare* two or more sets of data. |

Which type(s) of graph would be most appropriate for displaying the data to answer each question?

1. From which four countries does the United States import the most cars?

_____ **bar graph, circle graph** _____

2. How has the cost of school lunch changed over the last 10 years?

_____

Write the letter or letters of the graphs that can be used to answer each question.

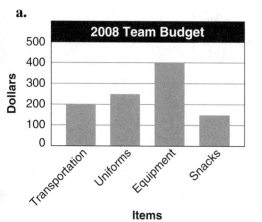

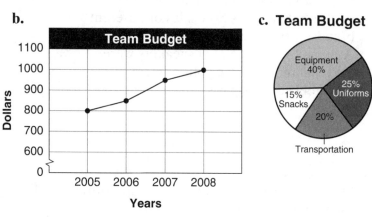

3. How much more money (in dollars) does the team budget for equipment than for uniforms? ___**a**___

4. How much greater was the team's budget in 2008 than in 2007? _____

5. What was the median amount budgeted from 2005 to 2008? _____

6. If the team spent a total of $976 in 2008, how much less did it spend than budgeted?

_____

7. How many students played on the team in 2008? _____

8. If the team increases its 2008 budget by 10% for 2009, what will be its 2009 budget?

_____

9. For which two items does the team budget the most? _____

10. What part of the budget is *not* allotted for equipment? _____

Choose the most appropriate type of graph for each set of data.
Then on a separate sheet of paper, construct the graphs from the data.

11.

Students' Film Preferences	
Kind	No. of Students
Comedy	17
Nature	11
Horror	8
Space	25
Musical	12
Other	5

12.

Number of Hits Per Game	
Game	Hits
1	11
2	9
3	8
4	11
5	12
6	15
7	16

13.

Sixth Graders' Favorite Sports	
Sport	Part of Total
basketball	$\frac{1}{4}$
soccer	$\frac{3}{8}$
track	$\frac{1}{8}$
volleyball	$\frac{1}{16}$
baseball	$\frac{1}{4}$

___bar graph___   _____   _____

Solve. Check to justify your answer.

14. Use graph paper to construct another kind of graph that shows how sales of different brands of sneakers compared in May. Assume that 300 pairs of sneakers were sold that month. Give your graph a title and label all of its parts.

Sneaker Sales in May

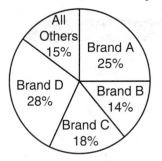

15. Describe a data set that would be appropriate to display on each type of graph.

a. bar graph _____

b. line graph _____

c. circle graph _____

MENTAL MATH

Solve.

16. $\dfrac{24 + 36 + 22 + 18}{4}$

17. 50% of 320

18. $-140 + 75$

19. $\frac{1}{4}$ of 220

20. $76 + 21 + (-17)$

21. What percent of 50 is 40?

8-5 Multiple Bar Graphs

Name _____ Date _____

What percent of their games did the Dragons win in 2006?

To find the percent, use the graph to locate the data needed. Then write and rename a ratio as a percent.

$12:16 \rightarrow \dfrac{12}{16} \rightarrow 0.75 \rightarrow 75\%$

The Dragons won 75% of their games in 2006.

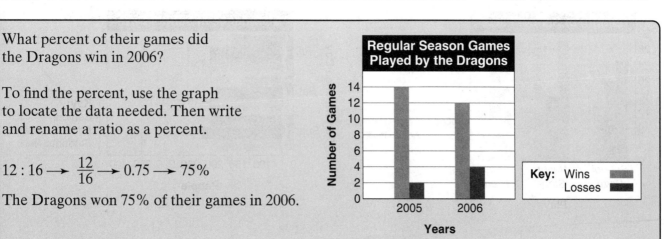

Use the bar graph to answer each question.
(*Hint:* Estimate the value for each bar length to the nearest half or quarter interval.)

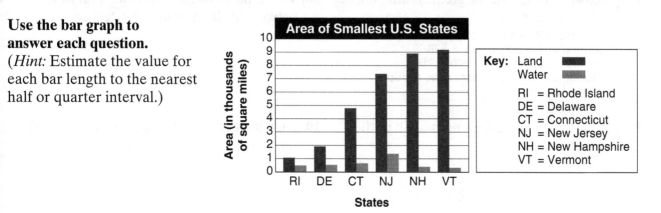

1. Estimate the percent of the area of Delaware that is covered by water.

   Land area: about 2000 mi²; water area: about 500 mi²; total area: about 2500 mi²

   $500 : 2500 = \dfrac{1}{5} = 0.2 = 20\%$
   The area covered by water is about 20%.

2. About what percent of the area of Rhode Island consists of dry land?

   _____

3. Use a percent to compare the land areas of New Jersey to New Hampshire.

4. Use a percent to compare the water areas of New Jersey to New Hampshire.

_____   _____

Use the data in the chart at the right to make a multiple bar graph. Then use your graph to answer exercises 5–6.

5. What is the ratio of shots made to shots missed for Wendy?

_____

6. What percent of her shots did Tara miss?

_____

Free Throw Shots		
Players	**Tried**	**Made**
Rachel	24	14
Wendy	25	16
Tara	15	9
Fran	10	7
Melody	7	5

Solve. Use the bar graphs to solve problems 7–10.

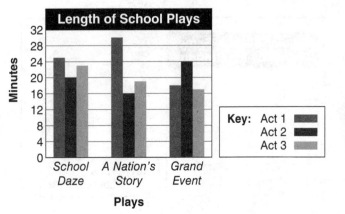

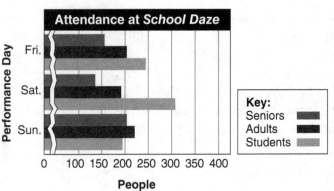

7. Which age group had the greatest attendance at *School Daze*?

> Seniors: 150 + 125 + 200 = 475
> Adults: 200 + 200 + 225 = 625
> Students: 250 + 300 + 200 = 750
> **Students were the greatest age group in attendance.**

8. Which play has the range of 5 minutes between its longest and shortest acts?

9. What is the mean of the length of all of the school plays?

10. On which day was the median attendance the least?

CHALLENGE

11. Which continent shown has the greatest range of temperatures?

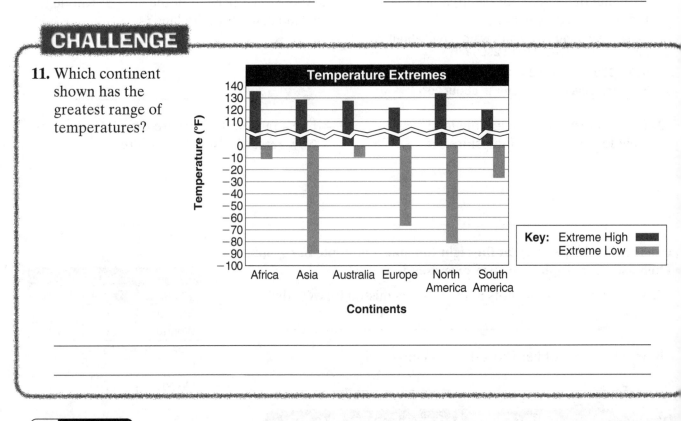

8-6 Histograms

Name _____ Date _____

A *histogram* is a graph that shows frequencies of data within equal intervals. Unlike bars on a bar graph, the bars on a histogram are next to each other without a gap, unless there is an interval that has a frequency of 0.

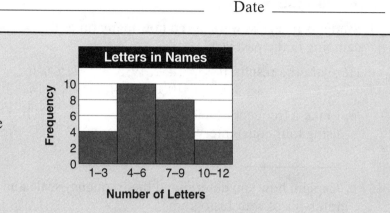

Is the graph a histogram? Explain.

1.

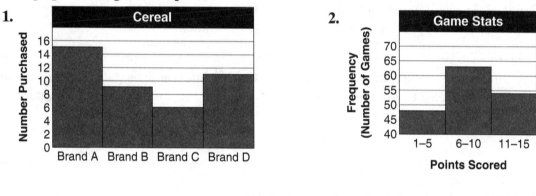

2.

_____

_____

Use the histogram to answer the questions.

3. In which interval did the greatest frequency occur?
The tallest bar is the interval with the greatest frequency; the interval 56°F–60°F.

4. How many days was the average temperature no greater than 70°F?

_____

5. How many more days was the average temperature less than 66°F than days when the temperature was at least 66°F?

_____

6. In which interval does the median of the data fall?

_____

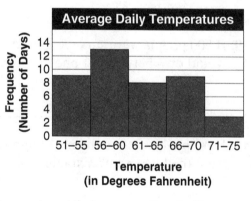

Solve. Show your work.

7. Students in a class were asked how many times they went camping in the past year.

   Here are the results: 0, 13, 5, 4, 2, 19, 3, 3, 5, 7, 5, 6, 6, 8, 9, 6, 10, 0, 12, 14, 11, 15, 1, 16

   a. Make a frequency table of the data, using four equal intervals.

   b. Use the frequency table you made to make a histogram of the data.

   _____

   _____

   c. Explain how you determined the frequency scale and intervals of your histogram.

   _____

   d. How many students went camping from 5 to 14 times?

   e. How many students went camping at least 5 times?

   _____

   _____

   f. How many students went camping a number of times that is in the least or greatest interval?

   g. In what interval does the median of the data fall? Use the data to justify your answer.

   _____

   _____

Solve. Use the histogram at the right to answer each problem.

8. How many people were surveyed?

   20 + 35 + 25 + 15 + 5 = 100; 100 people were surveyed.

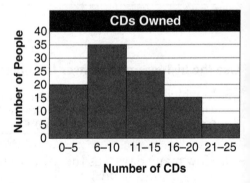

9. If 500 people were surveyed, predict how many would own between 11 and 20 CDs.

   _____

10. Is it possible to find the mean number of CDs that are owned from the histogram? Explain.

   _____

SPIRAL REVIEW

11. What are the mean, median, mode, and range of the heights of 4-year-old boys (in inches)?

   Heights: 39, 40, 39.5, 40, 40.5, 38.5, 42, 41.5, 40, 38.5

   _____

8-7 Stem-and-Leaf Plots

Name _____ Date _____

Mean Monthly Precipitation (inches)					
	Jan.	Feb.	Mar.	Apr.	May
Tampa	2.3	2.7	2.8	1.8	2.9
Houston	3.8	3.3	1.5	3.6	1.5

Mean Monthly Precipitation (inches), Tampa, FL	
Stem	Leaves
1	8
2	3 7 8 9

Key: 1|8 = 1.8 inches

Mean Monthly Precipitation (inches)		
Houston		Tampa
Leaves	Stem	Leaves
5 5	1	8
	2	3 7 8 9
8 6 3	3	

Key: 5.6 inches = 6|5|5 = 5.5 inches

A *stem-and-leaf plot* displays the digits of the numbers in a set of data to show how the data are distributed.

A *back-to-back stem-and-leaf plot* shows leaves on both sides of the stem. This display represents two sets of data.

Make an organized list of the data set shown on each stem-and-leaf plot.

1.

Cost of Running Shoes ($)	
Stem	Leaves
4	8 9 9
5	4 6 7 8
6	
7	0

Key: 4|8 = $48

cost of running shoes (dollars):
48, 49, 49, 54, 56, 57, 58, 70

2.

Ages of Teachers (years)	
Stem	Leaves
2	2 4 4 8 9
3	0 2 4 5 5 6 7
4	1 1 8 8 9
5	2 5 6

Key: 2|2 = 22 years

Organize each set of data and make a stem-and-leaf plot. Then answer the questions.

3. The number of minutes per day band students practice: 45, 30, 45, 50, 25, 25, 30, 15, 30, 20

  a. How many students practice 25 minutes daily?
  2|5 occurs twice; 2 students practice 25 minutes daily.

  b. How many students practice at least 30 minutes daily?

  c. What is the range of the practice times?

4. Number of miles ridden by Cycling Club members: 21, 40, 8, 15, 42, 13, 29, 9, 24, 26, 13, 17, 29, 20

  a. How many cyclists rode more than 25 miles?

  b. What is the median distance ridden?

  c. What is the mode of the distances?

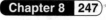

On a separate sheet of paper, make a back-to-back stem-and-leaf plot from the data in the table. Use your plot to answer exercises 5–8.

5. Identify any outliers.

48 is an outlier in the set of winning scores

6. How many times did the winning team score more than 30 points?

7. Compare the medians of the winning and losing scores.

8. Compare the ranges of the winning and losing scores.

Superbowl Scores		
Year	Winning Score	Losing Score
2007	29	17
2006	21	10
2005	24	21
2004	32	29
2003	48	21
2002	20	17
2001	34	7
2000	23	16
1999	34	19
1998	31	24

Solve. Use the stem-and-leaf plots to solve problems 9–11.

Annual Mean Monthly Temperatures (°F), San Diego, CA	
Stem	Leaves
5	8 8 9
6	0 2 3 5 7 8
7	1 2 3

Key: 5|8 = 58°F

Annual Mean Monthly Temperatures (°F), Phoenix, AZ	
Stem	Leaves
5	4 4 8
6	2 3
7	0 5 9
8	6 9
9	1 3

Key: 5|4 = 54°F

Annual Mean Monthly Temperatures (°F), New York City, NY	
Stem	Leaves
3	2 5 7
4	3 7
5	3 7
6	3 8
7	1 5 7

Key: 3|2 = 32°F

9. In which city would you experience the greatest range of temperatures? Explain.

10. Which measure of central tendency indicates that San Diego is warmer than Phoenix? Explain.

11. How do the lowest temperatures for San Diego and Phoenix compare? How do their means compare? How can you explain the difference?

CRITICAL THINKING

12. Which data set could better be displayed in a stem-and-leaf plot: a set of 20 values with 5 different front-end digits or a set of 50 values with 2 different front-end digits? Explain.

8-8 Box-and-Whisker Plots

Name _____ Date _____

Make a box-and-whisker plot of the data set.

- Determine the median, the lower quartile, and the upper quartile.
- Locate these three points on a number line and draw a box above the number line to represent the middle half (or second and third quartile) of the data.
- Draw lines (whiskers) from the upper quartile of the box to the *upper extreme*, **48**, and from the lower quartile to the *lower extreme*, **4**.

To determine if there are any outliers, multiply the *interquartile range* by 1.5.

For this data set, outliers are 10.5 points beyond the lower or upper quartiles.

So 48 is an outlier.

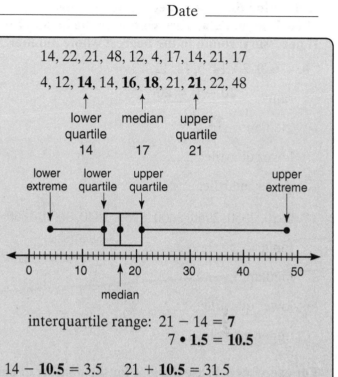

14, 22, 21, 48, 12, 4, 17, 14, 21, 17

4, 12, **14**, 14, **16**, **18**, 21, **21**, 22, 48

| lower quartile | median | upper quartile |
| 14 | 17 | 21 |

interquartile range: $21 - 14 = 7$

$7 \cdot 1.5 = 10.5$

$14 - 10.5 = 3.5$ $21 + 10.5 = 31.5$

Outliers are *less than* 3.5 or *greater than* 31.5.

Use the box-and-whisker plot to identify the values.

1. lower extreme: __39__

upper extreme: __87__

median: __65__

lower quartile: _____   range: $87 - 39 =$ _____

upper quartile: _____   interquartile range: _____

2. lower extreme: _____

upper extreme: _____

median: _____

lower quartile: _____   range: _____

upper quartile: _____   interquartile range: _____

Determine an appropriate scale and intervals, given the lower and upper extremes for each data set.

3. lower extreme: 260
upper extreme: 290

scale: __250 to 300__

interval: __of 5__

4. lower extreme: 11,000
upper extreme: 14,500

scale: _____

interval: _____

5. lower extreme: 96.4
upper extreme: 96.9

scale: _____

interval: _____

Determine the range, median, lower quartile, and upper quartile of each set of data. Then complete the box-and-whisker plot. If necessary, round to the nearest whole number.

6. 4, 6, 0, 20, 14, 9, 14, 12, 13

   range: __20 – 0 = 20__

   median: __12__

   lower quartile: _____

   upper quartile: _____

7. 2810, 2850, 2960, 3000, 2750, 2840, 3000, 2860, 2990

   range: _____

   median: _____

   lower quartile: _____

   upper quartile: _____

For exercises 8–9, use the plot for the number of push-ups students in each class did.

8. Which class has the greater range? How much greater?

   _____

9. In which class do the push-up counts cluster more closely around the median?

   _____

Solve. Check to justify your answer.

10. The box-and-whisker plot represents Jan's pulse rate record: 50, 58, 61, 63, 63, 65, 67, 68, 69, 70, 70, 72, 73, 74, 76, 79, 85, 87, and 99. How does the mean relate to the other measures on the plot?

    _____

MENTAL MATH

11. Does this data set contain outliers? Explain.

    _____

    _____

    _____

8-9 Venn Diagrams

Name _____ Date _____

A *Venn diagram* is a group of two or more overlapping circles, each representing a single data set.

In Mr. Wilson's class, 14 students speak Spanish, 5 students speak French, and 3 students speak both Spanish and French. How many students in Mr. Wilson's class speak Spanish, French, or both?

Use a Venn diagram:

$14 - 3 = \mathbf{11}$ ← Students who speak *only* Spanish.
$5 - 3 = \mathbf{2}$ ← Students who speak *only* French.

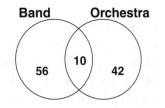

Add the numbers that represent each region: $11 + 3 + 2 = \mathbf{16}$.
There are 16 students who speak Spanish, French, or both.

14 students speak Spanish.
5 students speak French.
3 students speak Spanish and French.

Each Venn diagram shows all the prime factors of two or three numbers. Identify the numbers whose prime factors are represented. Then give the common factor(s) of all the numbers.

1.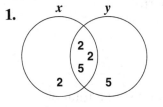

   x = 40; y = 100; common
   prime factors: 2, 2, 5

2.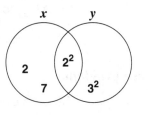

   _____

3.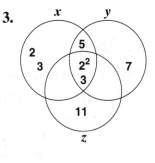

   _____

Draw a Venn diagram to show the prime factors of the numbers and their common factor(s). Then find their greatest common factor (GCF).

4. 30 and 42
   $30 = 2 \cdot 3 \cdot 5$; $42 = 2 \cdot 3 \cdot 7$
   $GCF = 2 \cdot 3 = 6$

5. 48 and 42

   _____

6. 140 and 105

   _____

Use the Venn diagram to answer the questions.

7. How many students are in the band?

   Band   Orchestra

   56   10   42

   _____

8. How many students are in the band, the orchestra, or both?

   _____

Use the Venn diagram to answer the questions.

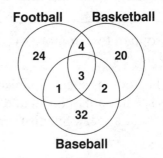

9. How many students play football and basketball?

   4 + 3 = 7 students

10. How many students play football and baseball?

    _____

11. How many students play baseball?

    _____

12. How many students play basketball?

    _____

13. How many students play exactly two sports?

    _____

14. How many students play all three sports?

    _____

On a separate sheet of paper, draw a Venn diagram to organize the data.

15. multiples of 3: 3, 6, 9, 12, 15, 18, 21, 24, 27, 30
    multiples of 5: 5, 10, 15, 20, 25, 30

16. party decoration committee: Jason, Angela, Maggie, Terrence, Kate
    party ticket committee: Sharon, Scott, Maggie, Kate, Roberto

Problem Solving

Draw and use a Venn diagram to solve each problem.

17. During the day, 38 people borrowed mysteries from the library, and 10 people borrowed biographies. Six people who borrowed a mystery also borrowed a biography. How many people borrowed a mystery, a biography, or both?

18. One evening a pizzeria sold a total of 33 pizzas topped with pepperoni, sausage, or pepperoni and sausage. Twenty-nine of the pizzas had pepperoni. Of these, 15 also had sausage. How many more pizzas had pepperoni only than had sausage only?

    _____   _____

CHALLENGE

19. Fifty-eight people take classes at an art center. Twenty-nine take painting, 23 take pottery, and 18 take weaving. Two people take all three classes. Four people take only painting and pottery. Four people take weaving and exactly one other class. Seven people take pottery and at least one other class. Draw a Venn diagram to show the numbers of students taking any combination among painting, pottery, and weaving classes.

8-10 Multiple Line Graphs

Name _____ Date _____

Use *multiple line graphs* to quickly compare two or more related sets of data that change over time. Line segments sloping up indicate increases, segments sloping down indicate decreases, and horizontal line segments indicate no change.

Key:
Paradise Resort ●——●
Tropical Resort ●----●

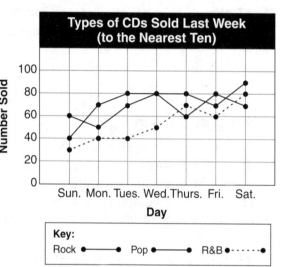

Resort Attendance

Use the graph to complete the table of data.

Types of CDs Sold Last Week (to the Nearest Ten)							
	Sun.	Mon.	Tues.	Wed.	Thurs.	Fri.	Sat.
1. Rock	___	___	___	___	___	___	___
2. Pop	___	___	___	___	___	___	___
3. R & B	___	___	___	___	___	___	___

Types of CDs Sold Last Week (to the Nearest Ten)

Key:
Rock ●——● Pop ●——● R&B ●----●

Use the table data above to make multiple line graphs on a separate sheet of paper.

4. scale: 0 to 100; intervals of 25

5. scale: 0 to 100; intervals of 10

6. broken scale: 80 to 100; intervals of 2

7. In exercises 4–6, how do the scale sizes contribute to the usefulness of a graph?

_____

_____

Make a double line graph on a separate sheet of paper for the data at the right. Then answer the questions.

Paper Route Customers				
	2005	2006	2007	2008
Fran	186	205	200	220
Paulo	193	197	204	216

8. How many fewer customers did Paulo have in 2006 than Fran?

205 − 197 = 8; Paulo had 8 fewer customers.

9. In which year(s) did Fran have fewer customers than Paulo?

10. Based on the data, make a prediction for the number of customers for Fran and Paulo in 2009.

_____

_____

Make a multiple line graph on a separate sheet of paper using the data below. Explain how the graph helped you answer each question. Use the graph to answer exercises 11–14.

Number of Craft Items Made for the School Fair			
Week	Class 701	Class 702	Class 703
1	7	8	10
2	5	8	6
3	4	7	10
4	9	8	11
5	12	6	13
6	16	10	9
7	21	11	18

11. How many more items did Class 703 make than Class 702 during Week 5?

7 more items; Possible answer: The length of the line segment between the two graphs during Week 5 represents the difference.

12. Which class had the greatest drop in the number of items made in a one-week period?

13. Which class had the greatest increase in the number of items made in a one-week period?

14. In which week were the fewest items made?

Problem Solving

Sam is considering closing one of his three stores to make his overall business more profitable. He created this graph from the last six months of sales.

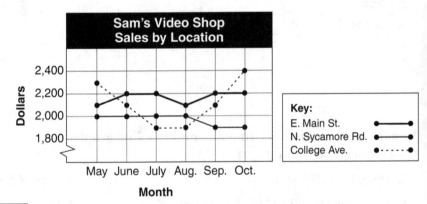

15. Which location had the highest sales figure for one month?

16. What was the difference in sales between the E. Main St. and N. Sycamore Rd. locations in August?

17. Do you think Sam has enough information to decide which store to close? Explain.

TEST PREPARATION

18. Select in which situation a multiple line graph would best display information.

A. You want to display data about the top running speed for five different animals.

B. You want to compare sales of cars from the United States, Germany, and Japan for the past six years.

C. You want to show what percent of last month's budget was spent for electricity.

D. Your friend has baseball cards dating from the 1950s. You want to show how many cards she has from each decade.

8-11 Scatter Plots

Name _____   Date _____

A *scatter plot* is a graph that compares two related sets of data on a coordinate plane. On any scatter plot, the data displayed can be described in three different ways.

- *Positive correlation:* The numbers for one data set increase as the numbers for the other data set increase.

- *Negative correlation:* The numbers for one data set decrease as the numbers for the other data set increase.

- *No correlation:* There is no pattern in the way the numbers for the data sets increase or decrease.

The data table at the right and its graph show a positive correlation between repair cost and remodeling value.

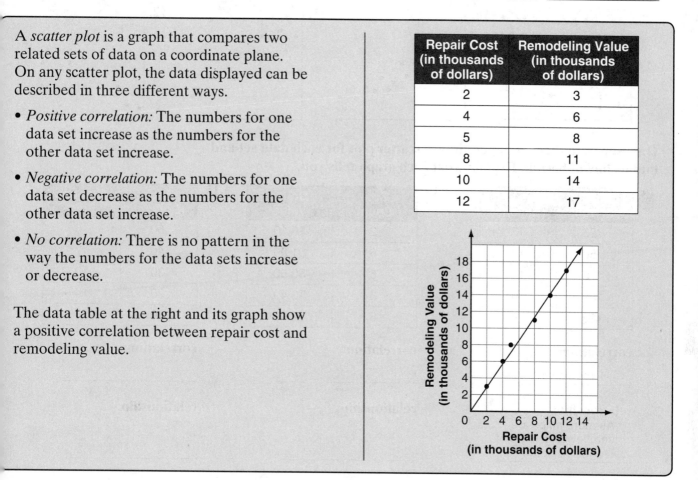

Repair Cost (in thousands of dollars)	Remodeling Value (in thousands of dollars)
2	3
4	6
5	8
8	11
10	14
12	17

Identify each scatter plot as showing a *positive correlation*, a *negative correlation*, or *no correlation*.

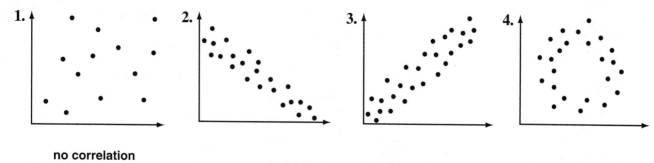

1. _____ no correlation _____

2. _____

3. _____

4.

Tell whether you would expect a *positive correlation*, a *negative correlation*, or *no correlation* for each situation. Explain.

5. musical ability and shoe size
   No correlation: musical ability probably does not relate to shoe size.
   _____

6. time spent studying and test score
   _____

7. a dog's age and activity level
   _____

8. car speed and travel time
   _____

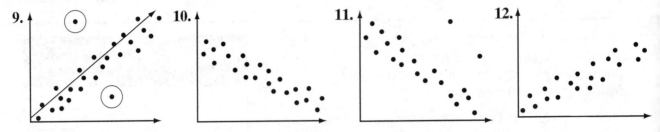

Draw a line of best fit. Circle any outliers.

9.   10.   11.   12.

On a separate sheet of paper, draw a scatter plot for each data set and find its line of best fit. Explain what each graph tells you.

13.

Miles Driven	Gas Left (Gallons)
25	13
50	12
75	11
100	10
125	9

correlation:

___negative___

relationship:
As more miles are driven, fewer gallons of gas are left.

14.

Coin Count	Dollar Value
2	$0.10
6	$1.00
6	$0.50
8	$0.40
8	$2.00

correlation:

_____

relationship:

_____

15.

Price (Dollars)	Number Sold
50	5
40	7
30	10
20	14
10	16

correlation:

_____

relationship:

_____

16.

Year	Funds Raised (Thousands of dollars)	Cost to Play Sports (per Student)
1999	3	85
2000	4	75
2001	5	68
2002	6	65
2003	8	60
2004	10	48
2005	9	58
2006	11	50

correlation:

_____

relationship:

_____

SPIRAL REVIEW

17. Twelve students responded to a survey asking how many books they read last year. The results were 6, 4, 8, 4, 5, 4, 2, 13, 3, 10, 7, and 15. Find the mean, median, mode, and range of the data.

_____

_____

8-12 Misleading Statistics and Graphs

Name _____ Date _____

To identify factors about the data that may be misleading,
look for:

- choice of statistical measure
- biased survey questions
- missing important information
- inappropriately small amount of data

- data from a single source when multiple sources are appropriate
- differences in the items grouped, such as price, quality, dates, and location

To identify data displays that may distort information, look for:

- small intervals
- large intervals

- a broken scale
- a scale that does not start at zero

Determine which graph may be misleading and why.

1. a.
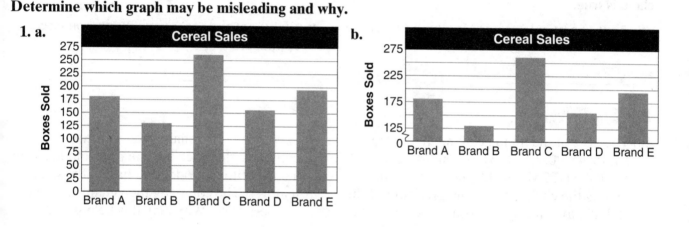

_____

Explain whether the claim in the title is supported by the graph.

2. 3.
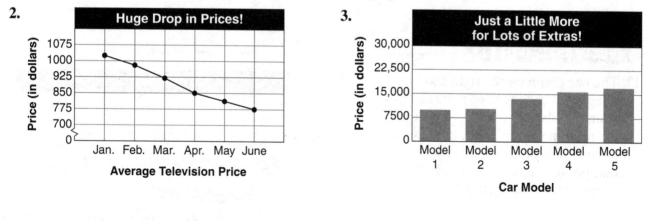

_____   _____

_____   _____

Find the mean, median, and mode for the data set. Then determine if the mean of the data may be misleading. If so, which measure better represents the data?

4. 57, 86, 90, 88, 94

5. 465, 486, 377, 392, 406

_____

6. 107.5, 100, 83.4, 106.2, 98.9, 78.2

7. $-20, -18, -18, -15, -6, -22$

_____

List two questions to ask the advertiser in order to decide if the claim is true.

8. 4 out of 5 people prefer Moo-brand Cheese.

9. We've got the best prices around on large appliances.

_____

Problem Solving

10. The ages of the hiking club members are 53, 15, 45, 40, 19, 16, 31, 65, 60, 24, 33, and 55. Toby is 22 years old, and considering joining the club. He asks the president of the club the average age of its members and the president gives the mean. Why might this fact be misleading?

11. A company that makes refrigerators compares the price for one of its models with a competitor's model that has all the same features. The company then claims to have the best price. Why may this be misleading?

_____

MENTAL MATH

12. The bar graph on the right shows the number of each type of movie borrowed from the library. What appears to be the relationship between the number of comedies or action movies versus the number of dramas borrowed? What is the actual relationship?

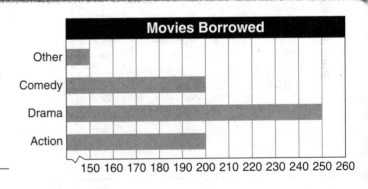

Movies Borrowed

_____

8-13 Technology: Create Graphs

Name _____ Date _____

You can use spreadsheet software to display data in bar graphs, line graphs, or circle graphs.

Use the following steps:

Step 1 Enter the data from a table into the first two columns of the spreadsheet.

Step 2 Highlight the data, including the column heads.

Step 3 From the *Insert* menu, select **Chart**. Select **Column** for a bar graph, **Pie** for a circle graph, or **Line** for a line graph. You can also use the *Chart Wizard* icon on the toolbar to display the data of either graph type.

	A	B
1	Month	School Store Sales (dollars)
2	January	250
3	February	325
4	March	307
5	April	211
6	May	90

When you change the data in the spreadsheet the graph is automatically updated.

Give the content or numerical value of each cell.

1. C2 _____**91**_____

2. C5 _____

3. B4 _____

4. D2 _____

5. B1 _____

6. D1 _____

7. A6 _____

8. A1 _____

Third Marking Quarter Report Card Grades

	A	B	C	D
1	Student	Math	Science	Reading
2	Emily	82	91	87
3	Dominick	85	76	91
4	Nicholas	78	90	88
5	Damian	90	78	76
6	Rita	81	94	71

Give the cell(s) that contain the given content or numerical value.

9. 82 _____**B2**_____

10. 76 _____

11. 90 _____

12. 88 _____

13. Damian _____

14. Science _____

15. 91 _____

16. 78 _____

17. 94 _____

Use a spreadsheet program to represent the data for each table.

18. Represent the data by making a vertical bar graph and a circle graph. On a separate sheet of paper sketch the displayed graphs.

Talbert Middle School Enrollment	
Grade	Number of Students
Grade 6	145
Grade 7	261
Grade 8	248
Grade 9	178

19. Which graph *best* represents the data? Why?

_____

_____

20. Represent the data by making a circle graph and a line graph. On a separate sheet of paper sketch the displayed graphs.

Telecorp's Sales for 2008	
Quarter	Sales (in thousands of dollars)
1	430
2	115
3	231
4	224

21. Which graph *best* displays that sales dropped significantly between the first and second quarters? Why?

_____

_____

22. Represent the data by making a double-bar graph and a double-line graph. On a separate sheet of paper sketch the displayed graphs.

Abigail's Summer Earnings ($)		
Month	Carnival Ride Operator	Lawn Mowing
May	40	72
June	65	80
July	75	60
August	100	70

23. Which graph *best* compares Abigail's summer earnings from month to month? Why?

_____

_____

CRITICAL THINKING

24. Describe how you would display measurements of a tree's growth over several years. What measurements would you use? How would you display them? Explain your answer.

_____

_____

_____

_____

8-14 Problem-Solving Strategy:
Review of Strategies

Name _____ Date _____

Solve. Show your work.

1. Find the product without using a calculator: $(0.25)(1.5)(0.8)$

_____

2. Of 15 balls in a hat, 10 are white and 5 are yellow. You may add exactly four more balls at a time, using as many of either color as you wish. By doing this, can you change the contents of the hat so that exactly half the balls are white? Explain.

_____

3. Can you rearrange the digits of the number 1,835,159 so that the resulting number is divisible by 4? Explain.

_____

4. Compute without using a calculator:
$(0.125)(8) + (1.25)(9) + (12.5)(6) + (125)(7)$.

_____

5. Erin has 19 coins worth $3.55. If she has only quarters and dimes, how many of each does she have?

_____

6. Randy has $8.75 in only quarters and dimes. His mother says, "Can I have half your quarters? I'm going to need them for parking meters today." Can Randy fulfill the request?

_____

7. Phil drove 5 miles east, 3 miles south, 4 miles east, 7 miles north, 6 miles west, and 2 miles north. How far, in each direction, is he now from where he started?

_____

8. A ball is dropped from a height of 243 feet. Each time it bounces, it returns to a third of its previous height. At the top of its fifth bounce, your friend grabs it. In all, how far did the ball travel?

_____

9. A pipe is cut into 8 equal parts. Of these, 5 are shipped to Peoria. Each of these are then cut into thirds. Of those, 8 pieces are used in a construction job. How much of the original pipe was used in this construction job?

_____

10. Twenty vehicles comprised of 2- and 3-wheeled motorcycles and 4-wheeled cars are parked in a lot. There are 61 tires in all, and there are exactly 8 cars. How many 2-wheeled and how many 3-wheeled vehicles are in this lot?

_____

Enrichment:
Financial Spreadsheets

Name _____ Date _____

Listed below is a budget for Mr. Rosen's class cookout. Mr. Rosen wants to know the total cost of the cookout.

He uses a formula to find the costs of the items. In D3, he enters the formula =B3*C3. This multiplies the value in cell B3 (number of bags of charcoal to buy) by the value in cell C3 (price per bag) to get the total cost for the charcoal.

Mr. Rosen then copies the formula into rows 4–10 of column D. The program updates the formula for each row to get the cost of the items needed.

	A	B	C	D
1	Mr. Rosen's Class Cookout			
2	Item	Quantity	Price per item	Cost
3	charcoal	1	$6.76	$6.76
4	pack of burgers	2	$10.81	$21.62
5	pack of hot dogs	2	$3.89	$7.78
6	bag of apples	2	$4.84	$9.68
7	bottle of juice	6	$2.38	$14.28
8	potato salad	2	$6.82	$13.64
9	pack of buns	8	$3.85	$30.80
10	condiments	1	$15.04	$15.04

Next, he finds the total cost by entering the formula =SUM(D3:D10) in cell D11. This computes the sum of all the values in the Cost column, from cell D3 to cell D10.

$119.60
=SUM(D3:D10)

For exercises 1–6, copy the chart below into a spreadsheet. Douglass High School Student Council is holding an end-of-the-year dance as a community fundraiser. The goal is to raise a thousand dollars. The committee has put together a budget for the dance, which is shown below.

	A	B	C	D
1	End-of-the-Year Fundraiser Dance			
2	Item	Quantity	Price per item	Cost
3	DJ	1	$825.00	
4	Decorations	1	$500.00	
5	Veggie Plate	15	$21.35	
6	Fruit Plate	15	$21.35	
7	plate of mini sandwiches	45	$12.78	
8	bottles of water	150	$0.86	
9	bottles of apple juice	150	$1.29	
10			Total Cost	
11			Cost for 1 student	

1. What formula would be entered to find the cost of the DJ? In which cell should the formula be entered?

=B3*C3; D3

2. What is the total cost of the veggie plates?

_____

3. What is the total cost of the plates of mini sandwiches?

_____

4. What is the total cost of the bottles of apple juice?

_____

5. What is the total cost of the dance?

_____

6. If 300 students showed up to the dance, how much should each student donate to help the dance raise a thousand dollars above the cost of the event?

_____

For exercises 7–11, copy the chart below into a spreadsheet. **The Bluesberg County Zoo has been approached to lower the price of admission by the county commission. The zoo says that the reason why the price is so high is because of the weekly feeding costs of the animals in the zoo. The weekly feeding costs for the animals are shown below.**

	A	B	C	D
1	Bluesberg County Zoo Weekly Feeding Costs			
2	Animal	Quantity	Price per animal	Cost
3	Lions	12	$225.00	
4	Bears	15	$156.00	
5	Hyenas	24	$135.00	
6	Giraffes	35	$144.00	
7	Elephants	18	$197.00	
8	Gorillas	19	$184.00	
9	Rhinoceros	23	$122.00	
10	Anacondas	15	$78.00	
11	Dolphins	54	$193.00	
12			Total Cost	
13			Cost per visitor	

7. What is the weekly cost of feeding the lions?

$2700 _____

8. What is the weekly cost of feeding the bears?

_____

9. What is the weekly cost of feeding the giraffes?

_____

10. What is the weekly cost of feeding the dolphins?

_____

11. To lower the price of admission, the county commission suggests transferring animals to a different zoo. The zoo is willing to transfer half of the dolphins, and 20 giraffes, and all of the hyenas to another zoo. If the zoo still averages 1500 visitors a week, what is the absolute minimum price per visitor?

_____

WRITE ABOUT IT

12. A spreadsheet helps organize data to be easily used and adjusted as needed. For which activities could you use a spreadsheet in your daily life? Sketch an example of how you would organize such a spreadsheet including equations that you might use.

_____

_____

_____

Test Prep: Multiple-Choice Questions

Strategy: Understand Distractors

Name _____   Date _____

Be sure to *answer the question asked* in multiple-choice questions. Distractors in multiple-choice questions are often correct answers to *different* questions that can be asked.

To select the correct answer in a multiple-choice question, try using these test-taking tips.

- Underline important words.
- Restate the question.
- Use the Test-Prep Strategy.
- Apply appropriate rules, definitions, properties, or strategies.
- Analyze and eliminate answer choices.

Choose the correct answer. *TIP: Use all the time you are given.*

1. Use the table below.

Day	Shop A Rentals	Shop B Rentals
Mon.	13	10
Tues.	7	12
Wed.	11	6
Thurs.	9	14
Fri.	10	13

What is the difference between the median numbers of bikes rented at Shop A and Shop B?

A. 1   **C.** 2

B. 6   **D.** 10.5

2. What is the median of the data shown in the stem-and-leaf plot below?

Stem	Leaves
1	6 9
2	0 3 5 8 9
3	0 0 1 5

Key: 2 | 5 = 25

F. 19   **H.** 26

G. 28   **J.** 30

3. What is the greatest common factor of 12, 18, and 24?

A. 3   **C.** 6

B. 36   **D.** 72

4. Together, Elise and Ari won 28 tennis matches. Elise won 4 more matches than Ari. How many matches did Elise win?

F. 12   **H.** 14

G. 16   **J.** 24

5. The set below contains only which type of numbers?

$(-3, 8, 2\frac{1}{2}, 10, 7.25, 16, \sqrt{36}, 64)$

A. mixed numbers   **C.** whole numbers

B. integers   **D.** rational numbers

6. All fifteen members of a soccer team are getting new uniforms. Shirts cost $18 each, shorts cost $25 each, and socks cost $7 a pair. What is the total cost of the new uniforms?

F. $50   **H.** $65

G. $750   **J.** $975

Vocabulary Development

Name _____ Date _____

Chapter 8 Vocabulary

back-to-back stem-and-leaf plot	line of best fit	median	representative sample
	line plot	mode	sample
bias	lower extreme	multiple line graph	scatter plot
box-and-whisker plot	lower quartile	outliers	stem-and-leaf plot
convenience sample	mean	population	survey
frequency tables	measures of central tendency	quartiles	upper extreme
histogram		random sample	upper quartile
interquartile range	measures of dispersion	range	Venn diagram

From the vocabulary list above, choose the term(s) that best complete each sentence. Write the term(s) in the space(s) provided.

1. The median of the lower half of a set of data is the _____.

2. The _____ of a data set 3, 9, 2, 3, 8, 12 is 3.

3. A data display that splits numbers into two sets of digits is a

   _____.

4. Numbers that are much greater or much less than other values in a set of

   data are _____.

5. Asking only football players how to spend the school's athletic budget could

   lead to a result with _____.

6. The number 12 is the _____ of the data set 4, 12, 11, 4, 6.

7. A _____ uses overlapping circles to show relationships
   among data sets.

Tell whether each statement is *true* or *false*. If the statement is false, change it to make it true.

8. You can use a multiple line graph to display related sets of data that change
   over time.

   _____

9. The range is the number that is in the middle of a data set.

   _____

10. Each member of a population has an equal chance of being chosen in a
    convenience sample.

    _____

Use after ▶ **SOURCEBOOK Lessons 8-1–8-12, pages 208–231.**

Practice Chapter 8 Test

Name _____ Date _____

1. Which sample is best to find out how many movies people see each month?

    a. ask people on line at a movie theater   **b.** call every tenth person in a phone book

2. What type of graph would best display the percent of

    students in the class who play various musical instruments? _____

Use the tally chart at the right for exercise 3.

3. How many of 2575 people will *not* vote for Anderson?

_____

Candidate	Number of Supporters
Miller	ЖИТ ЖИТ ЖИТ
Anderson	ЖИТ ЖИТ ЖИТ ЖИТ ЖИТ I
Other	ЖИТ IIII

4. Name the outlier, then find the mean, median, mode, and range of the data set without the outlier. 2, 4, 4, 6, 4, 16

_____

Use the bar graph at the right for exercises 5–6.

5. During what game was the greatest difference between the number of points Heather and Christine scored?

_____

6. Find the mean, median, mode, and range of Heather's points in these games.

_____

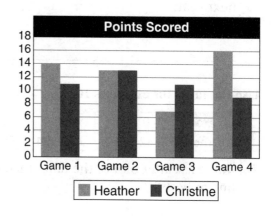

7. Make a stem-and-leaf plot of the following data.
    52, 68, 41, 32, 46, 38, 64, 67

Use the table at the right for exercises 8–10.

8. Draw a histogram with scale intervals of 2.

9. Draw a histogram with scale intervals of 10.

10. Compare your two histograms.

_____

Number of Books Read	Number of People
0–4	7
5–9	10
10–14	18
15–20	15
21–25	10
more than 25	5

Use the box-and-whisker plot for exercise 11.

11. low temperatures: median _____

    lower quartile _____

    upper extreme _____

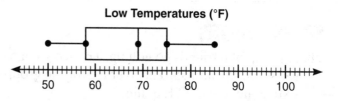

Low Temperatures (°F)

Use the following information for exercises 12–13.
Students are registering for elective courses at a middle school. Fifty-four students choose to take a computer course and 48 students choose to take an art class. Twenty-two students choose to take both courses.

12. Draw a Venn diagram to represent the situation.

13. How many students registered altogether?

_____

Use the double line graph at the right for exercises 14–15.

14. What was the greatest difference in the number of bikes the shops sold in one month?

_____

15. Predict which shop will sell more bikes next year.

_____

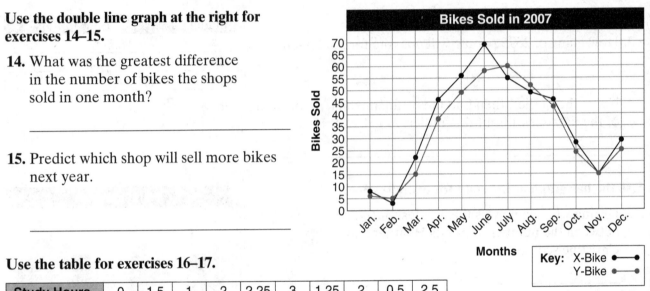

Bikes Sold in 2007

Key: X-Bike ●——●
      Y-Bike ●——●

Use the table for exercises 16–17.

Study Hours	0	1.5	1	2	2.25	3	1.25	2	0.5	2.5
Test Grade	42	87	73	94	95	97	78	89	67	92

16. Make a scatter plot of the data. Include a line of best fit.

17. What type of correlation is found in the data?

_____

Use the table at the right for exercises 18–19.

18. The table gives an employee's monthly sales for six months. Use the data to make line graph A and line graph B.

Graph A: a scale starting at 15, intervals of 2.
Graph B: a scale starting at 0, intervals of 5.

19. Which graph could be misleading? Explain.

Month	Jan.	Feb.	Mar.	Apr.	May	June
Kim's Sales (in thousands)	22	18	24	25	29	29

_____

Tell About It

20. A group of 6 friends go golfing. The scores of 5 of the golfers are 95, 88, 96, 90, and 95. The average for the group is 93. What is the sixth golfer's score? Explain.

_____

Cumulative Review: Chapters 1–8

Name _____ Date _____

Circle the best answer.

1. The number of subscribers of a newsletter increased from 800 to 1000. What was the percent increase?

   A. 20%   **B.** 25%
   C. 80%   **D.** 125%

2. What is the median of the data set?

   14, 12, 9, 19, 12, 16

   F. 11   **G.** 12
   H. 13   **J.** 14

3. What is 120,000,000 written in scientific notation?

   A. 1.2×10^7
   B. 1.2×10^8
   C. 1.2×10^9
   D. 12×10^8

4. An ordered pair has two negative coordinates. In which quadrant does the point lie?

   F. I   **G.** II
   H. III   **J.** IV

5. Which graph represents the solution of $-3 + x < -5$?

   A.
   B.
   C.
   D.

6. In a survey of 150 people, 38 said science fiction is their favorite type of movie. Predict how many people out of 1200 would say science fiction is their favorite.

   F. 304   **G.** 380
   H. 456   **J.** 570

7. A 2-pound 8-ounce package of chicken costs $5.75. What is the price per pound?

   A. $2.05   **B.** $2.16
   C. $2.30   **D.** $2.89

8. Solve.

   $6.37 - 5.2x = -11.83$

   F. -3.5 **G.** -1.05
   H. 1.05 **J.** 3.5

9. Sue cuts 1 yard 7 inches from a board that is 4 feet 3 inches long. How many inches of board are left?

   A. 4 in.   **B.** 8 in.
   C. 15 in.   **D.** 16 in.

10. Solve the inequality.

    $-6x + 2x - 6 > -30$

    F. $x < -6$ **G.** $x < 6$
    H. $x > -6$ **J.** $x > 6$

11. Simplify: $\dfrac{15 - (4 - 9)^2}{-2 \bullet (4 + 6)}$

    A. -20
    B. $-\frac{1}{2}$
    C. $\frac{1}{2}$
    D. 5

12. 52 is 40% of what number?

    F. 20.8
    G. 72.8
    H. 104
    J. 130

13. Which property is illustrated?

$(0.6 - 0.8) + 1.9 = 1.9 + (0.6 - 0.8)$

- **A.** Associative Property of Addition
- **B.** Commutative Property of Addition
- **C.** Identity Property of Addition
- **D.** Inverse Property of Addition

14. What is the solution of the inequality $-2x \geq -8$?

- **F.** $x \leq 4$
- **G.** $x \leq -4$
- **H.** $x \geq 4$
- **J.** $x \geq -4$

15. Gabriel needs $\frac{1}{2}$ cup of milk for a recipe. How much of a quart does he need?

- **A.** $\frac{1}{16}$
- **B.** $\frac{1}{8}$
- **C.** $\frac{1}{4}$
- **D.** $\frac{1}{2}$

16. Fiona is participating in a walkathon. For every 2 miles she walks, she earns $35 in donations. How much will she earn if she completes all 15 miles of the walk?

- **F.** $70
- **G.** $262.50
- **H.** $525
- **J.** $1050

17. Rosa takes out a loan for $8000. The bank charges 6.5% annual interest. What is the total amount she pays if she pays off the loan in 15 years? Use $I = prt$.

- **A.** $5200
- **B.** $7800
- **C.** $15,800
- **D.** $78,000

18. Triangle ABC is similar to triangle DEF. What is the length of $\overline{DE}$?

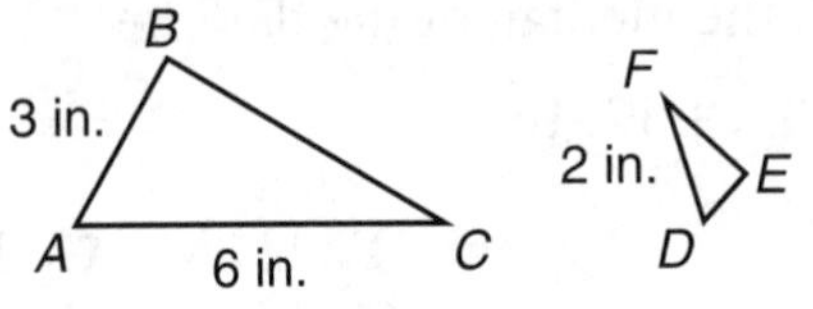

- **F.** 1 in.
- **G.** 1.5 in.
- **H.** 6 in.
- **J.** 9 in.

19. Maurice is at least two years older than twice his younger sister's age. Let m = Maurice's age and s = his sister's age. Which inequality models the situation?

- **A.** $s \geq 2m - 2$
- **B.** $s \geq 2m + 2$
- **C.** $m \geq 2s - 2$
- **D.** $m \geq 2s + 2$

20. A survey asked what types of pets people owned. How many people owned cats and fish but no dogs?

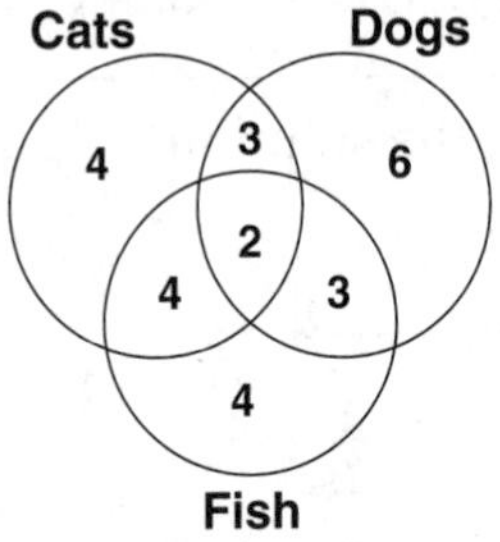

- **A.** 4
- **B.** 6
- **C.** 12
- **D.** 14

Tell About It

Explain how you solve each problem. Show all your work.

21. On the first 4 science tests, Pat received scores of 84, 92, 75, and 89. After the fifth test, his average was 86. What grade did Pat receive on the fifth test?

22. The tally chart shows the number of campers in each age group. Make a histogram of the data.

Age Group	Number of Campers
5–7	卌 卌 卌 III
8–10	卌 卌 卌 卌 卌 IIII
11–13	卌 卌 卌 卌 卌 卌 卌 I
14–15	卌 卌 卌 II

9-1 Points, Lines, and Planes

Name _____   Date _____

Geometric Figures and Names

point $M\bullet$

point M

line $\overleftrightarrow{PQ}$

$\overleftrightarrow{PQ}$ or $\overleftrightarrow{QP}$

line segment $R \rule{1.5cm}{0.4pt} S$

$\overline{RS}$ or $\overline{SR}$

---

ray $T \rule{1.5cm}{0.4pt} U$

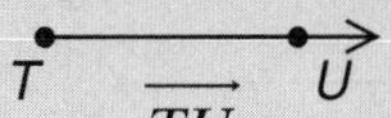

$\overrightarrow{TU}$

angle

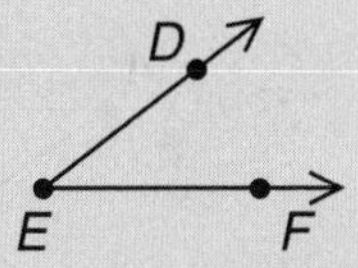

$\angle DEF$ or $\angle FED$ or $\angle E$

plane

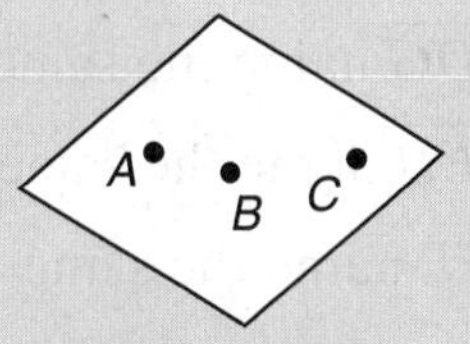

plane ABC

---

perpendicular lines ($\perp$): lines that form 4 right angles
parallel lines ($\parallel$): lines that extend in the same direction(s) and are the same distance apart

---

Match each term with the appropriate symbol or diagram.

a.

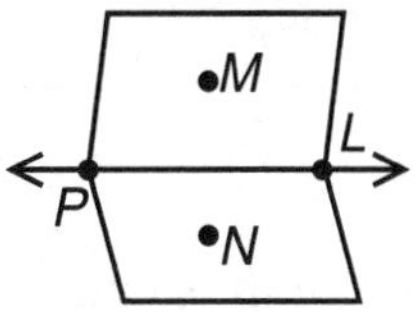

b. $\overline{AF}$ c. $\overleftrightarrow{RS}$ d. $\angle NOP$ e. $\bullet$

f.

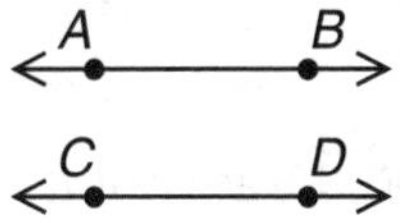

g. $\perp$ h. $\overrightarrow{KL}$ i.   j. 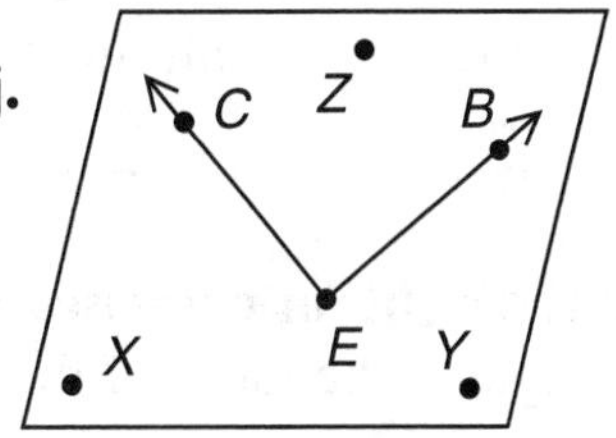   k. $\parallel$

1. point ___e___

2. line _____

3. collinear _____

4. line segment _____

5. ray _____

6. angle _____

7. coplanar _____

8. is perpendicular to _____

9. is parallel to _____

10. parallel lines _____

11. intersecting planes _____

Identify the figures in the diagram.

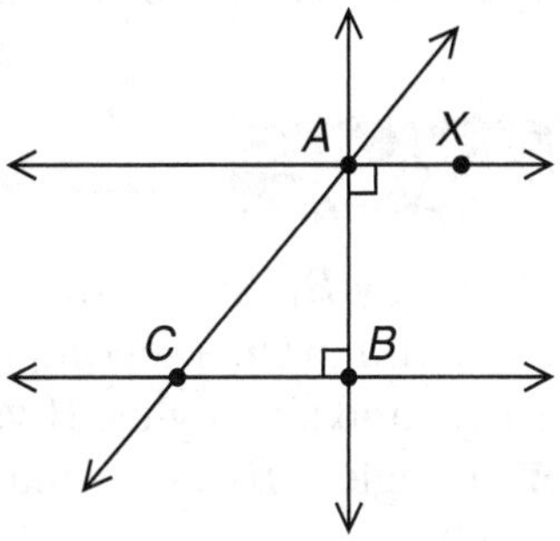

12. four points ___*A, B, C, X*___

13. six rays _____

14. one set of perpendicular lines _____

15. five angles _____

16. three line segments _____

Make a drawing to illustrate each exercise.

17. Angles *ABC* and *DBE* share a vertex.

18. $\overleftrightarrow{GH} \parallel \overleftrightarrow{RS}$

19. $\overrightarrow{WZ}$ and $\overrightarrow{WX}$ form ∠*ZWX*.

20. Line *BC* is perpendicular to line *MN*.

21. Points *C*, *D*, and *E* are on line *YZ*.

22. Points *H*, *K* and $\overline{LM}$ are on the same plane.

Use the figure for exercises 23–27.

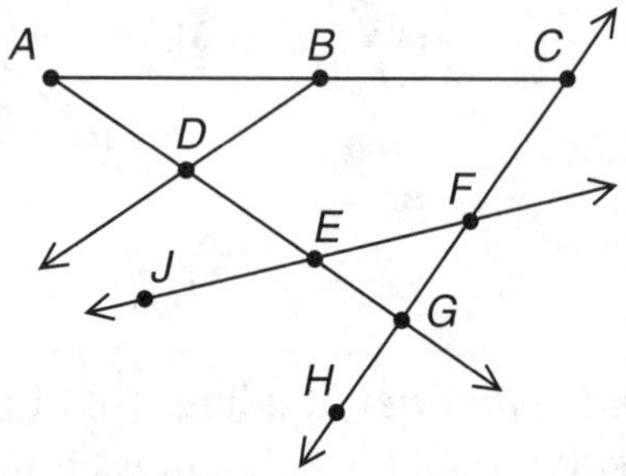

23. Do $\overline{DE}$ and $\overline{DG}$ name the same segment? ___No___

24. Do $\overline{DE}$ and $\overline{ED}$ name the same segment? _____

25. Do $\overrightarrow{EF}$ and $\overrightarrow{FE}$ name the same ray? _____

26. Name all the segments with endpoint *B*. _____

27. Name all the rays with endpoint *E*. _____

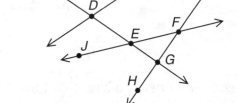

On a separate sheet of paper draw each figure. Then answer each question.

28. Draw and label point *A*. How many lines can you draw through point *A*?

_____

29. Draw and label point *B*. How many lines can you draw through points *A* and *B*?

_____

30. Draw point *C* so that it is not on line *AB*.

a. How many lines can contain all three points?

_____

b. How many planes can contain all three points?

_____

c. How many planes can pass through line *AB*?

_____

Solve. Use the figure at the right for exercises 31–34. (*Hint:* All angles shown are right angles. The faces of the figure are on planes.)

31. Name two parallel lines. _____

32. Name the planes that are perpendicular to plane *ADH*.

_____

33. Name two parallel planes. _____

34. Name the lines that are skew to $\overleftrightarrow{BC}$. _____

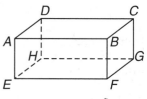

CHALLENGE

35. If you drew ray *BD* in the interior of angle *ABC*, there would be 3 rays and 3 angles. If you drew a second ray in the interior of angle *ABC*, there would be four rays and six angles. If you drew a total five rays from point *B* in the interior of angle *ABC*, how many angles would there be?

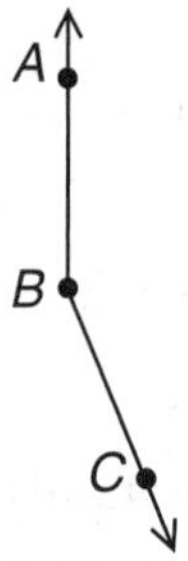

_____

_____

9-2 Classify and Measure Angles

Name _____ Date _____

Angles:	Acute Angle	Right Angle	Obtuse Angle	Straight Angle	Reflex Angle
	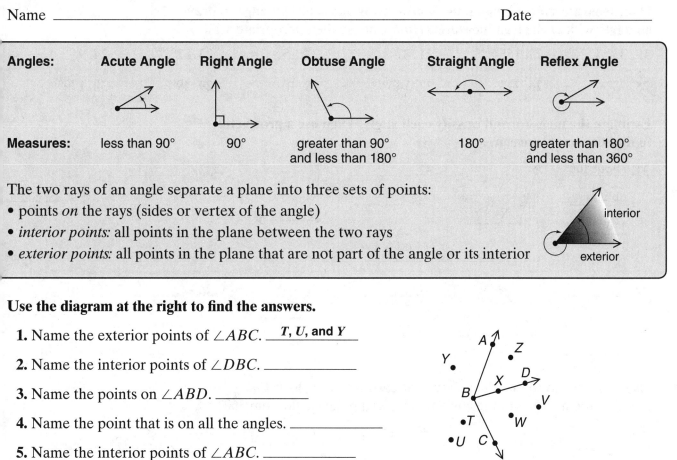				
Measures:	less than 90°	90°	greater than 90° and less than 180°	180°	greater than 180° and less than 360°

The two rays of an angle separate a plane into three sets of points:
- points *on* the rays (sides or vertex of the angle)
- *interior points:* all points in the plane between the two rays
- *exterior points:* all points in the plane that are not part of the angle or its interior

interior

exterior

Use the diagram at the right to find the answers.

1. Name the exterior points of ∠ABC. __T, U, and Y__

2. Name the interior points of ∠DBC. _____

3. Name the points on ∠ABD. _____

4. Name the point that is on all the angles. _____

5. Name the interior points of ∠ABC. _____

6. Name the exterior points of ∠ABD. _____

7. Name the interior points of ∠ABC that are also exterior points of ∠ABD. _____

Use the figure at the right for exercises 8–12.

8. ∠TSW is an ___obtuse___ angle.

9. Name a straight angle. _____

10. Name two different obtuse angles. _____

11. Name a right angle. _____

12. Name two different acute angles. _____

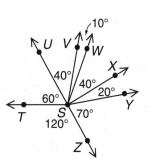

Use the protractor to identify the angle measure.
(*Hint:* Choose the appropriate scale.)

13. ∠AOB __35°__   14. ∠DOG _____

15. ∠GOB _____   16. ∠GOF _____

17. ∠BOE _____   18. ∠COF _____

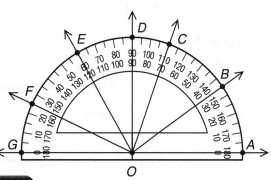

On a separate sheet of paper, use a protractor and a straightedge to draw
an angle with each given measure. (*Hint:* Choose the appropriate scale.)

19. 33°   **20.** 155°   **21.** 87°   **22.** 15°   **23.** 32°   **24.** 9°

25. 73°   **26.** 27°   **27.** 146°   **28.** 101°   **29.** 49°   **30.** 179°

Estimate the measure and classify each angle. Then use a protractor
to find the actual measure.

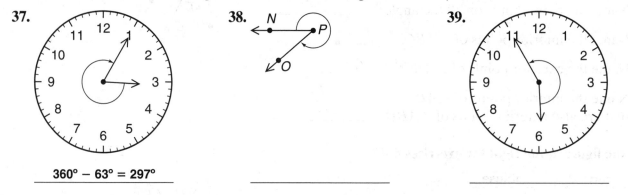

31. about 100°

obtuse

110°

32. _____

_____

33. _____

_____

34. _____

_____

35. _____

_____

36. _____

_____

Use a protractor to find the measure of each reflex angle. (*Hint:*
Subtract the measure of the angle that is *not* a reflex angle from 360°.)

37.

360° − 63° = 297°

38.

_____

39.

_____

Solve. (*Hint:* The minute hand of an analog clock rotates 360° every hour.)

40. Through how many degrees does the minute
hand rotate in 5 minutes? _____

41. Between 2:20 and 2:45, how many degrees
does the minute hand rotate? _____

42. What is the measure of the reflex angle
shown by the hands of a clock at 4:00? _____

43. About how many degrees are shown by the
hands of a clock at 2:20? _____

MENTAL MATH

44. Find each sum or difference using mental math.

   a. 90 + 85   **b.** 360 − 90   **c.** 90 + 45 + 30   **d.** 140 − 55   **e.** 180 − 105

   _____   _____   _____   _____   _____

9-3 Angle Pairs

Name _____ Date _____

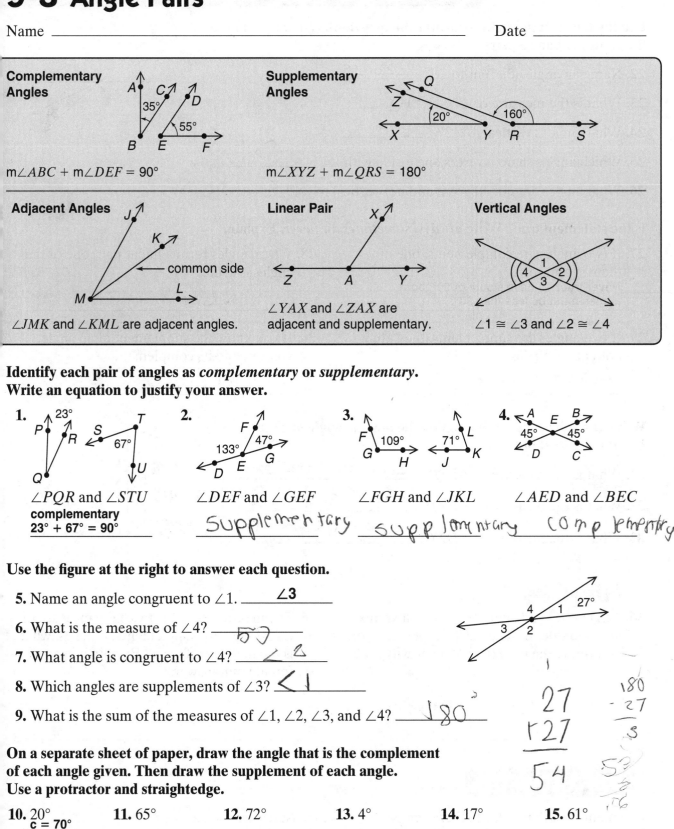

Complementary Angles

$m\angle ABC + m\angle DEF = 90°$

Supplementary Angles

$m\angle XYZ + m\angle QRS = 180°$

Adjacent Angles

$\angle JMK$ and $\angle KML$ are adjacent angles.

Linear Pair

$\angle YAX$ and $\angle ZAX$ are adjacent and supplementary.

Vertical Angles

$\angle 1 \cong \angle 3$ and $\angle 2 \cong \angle 4$

**Identify each pair of angles as *complementary* or *supplementary*.
Write an equation to justify your answer.**

1. $\angle PQR$ and $\angle STU$
complementary
$23° + 67° = 90°$

2. $\angle DEF$ and $\angle GEF$
Supplementary

3. $\angle FGH$ and $\angle JKL$
supplementary

4. $\angle AED$ and $\angle BEC$
complementary

Use the figure at the right to answer each question.

5. Name an angle congruent to $\angle 1$. ____$\angle 3$____

6. What is the measure of $\angle 4$? ____53____

7. What angle is congruent to $\angle 4$? ____$\angle 2$____

8. Which angles are supplements of $\angle 3$? ____$\angle 1$____

9. What is the sum of the measures of $\angle 1$, $\angle 2$, $\angle 3$, and $\angle 4$? ____180____

```
      1
   27      180
  r27     - 27
  ____      3
   54     53
```

**On a separate sheet of paper, draw the angle that is the complement
of each angle given. Then draw the supplement of each angle.
Use a protractor and straightedge.**

10. 20°
c = 70°
s = 160°

11. 65°

12. 72°

13. 4°

14. 17°

15. 61°

16. 83°

17. 24°

18. 69°

19. 19°

20. 6°

21. 45°

Use the figure at the right to answer the questions. (*Hint:* First mark the congruent angle pairs.)

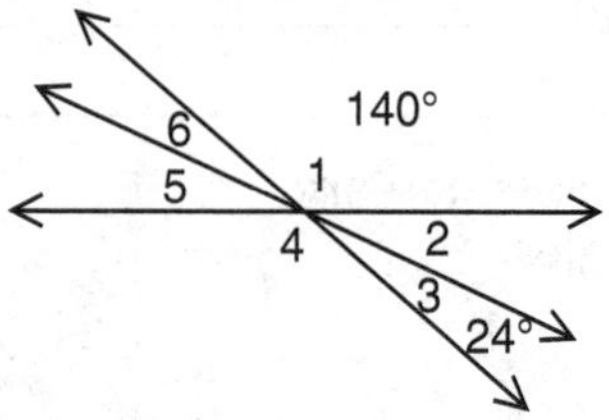

22. Name an angle adjacent to ∠1. <u>∠2 or ∠6</u>

23. What is the measure of ∠2? <u>40°</u>

24. What angle is vertical to ∠3? <u>< 5</u>

25. Which angles share a vertex and a side with ∠3? <u>< 6</u>

26. What angles are not adjacent and not vertical to ∠1? <u>< 6, 5, 2, 3</u>

Is the statement true? Write *always*, *sometimes*, or *never*. Explain.

27. If two angles are complements, one of them is obtuse.
Never true; To have a sum of 90°, both angles must be less than 90°.

28. When angles form a linear pair, one of the angles is acute.
<u>sometimes</u>

29. If two angles are supplements, they are both acute angles.
<u>sometimes</u>

30. If you know the supplement of an angle, you can find its complement.
<u>always</u>

Write and solve an equation to find the missing angle measure. Use the figure at the right.

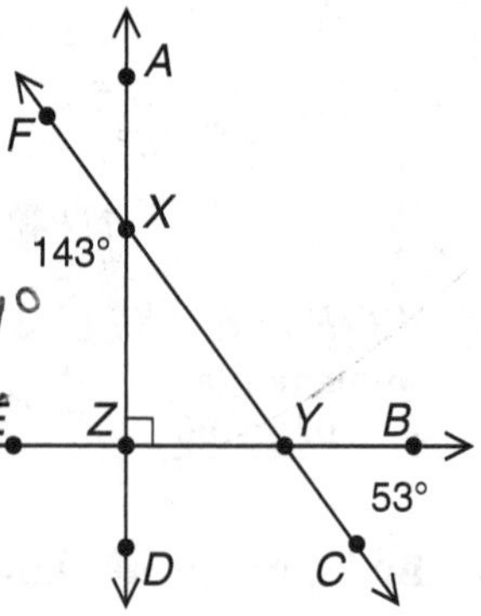

31. What is the measure of ∠FYB? <u>m∠FYB = 180° − 53° = 127°</u>

32. What is the measure of ∠EZD? <u>m < EZD = 180−143= 87°</u>

33. What is the measure of ∠DXC? <u>m< DXC = 180 −53= 127°</u>

Problem Solving

34. Angle *HKJ* and angle *JKL* share a vertex and one side. If the m∠*JKL* is 38°, can you determine the m∠*HKJ*? Why or why not?

35. The measure of ∠1 is twice the measure of ∠2. If they are supplementary angles, what is the measure of each? Explain how you found your answer.

MENTAL MATH

Use mental math to tell whether each pair of angle measures are *complements*, *supplements*, or *neither*.

36. 37°, 63°   **37.** 101°, 79°   **38.** 45°, 90°   **39.** 116°, 84°   **40.** 23°, 67°   **41.** 57°, 123°

9-4 Parallel Lines and Transversals

Name _____ Date _____

In the figure, line *c* ∥ line *f* and line *a* is a transversal.

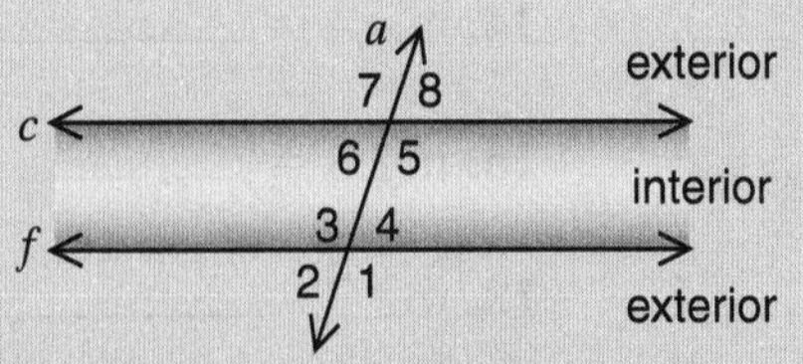

Corresponding Angles

∠1 and ∠5 ⟶ ∠1 ≅ ∠5
∠2 and ∠6 ⟶ ∠2 ≅ ∠6
∠3 and ∠7 ⟶ ∠3 ≅ ∠7
∠4 and ∠8 ⟶ ∠4 ≅ ∠8

Alternate Interior Angles

∠3 and ∠5 ⟶ ∠3 ≅ ∠5
∠4 and ∠6 ⟶ ∠4 ≅ ∠6

Alternate Exterior Angles

∠1 and ∠7 ⟶ ∠1 ≅ ∠7
∠2 and ∠8 ⟶ ∠2 ≅ ∠8

Use the figure at the right to answer exercises 1–5. $\overrightarrow{NO}$ ∥ $\overrightarrow{PQ}$.

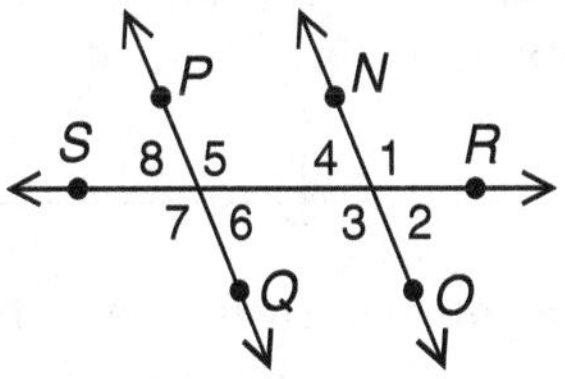

1. Which line is the transversal? _____ $\overrightarrow{RS}$ _____

2. List the exterior angles. _____

3. Which angle makes a pair of corresponding angles with ∠1? _____

4. What is the relationship between ∠2 and ∠4?   5. What is the relationship between ∠5 and ∠6?

_____   _____

Use the figure at the right to answer each question.
Note: line $\overleftrightarrow{UV}$ ∥ line $\overleftrightarrow{WX}$.

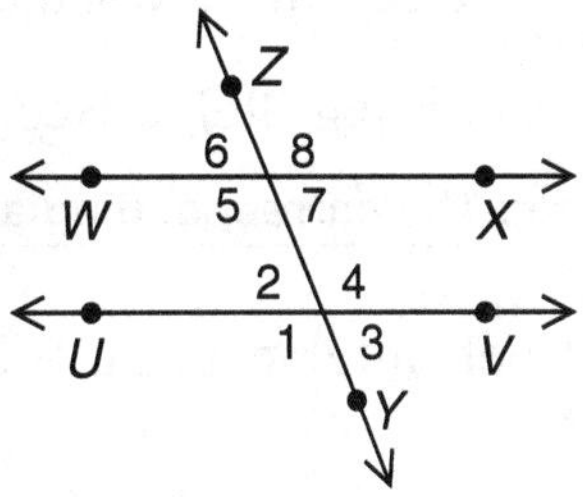

6. Which angles are alternate exterior angles?

   ∠1 and ∠8; ∠3 and ∠6

7. Which angles are alternate interior angles?   8. What is the sum of the measures of ∠1, ∠2, ∠3, and ∠4?

_____   _____

Use matching angle marks to indicate which angles are congruent.

9. line $\overleftrightarrow{AB}$ ∥ line $\overleftrightarrow{CD}$ 10. line *r* ∥ line *s* 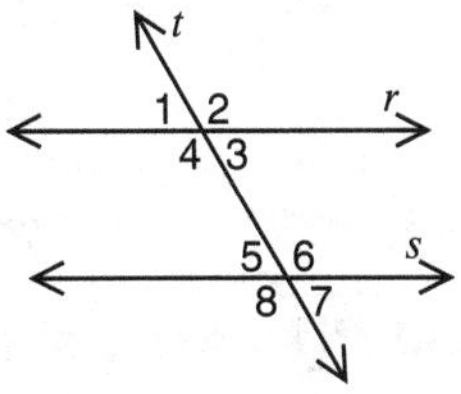   11. line $\overleftrightarrow{LM}$ ∥ line $\overleftrightarrow{NO}$

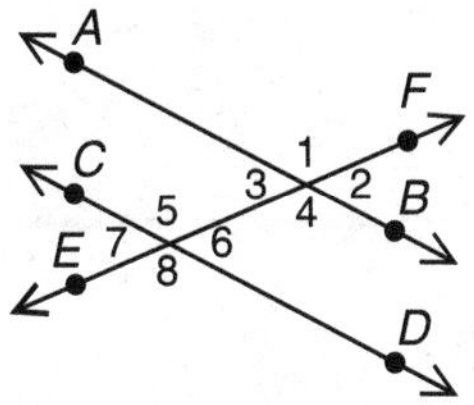

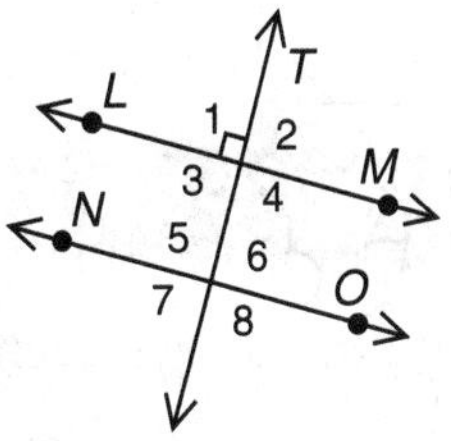

12. **Explain** What rule can you write about how many congruent angles are created when a transversal intersects a pair of parallel lines?

_____

Use the figure at the right to answer the questions.
Line $a \parallel$ line b, line $c \perp$ line a, and m∠1 = 115°.

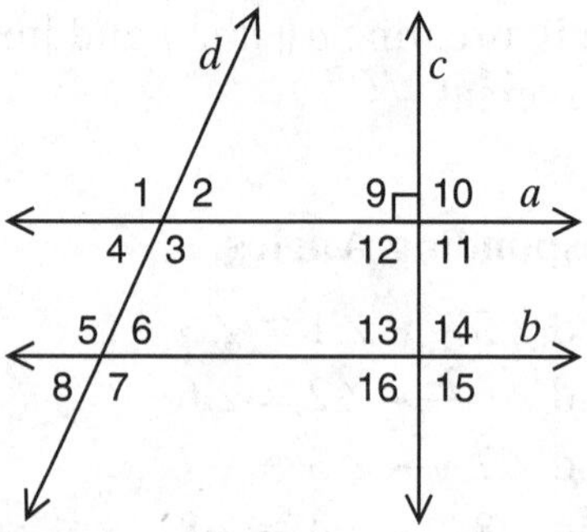

13. m∠2 = ____65°____   **14.** m∠4 = _____

15. m∠15 = _____   **16.** m∠8 = _____

17. m∠11 = _____   **18.** m∠7 = _____

19. The sum of m∠5 and   **20.** The sum of m∠3, m∠6, m∠12,
    m∠6 = _____.   and m∠13 is _____.

Is the statement true? Write *always, sometimes,* or *never.* Explain.

21. Exterior angles on the same side of the
    transversal are complementary.

_____

22. Vertical angles are complementary.

_____

23. The intersection of any two lines makes
    four angles whose sum is 360°.

_____

24. Interior angles on the same side of the
    transversal are supplementary.

_____

Solve. Use the street map at the right to answer the questions.
(*Hint:* All the streets are the same width.)

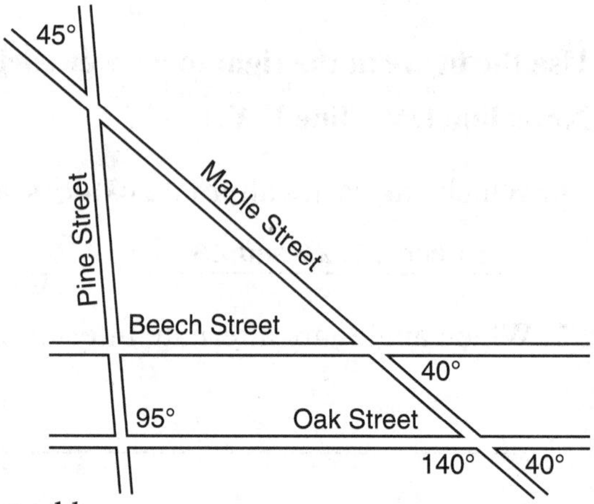

25. What street is parallel to Beech Street? Explain.

    Oak Street; The corresponding angles are congruent.

26. What streets intersect Maple Street?

_____

27. Is Pine Street perpendicular to Oak Street? Explain.

_____

28. Find the angle measures inside the three-sided shape formed by
    the intersections of Maple, Beech, and Pine streets. Then write
    an equation to find the sum of the measures. _____

TEST PREPARATION

Use the figure to answer each question. $\overleftrightarrow{NO}$ and $\overleftrightarrow{PQ}$ are parallel and m∠1 = 75°.

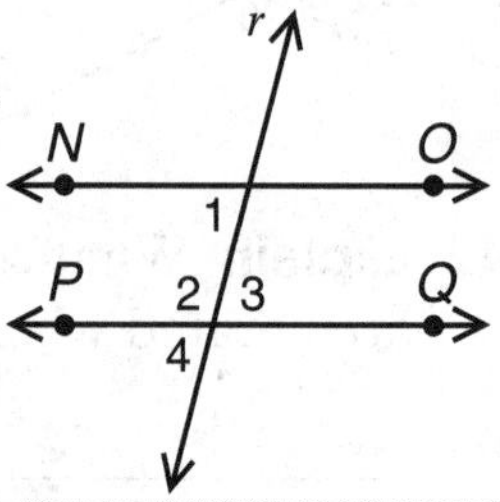

29. What is m∠2?

   A. 75°   **C.** 85°

   B. 105°   **D.** 110°

30. What is m∠3?

   F. 75°   **H.** 85°

   G. 105°   **J.** 180°

9-5 Congruent Angles and Line Segments

Name _____ Date _____

Construct the *perpendicular bisector of the line segment.*

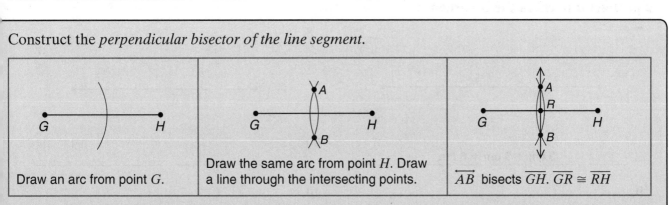

| Draw an arc from point G. | Draw the same arc from point H. Draw a line through the intersecting points. | $\overleftrightarrow{AB}$ bisects $\overline{GH}$. $\overline{GR} \cong \overline{RH}$ |

Construct the *bisector of the angle.*

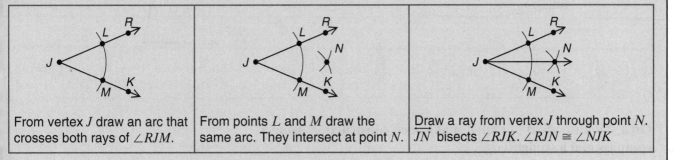

| From vertex J draw an arc that crosses both rays of ∠RJM. | From points L and M draw the same arc. They intersect at point N. | Draw a ray from vertex J through point N. $\overrightarrow{JN}$ bisects ∠RJK. ∠RJN ≅ ∠NJK |

Use the diagram at the right to answer each exercise.

1. Name two pairs of congruent line segments. $\underline{\overline{JK} \text{ and } \overline{ML}; \overline{JM} \text{ and } \overline{KL}}$

2. Name two pairs of congruent angles. _____

3. Suppose that a line bisects $\overline{KL}$ at point S. What

   can you say about line segments $\overline{KS}$ and $\overline{SL}$? _____

4. Suppose that $\overrightarrow{MT}$ bisects ∠JML. Name the

   congruent angles formed. _____

Mark the congruent sides with matching tick marks. Mark congruent angles with matching angle marks. Then name the congruent parts.

5.

6.

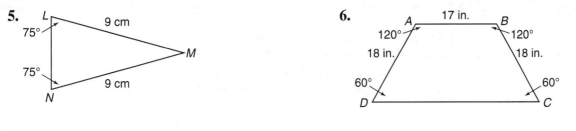

_____   _____

Bisect each segment and angle. Then use a metric ruler and
a protractor to check the congruence.

7.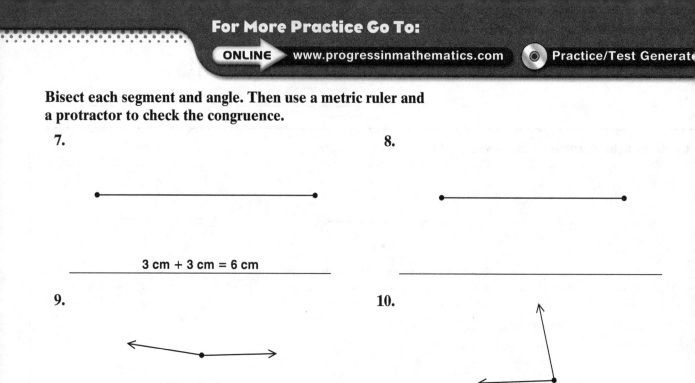

8.

3 cm + 3 cm = 6 cm

9.

10.

On a separate sheet of paper, make each construction using a
compass and a straightedge.

11. **a.** Draw an obtuse angle, ∠EFG.
    b. Bisect the angle.
    c. Label the congruent angles formed.

12. **a.** Draw a line segment, $\overline{HJ}$.
    b. Construct its perpendicular bisector, and
        label the intersection point Q.
    c. Identify the congruent line segments
        formed.

13. **a.** Draw two circles.
    b. Mark three points on each circle, and
        connect the points to make a triangle
        inside each circle.
    c. Construct the perpendicular bisector of
        each side on both triangles.

    d. Do the perpendicular
        bisectors of the sides intersect? _____
    e. Compare the locations of the intersection
        points of the perpendicular bisectors in
        both circles.

WRITE ABOUT IT

14. On a separate sheet of paper use a protractor to draw a triangle with
    three 60° angles. Use a compass to bisect each of the angles. Then
    mark the line segments that are congruent. What do you notice about
    where each angle bisector crosses the opposite side of this triangle?

9-6 Line Constructions

Name _____ Date _____

To construct a line perpendicular to $\overleftrightarrow{MN}$ through point A:

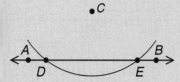

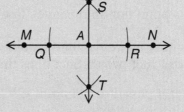

From point A draw the same arc twice on $\overleftrightarrow{MN}$.
Label points Q and R.

From points Q and R draw two intersecting arcs.
Label points S and T. Draw $\overleftrightarrow{ST}$.

To construct a line perpendicular to $\overleftrightarrow{AB}$ through point C:

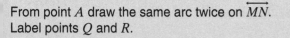

Draw an arc from point C.
Label points D and E.

Draw two intersecting arcs from points D and E.
Label point F. Draw $\overleftrightarrow{CF}$.

To construct a line parallel to $\overrightarrow{RS}$ through point K:

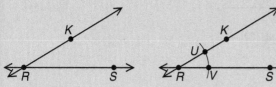 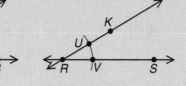 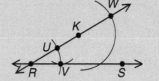 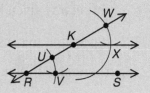

Draw $\overrightarrow{RK}$.

Make an arc from point R.
Label points U and V.

Make an arc from point K.
Label point W.

Copy arc UV from point W.
Draw $\overleftrightarrow{KX} \parallel \overleftrightarrow{RS}$.

Copy each. Use a compass and straightedge to complete each construction.

1. Construct a line perpendicular to line s through point K.

2. Construct a line perpendicular to line m through point D.

3. Construct a line parallel to line z through point N.

Answer each question *yes* or *no*. If *yes*, sketch an example on a separate sheet of paper. If *no*, explain why not.

4. Is it possible to construct a line that is perpendicular to any given line through a point not on the given line? _____**Yes**_____

5. Suppose you have a line *AB*, and a point *C* not on line *AB*. Is it possible to construct two distinct lines that are perpendicular to line *AB* and that pass through point *C*? _____

6. Is it possible to construct a perpendicular line that bisects a line?

   _____

7. Is it possible to construct a line that is parallel to any given line and that passes through a point that is not on the given line? _____

8. Is it possible to construct more than one line that is parallel to any given line? _____

9. Is it possible to construct a perpendicular line that bisects a line segment? _____

10. Is it possible to construct an infinite number of lines through a point on any given line? _____

11. Is it possible to construct an infinite number of lines that are perpendicular to any given line? _____

On a separate sheet of paper, use a compass and a straightedge to complete each construction.

12. Draw a line *g*. Draw and label a point *B* not on line *g*. Construct a line parallel to line *g* through point *B*.

13. Draw a line *c*. Draw and label a point *D* not on line *c*. Construct a line perpendicular to line *c* through point *D*.

CHALLENGE

14. How can you use only a compass and a straightedge to construct square *ABCD*?

   _____

   _____

   _____

   _____

9-7 Polygons

Name _____ Date _____

Find the sum of the interior angle measures of the polygon.

Start at a vertex and draw all possible diagonals.	Count the number of triangles formed. It is two less than the number of sides.	Then multiply the number of triangles by 180°. The sum of the interior angles of a triangle is 180°.
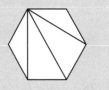	number of sides → number of triangles ← $6 - 2 = 4$	$4 \cdot 180° = \mathbf{720°}$

The sum of the interior angles of the hexagon is 720°.

Find the measure of one angle in a regular hexagon.

Use this formula to find the measure of one angle in a regular polygon:

sum of the angle measures →
number of sides of a polygon →
$$\frac{(n - 2) \cdot 180°}{n} \rightarrow \frac{(6 - 2) \cdot 180°}{6} = \frac{720°}{6} = 120°$$

One angle of the regular hexagon has a measure of 120°.

Write the meaning of each prefix used to name polygons.

1. tri- __3__
2. penta- _____
3. octa- _____
4. hepta- _____

5. deca- _____
6. nona- _____
7. hexa- _____
8. quadri- _____

Complete the tables.

	Figure	Number of Sides	Number of Angles
9.	_____	3	3
10.	_____	4	4
11.	_____	5	_____
12.	hexagon	_____	_____

	Figure	Number of Sides	Number of Angles
13.	_____	7	_____
14.	_____	8	_____
15.	nonagon	_____	_____
16.	_____	10	_____

Find the missing angle measure(s) for each triangle.

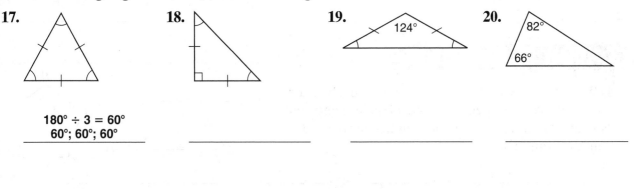

17.

18.

19. 124°

20. 82° 66°

$180° \div 3 = 60°$
$60°; 60°; 60°$

_____   _____   _____

Find the sum of the interior angles for each polygon.
(*Hint:* Draw diagonals from one vertex to form triangles.)

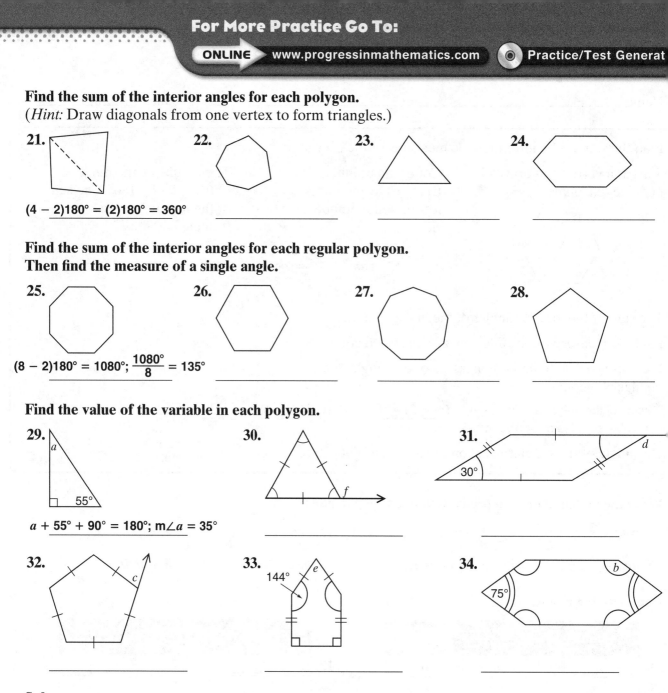

21.

$(4 - 2)180° = (2)180° = 360°$

22.

23.

24.

Find the sum of the interior angles for each regular polygon.
Then find the measure of a single angle.

25.

$(8 - 2)180° = 1080°; \dfrac{1080°}{8} = 135°$

26.

27.

28.

Find the value of the variable in each polygon.

29.

a

$55°$

$a + 55° + 90° = 180°; \; m\angle a = 35°$

30.

f

31.

$30°$

d

32.

c

33.

$144°$ e

34.

$75°$

b

Solve.

35. Find the measure of each interior angle of a regular nonagon.

36. If the sum of the measures of a regular polygon is 1800°, how many sides does the polygon have?

CRITICAL THINKING

37. Is there a difference between the sums of the interior angles of a concave pentagon and a regular pentagon? Is your answer true for all polygons in concave and convex forms? Explain.

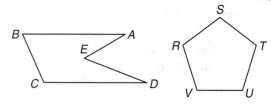

9-8 Triangles

Name _____   Date _____

You can classify triangles by the measures of their angles.

Acute Triangles
three acute angles

Obtuse Triangles
one obtuse angle

Right Triangles
one right angle

You can classify triangles by the lengths of their sides.

Equilateral triangles
all sides congruent

Isosceles triangles
two sides congruent

Scalene triangles
no sides congruent

To find the range of
possible lengths for $\overline{AB}$,
use the Triangle Inequality
Theorem.

Solve for $m\overline{AB}$.

$$m\overline{AB} < 5 + 9 \longrightarrow m\overline{AB} < 14$$
$$m\overline{AB} > 9 - 5 \longrightarrow m\overline{AB} > 4$$

So the length for $\overline{AB}$ is between 4 cm and 14 cm, or 4 cm $< m\overline{AB} <$ 14 cm.

Classify each triangle by angles and sides.

1.

obtuse triangle
scalene triangle
_____

2.

_____

3.

_____

4.

_____

The measure of two of the three angles of a triangle are given. Find the measure of the remaining angle. Then classify the triangle by its angles.

5. 30°, 65°,
$180° - (30° + 65°) = 85°$
acute triangle
_____

6. 73°, 37°,

_____

7. 60°, 60°,

_____

8. 108°, 32°,

_____

9. 56°, 19°,

_____

10. 30°, 30°,

_____

11. 90°, 45°,

_____

12. 100°, 36°,

_____

**Can each set of side lengths given be used to form a triangle?
Write *Yes* or *No*. Explain.**

13. 2 m, 6 m, 9 m

No; 2 + 6 < 9
_____

14. 3 cm, 5 cm, 11 cm

_____

15. 4 ft, 7 ft, 8 ft

_____

16. 8 cm, 10 cm, 16 cm

_____

17. 5.3 in., 9.3 in.,
15.2 in.

_____

18. 7.1 cm, 8.4 cm,
9.7 cm

_____

19. 9.6 in., 10.2 in.,
20.3 in.

_____

20. 6.6 ft, 10.4 ft, 17.5 ft

_____

Apply the Triangle Inequality Theorem to find the range of possible lengths for the third side of each triangle.

21. m $\overline{BC}$ = 4 units, m $\overline{AC}$ = 8 units

m $\overline{AB}$ < 4 + 8 ⟶ 12

m $\overline{AB}$ > 8 − 4 ⟶ 4; 4 units < m $\overline{AB}$ < 12 units

22. m $\overline{AB}$ = 6 units, m $\overline{AC}$ = 9 units

_____

23. m $\overline{AB}$ = 3.5 units, m $\overline{AC}$ = 6.8 units

_____

24. m $\overline{BC}$ = $6\frac{1}{4}$ units, m $\overline{AC}$ = $8\frac{2}{3}$ units

_____

True or false? If *false*, rewrite as a true statement.

25. An isosceles triangle can be a right triangle.

True

26. Every right triangle has an obtuse angle.

_____

27. An equilateral triangle is a right triangle.

_____

28. All acute triangles have three congruent sides.

_____

Use letters in the figure at the right to identify as many of each kind of triangle as possible.

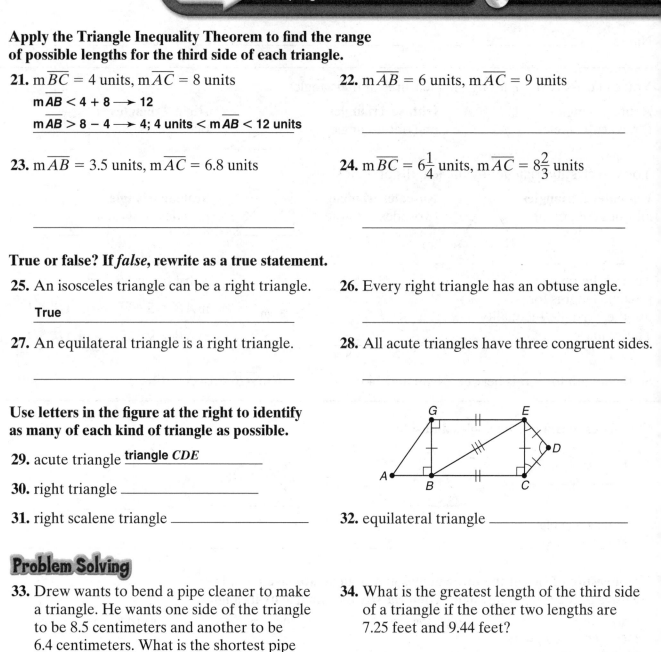

29. acute triangle triangle *CDE*

30. right triangle _____

31. right scalene triangle _____

32. equilateral triangle _____

Problem Solving

33. Drew wants to bend a pipe cleaner to make a triangle. He wants one side of the triangle to be 8.5 centimeters and another to be 6.4 centimeters. What is the shortest pipe cleaner Drew can use to make his triangle?

_____

34. What is the greatest length of the third side of a triangle if the other two lengths are 7.25 feet and 9.44 feet?

_____

SPIRAL REVIEW

Use a protractor to find the measure of each angle. Classify each as *acute, obtuse,* or *straight.*

35.

36.

_____   _____

9-9 Congruent Triangles

Name _____ Date _____

To identify congruent triangles, use one of these statements:

Side-Side-Side (SSS)
All 3 pairs of corresponding sides are congruent.

Side-Angle-Side (SAS)
Two pairs of corresponding sides and the included angles are congruent.

Angle-Side-Angle (ASA)
Two pairs of corresponding angles and the included sides are congruent.

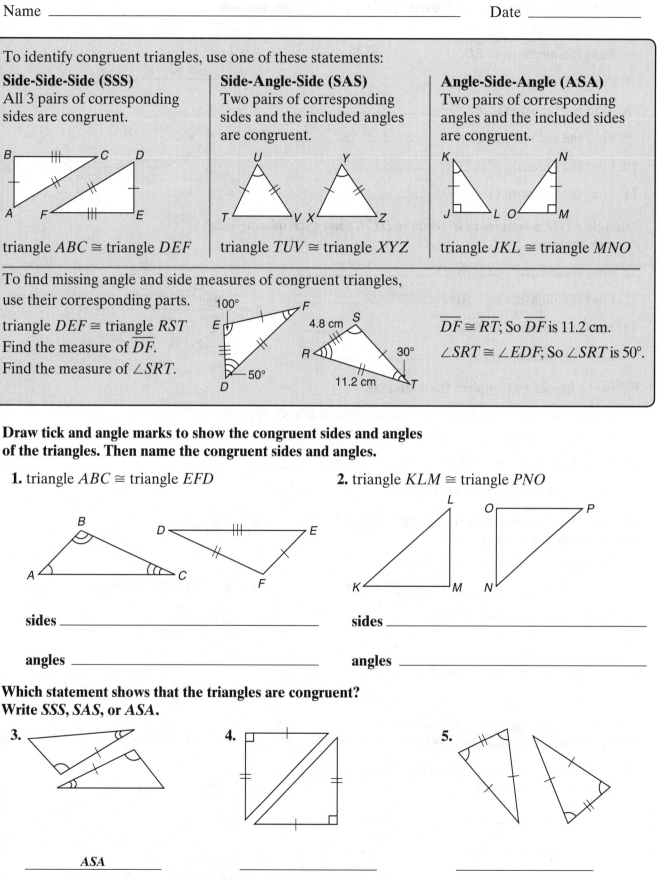

triangle $ABC \cong$ triangle DEF | triangle $TUV \cong$ triangle XYZ | triangle $JKL \cong$ triangle MNO

To find missing angle and side measures of congruent triangles, use their corresponding parts.

triangle $DEF \cong$ triangle RST
Find the measure of $\overline{DF}$.
Find the measure of $\angle SRT$.

100°
4.8 cm
30°
50°
11.2 cm

$\overline{DF} \cong \overline{RT}$; So $\overline{DF}$ is 11.2 cm.
$\angle SRT \cong \angle EDF$; So $\angle SRT$ is 50°.

Draw tick and angle marks to show the congruent sides and angles of the triangles. Then name the congruent sides and angles.

1. triangle $ABC \cong$ triangle EFD

2. triangle $KLM \cong$ triangle PNO

sides _____

angles _____

sides _____

angles _____

Which statement shows that the triangles are congruent? Write SSS, SAS, or ASA.

3.

4.

5.

_____ASA_____

_____

_____

Triangle *RJZ* is congruent to triangle *PFD*. Find each missing side or angle measure.

6. Find the measure of $\overline{FD}$. _____**21 in.**_____

7. Find the measure of $\overline{RZ}$. _____

8. Find the measure of $\overline{PF}$. _____

9. Find the measure of $\angle JRZ$. _____

10. Find the measure of $\angle FDP$. _____

11. Find the measure of $\angle PFD$. _____

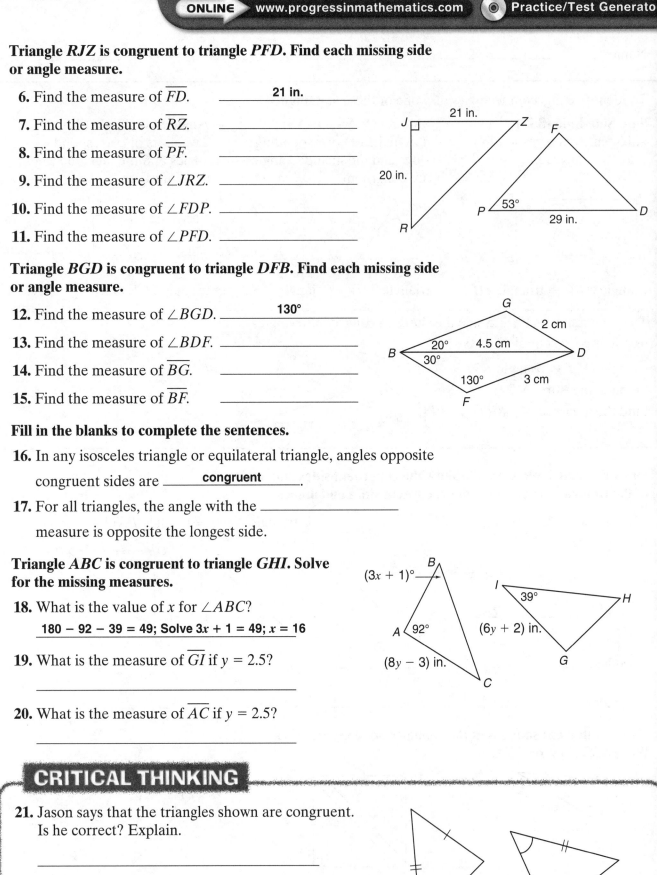

Triangle *BGD* is congruent to triangle *DFB*. Find each missing side or angle measure.

12. Find the measure of $\angle BGD$. _____**130°**_____

13. Find the measure of $\angle BDF$. _____

14. Find the measure of $\overline{BG}$. _____

15. Find the measure of $\overline{BF}$. _____

Fill in the blanks to complete the sentences.

16. In any isosceles triangle or equilateral triangle, angles opposite

    congruent sides are _____**congruent**_____.

17. For all triangles, the angle with the _____

    measure is opposite the longest side.

Triangle *ABC* is congruent to triangle *GHI*. Solve for the missing measures.

18. What is the value of *x* for $\angle ABC$?

    **180 − 92 − 39 = 49; Solve 3x + 1 = 49; x = 16**

19. What is the measure of $\overline{GI}$ if *y* = 2.5?

    _____

20. What is the measure of $\overline{AC}$ if *y* = 2.5?

    _____

CRITICAL THINKING

21. Jason says that the triangles shown are congruent.
    Is he correct? Explain.

    _____

    _____

    _____

9-10 Triangle Constructions

Name _____   Date _____

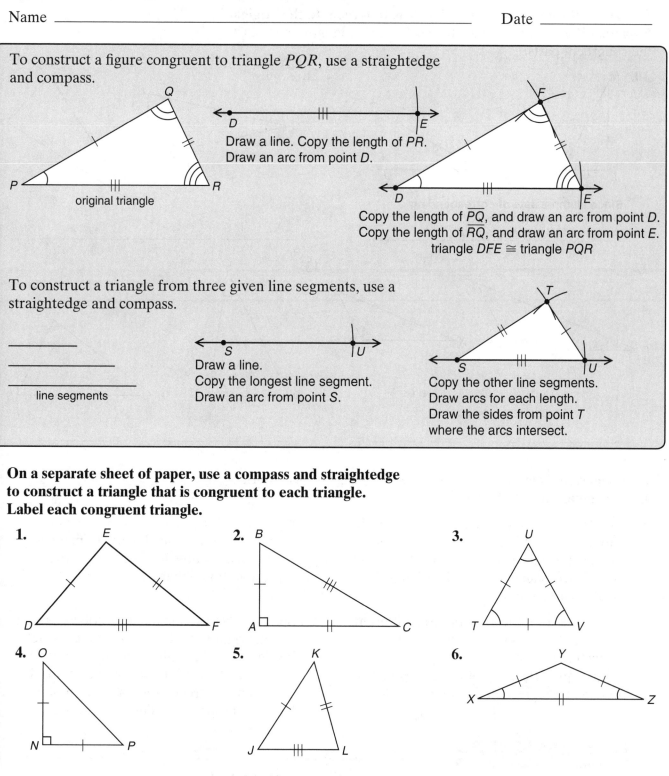

To construct a figure congruent to triangle *PQR*, use a straightedge and compass.

original triangle

Draw a line. Copy the length of *PR*.
Draw an arc from point *D*.

Copy the length of $\overline{PQ}$, and draw an arc from point *D*.
Copy the length of $\overline{RQ}$, and draw an arc from point *E*.
triangle *DFE* ≅ triangle *PQR*

To construct a triangle from three given line segments, use a straightedge and compass.

_____
_____
_____
line segments

Draw a line.
Copy the longest line segment.
Draw an arc from point *S*.

Copy the other line segments.
Draw arcs for each length.
Draw the sides from point *T*
where the arcs intersect.

**On a separate sheet of paper, use a compass and straightedge
to construct a triangle that is congruent to each triangle.
Label each congruent triangle.**

1.   2.   3.

4.   5.   6.

**On a separate sheet of paper, use a compass and straightedge to construct
a triangle from each set of line segments. Label each triangle.**

7. _____   8. _____   9. _____
   _____   _____   _____
   _____   _____   _____

Determine if each constructed triangle is congruent to the original.
Explain. (*Hint:* Use a compass to check the side lengths, and mark the congruent parts.)

10.

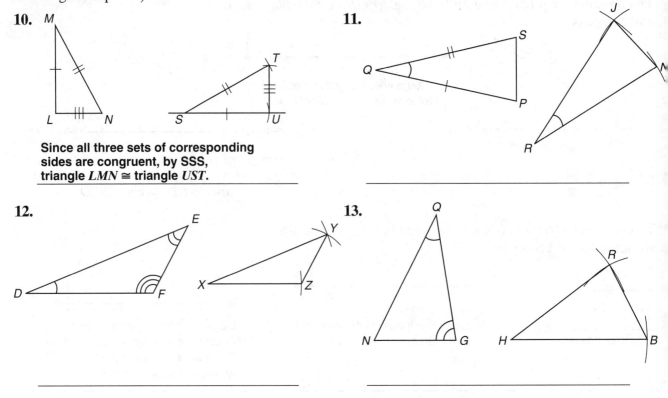

Since all three sets of corresponding sides are congruent, by SSS, triangle *LMN* ≅ triangle *UST*.

11.

12.

13.

On a separate sheet of paper, make the following constructions.
Use a compass and straightedge.

14. Charlie wants to restore a triangular border pattern on an old floor. The sides of each triangle are 3.6 cm, 6.8 cm and 7.9 cm. Show how Charlie can construct the triangle he needs to do the job.

15. Katie uses three pipe cleaners *a*, *b*, and *c*, that are all the same length, to make a triangle. Show how Katie can construct a representation of her triangle.

16. Sanjin uses pipe cleaners of three different sizes, 2*x*, 3*x*, and 4*x*, to make triangles. Draw three line segments proportional to Sanjin's pipe cleaners. Show how Sanjin can construct a representation of his triangle.

17. Sofia wants to create a pattern of congruent scalene right triangles for the 3-inch wide border strip of a quilt. The longest side of each triangle needs to be 4 inches. Show how Sofia can construct a representation of her border strip pattern using four triangles.

SPIRAL REVIEW

18. Find the measures of ∠*A* and ∠*B* in the regular octagon.

m ∠*A* = _____

m ∠*B* = _____

9-11 Quadrilaterals

Name _____ Date _____

To classify quadrilaterals, you can use the special properties
of their sides and angles.

Parallelogram
two pairs of parallel sides

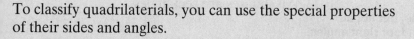

$\overline{AB} \parallel \overline{DC}; \overline{BC} \parallel \overline{AD}$

Rectangle
parallelogram with four
right angles

$\overline{EF} \parallel \overline{HG}; \overline{FG} \parallel \overline{EH}$

Rhombus
parallelogram with four
congruent sides

$\overline{IJ} \parallel \overline{LK}; \overline{JK} \parallel \overline{IL}$

Square
parallelogram with four right
angles and four congruent sides

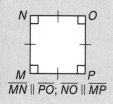

$\overline{MN} \parallel \overline{PO}; \overline{NO} \parallel \overline{MP}$

Trapezoid
exactly one pair of
parallel sides

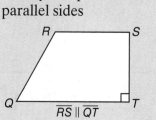

$\overline{RS} \parallel \overline{QT}$

Kite
two pairs
of adjacent
congruent
sides

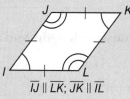

List all possible quadrilaterals for each description.

1. four right angles

   rectangle and square

2. four sides

_____

3. two pairs of congruent sides

_____

4. exactly one pair of parallel sides

_____

5. four congruent sides

_____

6. four congruent sides and four congruent angles

_____

7. two pairs of parallel sides

_____

8. two pairs of adjacent sides that are congruent

_____

**List all possible names for each figure. Then circle the name that
best describes it.**

9.

10.

11.

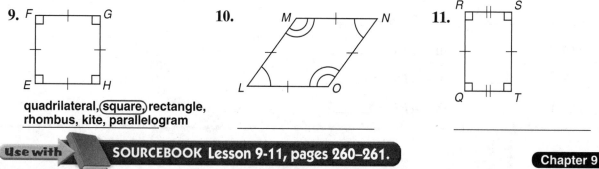

quadrilateral, (square) rectangle,
rhombus, kite, parallelogram

_____

_____

Tell whether each statement is *true* or *false*. If the statement is false, explain why.

12. All quadrilaterals are rectangles.
False; All rectangles are quadrilaterals, but not all quadrilaterals are parallelograms with four right angles.

13. All squares are rectangles.

14. A trapezoid can be a parallelogram.

15. Every kite is a rhombus.

List the missing lengths and angle measures for each figure.

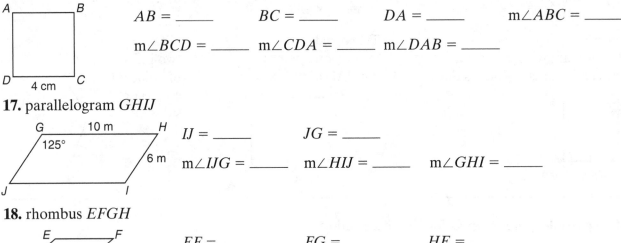

16. square *ABCD*

$AB =$ _____ $BC =$ _____ $DA =$ _____ $m\angle ABC =$ _____

$m\angle BCD =$ _____ $m\angle CDA =$ _____ $m\angle DAB =$ _____

17. parallelogram *GHIJ*

$IJ =$ _____ $JG =$ _____

$m\angle IJG =$ _____ $m\angle HIJ =$ _____ $m\angle GHI =$ _____

18. rhombus *EFGH*

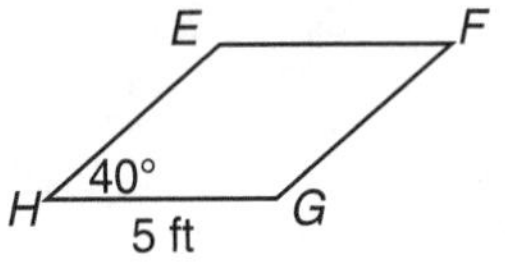

$EF =$ _____ $FG =$ _____ $HE =$ _____

$m\angle EFG =$ _____ $m\angle FGH =$ _____ $m\angle HEF =$ _____

Solve. Show your work.

19. A group of students wants to make a flag. Some want it to be a rectangle, some a kite, and others a rhombus. Can the group make a flag that will be all three shapes?

20. Petra made a kite to fly at the beach. It has a perimeter of 40 inches. One side of the kite measures 12 inches. What are the other side lengths?

CHALLENGE

21. Classify the figure at the right. Then find the unknown angle measures.

classification _____ $m\angle CDB =$ _____

$m\angle DAB =$ _____ $m\angle DBC =$ _____

$m\angle ABD =$ _____ $m\angle ADC =$ _____

$m\angle BDA =$ _____ $m\angle ABC =$ _____

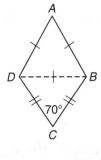

9-12 Circles

Name _____   Date _____

The dotted circle and the solid circle are
concentric circles with the same center.
The dotted circle, circle *G*, is *inscribed* in the square *XURZ*.
The square *XURZ* is *circumscribed* by the solid circle, *G*.

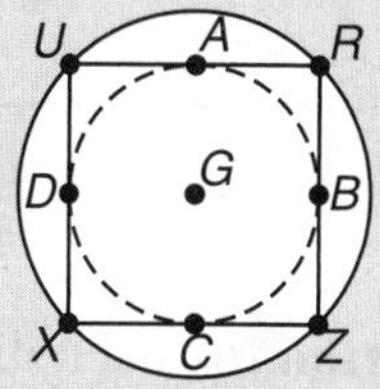

Look at circle *L*.

$\overline{LS}$ is a radius.
$\overline{TS}$ is a chord.
$\overline{PS}$ is a diameter.
$\overarc{RST}$ is a semicircle, 180°.
$\overarc{PGR}$ is a minor arc of 90°.
$\overarc{RSP}$ is a major arc of 270°.

∠*RLS* is a central angle.
∠*RTS* is an inscribed angle of 45°.
A sector of circle *L* is shaded.
$\overrightarrow{PH}$ is a tangent.
$\overleftrightarrow{GF}$ is a secant.

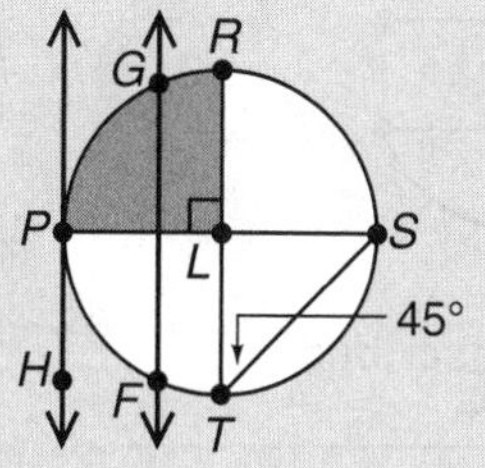

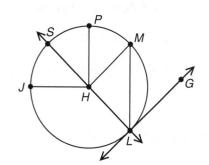

Use circle *H* to answer the exercises.

1. Name a diameter. __*SL*__

2. Name a chord. _____

3. Name the center. _____

4. Shade in a sector. _____

5. Name a radius. _____   6. Name a major arc. _____

7. Name a minor arc. _____   8. Name a semicircle. _____

9. Name an inscribed angle. _____   10. Name a central angle. _____

11. Name a secant. _____   12. Name a tangent. _____

**The measure of an inscribed angle is half of the central angle that forms
the same arc. Use circle *P* to find the measure of each arc or angle.**

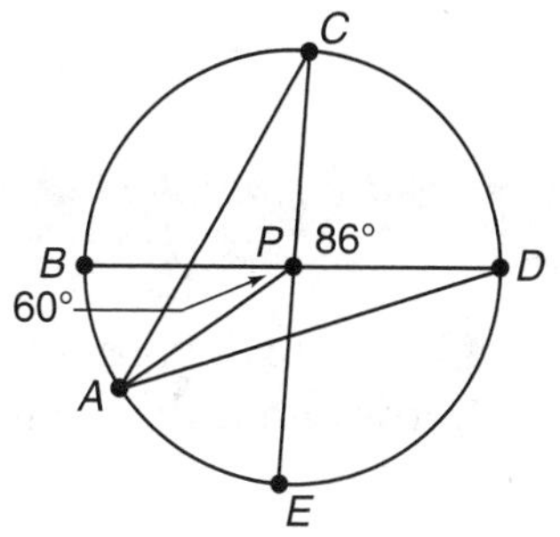

13. m$\overarc{CD}$ __86°__   14. m$\overarc{DE}$ _____

15. m$\overarc{BCD}$ _____   16. m$\overarc{DEC}$ _____

17. m∠*DPE* _____   18. m∠*ADB* _____

19. m∠*CAD* _____   20. m∠*CPE* _____

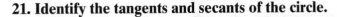
21. Identify the tangents and secants of the circle.

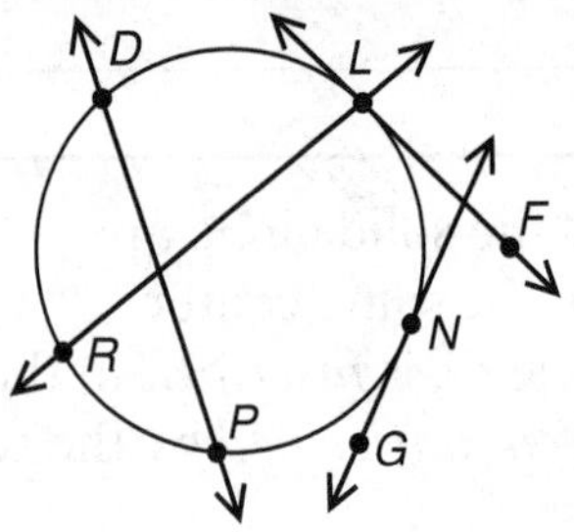

tangents _____

secants _____

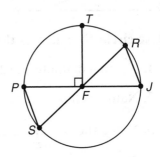

Write a description for each diagram.

22.

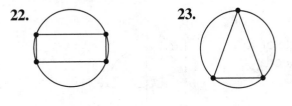

a circumscribed
rectangle

23.

_____

24.

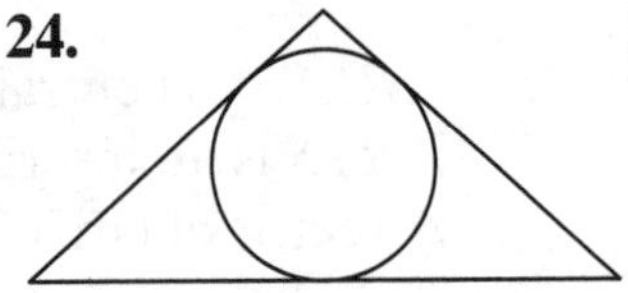

_____

25.

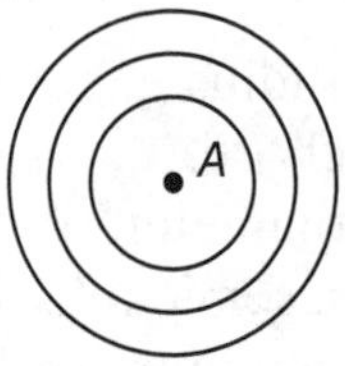

_____

Use the circle _F_ to complete the exercises.

26. Name a pair of supplementary central angles. _∠PFT_ **and** _∠TFJ_

27. Name a pair of complementary central angles. _____

28. Name a chord parallel to $\overline{RJ}$. _____

29. Name a radius perpendicular to $\overline{PF}$. _____

Solve. Show your work.

30. On a separate sheet of paper, draw a circle with two chords that do not have the same length. What is the relationship between the distance from the center and the length of the chords?

_____

31. Two different diameters of the same circle _K_ are $\overline{WY}$ and $\overline{XZ}$, where _W, X, Y,_ and _Z_ are points on the circle. The degree measure of $\overset{\frown}{YZ}$ is 110°. Find the measures of ∠_YKZ_, ∠_XKY_, ∠_YWZ_, and ∠_XWY_.

_____

CRITICAL THINKING

32. Do angle or arc degree measures change as a drawing of a circle with chords and radii is enlarged? Explain.

_____

_____

_____

9-13 Make a Circle Graph

Name _____ Date _____

A circle graph is a good way to display data because it shows *parts of a whole*.
The table at the right shows how Jennelle spends her allowance.

To make a circle graph to display this data, multiply each percent by 360° to find the degrees in each sector. Then use a compass, straightedge, and protractor to draw the graph.

How Jennelle Spends Her Allowance

Use	Percent (%)	Multiply	Degrees in Sector
Food	20	0.20 • 360	72°
Clothes	40	0.40 • 360	144°
Movies	25	0.25 • 360	90°
Music	15	0.15 • 360	54°
Totals	**100%**		**360°**

How Jennelle Spends Her Allowance

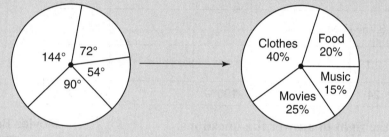

Find the degrees in each sector. Then complete each circle graph.

1.

Students' Favorite Subjects

	Subject	Percent (%)	Multiply	Degrees in Sector
a.	Math	20	_____	_____
b.	Science	10	_____	_____
c.	Language Arts	25	_____	_____
d.	History	20	_____	_____
e.	Music	15	_____	_____
f.	Art	10	_____	_____
	Totals	**100%**		**360°**

2. Students' Favorite Subject

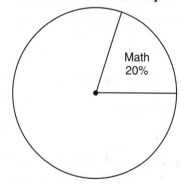

3.

David's Annual Budget

	Use	Percent (%)	Multiply	Degrees in Sector
a.	Food	13	_____	_____
b.	Clothing	32	_____	_____
c.	Movies	18	_____	_____
d.	Music	21	_____	_____
e.	Savings	10	_____	_____
f.	Charity	6	_____	_____
	Totals	**100%**		**360°**

4. David's Annual Budget

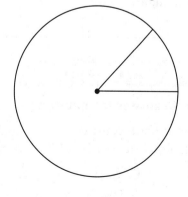

Find the degrees in each sector. Then complete the circle graph.
(*Hint:* Graph decimal degrees as numbers rounded to the nearest half degree.)

5.

	Time Spent Per Day				
Activity	Hours	Ratio and Decimal of Day	Percent (%)	Multiply	Degrees in Sector
a. Sleep	9				
b. Getting Ready	0.75				
c. School	6				
d. Sports	2.4				
e. Homework	3.75				
f. Eating	2.1				
Totals	24		100%		360°

6.

Use the graph at the right to answer the questions.
(*Hint:* percent • 360 = degrees of sector)

Movies Rented

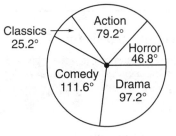

7. What percent of people rented horror movies?

   46.8 ÷ 360 = 0.13; 13% rented horror movies

8. What percent of people rented comedies?

   _____

9. What percent of people rented dramas?

   _____

10. What percent of people rented action movies?

   _____

Problem Solving

11. Each month Joe spends $90 on CDs, $200 on entertainment, and $100 on other purchases. He also saves $110. When Jed draws the part of the circle graph that represents other purchases, what measure should he use for that central angle?

   _____

12. Paula has $200 to spend on gifts. She spends $44 on jewelry, $39 on music, $57 on movies, and the rest on clothing. What measure should Paula use for the central angle of the sector for clothing in a circle graph?

   _____

TEST PREPARATION

Use the graph to answer the questions.

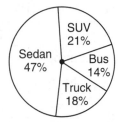

13. Which sector has a central angle with a measure of 169.2°?

   A. Sedan   **C.** SUV

   B. Bus   **D.** Truck

14. Which sector has a central angle with a measure of 64.8°?

   F. Sedan   **H.** SUV

   G. Bus   **J.** Truck

9-14 Problem-Solving Strategy:
Adopt a Different Point of View

Name _____   Date _____

Solve by using the strategy Adopt a Different Point of View.

1. The rhombus below is 8 cm across and 24 cm high. What is its area?

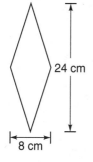

_____

2. Which is the shorter route from A to B, along *a* and *b* or along *c* and *d*? Explain.

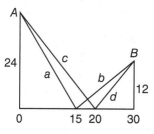

_____

3. A wind-up toy can move at 240 cm/s, but the dog chasing it can run 320 cm/s. If the toy begins 20 m from the dog, how long will it take the dog to catch it?

_____

4. In how many different ways can 9 students be selected from a group of 10 students?

_____

5. If x and y are both positive and if $3x + 2y = 21$ and $2x + 3y = 19$, which is greater, x or y?

---

6. If acute angle ABC is less than acute angle ACD, which segment is longer, AB or AC? Explain.

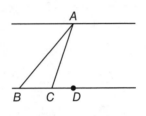

---

7. Two of the triangle's vertices shown in the figure below are midpoints of the sides of the square; the third vertex is a vertex of the square. What fraction of the region inside the square is occupied by the triangle?

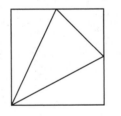

---

8. At the moment a hot air balloon is 1000 ft above ground, a second balloon lifts off the ground. The first balloon is dropping at 6 ft/sec while the second is rising at 4 ft/sec. In how many seconds will the balloons be at the *same* height above the ground?

---

9. If $4x + 2y = 19$ and $2x + 4y = 5$, what is the value of $x + y$?

Enrichment:
Quadrilaterals from Quadrilaterals

Name _____ Date _____

Look at the figures below. Connect the midpoints of the adjacent sides and describe the shape of the new quadrilateral that is formed.

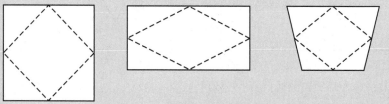

For the square, the new quadrilateral is another square. For the rectangle and trapezoid, it is a rhombus.

Look at the diagonals of the original figure. Notice that the diagonals are parallel to two of the sides of the midpoint quadrilateral. This demonstrates that each midpoint quadrilateral is a parallelogram.

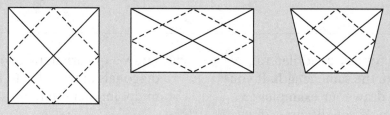

In exercises 1–8, connect the midpoints of the adjoining sides of the figure and describe the shape.

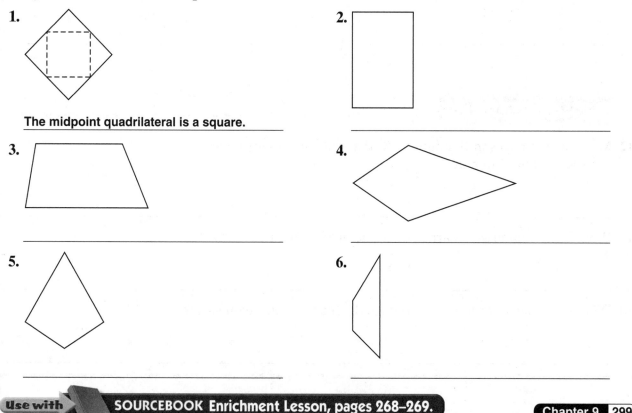

1.

The midpoint quadrilateral is a square.

2.

3.

4.

5.

6.

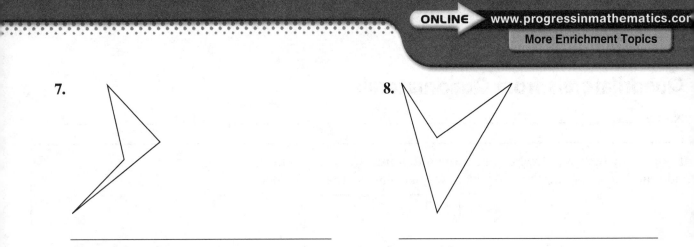

7. _____   **8.** _____

Problem Solving

9. Julie states that the midpoint quadrilateral for a rectangle will always be a rhombus. If you agree with her, draw four examples to support her claim. If you disagree, draw a counterexample.

_____

10. Alex states that for any quadrilateral, the diagonals are the same length. If you agree with him, draw four examples to support his claim. If you disagree, draw a counterexample.

_____

11. Draw a quadrilateral and show that the diagonals are parallel to the sides of the midpoint quadrilateral.

_____

SPIRAL REVIEW

12. Mary reads 5 pages in 10 minutes. At that rate, how many pages can she read in 25 minutes?

_____

13. What is the commission earned on a sale of $750 at a rate of 8%?

_____

14. What is the name for a type of triangle that has no congruent sides?

_____

Test Prep: Multiple-Choice Questions

Strategy: Apply Mathematical Reasoning

Name _____ Date _____

Look for relationships and visual or written cues that you can use to help solve multiple-choice questions.

To select the correct answer in a multiple-choice question, try using the following strategies.

- Underline important words.
- Restate the question.
- Apply appropriate rules, definitions, properties, or strategies.
- Analyze and eliminate answer choices.

Choose the correct answer. *TIP: Focus on the information you know is important.*

1. What is the measure of angle S?

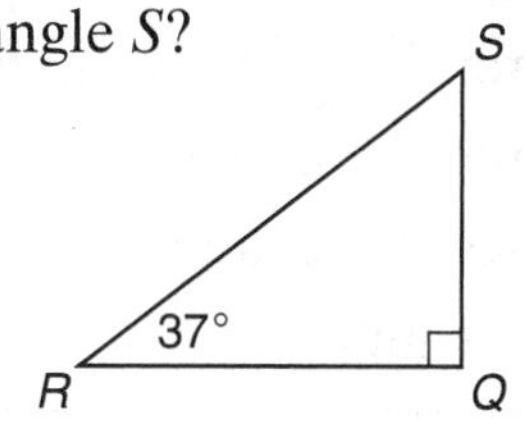

37°

A. 37°   **C.** 45°

B. 53°   **D.** 143°

2. Dennis is shopping for a jacket. All jackets are on sale for 30% off. Dennis also has a coupon for $10 off the sale price. Which equation can be used to find the cost, c, of a jacket with an original price, p?

F. $c = 0.3p - 10$ **H.** $c = 0.7p - 7$

G. $c = 0.7p - 10$ **J.** $c = 0.7p + 10$

---

3. The circle graph shows students who take each type of music lesson.

Student Lessons

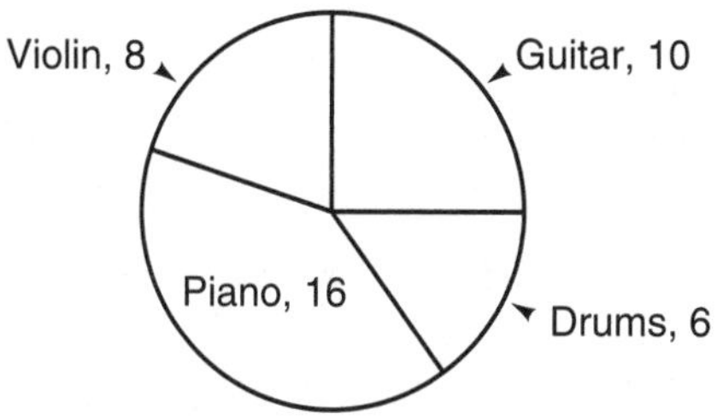

Violin, 8   Guitar, 10

Piano, 16   Drums, 6

What percent of the total number of students takes guitar lessons?

A. 16%   **B.** 40%   **C.** 25%   **D.** 75%

4. The equation $y = -3x + 1$ relates the variables x and y. For every increase in x of 2 units, what is the change in y?

F. −6

G. −5

H. −3

J. 1

---

5. Raul uses 3 scoops of iced-tea mix to make 2 quarts of iced tea. How many scoops does Raul need to make 3 gallons of iced tea?

A. $1\frac{1}{8}$ scoops   **C.** $4\frac{1}{2}$ scoops

B. 12 scoops   **D.** 18 scoops

6. Elsa can type 120 words in 2 minutes. How many words can she type in 5 minutes?

F. 60   **H.** 240

G. 300   **J.** 600

Vocabulary Development

Name _____ Date _____

Chapter 9 Vocabulary

acute triangle	convex polygon	minor arc	sector
adjacent angles	coplanar	obtuse triangle	semicircle
alternate exterior angles	corresponding angles	parallel lines	skew lines
alternate interior angles	equilateral triangle	parallel planes	straight angle
angle bisector	exterior angle	parallelogram	supplement
central angle	exterior point	perpendicular bisector	supplementary angles
chord	inscribed	perpendicular lines	tangent
circumscribed	interior angle	perpendicular planes	transversal
collinear	interior point	plane	trapezoid
complement	intersecting planes	ray	Triangle Inequality Theorem
complementary angles	isosceles triangle	reflex angle	
concave polygon	line segment	regular polygon	vertical angles
concentric	linear pair	scalene triangle	
congruent	major arc	secant	

From the vocabulary list above, choose the term(s) that best complete each sentence. Write the term(s) in the space(s) provided.

1. An angle formed on the outside of a polygon by extending one side is

   an _____.

2. A _____ is a line that intersects two or more lines at different points.

3. The three kinds of arcs of a circle are a _____,

   a _____, and a _____.

4. A quadrilateral with exactly one pair of parallel sides is a

   _____.

5. Two circles are _____ if they lie in the same plane and have the same center.

Choose two terms from the list that you did not use in Questions 1–5. For each term, write a definition in your own words and give an example.

6. _____

   _____

   _____

Practice Chapter 9 Test

Name _____ Date _____

Identify the figures in the diagram at the right.

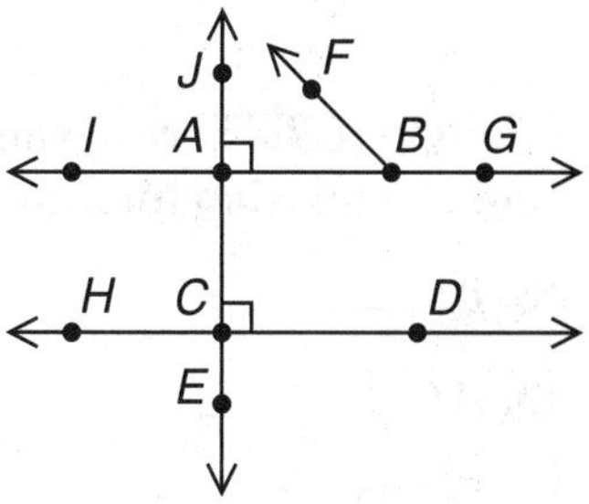

1. two lines _____

2. two line segments _____

3. two rays _____

4. an acute angle _____

5. a straight angle _____

6. an obtuse angle _____

7. a right angle _____

8. three collinear points _____

9. a pair of perpendicular lines _____

Use the diagram at the right to answer the questions and make drawings.
$\overrightarrow{BD}$ **bisects** $\angle ABC$.

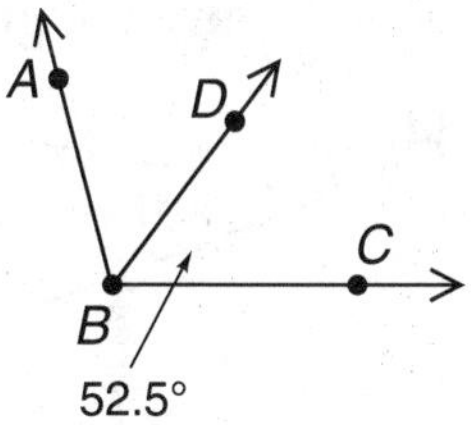

10. What is the measure of $\angle ABD$? _____

11. What type of angle is $\angle CBD$? _____

12. Draw the perpendicular bisector of $\overline{BC}$. Label the midpoint M.

13. Draw and label $\angle ABE$ with measure 75°.

14. Draw a point in the interior of $\angle ABE$ and label it T.

Find the measure of the complement and supplement of each angle.

15. 62° _____

16. 1° _____

17. 37° _____

18. 88° _____

Use the diagram at the right to answer exercises 19–29. $\overleftrightarrow{VW} \parallel \overleftrightarrow{XY}$ **and m**$\angle 2 = 125°$.

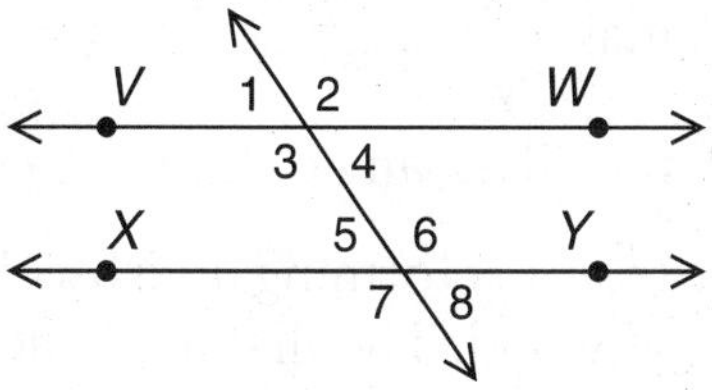

19. What angle makes a vertical angle pair with $\angle 2$? _____

20. Name an angle congruent to $\angle 1$. _____

21. Name two angles that form a linear pair with $\angle 7$. _____

22. Name two angles supplementary to $\angle 6$. _____

23. What angles are adjacent to both $\angle 1$ and $\angle 4$? _____

24. Name the interior angles. _____

25. Name the exterior angles. _____

26. What angle corresponds to $\angle 4$? _____

27. What is the measure of $\angle 5$? _____

28. Name two pairs of alternate interior angles.

_____

29. Name two pairs of alternate exterior angles.

_____

Use the figure to answer the questions.

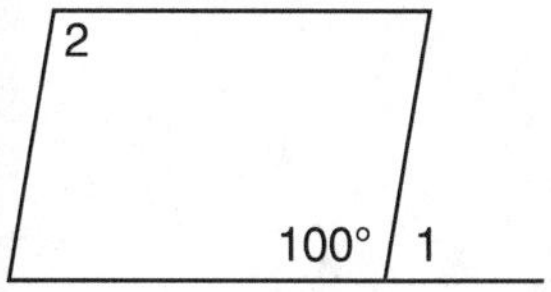

30. Find m$\angle 1$. _____

31. Find m$\angle 2$. _____

Classify each by angles and by sides.

32. _____

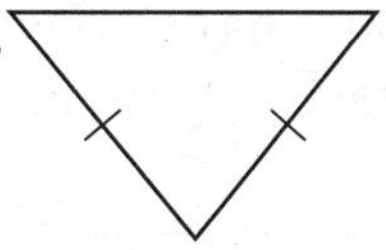

33. _____

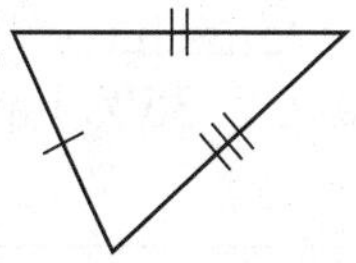

Determine if the set of side lengths given form a triangle. Answer *Yes* or *No*.

34. 17 cm, 12 cm, 4 cm   **35.** 25 in., 16 in., 9 in.   **36.** 6.4 m, 8.2 m, 14.5 m **37.** 1.7 ft, 1.3 ft, 3.3 ft

_____   _____   _____   _____

**Triangle *ABC* is congruent to triangle *DEF*.
Find the missing measures.**

38. *FE* _____

39. *AB* _____

40. *AC* _____

41. m∠*CAB* _____

42. m∠*DFE* _____

43. m∠*DEF* _____

Determine which statement shows that the triangles are congruent.

44.

_____

Classify the quadrilateral in as many ways as possible.

45.

_____

Identify the figures in the diagram.

46. chord _____

47. diameter _____

48. radius _____

49. minor arc _____

50. major arc _____

51. central angle _____

52. inscribed angle _____   **53.** tangent _____   **54.** secant _____

55. Henri is forming an isosceles triangle out of wood. The first angle he makes is 48°. Give two sets of possible measures for the other two angles.

_____

56. Find the measures of ∠1 and ∠2.

_____

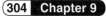 **Tell About It**

Explain how you solve the problem. Show all your work.

57. Make a circle graph of a survey about the number of siblings students have. The results are: have none: 8%, have 1: 32%, have 2: 35% have 3: 20% have 4 or more: 5%.

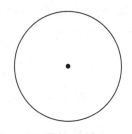

_____

_____

Cumulative Review: Chapters 1–9

Name _____   Date _____

Circle the best answer.

1. What percent of 850 is 497.25?

    A. 0.0085%
    B. 0.585%
    C. 5.85%
    D. 58.5%

6. Which set is closed under multiplication?

    A. integers
    B. prime numbers
    C. negative numbers
    D. {5, 10, 15, 20}

2. Solve the equation $\frac{3}{4}x + 10\frac{3}{4} = 12$.

    F. $x = \frac{15}{16}$ **G.** $x = 1\frac{1}{4}$

    H. $x = 1\frac{2}{3}$ **J.** $x = 30\frac{1}{3}$

7. What is the least common multiple of 42, 60, and 105?

    F. 3   **G.** 70
    H. 210   **J.** 420

3. What is 8.02×10^{-4} written in standard form?

    A. 0.0000802
    B. 0.000802
    C. 0.00802
    D. 0.0802

8. Rhonda earns 5.5% commission when she sells a house. The amount of commission she receives from a sale is $18,700. What is the sale price of the house?

    A. $1028.50
    B. $321,300
    C. $340,000
    D. $358,700

4. Which values make the equation $2y^2 - 4x + 6 = 16$ true?

    F. $x = 1, y = -2$
    G. $x = -1, y = 2$
    H. $x = 2, y = 1$
    J. $x = -2, y = -1$

9. Which word best describes the shaded region?

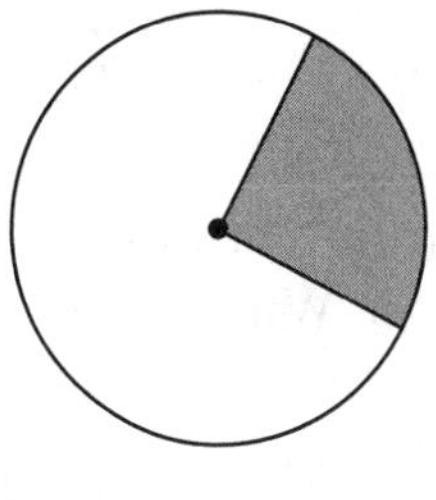

    F. sector
    G. chord
    H. tangent
    J. secant

5. Allen and Devon both own pizza shops. The bar graph below shows the total number of pizzas sold during three weeks. Which week(s) did Devon sell twice as many pizzas as Allen?

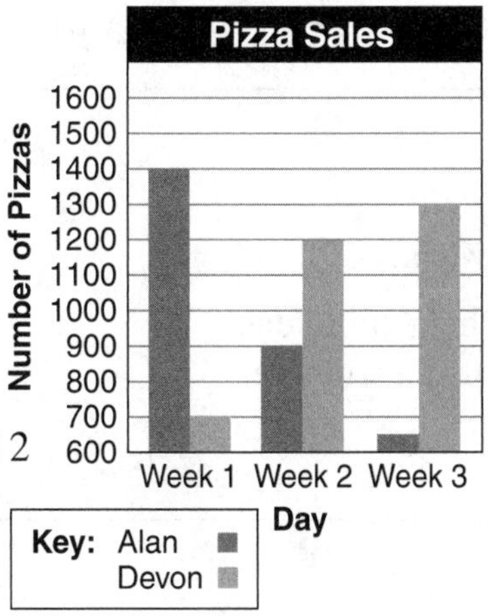

    A. Week 1
    B. Week 2
    C. Week 3
    D. Weeks 1 and 2

Pizza Sales

Number of Pizzas: 1600, 1500, 1400, 1300, 1200, 1100, 1000, 900, 800, 700, 600

Week 1   Week 2   Week 3

Day

Key: Alan ■ Devon ■

10. Which number is part of the solution set of $-6x < -24$?

    A. −11
    B. −4
    C. 4
    D. 11

11. Find the mean, median, and mode(s) of the numbers.

10, 16, 16, 19, 7, 10, 14, 5, 16, 17

    F. mean: 13; median: 15; mode: 16
    G. mean: 15; median: 13; mode: 16
    H. mean: 13; median: 15; modes: 10 and 16
    J. mean: 15; median: 13; modes: 10 and 16

12. Which is *not* a rational number?

    A. –5   **B.** $\frac{2}{3}$

    C. 3.14159…   **D.** $9.0\overline{8}$

13. Simplify: $6 + (-8) - 2(|-7| + 10)$

    F. −36   **G.** −8

    H. 4   **J.** 32

14. Find the value of x.

    A. 36°   **B.** 72°

    C. 108°   **D.** 144°

15. Solve:

$7.8x \geq 2.34$

    F. $x \geq 0.3$ **G.** $x \leq 0.3$

    H. $x \geq -0.3$ **J.** $x \leq -0.3$

16. Enrique buys 1 lb 12 oz of ground beef for $3.85. What is the cost per pound?

    A. $1.93   **B.** $2.20

    C. $3.44   **D.** $4.40

17. Evaluate $\dfrac{(16 - 2x) - x^2}{2}$ when $x = -1.2$.

    F. 6.08   **G.** 7.52

    H. 8.48   **J.** 9.32

18. Randy buys a video game that has an original price of $45. The game is on sale for 10% off. The sales tax on the sale price is 6%. How much does Randy pay for the game?

    F. $40.23   **G.** $42.93

    H. $43.20   **J.** $47.70

19. Which set of numbers could be the lengths of the sides of a triangle?

    A. 7.14, 10.2, 2.62   **B.** 1.75, 3.5, 1.75

    C. 5.8, 9.2, 3.3   **D.** 4.2, 9.6, 5.5

20. Which line is parallel to $\overleftrightarrow{AB}$?

    F. $\overleftrightarrow{AC}$

    G. $\overleftrightarrow{BD}$

    H. $\overleftrightarrow{EF}$

    J. $\overleftrightarrow{CD}$

21. The mean of 5 numbers is 1054. Four of the numbers are 1262, 975, 893, and 1037. What is the fifth number?

    A. 846   **B.** 1054

    C. 1071   **D.** 1103

22. Which is equivalent to $\dfrac{3^{12}}{3^4}$?

    F. 3^8 **G.** 3^3

    H. $(-3)^3$ **J.** $(-3)^8$

23. Which expression represents "2 divided by the difference of 16 and a number"?

    A. $2 \div 16 - n$ **B** $(2 \div 16) - n$

    C. $2 \div (16 - n)$ **D.** $(16 - n) \div 2$

Tell About It

Explain how you solve the problem. Show all your work.

24. Ben is setting up a tent. The sides that slope to the ground each measure 5.25 feet. If the sides and the ground form a triangle, what is the range of possible lengths for the base?

10-1 Precision and Accuracy in Measurement

Name _____ Date _____

The distance from Newport to Kenville is measured as 8.2 km to the nearest tenth of a kilometer. What is the greatest possible error? What is the relative error?

Greatest Possible Error	Range of Error (Possible measurements)	Relative Error
Think	**Think**	**Think**
$GPE = \frac{1}{2}$ smallest unit	Measurement $\pm$ GPE	$\dfrac{GPE}{\text{given measurement}}$
$GPE = \frac{1}{2} \cdot 0.1 \text{ km} = 0.05 \text{ km}$	$8.2 + 0.05 = 8.25$ km $8.2 - 0.05 = 8.15$ km 8.15 km to 8.25 km	$\dfrac{0.05}{8.2} \approx 0.0061$ $= 0.61\%$

Measurements obtained experimentally should be recorded using an appropriate number of significant digits.

Operating with significant digits:
- When adding or subtracting, identify the measurement with the fewest decimal places. Round the result to this number of decimal places.
- When multiplying or dividing identify the measurement with the fewest number of significant digits. Round the result to this number of significant digits.

Remember:
Significant digits
1) all nonzero digits
2) zeros between nonzero digits
3) zeros that follow nonzero digits that are after the decimal point
73,002 → 5 significant digits
0.060 → 2 significant digits

List the least precise and most precise measurements.

1. 3 ft, 3.73 ft, 3.729 ft, 3.7 ft

    _____**3 ft, 3.729 ft**_____

2. 13.37 lb, 13.371 lb, 13.4 lb, 13.3702 lb

    _____

3. 3684.0 g, 3.7 kg, 3684 g, 3.68 kg

    _____

Measure each line segment to the nearest unit indicated. Then find the range of possible measurements for the actual length.

4. ━━━━━━━━━━━━━━━

   a. nearest inch: _____

     range: _____

   b. nearest quarter inch: _____

     range: _____

5. ━━━━━

   a. nearest centimeter: _____

     range: _____

   b. nearest tenth of a centimeter: _____

     range: _____

Decide whether each statement is *true* or *false*. Explain your answers.

6. If a thermometer reads 78°, the actual temperature is between 77.5° and 78.5°.

_____

7. If a racer is timed at 11.7 sec, her actual time is between 11.7 sec and 11.75 sec.

_____

For each measurement, give the GPE, and calculate the percent of relative error to the nearest tenth of a percent.

	Measurement	GPE	% Relative Error
8.	33 km	_____	_____
9.	12 cm	_____	_____
10.	372 mm	_____	_____

	Measurement	GPE	% Relative Error
11.	8.2 lb	_____	_____
12.	3 ft 7 in.	_____	_____
13.	2 lb 5 oz	_____	_____

Find the number of significant digits.

14. 8020 __4__   **15.** 220.03 _____   **16.** 0.00750 _____   **17.** 80.40600 _____

Compute. Use the correct form of precision for each situation.

18. Yang measures the width and length of his computer screen. It has a width of 10.625 inches and a length of 12.5 inches. What is the best measure of its perimeter?

_____

19. The antenna on Barack's shortwave radio has a measured height of 25.875 cm. If he shortens the height by about 4.30 cm, about how tall is the antenna?

_____

20. Kim's notepad has a measured width of 3.5 centimeters and a measured length of 4.7 centimeters. What is the best measure of the notepad's area?

_____

21. A department store has a giant brass door at its entrance. It has a measured height of 17.21 feet and a measured width of 4 feet. What is the best estimate of the door's area?

_____

Solve. Show your work.

22. A mail package weighs 2 pounds on a scale that measures to the nearest pound. What is the relative error? Is this amount of relative error reasonable for the situation?

_____

MENTAL MATH

23. Estimate the relative error as less than 1%, between 1% and 10%, or greater than 10%. $\left(Hint: \dfrac{0.5}{4} = 0.5 \cdot \dfrac{1}{4} = \dfrac{1}{2} \cdot \dfrac{1}{4}\right)$

a. $\dfrac{0.5 \text{ m}}{1 \text{ m}}$ **b.** $\dfrac{0.5 \text{ people}}{2000 \text{ people}}$ **c.** $\dfrac{5.0 \text{ in.}}{70 \text{ in.}}$

_____   _____   _____

10-2 Perimeter

Name _____   Date _____

A new street sign is in the form of a regular pentagon. If it has a perimeter of 280 cm, what is the length of each side?

Solve: $P = 5s$ ← Perimeter formula for a regular pentagon.

$280 = 5s$ ← Substitute 280 for P.

$56 = s$ ← Divide both sides by 5. Simplify.

So the length of each side is 56 centimeters.

Check: $280 \overset{?}{=} 5(56)$

$280 = 280$ True

> **Remember:**
> **Perimeter Formulas**
> Regular Polygon: $P = ns$, where n is the number of sides and s is the side length.
> Rectangle: $P = 2\ell + 2w$, where ℓ is the length and w is the width.

Write an equation and find the perimeter.

1. Square: $s = 14.7$ ft

$P = 4s; P = 4(14.7)$
$P = 58.8$ ft

2. Regular octagon: $s = 6$ m

_____

3. Rectangle: $\ell = 35.3$ cm, $w = 12.4$

_____

Find the perimeter of each polygon.

4.

15 in.
9 in.
12 in.

$15 + 9 + 12; P = 36$ in.

5.

14 mm
28 mm
20 mm

_____

6.

36 dm
19 dm
22 dm
42 dm

_____

7.

21 ft
15 ft
12 ft
36 ft

_____

8.

4 cm
2 cm
5 cm

_____

9.

8.6 mi
7.5 mi

_____

Find the measure of the side of each regular polygon with the given perimeter.

10. Square
$P = 72$ cm

$72 = 4s; \dfrac{72}{4} = \dfrac{4s}{4}$
$18 = s; 18$ cm

11. Equilateral triangle
$P = 87$ yd

_____

12. Regular decagon
$P = 43$ m

_____

Find the measure of the missing side for each rectangle.

13. $P = 30$ cm, $\ell = 9$ cm

$P = 2\ell + 2w; 30 = 2(9) + 2w$
$12 = 2w$
$6 = w; 6$ cm

14. $P = 45.6$ mi, $\ell = 18.3$ mi

15. $P = 1230.4$ yd, $w = 412.7$ yd

Find the perimeter.

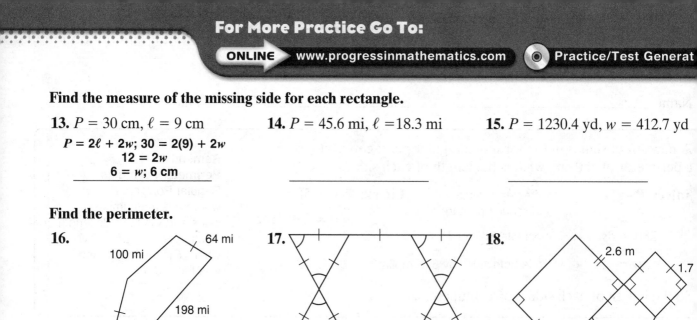

16.
100 mi, 64 mi, 198 mi, 24 mi, 45 mi

$P = 100 + 64 + 198$
$+ 45 + 24 + 64; P = 495$ mi

17. 18.24 ft

18. 2.6 m, 1.7

Each pair of polygons is similar. Using the rules of similarity, find the perimeter of the second polygon.

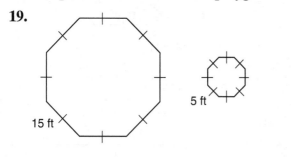

19.
15 ft, 5 ft

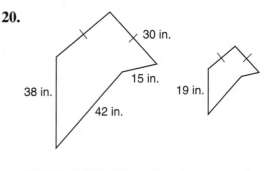

20.
30 in., 38 in., 15 in., 42 in., 19 in.

Problem Solving

21. Mr. Alba puts a 14.6-meter low fence around his trapezoid-shaped garden. If the parallel sides measure 3.5 meters and 5.2 meters, and a third side measures 2.8 meters, what is the length of the fourth side?

22. Alberto has a picture in the shape of a regular hexagon. How much would it cost to frame the picture if the frame is 52 cm on each side, molding material costs $4.10 per meter, and the labor charge is $15.25? Round up to the nearest cent.

MENTAL MATH

23. Solve.

    a. $2.5x = 12.5$ _____
    b. $1.2n = 14.4$ _____
    c. $5.6 \div w = 0.7$ _____
    d. $6.3 \div z = 9$ _____

10-3 Squares and Square Roots

Name _____ Date _____

The *square root of a number* is a number that when multiplied by itself, equals the original number.

$\sqrt{64} = 8$, because $8 \cdot 8 = 64$

Every positive number has a *positive square root* and a *negative square root*.

$(10)^2 = 100$ and $(-10)^2 = 100$

Both 10 and -10 are square roots of 100. 100 is a perfect square.

Simplify: $\sqrt{196} + \sqrt{16}$

Think

$x = \sqrt{196}$
$x^2 = 196$
$x^2 = 2 \cdot 2 \cdot 7 \cdot 7$ ⟵ Prime factorization.
$x^2 = (2 \cdot 7)(2 \cdot 7)$ ⟵ Regroup.
$x^2 = 14 \cdot 14 = 14^2$ ⟵ Simplify.
$x = 14$

$14 + \sqrt{16}$ ⟵ $\sqrt{196} = 14$
$14 + 4$ ⟵ $\sqrt{16} = 4$
18 ⟵ Add.

Find both square roots of each number.

1. 81 __9, −9__

2. 121 _____

3. 225 _____

4. 1296 _____

5. 11,881 _____

6. 270,400 _____

Simplify each expression.

7. $\sqrt{625}$
$x = \sqrt{625}$; $x^2 = 625$
$x^2 = (5 \cdot 5)(5 \cdot 5) = 25 \cdot 25$
$x^2 = 25^2$; $x = 25$; 25

8. $\sqrt{225}$

9. $\sqrt{3136}$

10. $\sqrt{2916}$

11. $\sqrt{5184}$

12. $\sqrt{576 \cdot 7^2}$

13. $\sqrt{441 \cdot 11^2}$

14. $\sqrt{124 + 900}$

15. $\sqrt{225 - 81}$

16. $\sqrt{25} + \sqrt{144}$

17. $\sqrt{64} - \sqrt{121}$

18. $\sqrt{16^2} + \sqrt{5^2} + \sqrt{196}$

19. $\sqrt{14^2} + \sqrt{7^2} + \sqrt{169}$

20. $\sqrt{225} - \sqrt{6^2} + \sqrt{23^2}$

21. $\sqrt{144} - \sqrt{17^2} - \sqrt{4^2}$

22. $\sqrt{64} + \sqrt{(7-9)^2} - 6$

23. $\sqrt{81} - \sqrt{(25-21)^2} + 7$

24. $\sqrt{36^2 + (-8)^2 + 3^2}$

Place the numbers on a number line.

25.

$$\begin{array}{c}\text{number line from } -10 \text{ to } 10 \\ -10\ -8\ -6\ -4\ -2\ 0\ 2\ 4\ 6\ 8\ 10\end{array}$$

$\frac{1}{4}, \sqrt{25}, -\sqrt{25}\ 2.5, -2.5$

26.

$$\begin{array}{c}\text{number line from } -10 \text{ to } 10 \\ -10\ -8\ -6\ -4\ -2\ 0\ 2\ 4\ 6\ 8\ 10\end{array}$$

$0.3, 9, -9, -\sqrt{9}, \sqrt{3^2}$

Evaluate the expressions for $x = 3$ and $y = -2$.

27. $\sqrt{4x^2 - 4xy + y^2}$

$$\sqrt{4(3)^2 - 4(3)(-2) + (-2)^2}$$
$$\sqrt{36 + 24 + 4} = \sqrt{64} = 8$$

28. $\sqrt{x^2 - 6xy + 9y^2}$

29. $\sqrt{2x^2 + 5xy + 16}$

30. $\sqrt{3x^2 + 4xy + 33}$

Evaluate the expressions for $a = 8$ and $b = -3$.

31. $\sqrt{3a^2 + ab + b^2 - 8}$

$$\sqrt{3(8)^2 + 8(-3) + (-3)^2 - 8}$$
$$\sqrt{192 - 24 + 9 - 8} = \sqrt{169} = 13$$

32. $\sqrt{2a^2 - ab - b^2 + 1}$

33. $\sqrt{2a^2 + 3a + 14 + 10b^2}$

34. $\sqrt{3a^2 + 5a + 2 - b^2}$

Problem Solving

35. A square museum is built with a square courtyard in its interior. The length of the side of the courtyard is 9.5 feet. The area of the museum's floor space is 1278.75 square feet. What is the length of each side of the museum?

36. A square chessboard is divided into 64 squares, each with an area of 16 square centimeters. What is the perimeter of the chessboard?

CRITICAL THINKING

37. The area of a framed picture is x^2 square inches. The molding of the frame is 1.5 inches wide all the way around. How can you find the dimensions of the picture that shows through the frame? Explain.

10-4 Irrational Numbers

Name _____ Date _____

Irrational numbers are numbers that cannot be expressed as the quotient of two integers, $\frac{a}{b}$, where $b \neq 0$.

Rational Numbers	Irrational Numbers
$4\frac{3}{10}$ ← can be written as $\frac{43}{10}$	π ← neither terminates nor repeats
$0.\overline{3}$ ← can be written as $\frac{1}{3}$	$\sqrt{98}$ ← not a perfect square
	$59.47447774447777\ldots$ ← neither terminates nor repeats

Approximate $\sqrt{52}$ to the nearest whole number.

1 Identify the perfect squares closest to $\sqrt{52}$. $\sqrt{49} < \sqrt{52} < \sqrt{64}$

2 Find the positive square roots of the perfect squares. $7 < \sqrt{52} < 8$

3 Use your calculator to find a better estimate.
Press `2ND` `x²` 5 2 `ENTER` | 7.211102551 |

Locate $\sqrt{52}$ on a number line. ←|+|+●|+|+|+|+|+|+|→ So $\sqrt{52}$ is closer to 7 than to 8.
                                          7   8

Classify each number as *rational* or *irrational*. Explain.

1. $\sqrt{49}$ __rational, 49 is a perfect square__

2. $\sqrt{3}$ _____

3. $-\sqrt{16}$ _____

4. $\sqrt{5^2}$ _____

5. $7\frac{2}{3}$ _____

6. $-3\frac{16}{17}$ _____

7. $\frac{\pi}{4}$ _____

8. $\frac{6\pi}{11}$ _____

9. 67% _____

10. $53.27\overline{474}$ _____

Identify the closest perfect squares.

11. $\sqrt{11}$ 12. $\sqrt{97}$ 13. $\sqrt{62}$ 14. $\sqrt{78}$

$\sqrt{9} < \sqrt{11} < \sqrt{16}$
$3 < \sqrt{11} < 4$
$\sqrt{11}$ is between 3 and 4.   _____   _____   _____

On the number line, approximate the location of the irrational numbers for exercises 11–14.

15.

←|+|+|+|+|+|+|+|+|→
0   5   10

Complete the table of square roots. Use your calculator to estimate irrational numbers to the nearest tenth.

16.

Integer	Square Root	Integer	Square Root	Integer	Square Root	Integer	Square Root
1	_____	6	_____	11	_____	16	_____
2	_____	7	_____	12	_____	17	_____
3	_____	8	_____	13	_____	18	_____
4	_____	9	_____	14	_____	19	_____
5	_____	10	_____	15	_____	20	_____

On the number line, approximate the location of the square root of each integer from 1 through 20.

17.

Problem Solving

18. The Alejandro family has a square yard with an area of 175 square feet. If they want to cover the yard with 1-foot long paving stones, what is the greatest number of whole stones they can place along one side?

19. A square playground has an area of 2830 square meters. Estimate the length of one side. Explain your method.

_____   _____

20. The Parkers have a square garden with an area of 108 square feet. They want to estimate the perimeter of the garden. Explain how this can be done.

_____

_____

SPIRAL REVIEW

Find the side length of the regular polygon with the given perimeter.

21. Octagon; $P = 500$ cm

22. Pentagon; $P = 199$ mm

_____   _____

23. Square; $P = 51.4$ in.

24. Hexagon; $P = 704.94$ ft

_____   _____

10-5 Pythagorean Theorem

Name _____   Date _____

You can apply the *Pythagorean Theorem* to find the value of a missing side of a right triangle, or to determine if three side lengths form a right triangle.

A right triangle has a height of 12 meters. Its hypotenuse has a length of 20 meters. What is the length of its base?

Let $a = 12$ and $c = 20$.

Solve: $12^2 + b^2 = 20^2$ ← Apply the Pythagorean Theorem.

$144 + b^2 = 400$ ← Evaluate the squares.

$144 - 144 + b^2 = 400 - 144$ ← Subtract 144 from both sides.

$b^2 = 256$ ← Simplify.

$\sqrt{b^2} = \sqrt{256}$ ← Find the positive square root of both sides.

$b = 16$ ← Simplify.

So the length of the base is 16 m.

Remember:
Pythagorean Theorem
In any right triangle, if a and b are the lengths of the legs, and c is the length of the hypotenuse, then $a^2 + b^2 = c^2$.

Determine whether a triangle with the given side lengths is a right triangle.

1. 10 m, 24 m, 26 m

$10^2 + 24^2 \overset{?}{=} 26^2$
$100 + 576 \overset{?}{=} 676$
$676 = 676;$ Yes

2. 3 ft, 13.3 ft, 14 ft

3. 4 in., 7.5 in., 8.5 in.

Each group of three numbers that can form the sides lengths of a right triangle is called a Pythagorean triple. Find each missing side length. Then write the Pythagorean triple.

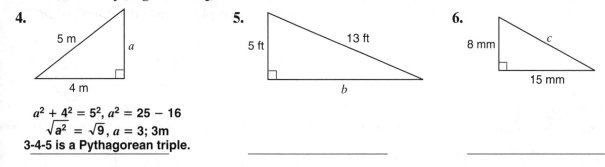

4. 5 m, 4 m, a

$a^2 + 4^2 = 5^2,\ a^2 = 25 - 16$
$\sqrt{a^2} = \sqrt{9},\ a = 3;\ 3\text{m}$
3-4-5 is a Pythagorean triple.

5. 5 ft, 13 ft, b

6. 8 mm, 15 mm, c

Find the length of each missing side in a right triangle to the nearest tenth. You may use a calculator.

7. $a = 5$ in., $b = 12$ in.   **8.** $a = 6.4$ m, $b = 4.8$ m   **9.** $a = 17$ in., $b = 10$ in.   **10.** $b = 13$ cm, $c = 19$ cm

$5^2 + 12^2 = c^2$
$c^2 = 25 + 144$
$\sqrt{c^2} = \sqrt{169},\ c = 13$ in.

Find the length of each hypotenuse to the nearest tenth. Assume that the side of each small square on the grid is 2 units.
(*Hint:* Use the grid to draw a right triangle.)

11.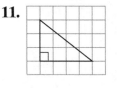

$6^2 + 8^2 = c^2, c^2 = 36 + 64$
$\sqrt{c^2} = \sqrt{100}, c = 10$

12.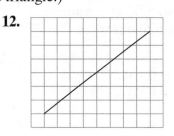

13.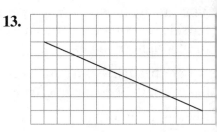

14.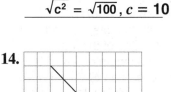

15.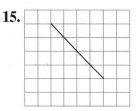

16.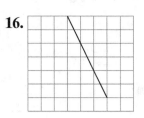

Problem Solving

17. As part of a training exercise, 16 firemen need to carry equipment up a ladder hooked to the top of an office building that is 15 meters tall. If the base of the ladder is 7 meters from the wall, about how long is the ladder?

18. The Lee family wants to buy a new round dining table. Their rectangular door frame is 3 feet wide and 6.5 feet high. If the legs are attached to the table, approximate the greatest length of its diameter so that the table can be placed into the dining room.

CHALLENGE

19. Find the length of line segments *A*, *B*, and *C* on the coordinate plane. Do negative endpoint coordinates affect the length of the line? Explain.

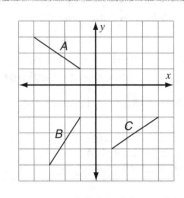

_____

_____

_____

_____

10-6 Area of Parallelograms

Name _____ Date _____

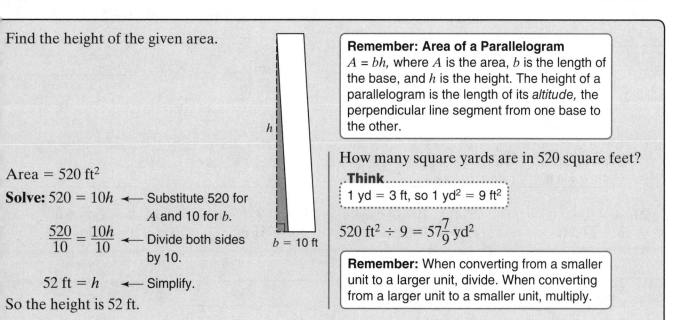

Find the height of the given area.

Remember: Area of a Parallelogram
$A = bh$, where A is the area, b is the length of the base, and h is the height. The height of a parallelogram is the length of its *altitude,* the perpendicular line segment from one base to the other.

h

$b = 10$ ft

Area $= 520$ ft^2

Solve: $520 = 10h$ ← Substitute 520 for A and 10 for b.

$\dfrac{520}{10} = \dfrac{10h}{10}$ ← Divide both sides by 10.

52 ft $= h$ ← Simplify.

So the height is 52 ft.

How many square yards are in 520 square feet?

Think
1 yd = 3 ft, so 1 yd^2 = 9 ft^2

520 ft$^2 \div 9 = 57\frac{7}{9}$ yd^2

Remember: When converting from a smaller unit to a larger unit, divide. When converting from a larger unit to a smaller unit, multiply.

Find the area of each parallelogram.

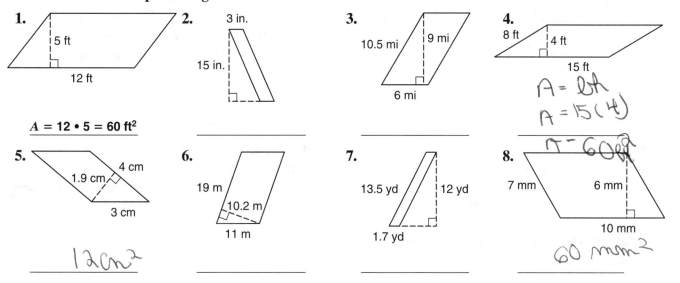

1. 5 ft, 12 ft

$A = 12 \cdot 5 = 60$ ft^2

2. 3 in., 15 in.

3. 10.5 mi, 9 mi, 6 mi

4. 8 ft, 4 ft, 15 ft

$A = bh$
$A = 15(4)$
$A = 60$ ft²

5. 4 cm, 1.9 cm, 3 cm

12 cm²

6. 19 m, 10.2 m, 11 m

7. 13.5 yd, 12 yd, 1.7 yd

8. 7 mm, 6 mm, 10 mm

60 mm²

Find the area of each parallelogram given the dimensions.
(*Hint:* Convert to compute like units, when necessary.)

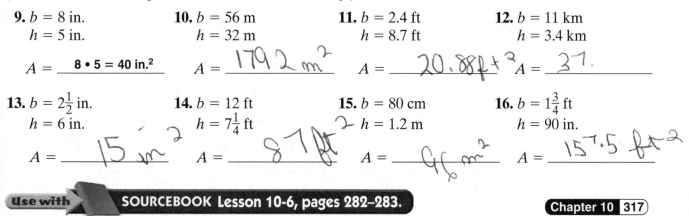

9. $b = 8$ in.
$h = 5$ in.

$A = $ 8 • 5 = 40 in.^{2}

10. $b = 56$ m
$h = 32$ m

$A = $ 1792 m²

11. $b = 2.4$ ft
$h = 8.7$ ft

$A = $ 20.88 ft²

12. $b = 11$ km
$h = 3.4$ km

$A = $ 37.

13. $b = 2\frac{1}{2}$ in.
$h = 6$ in.

$A = $ 15 in²

14. $b = 12$ ft
$h = 7\frac{1}{4}$ ft

$A = $ 87 ft²

15. $b = 80$ cm
$h = 1.2$ m

$A = $ 96 m²

16. $b = 1\frac{3}{4}$ ft
$h = 90$ in.

$A = $ 157.5 ft²

Use the area formula to find the missing dimension.

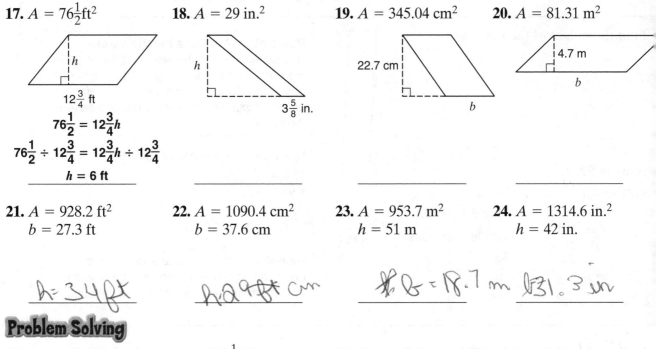

17. $A = 76\frac{1}{2}\text{ft}^2$

$76\frac{1}{2} = 12\frac{3}{4}h$

$76\frac{1}{2} \div 12\frac{3}{4} = 12\frac{3}{4}h \div 12\frac{3}{4}$

$h = 6\text{ ft}$

18. $A = 29\text{ in.}^2$

19. $A = 345.04\text{ cm}^2$

20. $A = 81.31\text{ m}^2$

21. $A = 928.2\text{ ft}^2$
$b = 27.3\text{ ft}$

$h = 34\text{ ft}$

22. $A = 1090.4\text{ cm}^2$
$b = 37.6\text{ cm}$

$h = 29\text{ ft cm}$

23. $A = 953.7\text{ m}^2$
$h = 51\text{ m}$

$b = 18.7\text{ m}$

24. $A = 1314.6\text{ in.}^2$
$h = 42\text{ in.}$

31.3 in

Problem Solving

25. A parallelogram has a base of $12\frac{1}{4}$ kilometers and a height of 6 kilometers. Find the area of the parallelogram, then explain how the area would change if the base were multiplied by 4.

26. A parallelogram has a base of 6 yards and a height of $18\frac{2}{3}$ yards. Find the area of the parallelogram, then explain how the area would change if the height were halved.

27. Sarah is painting a mural on a wall. Part of the mural is a large parallelogram that has a base of 3.5 yards and a height of 3 yards. One quart of paint covers approximately 87.5 square feet. How many cans of paint will Sarah need to buy to cover the parallelogram?

28. Luis wants to replace a section of a roof that is shaped like a parallelogram. Each shingle is a parallelogram with a height of 7 inches and a base of 5 inches. If the section has a base of 15 ft and a height of 5.25 ft, how many shingles will Luis need?

TEST PREPARATION

29. A parallelogram has a height of 1.6 meters and an area of 4.56 square meters. What is the length of its base?

   A. 2.85 m   **C.** 2.96 m

   B. 6.16 m   **D.** 7.296 m

30. What is the area of a parallelogram with a height of 2.3 centimeters and a base that is three times its height?

   F. 9.2 cm^2 **H.** 10.58 cm^2

   G. 12.167 cm^2 **J.** 15.87 cm^2

10-7 Area of Triangles and Trapezoids

Name _____ Date _____

Find the area of each triangle.

1.

7 m   6 m

12 m

$A = \frac{1}{2}(12)(6) = 36 \text{ m}^2$

2.

4 in.   23 in.

18 in.

$A - \frac{bh}{2}$

$207 un^2$

3. $b = 5\frac{3}{4}$ cm
$h = 16$ cm

4 cm²

+84 cm² (crossed out)

4. $b = 11.3$ ft
$h = 5.8$ ft

32.77 ft²

Find the area of each trapezoid.

5.

8 cm

4 cm

20 cm

$A = 56 cm^2$

6.

2 mm

8 mm

12 mm

$A = 56 cm^2$

7. $b_1 = 1.75$ yd
$b_2 = 2.25$ yd
$h = 3.5$ yd

8. $b_1 = 16$ in.
$b_2 = 12$ in.
$h = 1\frac{1}{2}$ in.

Find the missing dimension of each figure.

9.

h 11.4 m

12 m

$A = 60 \text{ m}^2$

$60 = \frac{1}{2}(12)h;\ 60 = 6h$

$\frac{60}{6} = \frac{6h}{6}$

$h = 10 \text{ m}$

10.

14 in.

h

$A = 147 \text{ in.}^2$

11. 4 dm

20 dm

b_2

$A = 100 \text{ dm}^2$

12.

b_1

8.7 cm   6 cm

11 cm

$A = 48 \text{ cm}^2$

Check
$A = \frac{b_1 + b_2}{2} h$
$48 = \frac{5(11)(6)}{2}$ b
$48 = 48$ ✓

$A = \frac{b_1 + b_2 h}{2} = 48$

$A = \frac{b_1 + 11}{2}$

$3(b_1 + 11)$
$\frac{3}{11} = b_1 + 11$

$5 = b_1$

13. Triangle:
$A = 136.4$ in.^{2}
$b = 12.4$ in.
$h = ?$

$\frac{136.4}{6.2h} = 22 un$

14. Triangle:
$A = 72.9$ km^2
$b = ?$
$h = 16.2$ km

$\frac{72.9}{8.1} = 9$ km

15. Trapezoid:
$A = 63 \text{ m}^2$
$b_1 = 12$ m
$b_2 = 8$ m
$h = ?$

$A = \frac{b_1 + b_2 h}{2}$

$A = \frac{12(8)(12)}{2}$

$63 = \frac{20}{2}$

16. Trapezoid:
A = 96 ft^2
$b_1 = 11$ ft
$b_2 = 13$ ft
$h = ?$

$16 = b_1 + 11$

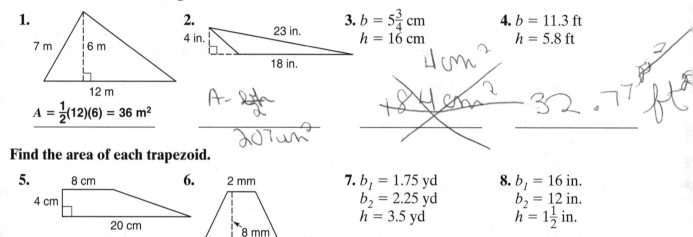
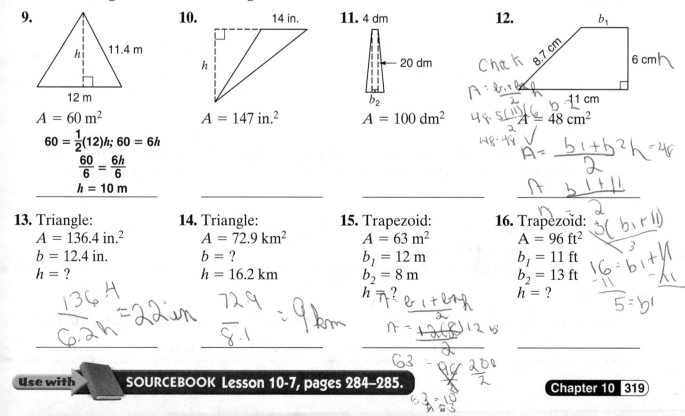

Find the area of each figure. Then rename the area in the given units.

17. Triangle:
b = 30 cm
h = 35 cm
Find the area in mm².

$A = \frac{1}{2}(30)(35) = 525$ cm²
1 cm = 10 mm; 1 cm² = 100 mm²
$A = 525 \cdot 100 = 52{,}500$ mm²

18. Triangle:
b = 18 yd
h = 3 yd
Find the area in ft².

19. Trapezoid:
b_1 = 20 cm
b_2 = 110 cm
h = 5 cm
Find the area in m².

Solve. Explain your answers.

20. A triangle has a base of 9 meters and a height of 8 meters. Explain how the area of the triangle will change if the height is halved.

Let A_1 = original area, and A_2 = area of the triangle with height halved.
$A_1 = \frac{1}{2} \cdot 9 \cdot 8 = 36$ m²
$A_2 = \frac{1}{2} \cdot 9 \cdot (\frac{1}{2} \cdot 8) = \frac{1}{2} \cdot 9 \cdot 4 = 18$ m²
$A_1 : A_2 = 36 : 18 = 1 : \frac{1}{2}$
The area of the triangle is halved when its height is halved.

21. A triangle has a base of 3 centimeters and a height of 6 centimeters. Explain how the area of the triangle will change if the base is doubled.

22. A trapezoid has a base of 4 inches, another base of 6 inches, and a height of 7 inches. Explain how the area of the trapezoid will change if the height is doubled.

23. A trapezoid has a base of 5 millimeters, another base of 7 millimeters, and a height of 6 millimeters. Explain how the area of the trapezoid will change if the height and both bases are doubled.

24. The sum of the lengths of the bases of the trapezoid is 36 inches. The second base is double the length of the first base. The height is half the length of the first base. What is the area of the trapezoid?

MENTAL MATH

25. Evaluate.

a. 0.8^2 **b.** 0.08^2 **c.** 0.9^2 **d.** 0.09^2 **e.** 0.12^2 **f.** 0.012^2

10-8 Circumference and Area of a Circle

Name _____ Date _____

The top of Henri's circular thermos has a diameter of 2.75 inches. What is the distance around his thermos? What is the area of the top of his thermos?

Find the distance around the circle, *circumference*.

Remember: Circumference formulas
$C = 2\pi r$ or $C = \pi d$, where r is the length of the radius, and d is the length of the diameter.

$C = \pi d$
$C = 2.75\pi$ ⟵ Substitute 2.75 for d.
$C \approx 2.75(3.14)$ ⟵ Substitute 3.14 for π.
$C \approx 8.635$ in. ⟵ Simplify.

So the distance around his thermos is about 8.635 in.

Find the *area* of the top of the thermos.

Remember: Area of a Circle
$A = \pi r^2$, where r is the length of the radius.

$A = \pi r^2$

Think
$d = 2r; 2.75 = 2r; 1.375 = r$

$A = \pi(1.375)^2$ ⟵ Substitute 1.375 for r.
$A = \pi(1.890625)$ ⟵ Evaluate the square.
$A \approx (3.14)(1.89)$ ⟵ Substitute 3.14 for π.
$A \approx 5.9$ in.^{2} ⟵ Simplify. Round to the nearest tenth.

So the area of the top of his thermos is about 5.9 in.^{2}.

Write the circumference of each circle in terms of π. Then approximate the circumference using 3.14 for π. As needed, round to the nearest tenth.

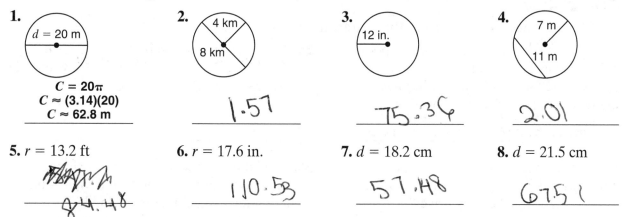

1. $d = 20$ m

$C = 20\pi$
$C \approx (3.14)(20)$
$C \approx 62.8$ m

2. 4 km, 8 km

1.57

3. 12 in.

75.36

4. 7 m, 11 m

2.01

5. $r = 13.2$ ft

84.48

6. $r = 17.6$ in.

110.53

7. $d = 18.2$ cm

57.48

8. $d = 21.5$ cm

67.51

Assume each square in the grid represents 1 unit. Write the area of each circle in terms of π. Then approximate the area using 3.14 for π. As needed, round to the nearest tenth.

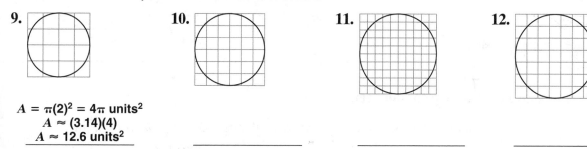

9.

$A = \pi(2)^2 = 4\pi$ units^2
$A \approx (3.14)(4)$
$A \approx 12.6$ units^2

10.

11.

12.

Find the radius of each circle. Use 3.14 for π. If necessary, round to the nearest tenth.

13. $C = 20.1$ in.
$2\pi r = 20.1$
$\dfrac{2\pi r}{2\pi} = \dfrac{20.1}{2\pi}$
$r \approx 3.2$ in.

14. $C = 14.8$ km

2.6

15. $C = 74.7$ mi

11.9

16. $C = 108.6$ yd

17.3

17. $A = 50.24$ cm^2

8

18. $A = 153.86$ ft^2

24.5

19. $A = 254.34$ dm^2

465

20. $A = 113.04$ mm^2

18

Find the area of each circle. Use 3.14 for π. If necessary, round to the nearest tenth. (*Hint:* Use a circumference formula to find r. Substitute that value into the area formula.)

21. $C = 75.36$ in.
$75.36 = 2\pi r$
$\dfrac{75.36}{2\pi} = \dfrac{2\pi r}{2\pi}$; 12 in. $\approx r$
$A \approx \pi(12)^2 \approx (3.14)144$
$A \approx 452.2$ in.^{2}

22. $C = 87.92$ cm

196

23. $C = 94.83$ km

220.0

24. $C = 67.2$ mi

114.4

Problem Solving

Use 3.14 for π. If necessary, round to the nearest tenth.

25. Dulce has a level, circular swimming pool. The pool has a radius of 23 feet. If she wants to cover the floor of the pool with tiles, how many square feet of tiles are needed?
$A = \pi r^2 = \pi(23)^2 \approx (3.14)(529) \approx 1661.1$ ft^2
Dulce needs about 1661.1 square feet of tiles.

26. A dog has a leash on that is 4 meters long. What is the total area of the space where the dog can travel?

27. Seyla raced her horse 3 times around a circular track with a radius of 180 yards. How many yards did they travel?

28. The largest wheel of a penny-farthing—the precursor to the modern bicycle—has a diameter of 1.5 meters. If the largest wheel of a penny-farthing has rotated 75 times, about how far has a person on a penny-farthing ridden?

MENTAL MATH

Use $\dfrac{22}{7}$ for π to approximate each circumference.

29. $r = 3.5$ ft

30. $r = 10.5$ km

31. $d = 49$ cm

32. $d = \dfrac{49}{2}$ in.

10-9 Area of Complex Figures

Name _____ Date _____

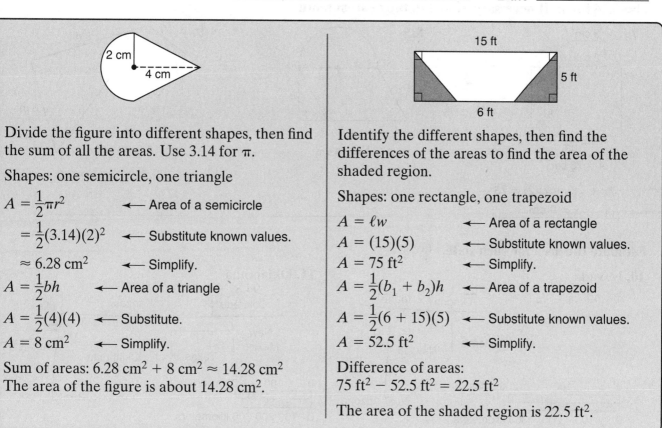

Divide the figure into different shapes, then find the sum of all the areas. Use 3.14 for π.

Shapes: one semicircle, one triangle

$A = \frac{1}{2}\pi r^2$ ← Area of a semicircle

$= \frac{1}{2}(3.14)(2)^2$ ← Substitute known values.

$\approx 6.28 \text{ cm}^2$ ← Simplify.

$A = \frac{1}{2}bh$ ← Area of a triangle

$A = \frac{1}{2}(4)(4)$ ← Substitute.

$A = 8 \text{ cm}^2$ ← Simplify.

Sum of areas: 6.28 cm^2 + 8 cm^2 $\approx$ 14.28 cm^2
The area of the figure is about 14.28 cm^2.

Identify the different shapes, then find the differences of the areas to find the area of the shaded region.

Shapes: one rectangle, one trapezoid

$A = \ell w$ ← Area of a rectangle

$A = (15)(5)$ ← Substitute known values.

$A = 75 \text{ ft}^2$ ← Simplify.

$A = \frac{1}{2}(b_1 + b_2)h$ ← Area of a trapezoid

$A = \frac{1}{2}(6 + 15)(5)$ ← Substitute known values.

$A = 52.5 \text{ ft}^2$ ← Simplify.

Difference of areas:
75 ft^2 − 52.5 ft^2 = 22.5 ft^2

The area of the shaded region is 22.5 ft^2.

Find the total area of each complex figure. If necessary, round to the nearest tenth.

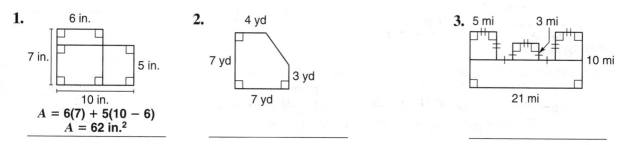

1. $A = 6(7) + 5(10 - 6)$
$A = 62 \text{ in.}^2$

2.

3.

Find the area of the shaded region. Use 3.14 for π. If necessary, round to the nearest tenth.

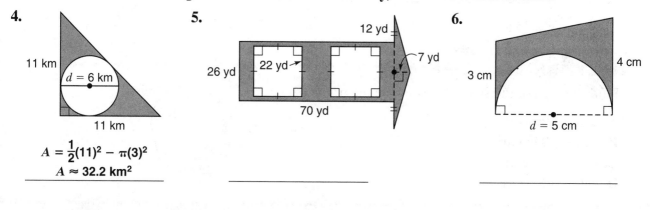

4. $A = \frac{1}{2}(11)^2 - \pi(3)^2$
$A \approx 32.2 \text{ km}^2$

5.

6.

**Find the unknown measurement(s) given the area of each figure.
Use 3.14 for π. If necessary, round to the nearest tenth.**

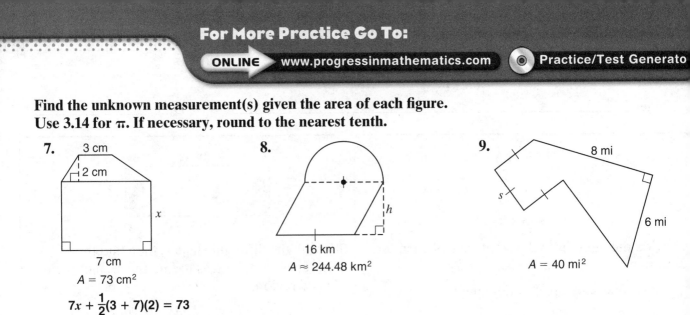

7.
3 cm

2 cm

x

7 cm

$A = 73$ cm²

$7x + \frac{1}{2}(3 + 7)(2) = 73$

$x = 9$ cm

8.
h

16 km

$A \approx 244.48$ km²

9.
8 mi

s

6 mi

$A = 40$ mi²

Estimate the area for each state.

10. Nevada

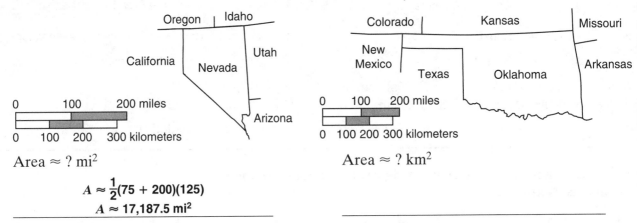

Oregon | Idaho

California | Nevada | Utah

0   100   200 miles

0   100   200   300 kilometers

Arizona

Area ≈ ? mi²

$A \approx \frac{1}{2}(75 + 200)(125)$

$A \approx 17{,}187.5$ mi²

11. Oklahoma

Colorado | Kansas | Missouri

New
Mexico | | Arkansas

Texas | Oklahoma

0   100   200 miles

0   100 200 300 kilometers

Area ≈ ? km²

Problem Solving

12. Tina has been hired to paint the front of this house. It has a door
that is 4 feet by 7 feet and two windows, each 3 feet by 4 feet. The
height of the triangular part of the house is a third the total height.
How many gallons of paint are needed if 1 gallon covers
250 square feet?

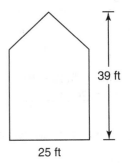

39 ft

25 ft

TEST PREPARATION

13. Find the area of the shaded part of the diagram.

A. $220 - 20\pi$ cm²

B. $220 - 100\pi$ cm²

C. $440 - 20\pi$ cm²

D. $440 - 100\pi$ cm²

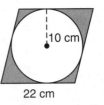

10 cm

22 cm

10-10 Symmetry

Name _____ Date _____

A figure can have several types of symmetry.

- **Line symmetry:** When a real or imaginary line divides the figure into mirror-images. This line is called the *line of symmetry.* A figure can have more than 1 line of symmetry.
- **Rotational symmetry:** When the image matches the original figure after rotating *less than a full turn* around a central point, the *center of rotation.* The smallest turn that creates a match is an *angle of rotation.*
- **Point symmetry:** When the image matches the original figure after rotating *half a turn* around the center of rotation. The angle of rotation is *always* 180°.

To describe the symmetry of a regular pentagon, use the definitions.

- 5 lines of symmetry
- rotational symmetry for 72°, 144°, 216°, 288°, and 360°

  angle of rotation: $\dfrac{360°}{5 \text{ rotations}} = 72°$

- no point symmetry

Tell whether or not the dotted line shows a line of symmetry.

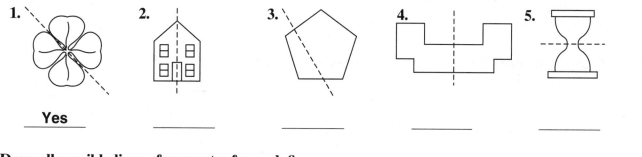

1. _____Yes_____ 2. _____ 3. _____ 4. _____ 5. _____

Draw all possible lines of symmetry for each figure.

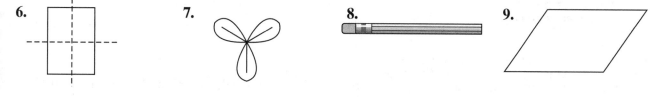

6. **2 lines of symmetry** 7. _____ 8. _____ 9. _____

Tell whether each figure has rotational symmetry. Then find the angle of rotation.

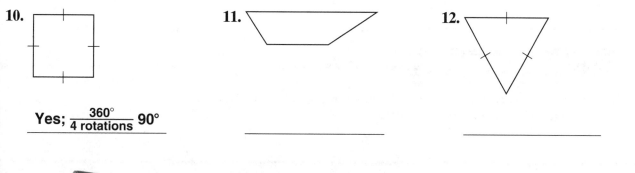

10. **Yes;** $\dfrac{360°}{4 \text{ rotations}}$ **90°** 11. _____ 12. _____

Find the angle of rotation for each figure.

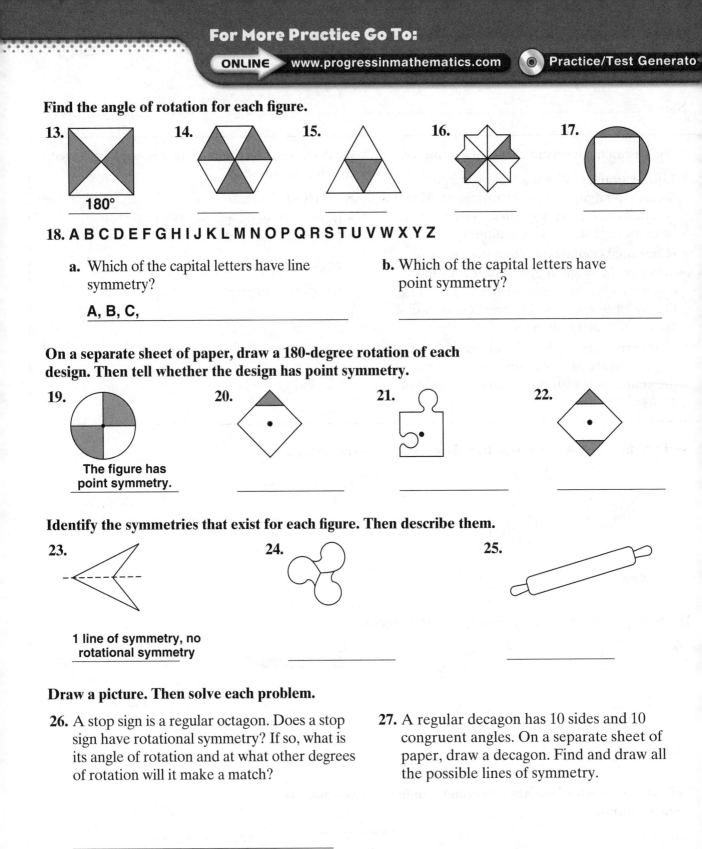

13. 180°

14. _____

15. _____

16. _____

17. _____

18. A B C D E F G H I J K L M N O P Q R S T U V W X Y Z

a. Which of the capital letters have line symmetry?

A, B, C, _____

b. Which of the capital letters have point symmetry?

_____

On a separate sheet of paper, draw a 180-degree rotation of each design. Then tell whether the design has point symmetry.

19. The figure has point symmetry.

20. _____

21. _____

22. _____

Identify the symmetries that exist for each figure. Then describe them.

23. 1 line of symmetry, no rotational symmetry

24. _____

25. _____

Draw a picture. Then solve each problem.

26. A stop sign is a regular octagon. Does a stop sign have rotational symmetry? If so, what is its angle of rotation and at what other degrees of rotation will it make a match?

27. A regular decagon has 10 sides and 10 congruent angles. On a separate sheet of paper, draw a decagon. Find and draw all the possible lines of symmetry.

_____

CRITICAL THINKING

28. On a separate sheet of paper, draw a figure that has at least four lines of symmetry and point symmetry.

10-11 Tessellations

Name _____ Date _____

Tessellations are the covering of a plane with congruent copies of the same figure or figures, with no overlaps or gaps.

A *translation tessellation* is a pattern made by translating, or sliding, a figure.

A *rotation tessellation* is a pattern made by rotating a figure. Only figures with angles that are factors of 360° can be used to make rotation tessellations.

Tessellations can be made by using more than one figure.

Draw each regular polygon on a separate sheet of paper. Tell whether each figure tessellates. If possible, create a tessellation.

1. _____Yes_____

2. _____

3. _____

4. _____

Draw each polygon on another sheet of paper. Tell whether each figure tessellates. If so, make a tessellation.

5. _____Yes_____

6. _____

7. _____

8. _____

Identify each type of tessellation.

9. ___rotation___

10. _____

11. _____

12. _____

Identify the polygons used to create the tessellation.

13.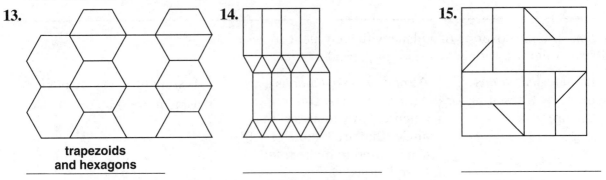

trapezoids
and hexagons

14.

15.

Determine whether the statement is *true* **or** *false***. Explain.**

16. All parallelograms can tessellate using rotation.

False; Figures that can make rotation tessellations must have angle measures that are all factors of 360°; not all parallelograms do.

17. All triangles can tessellate.

18. All regular polygons can tessellate using rotation.

19. Most tiles on floors are laid out with a pattern using tessellations.

Problem Solving

20. Mae is designing a pattern for a tablecloth. She wants to make a tessellation using a regular hexagon and an equilateral triangle. On a separate sheet of paper, draw a pattern she can make.

21. Jerome wants to stencil a wall in his room with a tessellation pattern. His stencil kit includes a regular octagon and a square. The sides of the square are the same length as the sides of the octagon. On a separate sheet of paper, draw a pattern he can make.

CRITICAL THINKING

22. Without drawing the figures, explain why you can make a tessellation using a combination of a regular hexagon, two squares and an equilateral triangle.

10-12 Technology: Relate Perimeter and Area

Name _____ Date _____

Find the area and perimeter of a rectangle with a length of 15 inches and a width of 5 inches. Then see what happens when one dimension is halved.

	A	B	C	D
1	Length (in.)	Width (in.)	Perimeter (in.)	Area (in.²)
2	15	5		

Step 1 Set up a table in your spreadsheet program like the one above.

Step 2 Enter the formula for perimeter in cell C2. Type **=2*A2+2*B2.** The program will multiply the value in cell A2 by 2, multiply the value in cell B2 by 2, and find their sum.

Step 3 Enter the formula for area in cell D2. Type **=A2*B2.** The program will multiply the value in cell A2 by the value in cell B2.

So the original perimeter is 40 in. and the original area is 75 in.².

Step 4 To see what happens when one of the dimensions is changed, in cell A2, divide the original length by 2. Type-in 7.5. The program will automatically calculate the new perimeter and area.

So the new perimeter is 25 in. and the new area is 37.5 in.² The change in perimeter is a decrease of 15 in., or the original length. The new area is half the original area.

1. Write the formula that was typed into cell E2 in the spreadsheet below to calculate the Account Balance. Determine the missing value of C2.

	A	B	C	D	E
1	Date	Deposits	Withdrawals	Checks Cashed	Account Balance
2	10 Jan	4755		1500	1854

_____

_____

_____

2. What would the formula placed in E2 change to if the deposits were double the amount? What would be the value of C2, in this case?

_____

_____

_____

3. Use a spreadsheet program to find the perimeter and area of a square whose side length is 5.5 cm. Draw the cells as they appear on the spreadsheet. Then write and identify the formulas used in the spreadsheet program.

_____

4. Use the same spreadsheet you made above to find the perimeter and area of a similar square with side lengths that are tripled. Draw the cells as they appear on the spreadsheet. Then write and identify the formulas used in the spreadsheet program.

_____

5. Describe the changes that occurred to the perimeter and area.

_____

_____

_____

_____

CRITICAL THINKING

6. Can a spreadsheet program be used to compute the circumference and area of a circle? If so, use a spreadsheet program to find the circumference and area of a circle whose diameter is 8 cm. Use 3.14 for π. Draw the cells as they appear on the spreadsheet. Then write and identify the formulas used in the spreadsheet program.

_____

10-13 Problem-Solving Strategy:
Account for All Possibilities

Read Plan Solve Check

Name ______________________ Date __________

Solve by using the strategy Account for All Possibilities.

1. There are eight wooden rods on a table. Their lengths in inches are: 1, 1, 2, 3, 5, 8, 13, and 21. How many different triangles can be made by choosing three of these rods at a time?

____

2. Mary has $62. She has four more $1 bills than $5 bills. She also has at least one $20 bill. If she holds no other denominations of currency, describe the bills she has.

____

3. How many diagonals does a regular hexagon have? A regular pentagon?

____

4. In how many different ways can 100 baseball cards be placed in stacks of equal heights (other than 100 stacks of 1 or 1 stack of 100)?

____

5. In how many distinct ways can the letters AABB be arranged?

____

Use with SOURCEBOOK Lesson 10-13, pages 296–297.

6. How many *right* triangles have side lengths that are whole numbers and hypotenuses that are less than 14?

7. If you don't get any pennies, in how many ways can you receive 45¢ in change?

8. In how many different ways can Alice, Bill, Cathy, and Derrick line up at the snack bar?

9. If the area of a rectangle is 40 m² and the length in meters of each side is a whole number, what is the smallest perimeter the rectangle can have?

10. If we must move between nodes in the directions indicated, how many different paths can we take from node A to node B?

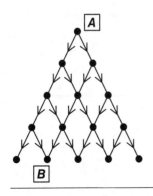

Enrichment:
Areas of Irregular Polygons

Name _____   Date _____

Find the area of the polygon.

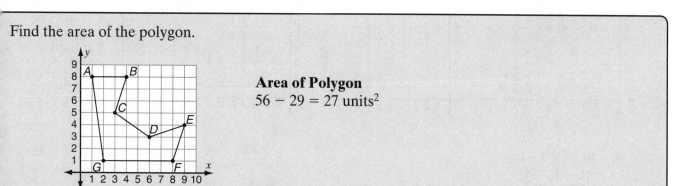

Area of Polygon
$56 - 29 = 27$ units^2

Use Pick's Formula

Step 1	Step 2	Step 3
Mark and count all lattice points on the boundary (sides) of the polygon. Be sure to count the vertices.	Mark and count all the interior lattice points (those that are inside the polygon).	Use Pick's formula: $A = I + \dfrac{B}{2} - 1$. where I is the number of interior points and B is the number of boundary points.

Use Method 1: Subtract from a rectangle, to find the area of the given polygon.

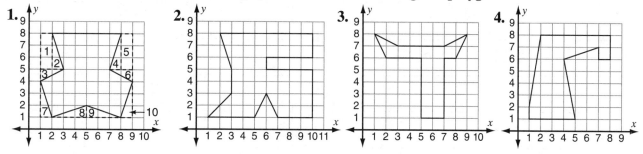

Area of Rectangle
$8 \times 7 = 56$ units^2
Areas of Figures
Outside the Polygon

(1) 3 units^2 (2) 1.5 units^2
(3) 1 units^2 (4) 1.5 units^2
(5) 3 units^2 (6) 1 units^2
(7) 1.5 units^2 (8) 1.5 units^2
(9) 1.5 units^2 (10) 1.5 units^2

Total = 17 units^2
Area of Polygon: $56 - 17$
    = **39 units^2**

_____   _____   _____   _____

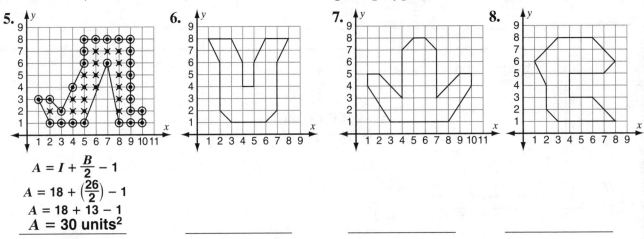

Use Method 2, Pick's formula, to find the area of the given polygon.

5.

$$A = I + \frac{B}{2} - 1$$
$$A = 18 + \left(\frac{26}{2}\right) - 1$$
$$A = 18 + 13 - 1$$
$$A = 30 \text{ units}^2$$

6. _____

7. _____

8. _____

Use Method 3: Cross Products of the Coordinates, to find the area of the polygons that have vertices at the given points. (*Hint:* Start and end with the same point.)

9. $A(0, 7)$, $B(2, 7)$, $C(3, 4)$, $D(4, 6)$, $E(5, 4)$, $F(6, 7)$, $G(8, 7)$, $H(7, 0)$, $I(5, 0)$, $J(4, 2)$, $K(3, 0)$, $L(1, 0)$

Cross Products	Coordinates		Cross Products
	x	y	
	0	7	
14	2	7	0
	0	7	

10. $M(0, 7)$, $N(2, 7)$, $O(2, 5)$, $P(4, 5)$, $Q(4, 7)$, $R(6, 7)$, $S(6, 0)$, $T(4, 0)$, $U(4, 3)$, $V(2, 3)$, $W(2, 0)$, $X(0, 0)$

Cross Products	Coordinates		Cross Products
	x	y	

_____ _____

CHALLENGE

Choose a method to find the area of the given polygon.

11. _____

_____

_____

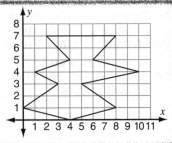

Test Prep: Multiple-Choice Questions

Strategy: Apply Mathematical Reasoning

Name _____   Date _____

An *estimate* can sometimes be used to determine which answer choices are reasonable and which should be deleted. When only one answer seems reasonable, check to be sure that it is correct.

To select the correct answer in a multiple-choice question, try using the following strategies.

- Reread the item.
- Use the Test-Prep Strategy.
- Apply appropriate rules, definitions, properties, or strategies.
- Analyze your answers.

Choose the correct answer. *TIP: Don't forget to use the tools and formulas provided.*

1. What is the area of trapezoid *PQRS* in square units?

A. $82\frac{1}{4}$ **C.** $41\frac{41}{64}$

B. $35\frac{7}{8}$ **D.** $25\frac{11}{32}$

2. To the nearest square foot, what is the area of the circle?

Area $= \pi r^2$

F. 15   **H.** 25

G. 36   **J.** 50

3. Which irrational number is *closest* to 6?

F. $\sqrt{60}$ **H.** $\sqrt{7}$

G. $\sqrt{37}$ **J.** $\sqrt{6}$

4. The scale on a map is $\frac{1}{2}$ inch = 5 miles. How many inches on the map represents a distance of 42 miles?

A. 4.2   **C.** 8.4

B. 10.8   **D.** 12.0

5. Mrs. Gonzales bought 4 gallons of milk. One gallon is about 3.8 liters. About how many liters of milk did she buy?

A. 0.2 liters   **C.** 7.8 liters

B. 12 liters   **D.** 15 liters

6. Ted's restaurant bill came to $41.75. He wants to leave a 15% tip. Which is a good estimate of the amount for the tip?

F. $4.00   **H.** $6.00

G. $46.00   **J.** $48.00

Vocabulary Development

Name _____ Date _____

Chapter 10 Vocabulary

absolute error	height	positive square root	square of a number
accuracy	irrational number	precision	square root
altitude	line of symmetry	Pythagorean Theorem	symmetry
angle of rotation	line symmetry	Pythagorean triple	tessellation
area	negative square root	radical sign	translation tessellation
base	perfect square	relative error	
circumference	perimeter	rotation tessellation	
greatest possible error (GPE)	point symmetry	rotational symmetry	

From the vocabulary list above, choose the term(s) that best complete each sentence. Write the term(s) in the space(s) provided.

1. A(n) _____ cannot be expressed as a quotient of two integers.

2. The _____ is equal to one half of the smallest unit that an instrument can measure.

3. A design that covers a plane with congruent copies of the same

   figure with no overlaps or gaps is called a _____.

4. The distance around a circle is called its _____.

5. A figure that has _____ matches the original figure after rotating a half turn around its center.

Tell whether each statement is *true* or *false*. If the statement is false, change it to make it true.

6. A square has 2 lines of symmetry.

   _____

7. A trapezoid with an area of 240 cm^2 has bases that measure 18 cm and 22 cm. The height of the trapezoid is 12 cm.

   _____

8. An example of a perfect square is 99.

   _____

9. When the side lengths of a right triangle are 1, 2, and 3, they form a Pythagorean triple.

   _____

Practice Chapter 10 Test

Name _____ Date _____

Give the greatest possible error, GPE, and the percent of relative error to the nearest tenth of a percent.

1. 55 cm

GPE = _____

Relative error = _____

2. 3 kg

GPE = _____

Relative error = _____

Find the perimeter of each polygon.

3.

16.8 ft

P = _____

4.

15 in.   6 in.

8 in.

18 in.

P = _____

5.

41 km

34.2 km

65.5 km

33 km

46.8 km

P = _____

Simplify each expression.

6. $\sqrt{225}$

_____

7. $\sqrt{400}$

_____

8. $\sqrt{900} - \sqrt{36}$

_____

9. $\sqrt{144} + \sqrt{121}$

_____

Identify which whole numbers the square root is between.

10. $\sqrt{50}$

_____

11. $\sqrt{77}$

_____

12. $\sqrt{432}$

_____

13. $\sqrt{2759}$

_____

Find the length of each missing side in a right triangle to the nearest tenth.

14. $a = 5$ in., $b = 12$ in.

_____

15. $a = 18$ ft, $b = 24$ ft

_____

16. $a = 6$ cm, $c = 9$ cm

_____

17. $b = 11$ km, $c = 16$ km

_____

Find the unknown dimension of the polygon.

18. Regular Octagon:

$P = 496$ cm

$s =$ _____

19. Rectangle:

$P = 6.6$ mm

$\ell = 1.8$ mm

$w =$ _____

20. Trapezoid:

$b_1 = 33$ m, $b_2 = 34$ m

$A = 737$ m^2

$h =$ _____

Find the area and circumference of each circle with the given diameter or radius to the nearest tenth. Use 3.14 for π.

21. $r = 17$ in.

_____

_____

22. $r = 6.5$ yd

_____

_____

23. $d = 19$ ft

_____

_____

24. $d = 10.2$ mm

_____

_____

Find the total area of each figure. Use 3.14 for π. Round to the nearest tenth when necessary.

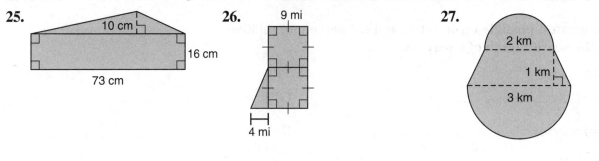

25. 26. 9 mi 27.

_____ _____ _____

Find the total area of each shaded region. Use 3.14 for π.
Round to the nearest tenth when necessary.

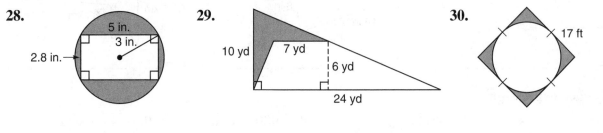

28. 29. 30.

_____ _____ _____

Identify the symmetries that exist for each figure. Then describe them.

31. 32. 33.

_____ _____ _____

Identify each type of tessellation.

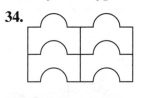

34. _____ 35. _____

Tell About It

Explain how you solve the problem. Show all your work.

36. Cassandra designed a triangular poster with an area of 72 square inches. The length of the triangle's base is equal to its height. What are the base and height lengths of the triangle?

_____

_____

_____

Cumulative Review: Chapters 1–10

Name _____ Date _____

Circle the best answer.

1. What is the mean of the data in the stem-and-leaf plot?

stem	leaves
1	6 6 6 8
2	1 1
3	7 8 9
4	5 5 8

Key: 1|6 = 16

A. 16   **B.** 29

C. 30   **D.** 32

2. A gardener has 108 feet of fence to use to surround a rectangular garden. Which inequality can be used to represent the length of a garden if the width is 20 feet?

F. $2\ell \geq 108 - 40$ **G.** $2\ell > 108 + 40$

H. $2\ell < 108$ **J.** $2\ell \leq 108 - 40$

3. Solve:

$12x + 17 = -7$

A. $x = -2$ **B.** $x = -\frac{5}{6}$

C. $x = \frac{5}{6}$ **D.** $x = 2$

4. What is the greatest common factor of 900 and 1890?

F. 30   **G.** 90

H. 900   **J.** 18,900

5. The ratio of boys to girls in the 7th grade at the Miller School is 12 : 13. If there are 650 students in 7th grade, how many are girls?

A. 50   **B.** 312

C. 338   **D.** 600

6. Which is *not* equal to 200.5?

F. 2.005×10^2

G. 2.005%

H. $200\frac{1}{2}$

J. $\frac{401}{2}$

7. A regular octagon has a side length of 16.8 meters. What is its perimeter?

A. 67.2 m
B. 100.8 m
C. 134.4 m
D. 168 m

8. Jillian deposits $750 into an account that earns 4% simple annual interest. What is the balance in the account after 18 months? ($I = prt$)

F. $780   **G.** $795

H. $1125   **J.** $1322.40

9. A map has a scale of 2 cm = 250 km. What is the actual distance if the distance on the map is 5.5 cm?

A. 343.75 km   **B.** 687.5 km

C. 750 km   **D.** 1375 km

10. Simplify.

$$\frac{9^8}{9^2}$$

F. 9^7
G. 9^6
H. 3^7
J. 3^6

11. Maria's age is 3 years more than twice George's age. Which expression represents George's age in terms of Maria's?

  A. $2m - 3$
  B. $2m + 3$
  C. $\dfrac{m - 3}{2}$
  D. $\dfrac{m}{2} - 3$

12. 598 is 115% of what number?

  F. 508.3
  G. 520
  H. 687.7
  J. 5200

13. Classify the triangle.

  A. acute isosceles
  B. acute scalene
  C. obtuse isosceles
  D. obtuse scalene

14. Which postulate proves that the triangles are congruent?

  F. *ASA* **G.** *SAA*

  H. *SAS* **J.** *SSS*

15. Evaluate when $x = 5$ and $y = -5$.

  $y^2 + x - 3x^2$

  A. -95
  B. -45
  C. 45
  D. 95

16. Bo uses a 64-fluid ounce jug to fill a 10-gallon aquarium. How many times does he need to fill the jug to fill the aquarium completely?

  F. $2\frac{1}{2}$ **G.** 5

  H. 10 **J.** 20

17. Find the sum $4\frac{3}{8} + 6\frac{5}{6}$.

  A. $10\frac{5}{24}$ **B.** $10\frac{1}{3}$

  C. $10\frac{4}{7}$ **D.** $11\frac{5}{24}$

18. Find the area of the shaded region. Use 3.14 for π.

  F. 43.74 in.² **G.** 62.58 in.²

  H. 81.42 in.² **J.** 100.26 in.²

Tell About It

Explain how you solve the problem. Show all your work.

19. A rectangular deck has side lengths of 9 feet and 12 feet. Stuart stretches a rope from one corner of the deck to the opposite corner. What is the length of the rope between those two corners?

11-1 Three-Dimensional Figures

Name _____   Date _____

To classify three-dimensional figures, use the definitions.

Edge: The line segment where two faces meet.
Vertex: A point where three or more edges meet.
Polyhedron: All the faces are polygons.
Regular Polyhedron: All the faces are congruent.
Prism: A polyhedron with two congruent and parallel faces, called bases. The shape of the base determines the name of the prism. A prism's lateral faces are rectangles.

Pyramid: Has only one base, which can be any polygon. The other faces of a pyramid are triangles. The shape of the base determines the name of the pyramid.
Three-dimensional figures with curved surfaces include cylinders, cones, spheres, and hemispheres.

How many edges?	**Euler's Formula**	5 faces, n edges, 5 vertices
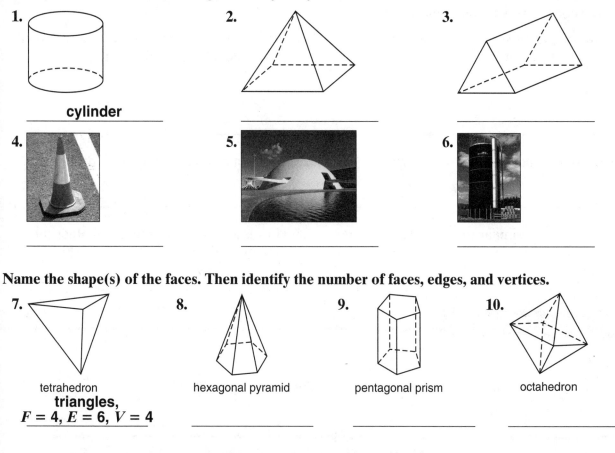 →	For any polyhedron, if F is the number of faces, E is the number of edges, and V is the number of vertices, then $F + V = E + 2$.	→ $F + V = E + 2$ $5 + 5 = E + 2$ ← Substitute the known values. $8 = E$ The square pyramid has 8 edges.

Classify the three-dimensional figure or object by name.

1.
cylinder

2.
_____

3.
_____

4.
_____

5.
_____

6.
_____

Name the shape(s) of the faces. Then identify the number of faces, edges, and vertices.

7.
tetrahedron
triangles,
$F = 4, E = 6, V = 4$

8.
hexagonal pyramid
_____

9.
pentagonal prism
_____

10.
octahedron
_____

Complete the chart. Use Euler's formula to check your answers.

	Figure	Face	Edges	Vertices	Euler's Formula
11.	cube	_____	_____	_____	_____
12.	triangular pyramid	_____	_____	_____	_____
13.	pentagonal pyramid	_____	_____	_____	_____
14.	hexagonal prism	_____	_____	_____	_____
15.	*n*-gonal pyramid	_____	_____	_____	_____

Identify each three-dimensional figure as *regular* or *not regular*.

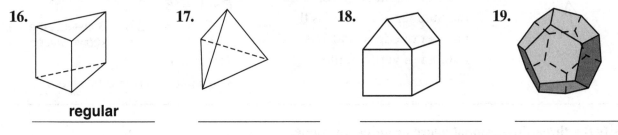

16.

regular

17.

_____

18.

_____

19.

_____

Explain your answers to these questions.

20. How are prisms similar to pyramids? How are they different?

_____

21. What is the difference between a rectangular prism and a hexagonal prism?

_____

22. How is a cylinder similar to a prism?

_____

23. Why is a cylinder not a polyhedron?

_____

24. How is a cone similar to a cylinder?

_____

25. How is a sphere different from other three-dimensional figures?

_____

SPIRAL REVIEW

Compute.

26. $(1.5)^2$ **27.** $(4.2)^3$ **28.** $(0.31)^2$ **29.** $(0.05)^3$ **30.** $\left(\frac{1}{3}\right)^2$ **31.** $\left(\frac{1}{2}\right)^3$

_____ _____ _____ _____ _____ _____

11-2 Draw Three-Dimensional Figures

Name _____ Date _____

To represent three-dimensional figures, make two-dimensional drawings.

Isometric Drawing

A pictorial view created on an isometric dot grid of a three-dimensional figure using 3 types of lines.

Orthographic Drawing

A two-dimensional drawing where each view shows only one face. The angles in the drawing are congruent to the angles in the *actual figure.*

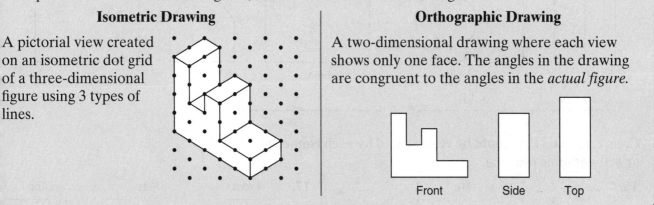

Front   Side   Top

Use isometric dot paper and a straightedge to make an isometric drawing of each rectangular prism. (h = height; w = width; ℓ = length).

1. $h = 1, w = 2, \ell = 5$ **2.** $h = 2, w = 1, \ell = 4$ **3.** $h = 2, w = 3, \ell = 4$ **4.** $h = 1, w = 4, \ell = 5$

Use graph paper and a straightedge to make orthographic drawings to show the front, side, and top views of each figure. Label each view.

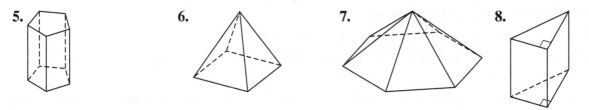

5.   **6.**   **7.**   **8.**

Name the figure that has the front, side, and top views shown.

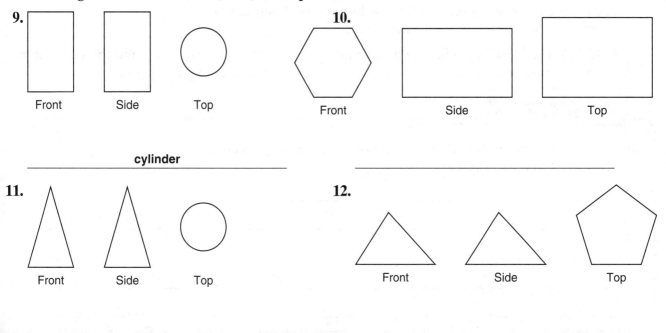

9.

Front   Side   Top

10.

Front   Side   Top

_____ cylinder _____   _____

11.

Front   Side   Top

12.

Front   Side   Top

_____   _____

Name an object that could be represented by each set of
orthographic drawings.

13.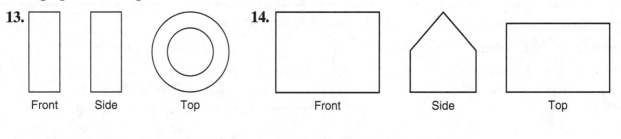

14.

Create a model that could be represented by each isometric
or orthographic drawing.

15. **16.** **17.**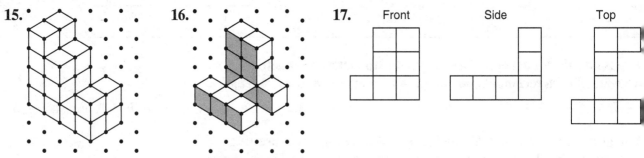

Make a drawing to represent each situation.

18. The longer side of an L-shaped building is 4 units long and the
shorter side is 3 units long. The entire building is 1 unit high,
and each side is 1 unit wide.

    a. Make an isometric drawing of the building
on isometric dot paper.

    b. Draw the front, side, and top views of the
building in question a. on graph paper.

19. A short staircase at the back of a house has 4 steps. Each step is
2.5 units wide, 1 unit high, and 1 unit deep.

    a. Make an isometric drawing of the staircase
on isometric dot paper.

    b. Draw the front, side, and top views of the
staircase on graph paper.

CHALLENGE

20. Describe the methods you would use to draw a cylinder, a cone,
a sphere, and a hemisphere.

_____

_____

_____

_____

_____

11-3 Surface Area of Prisms

Name _____   Date _____

To *find the surface area, S, of a prism,* use a net or a formula to calculate the sum of the areas of its faces.

Use a Net

Area of top	→ $\ell \cdot w = 5(4) = 20$ in.²
Area of bottom	→ $\ell \cdot w = 5(4) = 20$ in.²
Area of side	→ $\ell \cdot h = 5(1) = 5$ in.²
Area of side	→ $\ell \cdot h = 5(1) = 5$ in.²
Area of front	→ $w \cdot h = 4(1) = 4$ in.²
Area of back	→ $w \cdot h = 4(1) = 4$ in.²

$20 + 20 + 5 + 5 + 4 + 4 = 58$ in.² ← Use square units.

Use a Formula

Rectangular prism: $S = 2\ell w + 2\ell h + 2wh$, where S = surface area, ℓ = length, w = width, and h = height.

$S = 2(5)(4) + 2(5)(1) + 2(4)(1)$
$40 + 10 + 8 = 58$ in.² ← Use square units.

The surface area is 58 in.²

Use a net to find the surface area of each prism, then complete the exercises.

1. a. $S = (3 \cdot 6) + (3 \cdot 6) + (3 \cdot 9) + (3 \cdot 9) + (6 \cdot 9) + (6 \cdot 9)$
$S = 198$ in.² _____

b. How many pairs of congruent rectangles are there?

_____

2. a. _____

b. Classify the triangle that forms the base of the prism. Explain.

_____

Use graph paper and a straightedge to draw a net for each prism. Then find the surface area of the prism.

3.   1 yd   2 yd   2 yd   3 yd   3 yd

$S = 2\left(\frac{1}{2}\right) \cdot 3 \cdot 1 +$
$2(2 \cdot 3) + (3 \cdot 3) = 24$ yd²

4.   10.2 mm   9 mm   1.5 mm

$SA = 2[(l \cdot w + l \cdot h + w \cdot h)]$
$SA = 2[(10.2 \cdot 1.5) + (10.2 \cdot 9) + (5 \cdot 9)]$
$SA = 2(15.3 + 91.8 + 13.5)$
$SA = 241.2 \text{ mm}^2$

5.   7 mm   7 mm   7 mm

6.   16 in.   8 in.   2 in.   12 in.   4 in.

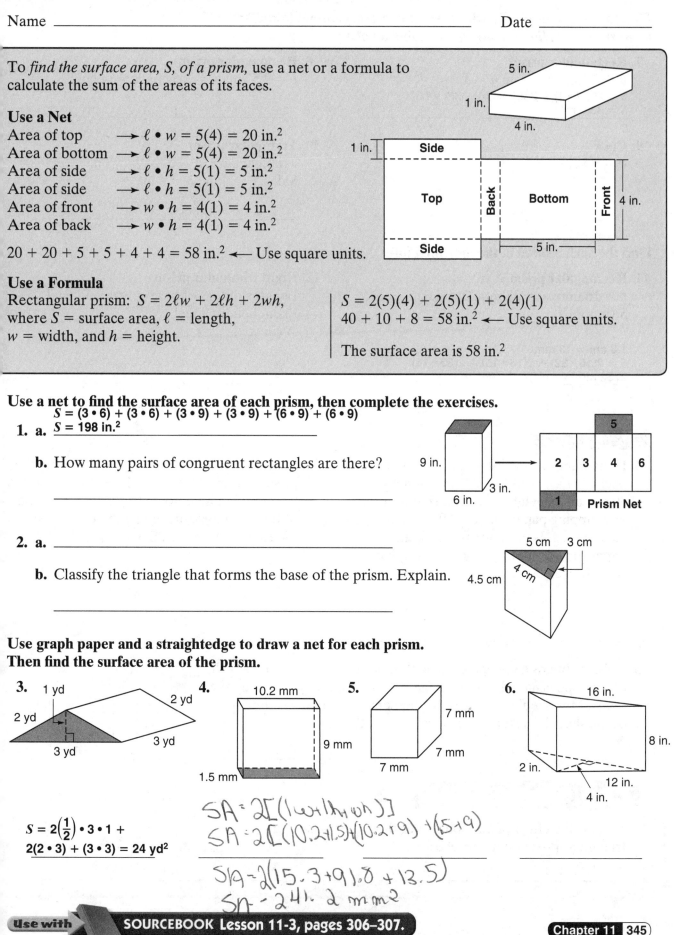

Find the surface area of each figure. If necessary, round to the nearest tenth. (*Hint:* First draw and label a net.)

7. Rectangular prism
$\ell = 2.2$ m; $w = 1$ m; $h = 4.5$ m
$S = 2(2.2 \cdot 1) + 2(2.2 \cdot 4.5) + 2(1 \cdot 4.5)$
$S = 33.2$ m²

8. Rectangular prism
$\ell = 2.5$ cm; $w = 2.5$ cm; $h = 14$ cm

0.25 + 35.735
152.5

9. Cube
$\ell = 4.7$ ft

10. Triangular prism
Triangle base: $b = 5$ in.; $h = 3$ in.
Sides: $\ell = 4$ in.; $h = 6$ in.

Find the surface area in the indicated units.

11. Rectangular prism
$\ell = 16$ mm; $w = 32$ mm; $h = 1.8$ cm
S (in mm²)

1.8 cm = 18 mm
$S = 2(16 \cdot 32) + 2(16 \cdot 18) + 2(32 \cdot 18) =$
2752 mm²

12. Right triangular prism
Lengths of legs of base = 8 yd and 6 yd
Prism height: 9 feet
S (in yd²)

Problem Solving

13. Hans want to wrap 10 packages. Each package has a width of 20 cm, a length of 30 cm, and a height of 10 cm. He has a roll of wrapping paper that is 20,000 square centimeters. Is this enough wrapping paper to wrap all the packages? Explain your answer.

14. Sally builds a clubhouse that is a rectangular prism that is 12 feet long, 15 feet wide, and 9 feet high. She is going to paint the outside of the clubhouse, including the top. What is the total surface area that Sally will paint?

15. Roberta builds a storage shed next to her garage. The largest side of the shed is nailed to the garage wall. If Roberta paints only the sides of the shed exposed to the elements, how many square feet of the shed does Roberta cover with paint?

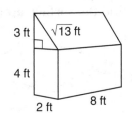

CRITICAL THINKING

16. What is the effect of doubling all of the dimensions of a triangular prism on its surface area?

11-4 Surface Area of Pyramids

Name _____ Date _____

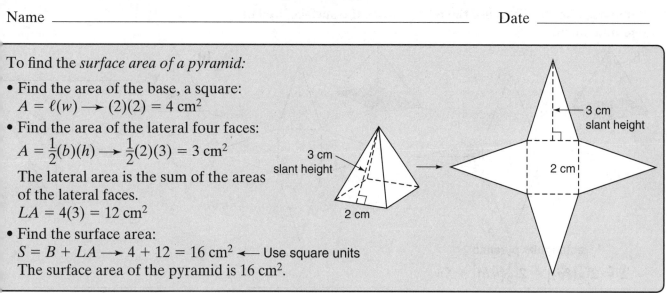

To find the *surface area of a pyramid:*

- Find the area of the base, a square:
  $A = \ell(w) \longrightarrow (2)(2) = 4$ cm^2
- Find the area of the lateral four faces:
  $A = \frac{1}{2}(b)(h) \longrightarrow \frac{1}{2}(2)(3) = 3$ cm^2

  The lateral area is the sum of the areas of the lateral faces.
  $LA = 4(3) = 12$ cm^2
- Find the surface area:
  $S = B + LA \longrightarrow 4 + 12 = 16$ cm^2 ← Use square units
  The surface area of the pyramid is 16 cm^2.

Draw a net for each pyramid, then find its surface area. If necessary, use a calculator to round square roots to the nearest tenth.

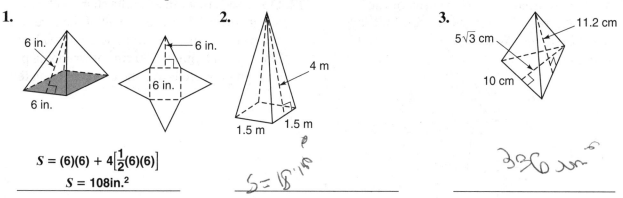

1.
6 in.   6 in.
6 in.   6 in.

$S = (6)(6) + 4\left[\frac{1}{2}(6)(6)\right]$
$S = 108$ in.^{2}

2.
4 m
1.5 m   1.5 m

$S = 18.18$

3.
11.2 cm
$5\sqrt{3}$ cm
10 cm

326 cm^2

Find the surface area. (*Hint:* Write the answer in the indicated units).

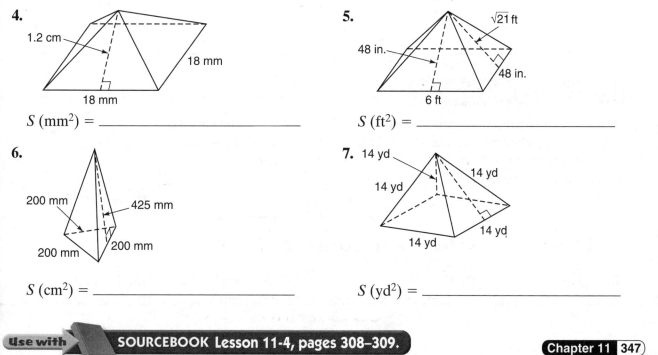

4.
1.2 cm
18 mm
18 mm

S (mm^2) = _____

5.
$\sqrt{21}$ ft
48 in.
48 in.
6 ft

S (ft^2) = _____

6.
200 mm   425 mm
200 mm   200 mm

S (cm^2) = _____

7. 14 yd
14 yd   14 yd
14 yd   14 yd

S (yd^2) = _____

Name each figure. Then use the nets to write the surface area in algebraic form.

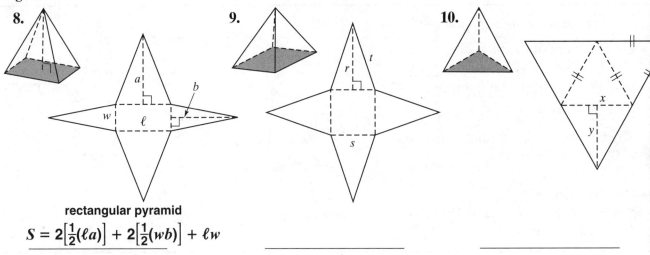

8.

9.

10.

rectangular pyramid

$$S = 2\left[\frac{1}{2}(\ell a)\right] + 2\left[\frac{1}{2}(wb)\right] + \ell w$$

Problem Solving

11. Violet says that the surface area of the square pyramid is 96 square feet. Phil says $S = 12{,}096$ in.^{2}. Whose answer is correct? Explain.

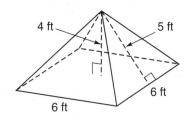

12. Don needs to wrap a candle shaped like a tetrahedron. The base and all of the faces are congruent equilateral triangles. Each side length is 140 mm. Is 290 cm^2 of wrapping paper enough paper to cover the candle completely?

TEST PREPARATION

13. A triangular pyramid is composed of congruent equilateral triangles. Each face has a surface area of 45 in.^{2} What is the total surface area of the figure?

   A. 11.25 in.^{2} **C.** 45 in.^{2}

   B. 135 in.^{2} **D.** 180 in.^{2}

14. What is the surface area of the square pyramid?

   F. 121 mm^2 **H.** 187 mm^2

   G. 308 mm^2 **J.** 495 mm^2

11-5 Surface Area of Cylinders and Cones

Name _____   Date _____

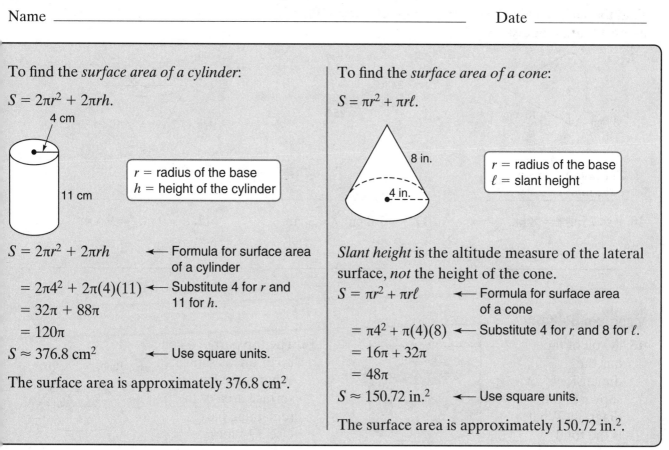

To find the *surface area of a cylinder*:

$S = 2\pi r^2 + 2\pi rh.$

4 cm

11 cm

r = radius of the base
h = height of the cylinder

$S = 2\pi r^2 + 2\pi rh$ ← Formula for surface area of a cylinder

$= 2\pi 4^2 + 2\pi(4)(11)$ ← Substitute 4 for r and 11 for h.

$= 32\pi + 88\pi$

$= 120\pi$

$S \approx 376.8 \text{ cm}^2$ ← Use square units.

The surface area is approximately 376.8 cm².

To find the *surface area of a cone*:

$S = \pi r^2 + \pi r\ell.$

8 in.

4 in.

r = radius of the base
ℓ = slant height

Slant height is the altitude measure of the lateral surface, *not* the height of the cone.

$S = \pi r^2 + \pi r\ell$ ← Formula for surface area of a cone

$= \pi 4^2 + \pi(4)(8)$ ← Substitute 4 for r and 8 for ℓ.

$= 16\pi + 32\pi$

$= 48\pi$

$S \approx 150.72 \text{ in.}^2$ ← Use square units.

The surface area is approximately 150.72 in.².

Draw a net for each cylinder. Then find its surface area. Use $\pi \approx 3.14$. If necessary, round to the nearest tenth.

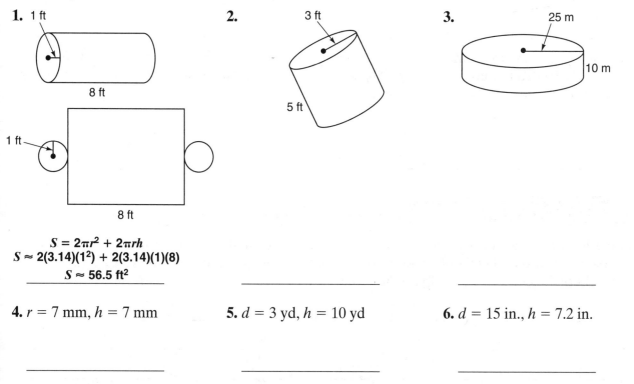

1. 1 ft

8 ft

1 ft

8 ft

$S = 2\pi r^2 + 2\pi rh$
$S \approx 2(3.14)(1^2) + 2(3.14)(1)(8)$
$S \approx 56.5 \text{ ft}^2$

2. 3 ft

5 ft

3. 25 m

10 m

4. $r = 7$ mm, $h = 7$ mm

5. $d = 3$ yd, $h = 10$ yd

6. $d = 15$ in., $h = 7.2$ in.

Find the surface of each cone. Use π ≈ 3.14. Round to the nearest tenth if necessary.

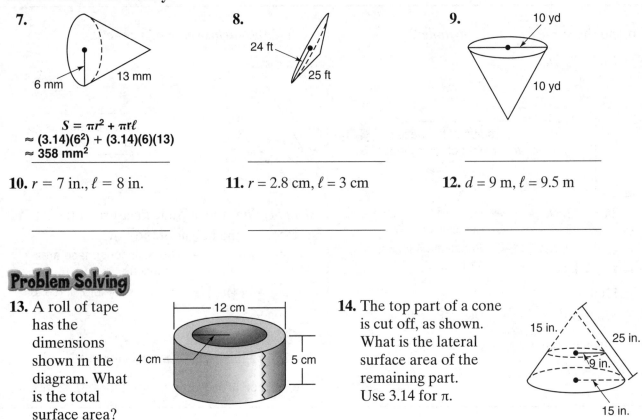

7.

6 mm   13 mm

$$S = \pi r^2 + \pi r \ell$$
$$\approx (3.14)(6^2) + (3.14)(6)(13)$$
$$\approx 358 \text{ mm}^2$$

8.

24 ft   25 ft

9.

10 yd   10 yd   10 yd

10. $r = 7$ in., $\ell = 8$ in.

11. $r = 2.8$ cm, $\ell = 3$ cm

12. $d = 9$ m, $\ell = 9.5$ m

Problem Solving

13. A roll of tape has the dimensions shown in the diagram. What is the total surface area? Use 3.14 for π.

12 cm   4 cm   5 cm

14. The top part of a cone is cut off, as shown. What is the lateral surface area of the remaining part. Use 3.14 for π.

15 in.   25 in.   9 in.   15 in.

15. A new juice can label completely covers the side of the can without overlapping. How much paper is needed to make labels for 100 juice cans that have a diameter of 3.5 centimeters and a height of 8 centimeters? Use 3.14 for π.

CRITICAL THINKING

16. Predict which has the greater surface area: A square pyramid with a base side length of 12 meters and a slant height of 9 meters, or a cone with a diameter of 12 meters and a slant height of 9 meters. Then compare the actual surface areas.

11-6 Estimate Surface Area

Name _____ Date _____

To *find an overestimate*, an estimate greater than the actual value, round a number up to a greater number.

To *find an underestimate*, an estimate less than the actual value, round a number down to a lesser number.

Decide whether the situation calls for an *overestimate* or an *underestimate*. Explain your reasoning.

1. the amount of pizza to buy for a party

Overestimate; This way there will be enough for everyone.

2. the amount of money you can spend at the store

_____

3. the size of a doorway through which you will bring a sofa

_____

4. the amount of wallpaper needed for a room

_____

Estimate the surface area in the specified units of measure.
(*Hint:* Use rounding and equivalent measures.)

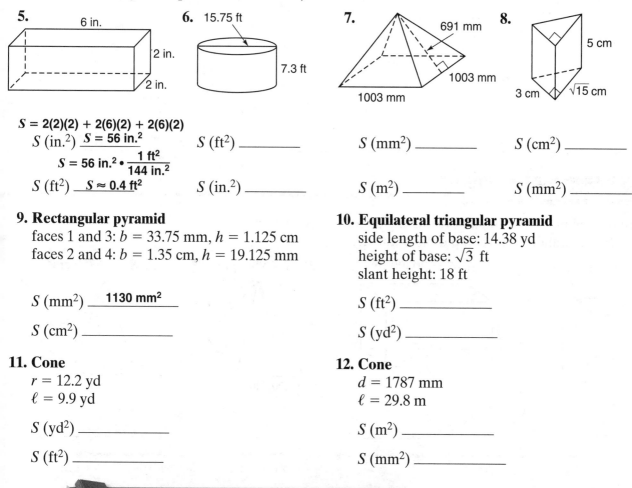

5. 6 in. 2 in. 2 in.

$S = 2(2)(2) + 2(6)(2) + 2(6)(2)$
S (in.²) __$S = 56$ in.²__
$S = 56$ in.² • $\dfrac{1\ ft^2}{144\ in.^2}$
S (ft²) __$S \approx 0.4$ ft²__

6. 15.75 ft 7.3 ft

S (ft²) _____

S (in.²) _____

7. 691 mm 1003 mm 1003 mm

S (mm²) _____

S (m²) _____

8. 5 cm 3 cm $\sqrt{15}$ cm

S (cm²) _____

S (mm²) _____

9. Rectangular pyramid
faces 1 and 3: $b = 33.75$ mm, $h = 1.125$ cm
faces 2 and 4: $b = 1.35$ cm, $h = 19.125$ mm

S (mm²) __1130 mm²__

S (cm²) _____

10. Equilateral triangular pyramid
side length of base: 14.38 yd
height of base: $\sqrt{3}$ ft
slant height: 18 ft

S (ft²) _____

S (yd²) _____

11. Cone
$r = 12.2$ yd
$\ell = 9.9$ yd

S (yd²) _____

S (ft²) _____

12. Cone
$d = 1787$ mm
$\ell = 29.8$ m

S (m²) _____

S (mm²) _____

Draw and label a net. Then estimate the surface area. (*Hint:* Use rounding and compatible numbers)

13.

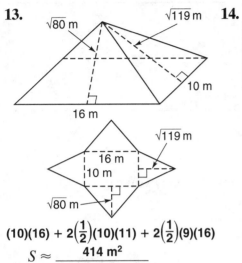

$$(10)(16) + 2\left(\tfrac{1}{2}\right)(10)(11) + 2\left(\tfrac{1}{2}\right)(9)(16)$$

$S \approx$ _____ 414 m² _____

14.

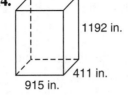

$S \approx$ _____

15.

$S \approx$ _____

16. Equilateral triangular pyramid
side length of base: 34.9 cm
height of base: $\sqrt{3}$ cm
slant height: 21 cm

17. Cube
side length: 2121 mm

18. Right triangular prism
base legs: 29.6 ft and 71.04 ft
hypotenuse: 76.96 ft
height of prism: 406.7 ft

$S \approx$ _____

$S \approx$ _____

$S \approx$ _____

MENTAL MATH

Use mental math to estimate the missing dimension. Use $\pi \approx 3$.
(*Hint:* Use rounding and compatible numbers.)

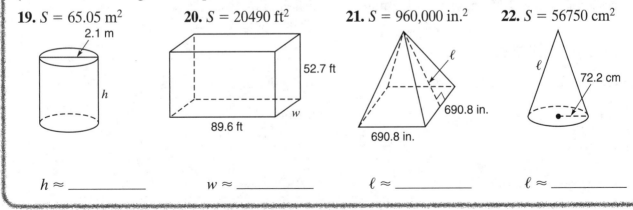

19. $S = 65.05$ m²

2.1 m

h

20. $S = 20490$ ft²

52.7 ft

89.6 ft

w

21. $S = 960{,}000$ in.²

ℓ

690.8 in.

690.8 in.

22. $S = 56750$ cm²

ℓ

72.2 cm

$h \approx$ _____

$w \approx$ _____

$\ell \approx$ _____

$\ell \approx$ _____

11-7 Volume of Prisms

Name _____   Date _____

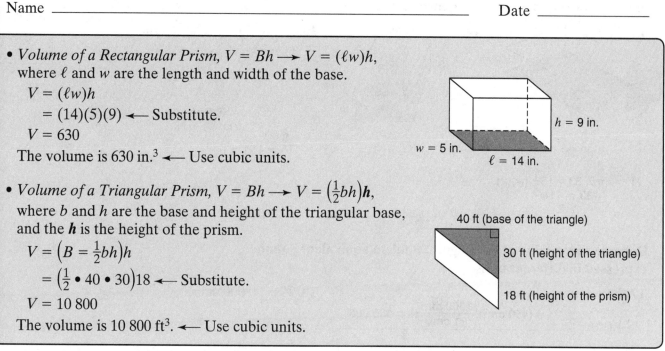

- *Volume of a Rectangular Prism, V = Bh* ⟶ *V = (ℓw)h,*
  where ℓ and *w* are the length and width of the base.

  $V = (\ell w)h$

  $= (14)(5)(9)$ ⟵ Substitute.

  $V = 630$

  The volume is 630 in.³ ⟵ Use cubic units.

  h = 9 in.
  w = 5 in.
  ℓ = 14 in.

- *Volume of a Triangular Prism, V = Bh* ⟶ $V = \left(\frac{1}{2}bh\right)h,$
  where *b* and *h* are the base and height of the triangular base,
  and the *h* is the height of the prism.

  $V = \left(B = \frac{1}{2}bh\right)h$

  $= \left(\frac{1}{2} \cdot 40 \cdot 30\right)18$ ⟵ Substitute.

  $V = 10\,800$

  The volume is 10 800 ft³. ⟵ Use cubic units.

  40 ft (base of the triangle)
  30 ft (height of the triangle)
  18 ft (height of the prism)

Find the volume of each rectangular prism (ℓ = length, *w* = width, and *h* = height).

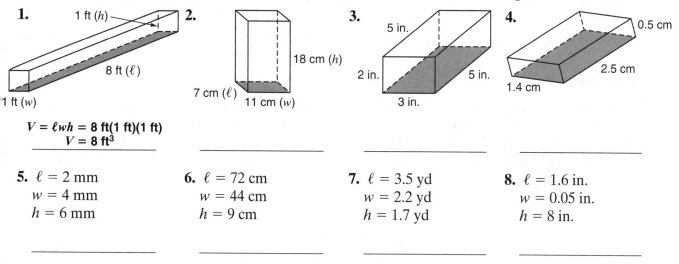

1.   1 ft (*h*)   8 ft (ℓ)   1 ft (*w*)

$V = \ell wh = 8\text{ ft}(1\text{ ft})(1\text{ ft})$
$V = 8\text{ ft}^3$

2.   18 cm (*h*)   7 cm (ℓ)   11 cm (*w*)

_____

3.   5 in.   2 in.   5 in.   3 in.

_____

4.   0.5 cm   2.5 cm   1.4 cm

_____

5. ℓ = 2 mm
w = 4 mm
h = 6 mm

_____

6. ℓ = 72 cm
w = 44 cm
h = 9 cm

_____

7. ℓ = 3.5 yd
w = 2.2 yd
h = 1.7 yd

_____

8. ℓ = 1.6 in.
w = 0.05 in.
h = 8 in.

_____

Find the volume of each triangular prism.

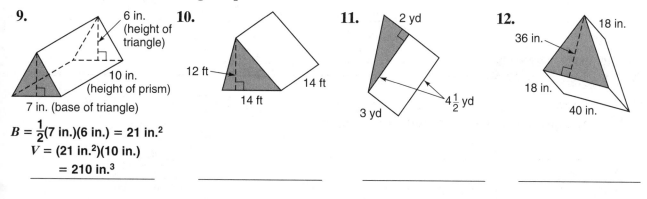

9.   6 in. (height of triangle)   10 in. (height of prism)   7 in. (base of triangle)

$B = \frac{1}{2}(7\text{ in.})(6\text{ in.}) = 21\text{ in.}^2$
$V = (21\text{ in.}^2)(10\text{ in.})$
$= 210\text{ in.}^3$

10.   12 ft   14 ft   14 ft

_____

11.   2 yd $4\frac{1}{2}$ yd   3 yd

_____

12.   18 in.   36 in.   18 in.   40 in.

_____

Find the missing dimension for each figure.

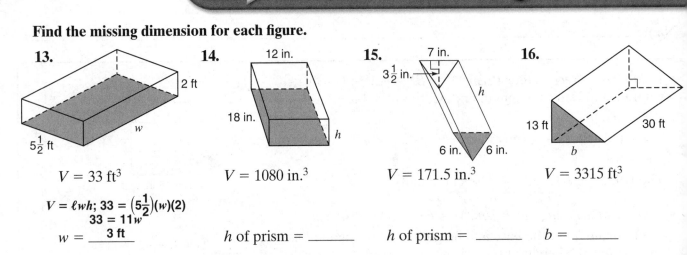

13.

$5\frac{1}{2}$ ft w 2 ft

$V = 33$ ft^3

$V = \ell wh; 33 = \left(5\frac{1}{2}\right)(w)(2)$
$33 = 11w$
$w = \underline{\quad 3 \text{ ft} \quad}$

14.   12 in.

18 in. h

$V = 1080$ in.^{3}

h of prism = _____

15.   7 in.

$3\frac{1}{2}$ in. h

6 in.   6 in.

$V = 171.5$ in.^{3}

h of prism = _____

16.

13 ft b 30 ft

$V = 3315$ ft^3

b = _____

Rename the volume of each figure. Find an equivalent volume expressed in different units.

17. $V = 450$ cm^3

$V(\text{mm}^3)$ $\underline{\quad V = (450 \text{ cm}^3)\left(\dfrac{1000 \text{ mm}^3}{1 \text{ cm}^3}\right) = 450\,000 \quad}$

18. $V = 30\,000$ cm^3

V (m^3) _____

19. rectangular prism; $\ell = 3$ yd, $w = 2$ yd, $h = 4$ yd

V (ft^3) _____

20. rectangular prism; $\ell = 1$ ft, $w = 2$ ft, $h = 3$ ft

V (in.^{3}) _____

Problem Solving

21. A rectangular prism is built entirely of 1-cm cubes and has a volume of 24 cubic centimeters. Give all the possible whole number dimensions of the rectangular prism.

22. All of Sean's paperback books are 10.5 cm wide, 2 cm thick, and 17 cm high. What is the greatest number of books he can pack in one shipping carton with inside dimensions of 64 cm × 34 cm × 10.5 cm?

_____   _____

CHALLENGE

23. The diagram shows three views of the same figure. Use the drawings to find the volume of the figure.

$V = $ _____

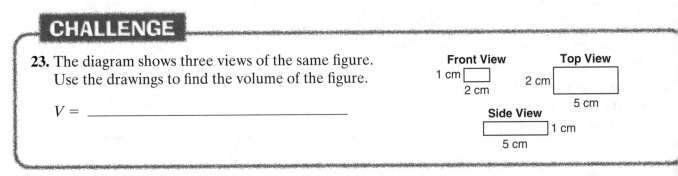

Front View
1 cm
2 cm

Top View
2 cm
5 cm

Side View
5 cm   1 cm

11-8 Volume of Pyramids

Name _____ Date _____

To *find the volume of a pyramid,* use the formula: $V = \frac{1}{3}Bh$.

Find the volume of the rectangular pyramid.

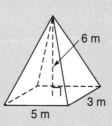

$V = \frac{1}{3}(\ell w)h$ ← Use the formula for volume of a pyramid.

$= \frac{1}{3}(5 \cdot 3)6$ ← Substitute.

$V = 30 \text{ m}^3$ ← Use cubic units.

The volume is 30 cubic meters.

To *find an unknown dimension* of a pyramid when the volume is given, use the formula $V = \frac{1}{3}Bh$ and substitute the known values.

Triangular pyramid: $V = 40 \text{ ft}^3$

$V = \frac{1}{3}Bh \longrightarrow V = \frac{1}{3}\left(\frac{1}{2}bh_{\text{base}}\right)h_{\text{pyramid}}$

$40 = \frac{1}{3}\left(\frac{1}{2} \cdot 5 \cdot 4\right)h$ ← Substitute.

$40 = \frac{1}{3}(10)h$ ← Divide both sides by $\frac{10}{3}$.

$h = 12$ ← Solve for h.

The height is 12 feet.

> For $B = \frac{1}{2}bh$,
> h = height of the triangular base
>
> For $V = \frac{1}{3}Bh$,
> h = height of the pyramid

Find each volume. Round to the nearest tenth, if necessary.

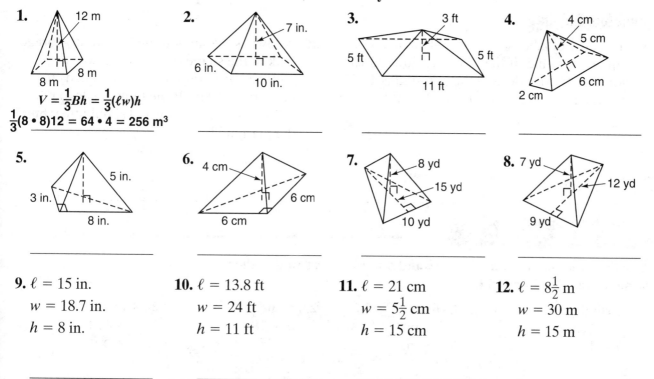

1. 12 m, 8 m, 8 m
$V = \frac{1}{3}Bh = \frac{1}{3}(\ell w)h$
$\frac{1}{3}(8 \cdot 8)12 = 64 \cdot 4 = 256 \text{ m}^3$

2. 7 in., 6 in., 10 in.

3. 3 ft, 5 ft, 5 ft, 11 ft

4. 4 cm, 5 cm, 6 cm, 2 cm

5. 5 in., 3 in., 8 in.

6. 4 cm, 6 cm, 6 cm

7. 8 yd, 15 yd, 10 yd

8. 7 yd, 12 yd, 9 yd

9. $\ell = 15$ in.
$w = 18.7$ in.
$h = 8$ in.

_____

10. $\ell = 13.8$ ft
$w = 24$ ft
$h = 11$ ft

_____

11. $\ell = 21$ cm
$w = 5\frac{1}{2}$ cm
$h = 15$ cm

_____

12. $\ell = 8\frac{1}{2}$ m
$w = 30$ m
$h = 15$ m

_____

Find the missing dimension of each pyramid.

13. Rectangular pyramid

$\ell = 6$ ft, $w = 2\frac{1}{2}$ ft, $V = 35$ ft^3, $h = ?$

$V = \frac{1}{3}Bh = \frac{1}{3}(\ell w)h$

$35 = \frac{1}{3}(6 \cdot 2\frac{1}{2})h$

$35 = 5h$

$h = \underline{\quad 7 \text{ ft} \quad}$

14. Tetrahedron

base of triangular base = b
base height = 62 cm
pyramid height = 21 cm

$V = 70\ 308$ cm^3

$b = \underline{\hspace{5cm}}$

15. Triangular Pyramid

h (base) = 14 in., b (base) = 18 in.,

h (pyramid) = ?, $V = 84$ in.^{3}

$h = \underline{\hspace{5cm}}$

16. Rectangular Pyramid

$\ell = 12$ m, $w = ?$ m, $V = 432$ m^3, $h = 6$ m

$w = \underline{\hspace{5cm}}$

17.

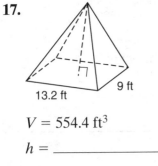

13.2 ft, 9 ft

$V = 554.4$ ft^3

$h = \underline{\hspace{5cm}}$

18.

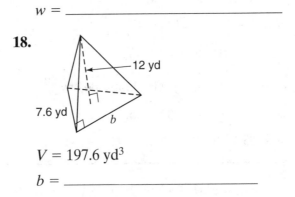

12 yd, 7.6 yd, b

$V = 197.6$ yd^3

$b = \underline{\hspace{5cm}}$

Problem Solving

19. The attic of a house has the shape of a square pyramid. If the base measures 33 yd long by 33 yd wide, and the pyramid is 21.5 yd tall, how much cubic room does it have?

20. A town is planning to build a water storage tank in the shape of an upside down rectangular pyramid. The base needs to be 15 m by 12 m. If the tank needs to hold 1320 m^3 of water, how tall should they build the pyramid?

SPIRAL REVIEW

Use the formulas $S = 2\pi r^2 + 2\pi rh$ and $S = \pi r^2 + \pi r\ell$ to find the surface area. Use $\pi \approx 3.14$.

21. Cylinder
$r = 8$ cm
$h = 11$ cm

22. Cylinder
$d = 6$ in.
$h = 9$ in.

23. Cone
$d = 18$ m
$\ell = 7$ m

24. Cone
$r = 11$ ft
$\ell = 5$ ft

11-9 Volume of Cylinders and Cones

Name _____ Date _____

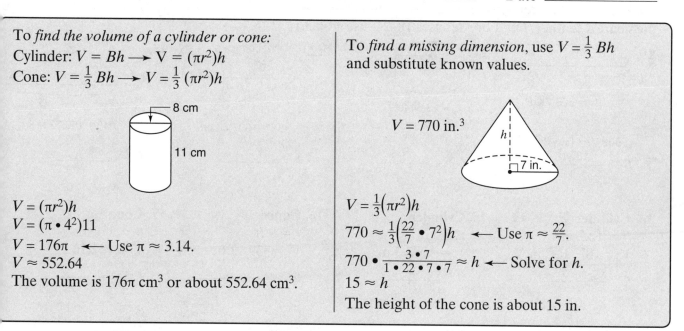

To *find the volume of a cylinder or cone:*
Cylinder: $V = Bh \longrightarrow V = (\pi r^2)h$
Cone: $V = \frac{1}{3}Bh \longrightarrow V = \frac{1}{3}(\pi r^2)h$

To *find a missing dimension*, use $V = \frac{1}{3}Bh$ and substitute known values.

$V = 770$ in.^{3}

$V = (\pi r^2)h$
$V = (\pi \cdot 4^2)11$
$V = 176\pi$ ← Use $\pi \approx 3.14$.
$V \approx 552.64$
The volume is 176π cm^3 or about 552.64 cm^3.

$V = \frac{1}{3}(\pi r^2)h$
$770 \approx \frac{1}{3}\left(\frac{22}{7} \cdot 7^2\right)h$ ← Use $\pi \approx \frac{22}{7}$.
$770 \cdot \dfrac{3 \cdot 7}{1 \cdot 22 \cdot 7 \cdot 7} \approx h$ ← Solve for h.
$15 \approx h$
The height of the cone is about 15 in.

Find the volume in terms of π.

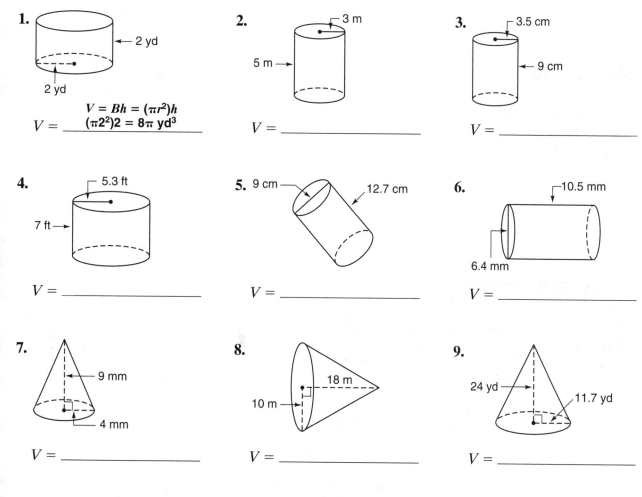

1.

← 2 yd

2 yd

$V = Bh = (\pi r^2)h$
$V = \underline{(\pi 2^2)2 = 8\pi \ yd^3}$

2. 3 m

5 m →

$V = $ _____

3. 3.5 cm

← 9 cm

$V = $ _____

4. 5.3 ft

7 ft →

$V = $ _____

5. 9 cm   12.7 cm

$V = $ _____

6. 10.5 mm

6.4 mm

$V = $ _____

7. 9 mm

4 mm

$V = $ _____

8. 18 m

10 m →

$V = $ _____

9. 24 yd → 11.7 yd

$V = $ _____

Find the unknown dimension. Use $\pi \approx \frac{22}{7}$ and round to the nearest tenth. (*Hint:* For exercises 18–21, use $\pi = 3.14$.)

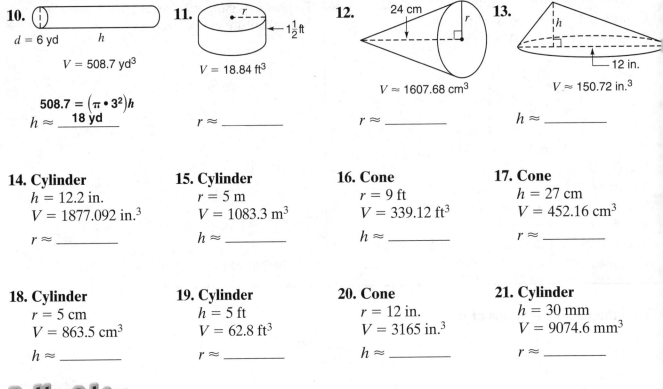

10.

$d = 6$ yd h

$V = 508.7$ yd^3

$508.7 = (\pi \cdot 3^2)h$

$h \approx$ __**18 yd**__

11.

$1\frac{1}{2}$ ft

$V = 18.84$ ft^3

$r \approx$ _____

12.

24 cm r

$V \approx 1607.68$ cm^3

$r \approx$ _____

13.

h

12 in.

$V \approx 150.72$ in.^{3}

$h \approx$ _____

14. Cylinder
$h = 12.2$ in.
$V = 1877.092$ in.^{3}

$r \approx$ _____

15. Cylinder
$r = 5$ m
$V = 1083.3$ m^3

$h \approx$ _____

16. Cone
$r = 9$ ft
$V = 339.12$ ft^3

$h \approx$ _____

17. Cone
$h = 27$ cm
$V = 452.16$ cm^3

$r \approx$ _____

18. Cylinder
$r = 5$ cm
$V = 863.5$ cm^3

$h \approx$ _____

19. Cylinder
$h = 5$ ft
$V = 62.8$ ft^3

$r \approx$ _____

20. Cone
$r = 12$ in.
$V = 3165$ in.^{3}

$h \approx$ _____

21. Cylinder
$h = 30$ mm
$V = 9074.6$ mm^3

$r \approx$ _____

Problem Solving

22. A circular wading pool has a diameter of 7 feet and is 2 feet deep. How many cubic feet of water can the pool hold? Use $\pi \approx 3.14$.

_____

23. A cube has a volume of 512 m^3. What are the dimensions and the volume of the largest cone that can fit inside the cube?

_____

WRITE ABOUT IT

24. Two movie theaters fill their popcorn containers to the top. Cinecom charges $4.00 for its popcorn box. Maxwell Cinemas charges $4.25. Which popcorn container is the better buy? Explain. Use $\pi \approx 3.14$.

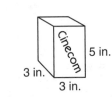

3 in.   5 in.   3 in.   3 in.

3 in.   6 in.

_____

_____

_____

11-10 Surface Area and Volume of Complex Three-Dimensional Figures

Name _____ Date _____

To find the surface area or volume of a three-dimensional complex figure use a net. Then calculate the sum of the areas.

Surface Area Formulas

Rectangular Prism: $S = 2\ell w + 2\ell h + 2\ell w$

Triangular Prism: $S = 2B + A_1 + A_2 + A_3$

Pyramid: $S = B + LA$

Cylinder: $S = 2\pi r^2 + 2\pi rh$

Cone: $S = \pi r^2 + \pi r\ell$

Volume Formulas

Rectangular Prism: $V = \ell wh$

Triangular Prism: $V = Bh$

Rectangular Pyramid: $V = \frac{1}{3}Bh$

Triangular Pyramid: $V = \frac{1}{3}Bh$

Cylinder: $V = Bh = \pi r^2 h$

Cone: $V = \frac{1}{3}Bh = \frac{1}{3}\pi r^2 h$

Identify the individual figures that form each complex figure and draw a net. Then find the total surface area of the figures. Use $\pi \approx 3.14$.

1.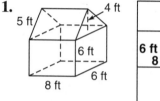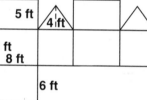

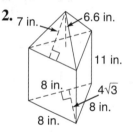 **2.** 7 in. 6.6 in. 11 in. 8 in. $4\sqrt{3}$ 8 in. 8 in.

figures: **1 rectangular prism, 1 triangular prism**

$S = 3(6 \cdot 8) + 2(8 \cdot 5) + 2(6 \cdot 6) + 2\left(\frac{1}{2} \cdot 6 \cdot 4\right)$,

$S = \underline{144 + 80 + 72 + 24 = 320 \text{ ft}^2}$

figures: _____

$S = $ _____

3.  13.3 m 15 m 14 m 21 m

4. 5 in. 12 in. 6 in. 10 in.

figures: _____

$S \approx$ _____

figures: _____

$S \approx$ _____

Find the total volume of the complex figures in exercises 1–4. Use $\pi \approx 3.14$.

5. Exercise 1

$V = (8 \cdot 6 \cdot 6) + \frac{1}{2}(6 \cdot 4 \cdot 8)$,

$V = \mathbf{384 \text{ ft}^3}$

6. Exercise 2

7. Exercise 3

8. Exercise 4

Find the surface area and volume for each figure. Use π ≈ 3.14.
If necessary, round to the nearest tenth.

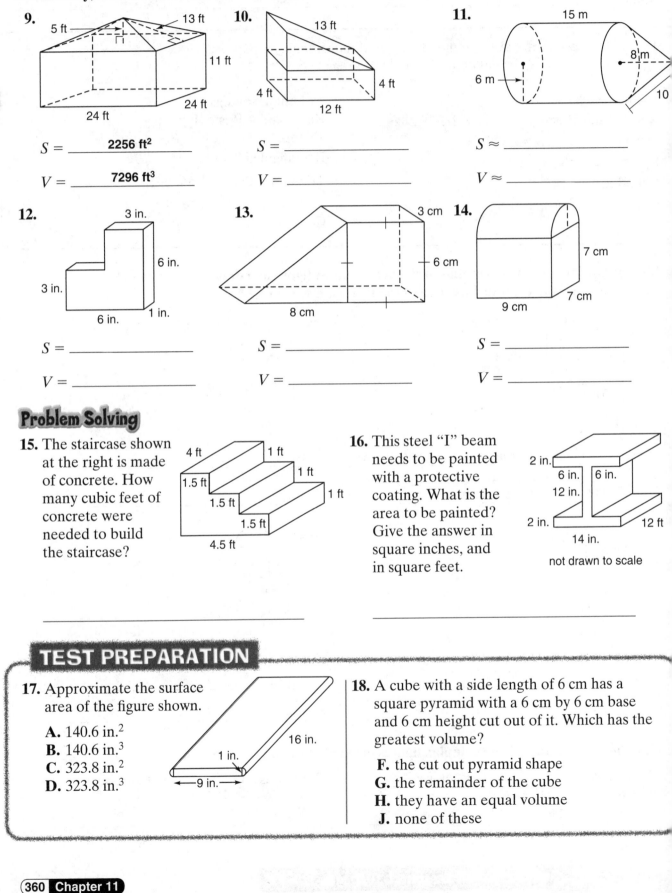

9.

5 ft — 13 ft
11 ft
24 ft
24 ft

S = _____2256 ft²_____

V = _____7296 ft³_____

10.

13 ft
4 ft
4 ft
12 ft

S = _____

V = _____

11.

15 m
8 m
6 m
10

S ≈ _____

V ≈ _____

12.

3 in.
6 in.
3 in.
6 in.   1 in.

S = _____

V = _____

13.

3 cm
6 cm
8 cm

S = _____

V = _____

14.

7 cm
9 cm   7 cm

S = _____

V = _____

Problem Solving

15. The staircase shown at the right is made of concrete. How many cubic feet of concrete were needed to build the staircase?

4 ft   1 ft
1 ft
1.5 ft
1.5 ft   1 ft
1.5 ft
4.5 ft

_____

16. This steel "I" beam needs to be painted with a protective coating. What is the area to be painted? Give the answer in square inches, and in square feet.

2 in.
6 in. 6 in.
12 in.
2 in.   12 ft
14 in.

not drawn to scale

_____

TEST PREPARATION

17. Approximate the surface area of the figure shown.

A. 140.6 in.²
B. 140.6 in.³
C. 323.8 in.²
D. 323.8 in.³

16 in.
1 in.
←—9 in.—→

18. A cube with a side length of 6 cm has a square pyramid with a 6 cm by 6 cm base and 6 cm height cut out of it. Which has the greatest volume?

F. the cut out pyramid shape
G. the remainder of the cube
H. they have an equal volume
J. none of these

11-11 Changing Dimensions of Three-Dimensional Figures

Name _____   Date _____

A model is a *scale model* when *every* dimension of the model has been transformed by the same scale factor.

To *find a scale factor*, use the formula: $\dfrac{\text{scale model dimension}}{\text{actual object dimension}}$.

To *find the dimensions of the scale model*, multiply each dimension by the scale factor: scale model dimension = scale factor • actual object dimension. Changes in dimensions affect changes in volume and surface area.

Find the dimensions of the scale model.

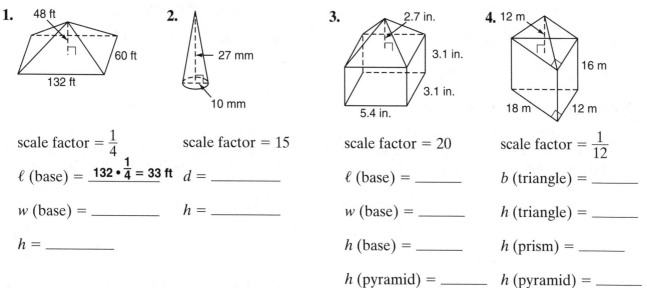

1. 48 ft, 60 ft, 132 ft

scale factor = $\dfrac{1}{4}$

ℓ (base) = $\underline{132 \cdot \frac{1}{4} = 33\ \text{ft}}$

w (base) = _____

h = _____

2. 27 mm, 10 mm

scale factor = 15

d = _____

h = _____

3. 2.7 in., 3.1 in., 3.1 in., 5.4 in.

scale factor = 20

ℓ (base) = _____

w (base) = _____

h (base) = _____

h (pyramid) = _____

4. 12 m, 16 m, 18 m, 12 m

scale factor = $\dfrac{1}{12}$

b (triangle) = _____

h (triangle) = _____

h (prism) = _____

h (pyramid) = _____

Determine if the figure is a scale model of the original. (*Hint:* Use ratios.)

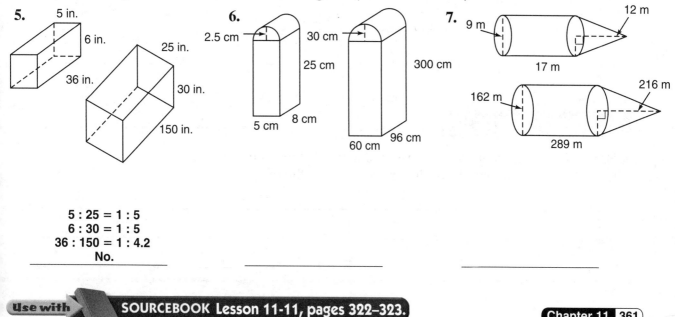

5. 5 in., 6 in., 36 in., 25 in., 30 in., 150 in.

6. 2.5 cm, 25 cm, 5 cm, 8 cm, 30 cm, 300 cm, 60 cm, 96 cm

7. 9 m, 12 m, 17 m, 162 m, 216 m, 289 m

5 : 25 = 1 : 5
6 : 30 = 1 : 5
36 : 150 = 1 : 4.2
_____ No. _____

_____   _____

For each figure, find the volume for the given dimension changes.

8. Cube

$\ell = 5$ in., $w = 5$ in., $h = 5$ in.

$5 \cdot 5 \cdot 5 =$

a. $V = \underline{\quad 125 \text{ in.}^3 \quad}$

$10 \cdot 5 \cdot 5 =$

b. double ℓ; $V = \underline{\quad 250 \text{ in.}^3 \quad}$

c. double ℓ and w; $V = \underline{\qquad}$

d. V when ℓ, w, and h are doubled $= \underline{\qquad}$

9. Triangular prism

$b = 10$ m, h (triangle) $= 16$ m, h (prism) $= 7$ m

a. $V = \underline{\qquad}$

b. b halved; $V = \underline{\qquad}$

c. b and h(triangle) halved; $V = \underline{\qquad}$

d. b, h(triangle), and h(prism) halved; $V = \underline{\quad}$

10. Rectangular pyramid

$\ell = 3$ cm, $w = 2.5$ cm, $h = 5$ cm

a. $V = \underline{\qquad}$

b. ℓ quadrupled; $V = \underline{\qquad}$

c. ℓ and w quadrupled; $V = \underline{\qquad}$

d. ℓ, w, and h quadrupled; $V = \underline{\qquad}$

11. Cylinder (write volumes in terms of π)

$r = 3$ yd, $h = 2$ yd

a. $V = \underline{\qquad}$

b. r multiplied by 10; $V = \underline{\qquad}$

c. r and h multiplied by 10; $V = \underline{\qquad}$

Solve and explain your reasoning.

12. In part b. of exercise 11, where only the radius is multiplied by 10, why is the volume 100 times greater than in part a.?

13. A cube measures 6 cm • 6 cm • 6 cm. How does doubling only one, only two, and all three dimensions change its surface area?

14. A triangular pyramid has a volume of 473 472 mm³. If a model of the pyramid has a scale factor of $\frac{1}{6}$, what is its volume?

15. A solid cement cylinder has a radius of 5 m and a height of 25 m. What is the volume of a model with a scale factor of $\frac{1}{5}$?

WRITE ABOUT IT

16. How does multiplying one dimension of any polyhedron by a given factor affect the volume? two dimensions? three dimensions?

11-12 Problem-Solving Strategy:
Work Backward

> **Read** > **Plan** > **Solve** > **Check**

Name _____ Date _____

Solve by using the strategy Work Backward.

1. If $8 + 8 + 8 + \ldots + 8 = 14 + 14 + 14 + \ldots + 14 = 18 + 18 + 18 + \ldots + 18$, what is the fewest number of terms each of these sums have?

_____

2. After receiving a 6% raise, Alicia's weekly salary is $585.12. What was her weekly salary *before* the raise?

_____

3. How many routes (along the segments and in the directions shown) are there from the node at A to the node at B?

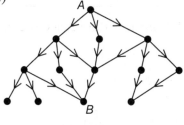

_____

4. With only a 3-minute timer and a 5-minute timer, how can you measure an interval of 4 minutes?

_____

5. Lupe's average after five 100-point tests is 78. If the teacher now decides to drop Lupe's least score, which is 66, what will be her new average?

_____

6. A jar held some coins. In the course of 2 weeks, Jamal did the following in order: added 45¢, took half the contents, took another 30¢, added 50¢, added a quarter, and took 2 quarters and a dime. If the jar now has $1.45, how much was in the jar 2 weeks ago?

7. Three classes go on a hiking trip together. The campground director provides a bag of breakfast bars for the three hiking groups. In the morning, Ms. Warren, thinking hers is the first group out, takes a third of the bars from the sack. Later, Ms. Khan, thinking hers is the first group out, takes a third of the remaining bars from the sack. Later still, Ms. Lopez, also thinking hers is the first group out, grabs a third of the remaining bars from the sack. Afterward, the campground director found 24 bars in the sack. How many breakfast bars were originally in the sack?

8. Four less than twice the cube of a number is 50. What is the number?

9. A beetle needs to climb out of a crater that is 800 cm deep. It advances 120 cm each day, but it slips back 90 cm while resting each night. How many days will it take before this beetle successfully climbs out of the crater?

10. A game consists of 21 toothpicks. Two players alternate turns, picking up anywhere from 1 to 4 toothpicks. The player who picks up the last toothpick loses! If you go second, what should be your strategy in order to ensure a win?

Enrichment:
Three-Dimensional Figures and the Ratio of Similarity

Name _____   Date _____

The two triangular prisms below are similar.
a. Find the ratio of similarity.
b. Find their surface areas and the ratio of the surface area of prism
   M to the surface area of prism N.
c. Find their volumes and the ratio of the volume of prism M to the
   volume of prism N.

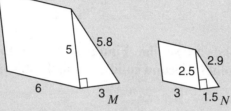

a. Prism M has a height of 6 units. Prism N has a height of 3 units.
   The ratio of similarity is $6 : 3$ or $2 : 1$.

b. Surface area of Prism M: Surface area of Prism N:
   $S_M = 2B + A_1 + A_2 + A_3$ $S_N = 2B + A_1 + A_2 + A_3$
   $S_M = 2\left(\frac{1}{2}(3)(5)\right) + (6)(5) + (5.8)(6) + (3)(6)$ $S_N = 2\left(\frac{1}{2}(1.5)(2.5)\right) + (3)(2.5) + (2.9)(3) + (1.5)(3)$
   $S_M = 97.8$ units^2 $S_N = 24.45$ units^2
   Ratio $\longrightarrow S_M : S_N = 97.8 : 24.45 = 4 : 1 = 2^2 : 1^2$

c. Volume of Prism M: Volume of Prism N:
   $V_M = Bh$ $V_N = Bh$
   $V_M = (7.5)(6)$ $V_N = (1.875)(3)$
   $V_M = 45$ units^3 $V_N = 5.625$ units^3
   Ratio $\longrightarrow V_M : V_N = 45 : 5.625 = 8 : 1 = 2^3 : 1^3$

**In exercises 1–5, the pair of solids are similar. Find the ratio of similarity
of the first solid to the second solid.**

1. Cube Y: side 6 cm
   Cube Z: side 32 cm

2. Rectangular prism W:
   length 0.5 m, height 0.25 m,
   width 0.15 m
   Rectangular prism X:
   length 8 m, height 4 m,
   width 2.4 m

3. Cylinder U:
   radius 24 in., height 14 in.
   Cylinder V: radius 3 in.,
   height 1.75 in.

Ratio $\longrightarrow Y : Z = 6 : 32 = 3 : 16$

4. Cone S: radius 15 mm,
   slant height 20 mm
   Cone T: radius 112.5 mm,
   slant height 150 mm

5. Triangular prism R:
   Triangular prism Q

R 46.05" 18.45" 30" 23.25"

Q 12.3" 20" 30.7" 15.5"

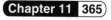

In exercises 6–8, the pair of solids are similar. Find their surface areas and the ratio of the surface area of the first solid to the surface area of the second solid. Compare this to the ratio of similarity.

6. Cube M: side 15 m
Cube L: side 40 m

$$S = 6s^2$$
$$S_M = 1350 \text{ m}^2$$
$$S_L = 9600 \text{ m}^2$$
$$1350 : 9600 = 9 : 64 \text{ or } 3^2 : 8^2$$

7. Rectangular prism K: length 5 in., height 25 in., width 15 in. Rectangular prism J: length 0.8 in., height 4 in., width 2.4 in.

_____

8. Cylinder H: radius 15 ft, height 27.5 ft. Cylinder G: radius 9 ft, height 16.5 ft

_____

In exercises 9–11, the pair of solids are similar. Find the volumes and the ratio of the volumes (first solid to second solid). Compare this to the ratio of similarity.

9. Cube AA: side 35 in.
Cube BB: side 7 in.

$$V = s^3$$
$$VAA = (35)^3$$
$$VAA = 42{,}875 \text{ in.}^3$$
$$VBB = (7)^3$$
$$VBB = 343 \text{ in.}^3$$
Ratio $\longrightarrow$ $42{,}875 : 343 = 125{:}1 \text{ or } 5^3 : 1^3$

10. Rectangular prism CC: length 16.5 ft, height 16.5 ft, width 12 ft
Rectangular prism DD: length 8.25 ft, height 8.25 ft, width 6 ft

_____

11. Cylinder EE: radius 100 m, height 88 m
Cylinder FF: radius 25 m, height 22 m

_____

Problem Solving

12. Two rectangular prisms are similar and are labeled A and B. The ratio of similarity from $A : B$ is $2 : 1$. If the volume of A is 36 units^3, what is the volume of B?

_____

13. Two cones have a ratio of similarity of $16 : 1$. If the larger of the two cones has a surface area of 64 ft^2, what is the surface area of the smaller cone?

_____

14. Two spheres have a ratio of similarity of $5 : 2$. If the radius of the larger sphere is 75 mm, what is the radius of the smaller sphere?

_____

CRITICAL THINKING

15. The ratio of similarity of a larger cone to a smaller cone is $y : 3$. The volume of the smaller one is 1458 m^3, what is the volume of the larger cone?

_____

Test Prep: Multiple-Choice Questions

Strategy: Apply Mathematical Reasoning

Name _____   Date _____

You can draw or sketch a model or diagram to help you *visualize the problem.* Be sure to check that your sketch matches the given information.

To select the correct answer in a multiple-choice question, try using the following strategies.

- Reread the item.
- Use the Test-Prep Strategy.
- Apply appropriate rules, definitions, properties, or strategies.
- Analyze your answers.

Choose the correct answer. *TIP: Mark only one answer for each question.*

1. Which figure is a net of a triangular prism?

A.

C.

B.

D.

2. Points *M* and *N* will be added to the grid at the right to form rectangle *KLMN*, which has an area of 15 square units.

Which ordered pairs could be the coordinates of points *M* and *N*?

F. (3, 4) and (–2, 4)   **H.** (3, 0) and (–2, 0)

G. (3, –1) and (–2, –1)   **J.** (3, –2) and (–2, –2)

3. Which combination of shapes makes up the faces of a rectangular prism that has length 3, width 3, and height 4?

F. 1 square, 2 rectangles

G. 2 squares, 4 rectangles

H. 4 squares, 2 rectangles

J. 6 squares

4. A square and a rectangle have the same perimeter. The area of the square is 100 square inches. Which of the following could be the dimensions of the rectangle?

F. 2 in. by 8 in.   **H.** 6 in. by 14 in.

G. 4 in. by 25 in.   **J.** 12 in. by 28 in.

5. The legs of a right triangle measure 5 inches and 12 inches. What is the length of the third side?

A. 7 in.   **C.** 17 in.

B. 13 in.   **D.** 169 in.

6. Zach stacked 10 rows of cans in a pyramid shape. There was 1 can in the top row, 2 cans in the second row, 3 cans in the third row, and so on. How many cans are in all 10 rows?

A. 6   **C.** 16

B. 10   **D.** 55

Vocabulary Development

Name _____ Date _____

Chapter 11 Vocabulary

base	lateral area	regular polyhedron
cone	lateral face	slant height
cubic units	lateral surface	sphere
cylinder	net	surface area
edge	orthographic drawing	three-dimensional figure
face	overestimation	underestimation
hemisphere	polyhedron	vertex
isometric drawing	prism	volume
	pyramid	

From the vocabulary list above, choose the term(s) that best complete each sentence. Write the term(s) in the space(s) provided.

1. The _____ of a cylinder is the curved surface that is not a base.

2. A _____ is a point where 3 or more edges meet.

3. The _____ is the height of each lateral face of a pyramid.

4. A three-dimensional figure with faces that are all polygons is called a _____.

5. A _____ and a _____ each have only one base.

6. Hugh estimates the volume of a cylindrical jar that has a diameter of 4 in. and a height of 5 in. to be 64π in.^{3}. He used _____.

7. The _____ does not include the areas of the bases.

8. A three-dimensional figure that has two circular bases that are parallel and congruent is a _____.

Choose three terms from the list that you did not use in Questions 1–8. For each term, write a definition in your own words and give an example.

9. _____

_____

_____

_____

_____

Practice Chapter 11 Test

Name _____ Date _____

Classify the three-dimensional figure.

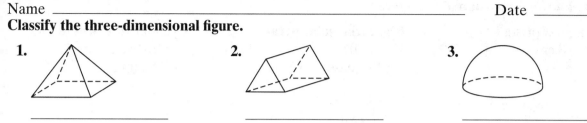

1. _____

2. _____

3. _____

Make an isometric drawing of a rectangular prism with the given dimensions. Then draw the top, front, and side views.

4. $\ell = 2, w = 2, h = 2$

5. $\ell = 4, w = 2, h = 3$

Draw a net of each figure on a separate piece of paper. Then find its surface area and volume. Use $\pi \approx 3.14$. (*Hint:* Round square roots to the nearest whole number.)

6.

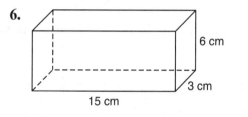

6 cm

3 cm

15 cm

_____

7.

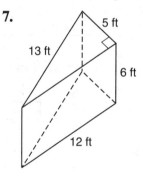

5 ft

13 ft

6 ft

12 ft

_____

8.

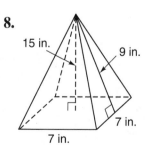

15 in.

9 in.

7 in.

7 in.

_____

9.

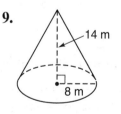

14 m

8 m

_____

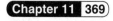

Find the unknown dimension of the figure.

10. Rectangular prism
$V = 226.8 \text{ cm}^3$
$\ell = 6 \text{ cm}$

$w = \underline{\hspace{3cm}}$
$h = 8.4 \text{ cm}$

11. Right triangular pyramid
$V = 20.075 \text{ yd}^3$
leg 1 of base = 6.6 yd

leg 2 of base = $\underline{\hspace{2cm}}$
$h = 2.5 \text{ yd}$

12. Cylinder (use 3.14 for π)
$V = 26\,988.3 \text{ mm}^3$
$r = 15 \text{ mm}$

$h = \underline{\hspace{2.5cm}}$

Find the surface area and volume of the three-dimensional figure with the given dimensions. Give your answer in smaller units, if indicated.

13. Rectangular prism

$\ell = 20 \text{ mm}, w = 17 \text{ mm}, h = 10 \text{ mm}$

$S = \underline{\hspace{6cm}}$

$V = \underline{\hspace{4cm}}$

14. Cylinder

$h = 8 \text{ ft}, d = 25 \text{ ft}$

$S = \underline{\hspace{6cm}}$

$V = \underline{\hspace{6cm}}$

15. Cone

$r = 2.0 \text{ yd, height} = 2.4 \text{ yd, slant height} = 2.6 \text{ yd}$

$S = \underline{\hspace{6cm}}$

$V = \underline{\hspace{6cm}}$

16. Right triangular prism

leg 1 = 1.5 ft, leg 2 = 2 feet, height of prism = 38 in.

$S = \underline{\hspace{6cm}}$

$V = \underline{\hspace{6cm}}$

Find the surface area and volume of the complex figure.

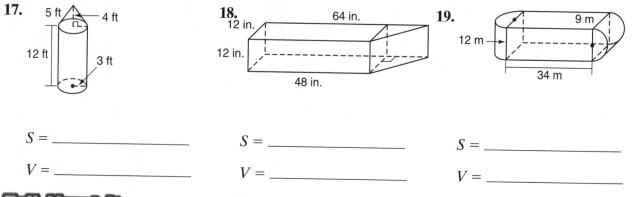

17. 5 ft   4 ft   12 ft   3 ft

$S = \underline{\hspace{3cm}}$

$V = \underline{\hspace{3cm}}$

18. 12 in.   64 in.   12 in.   48 in.

$S = \underline{\hspace{3cm}}$

$V = \underline{\hspace{3cm}}$

19. 9 m   12 m   34 m

$S = \underline{\hspace{3cm}}$

$V = \underline{\hspace{3cm}}$

Tell About It

Explain how you solve the problem. Show all your work.

20. A cube has a side length of 4.5 centimeters. What is the surface area of the cube? What is the surface area of two cubes stacked to form a rectangular prism? How does the surface area change if another cube is stacked on top of the two? What pattern do you notice?

Name _____ Date _____

Circle the best answer.

1. Evaluate $\dfrac{a^{-8}b^{-2}}{a^{-4}b^{-4}}$ when $a = 2$ and $b = 8$.

  A. -4

  B. $-\dfrac{1}{4}$

  C. $\dfrac{1}{4}$

  D. 4

2. What is the side length of a regular hexagon with a perimeter of 153 feet?

  F. 19.125 feet
  G. 25.5 feet
  H. 38.25 feet
  J. 51 feet

3. Which graph represents the solution of $2x \geq -6$?

  A.

  $\begin{array}{ccccccc} -5 & -4 & -3 & -2 & -1 & 0 & 1 \end{array}$

  B.

  $\begin{array}{ccccccc} -5 & -4 & -3 & -2 & -1 & 0 & 1 \end{array}$

  C.

  $\begin{array}{ccccccc} 1 & 2 & 3 & 4 & 5 & 6 & 7 \end{array}$

  D.

  $\begin{array}{ccccccc} 1 & 2 & 3 & 4 & 5 & 6 & 7 \end{array}$

4. A cone has a diameter of 4 yards and a slant height of 9 yards. What is its lateral area?

  F. 6π yd^2 **G.** 12π yd^2
  H. 18π yd^2 **J.** 36π yd^2

5. Cho left $8.10 as a tip on a $45 dinner bill. What percent of the bill did Cho leave as a tip?

  A. 0.18%   **B.** 0.22%
  C. 18%   **D.** 22%

6. From the box-and-whisker plot, which statement is true?

  F. 2 and -2 are outliers.
  G. The upper extreme is 3.
  H. The lower quartile is 0.
  J. The mean is 0.5.

7. Which type of data display would best show the number of people at an amusement park that chose the roller coaster as their favorite ride?

  A. bar graph   **B.** circle graph
  C. histogram   **D.** line graph

8. What is the area of a circle with a diameter of 6 inches? Use $\pi \approx 3.14$.

  F. 18.84 in.^{2}
  G. 28.26 in.^{2}
  H. 37.68 in.^{2}
  J. 113.04 in.^{2}

9. Solve: $\dfrac{5}{8} - \dfrac{3}{4}x = -4\dfrac{3}{8}$

  A. $x = 5$ **B.** $x = 5\dfrac{3}{4}$

  C. $x = 7$ **D.** $x = 6\dfrac{2}{3}$

10. Which statement illustrates the inverse property of addition?

  F. $7 - 7 = 0$ **G.** $5 + 0 = 5$
  H. $5 + 7 = 7 + 5$ **J.** $-5 + 7 = 7 - 5$

11. Roberto buys 4 tire tubes and a dozen energy bars at a bike shop. The total cost is $44.40. If the tubes cost $4.50 each, what is the cost per energy bar?

A. $2.20   **B.** $3.54
C. $26.40   **D.** $35.40

12. A snow cone cup shaped like a cone has a diameter of 3 inches and a height of 3.6 inches. What is its volume to the nearest tenth of a cubic inch? Use 3.14 for π.

F. 5.4 in.^{3} **G.** 8.5 in.^{3}
H. 22.6 in.^{3} **J.** 25 in.^{3}

13. Which statement is always true?

A. A kite is a trapezoid
B. A parallelogram is a rectangle
C. A trapezoid is a parallelogram
D. A square is a rhombus

14. Marilyn needs at least $150 to buy a new bike. So far, she has saved $90. Which inequality represents the amount she still needs to save?

F. $x + 90 > 150$ **G.** $x - 90 > 150$
H. $x + 90 \geq 150$ **J.** $x - 90 \geq 150$

15. What is the value of x?

4 cm x
6 cm

A. $\sqrt{20}$ cm   **B.** $\sqrt{52}$ cm
C. 8 cm   **D.** 10 cm

16. How many decigrams are in 18.7 milligrams?

A. 0.187
B. 1.87
C. 187
D. 1870

17. Write the product in scientific notation.

$17(5.75 \times 10^{-6})$

F. 9.775×10^{-4}
G. 9.775×10^{-5}
H. 9.775×10^{-6}
J. 9.775×10^{-7}

18. What is the volume of the pyramid?

10 m
9 m
12 m

A. 270 m^3 **B.** 360 m^3
C. 540 m^3 **D.** 1080 m^3

19. Solve: $4x + 7 = -25$

F. $x = -8$
G. $x = -4.5$
H. $x = 4.5$
J. $x = 8$

20. Which list is in order from greatest to least?

A. $-12, -11, -|10|, |-11|, 12$
B. $-|10|, -11, -12, |-11|, 12$
C. $12, |-11|, -12, -11, -|10|$
D. $12, |-11|, -|10| -11, -12$

Tell About It

Explain how you solve the problem. Show all your work.

21. A company produces cylindrical thermoses in 2 sizes. The larger thermos has a height of h centimeters and a diameter of 12 centimeters. The smaller thermos has the same diameter, but its height is $\frac{3}{4}$ that of the larger thermos. What is the difference in the volume of the thermoses? Give your answer in terms of π.

2-1 Sample Space

Name _____   Date _____

An *experiment* is the performance of an action. The result of an experiment is an *outcome*. The list of all possible outcomes is the *sample space*.
An *event* is any grouping of one or more outcomes from a sample space.
The chance of an event happening is the *likelihood of an event*.
Events can be: *impossible, certain, equally likely,* or *not equally likely*.

María has three marbles in a bag: 1 blue, 1 red, and 1 yellow.
Suppose she will pick a marble, replace it, and pick another.
What is the sample space for this experiment?

To create the sample space use a *tree diagram*, like the one at
the right, that shows all possible outcomes for the experiment.

Sample Space: {BR, BB, BY, RR, RB, RY, YR, YB, YY}

**Tell whether the events(s) are *impossible, certain, equally likely,*
or *not equally likely*. Then explain your result.**

1. Six cards are numbered 1, 1, 3, 3, 3, and 4
   a. choose a 3 or choose a 4.

   not equally likely; there are more 3's than 4's.

   c. choose a number less than 1.

   _____

   b. choose a number less than 5.

   _____

   d. choose an odd number or choose
   an even number.

   _____

2. A drawer contains only 3 blue pens, 3 black pens, and 3 red pens

   a. choose a blue pen or a red pen. _____

   b. choose a pencil. _____

   c. choose a pen. _____

**Draw a tree diagram to show each sample space. Then count the
number of possible outcomes.**

3. Flip a quarter twice.
   Given:

   _____
   4 outcomes

4. A bag has 3 balls: 1 black, 1 white, 1 red.
   Without looking, pull a ball. Then toss a coin.

   Number of outcomes: _____

5. A box has two shapes: 1 triangle, 1 square.
   Without looking, pull a shape, and then roll
   a number cube.

   _____

6. Flip a coin. Then roll a regular tetrahedron
   (triangular pyramid) labeled 1 through 4.

   _____

**Make an organized list to show the sample space.
Then count the number of possible outcomes.**

7. Flip a coin twice then roll a number cube labeled 1 through 6.

$$4 \times 6 = 24$$

**On a separate sheet of paper, make a table to show the sample space.
Then count the number of possible outcomes.**

8. Roll a number cube labeled 1 through 6.
Then flip a coin.

	1	2	3	4	5	6
H	1H	2H	3H	4H	5H	6H
T	1T	2T	3T	4T	5T	5T

12 outcomes

9. Spin the spinner shown.
Then flip a coin.

$$4 \times 2 = 8$$

**Use the spinner and cards shown. Find all of the
possible outcomes. Then write the number of
outcomes that are in the sample space.**

| M | A | T | H |

10. Spin the spinner and pick a card.

Outcomes: ___ $\frac{2}{7}$ ___

Number of outcomes: ___ 12 ___

11. Spin the spinner twice.

Outcomes: ___ $\frac{2}{3}$ ___

Number of outcomes: ___ 6 ___

Problem Solving

12. You play a game in which you spin a spinner
with equally-sized sections labeled 1 through
3, twice. You need to get a sum of 5 or more
to win. Are winning the game and losing the
game equally likely events?

13. Suppose you have cards each of which has
a number from 1 to 4. You choose a card,
replace the card, and choose a second card.
Is it more, less, or equally likely to pull
2 numbers with a product of 4 or a sum of 4?

SPIRAL REVIEW

Determine whether the triangle with the given side lengths is a right triangle.

14. 3.3 ft, 4.4 ft, and 5.5 ft   **15.** 4 m, 5 m, and 7 m   **16.** 0.3 cm, 0.4 cm, and 0.5 cm

2-2 Fundamental Counting Principle and Factorials

Name _____ Date _____

A restaurant has a daily lunch special: a soup, a sandwich, a drink, and a dessert for $7.95. It offers a choice of 3 soups, 8 sandwiches, and 6 drinks. How many different lunches are possible?

    ways to choose a soup: 3
ways to choose a sandwich: 8
    ways to choose a drink: 6
ways to choose all together: $3 \cdot 8 \cdot 6 = 144$
There are 144 different lunches that are possible.

> **Think**
> With the *Fundamental Counting Principle* you simply multiply the number of ways each event can occur.

Vijay's CD collection has five styles of music: hip-hop, classical, rock, country, and jazz. How many different ways can he arrange his collection by style? Use the Fundamental Counting Principle.
$5 \cdot 4 \cdot 3 \cdot 2 \cdot 1 = 120$ arrangements

> **Remember:** $5 \cdot 4 \cdot 3 \cdot 2 \cdot 1$ can also be written as 5!, or "5 factorial." A factorial of a given integer is the product of all positive integers less than or equal to that integer.

Find the value of each expression. Be sure to use the order of operations.
(*Hint:* 1! = 1 and 0! = 1)

1. 7!

$7 \cdot 6 \cdot 5 \cdot 4 \cdot 3 \cdot 2 \cdot 1 = 5040$

2. 3!

3. 9!

4. 3! + 4!

5. 5! − 2!

6. 6! + 0!

7. $\dfrac{6!}{3!}$

8. $\dfrac{3! \cdot 4!}{5! \cdot 3!}$

9. $\dfrac{6! \cdot 3!}{4!}$

Use the Fundamental Counting Principle to find the total number of possible combinations.

10. Earl is choosing a class ring. He can choose gold or silver, one of five different gemstones, and either a round or square stone. How many choices does he have?

11. Giselle wants to participate in exactly 1 sport, 1 club, and 1 committee activity. There are 5 sports, 7 clubs, and 4 committees from which to choose. How many different choices of three activities are there?

Use the Fundamental Counting Principle to find the number of different ways each group of items can be ordered.

12. Determine how many two-digit numbers can be formed with the digits 1, 3, and 5, if digits can be repeated.

$$3 \cdot 3 \cdot 3 = 27$$

13. Determine how many two-digit numbers can be formed with the digits 1, 3, and 5, if digits cannot be repeated.

14. Find the number of 4-digit locker combinations that can be made using the numbers 0 through 3 if numbers can be repeated and then if numbers cannot be repeated.

15. Find the number of ways that 11 children can be arranged in one row of 11 chairs.

Problem Solving

16. You are the DJ for your school's radio station. On Monday afternoons, you take requests and 5 students call in, each with a different request. How many ways can you order these five songs? Consider a situation in which one of these five songs must be played first. Now, how many ways are there to order the five songs?

17. You are on a school field trip and want to take a class photo with the students standing in a row. There are 10 students that will be in the photo. The class president will stand in the rightmost position and the vice president will stand in the leftmost position. How many ways can you arrange the remaining students?

18. Your class won the school wide math competition and the prize is ice cream sundaes for the class. There are 4 flavors of ice cream, 3 different toppings, and 2 types of sprinkles. You are allowed to pick two scoops of ice cream, which can be the same flavor, one topping, and 1 type of sprinkles. How many different sundaes could you make?

WRITE ABOUT IT

19. On a separate sheet of paper, draw a tree diagram to find the number of two-digit numbers that can be formed with the digits 1 through 6, where digits cannot repeat. Then use the Fundamental Counting Principle. Do you get the same answer? Describe the advantages and disadvantages of each method.

12-3 Theoretical Probability

Name _____ Date _____

The *probability of an event*, $P(E)$, is a measure of how likely it is that the event will occur. Probability is expressed as a ratio that is equal to 0, 1, or lies between 0 and 1. The *theoretical probability* of an event is the ratio of the number of favorable outcomes to the total number of possible outcomes.

Roll a number cube labeled 1 through 6. Find the probability of rolling a 4.

$P(4) = \dfrac{\text{number of favorable outcomes}}{\text{number of possible outcomes}} = \dfrac{1}{6}$

> **Remember:** Probabilities can be expressed as fractions, decimals, and percents.

The probability of rolling a 4 is $\dfrac{1}{6}$, which is approximately 0.17, or 17%.

Two events, E and *not* E, are *complementary events* if both cannot occur at the same time: $P(E) + P(\text{not E}) = 1$.
Two events, A and B, that have no outcomes in common are *mutually exclusive events*: $P(A \text{ or } B) = P(A) + P(B)$.

A marble is chosen from a bag containing 2 blue marbles, 3 green marbles, 6 red marbles, and 1 white marble. Compute the probability for each event.

1. $P(\text{blue})$
$\frac{2}{12} = \frac{1}{6}$

2. $P(\text{green})$
$\frac{3}{12} = \frac{1}{4}$

3. $P(\text{red})$
$\frac{6}{12} = \frac{1}{2}$

4. $P(\text{white})$
$\frac{1}{12}$

5. $P(\text{not blue})$
$\frac{10}{12}$

6. $P(\text{blue or red})$
$\frac{8}{12}$

7. $P(\text{yellow})$
$\frac{0}{12}$

8. $P(\text{not orange})$
$\frac{12}{12}$

9. $P(\text{not white})$
$\frac{11}{12}$

10. $P(\text{not red})$
$\frac{6}{12}$

11. $P(\text{white or blue})$
$\frac{3}{12}$

12. $P(\text{green or red})$
$\frac{9}{12}$

Find the probability for each event when spinning the spinner shown at the right. Write each probability as a fraction, a decimal, and a percent.

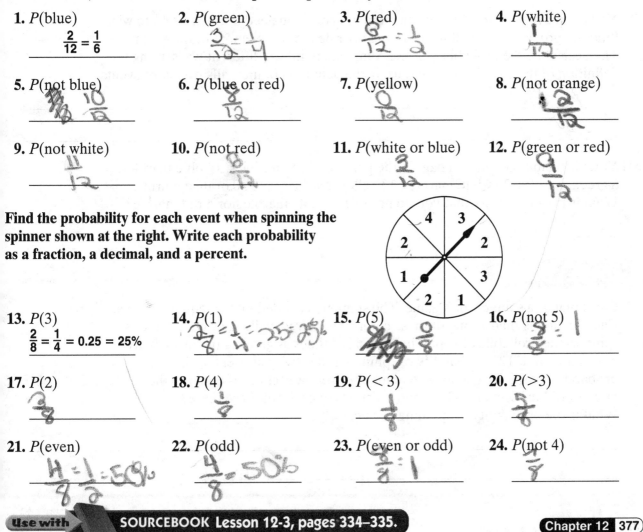

13. $P(3)$
$\frac{2}{8} = \frac{1}{4} = 0.25 = 25\%$

14. $P(1)$
$\frac{2}{8} = \frac{1}{4} = .25 = 25\%$

15. $P(5)$
$\frac{0}{8}$

16. $P(\text{not } 5)$
$\frac{8}{8} = 1$

17. $P(2)$
$\frac{3}{8}$

18. $P(4)$
$\frac{1}{8}$

19. $P(< 3)$
$\frac{4}{8}$

20. $P(>3)$
$\frac{5}{8}$

21. $P(\text{even})$
$\frac{4}{8} = \frac{1}{2} = 50\%$

22. $P(\text{odd})$
$\frac{4}{8} = 50\%$

23. $P(\text{even or odd})$
$\frac{8}{8} = 1$

24. $P(\text{not } 4)$
$\frac{7}{8}$

A coin is tossed. State the complement for each event. Then express the probability of the complement as a fraction, decimal, and a percent.

25. landing on heads

Complement: _____ **landing on tails** _____

Probability of complement = $\dfrac{1}{2} = 0.5 = 50\%$

26. not landing on heads

Complement: _____

Probability of complement = _____

27. not landing on heads nor landing on tails

Complement: _____

Probability of complement = _____

28. landing on heads or landing on tails

Complement: _____

Probability of complement = _____

Problem Solving

29. The probability that a spinner lands on red is $\dfrac{5}{8}$. If the spinner has 8 sections, what does this tell you about the number of sections that are red? What does that tell you about the number of sections that are *not* red?

_____

30. You are playing a game that uses a number cube. You need to roll a 4 or 5 to win. Find the probability of rolling a 4 or 5. Describe the complement of the event. Then calculate the probability of the complement in two different ways: using the definition of the complement, and using the definition of mutually exclusive events.

_____

_____

31. You pick a marble out of a bag. In the bag are 12 red marbles, 14 blue marbles, 8 green marbles, 23 white marbles, 13 yellow marbles, and 30 orange marbles. What is the probability that you do not pick a white marble nor a red marble?

_____

CHALLENGE

32. Carol makes a spinner for a game. The spinner is divided into 10 equal sections. Each section is shaded one of these colors: green, red, yellow, or blue. On this spinner, the probability of spinning green is 3 times as great as the probability of spinning red. The probability of spinning red is twice as great as the probability of spinning blue. The number of yellow sections is equal to the number of blue sections. How many sections of each color are there? What is the probability of spinning each color?

_____

_____

12-4 Experimental Probability

Name _____ Date _____

To find the *experimental probability* of an event, compare the number of times an event occurs to the total number of *trials*.

A bag contains 5 blue marbles, 6 red marbles, 2 yellow marbles, and 7 green marbles. Leah pulls out a marble, records the color, and returns it to the bag 10 times. Her results are: 2 blue marbles, 4 red marbles, 1 yellow marble, and 3 green marbles. Based on her results, about how many times in 100 trials can Leah expect to pick a red marble?

Experimental probability formula: $P(E) = \dfrac{\text{number of times an event occurs}}{\text{number of trials}} = \dfrac{4}{10}$

To estimate the number of times Leah will pick a red marble in 100 trials, use a proportion.

Let x = the number of times Leah can expect to pick a red marble.

So Leah can expect to pick a red marble about 40 times after 100 trials.

$\dfrac{4}{10} = \dfrac{x}{100}$

$4 \bullet 100 = 10 \bullet x$ ⟵ Cross multiply.

$400 = 10x$ ⟵ Simplify.

$\dfrac{400}{10} = \dfrac{10x}{10}$ ⟵ Divide both sides by 10.

$40 = x$ ⟵ Simplify.

There are tiles labeled A, B, C, D, and E in a bag. Abby picks a tile, records the letter, and returns the tile to the bag. The results of 20 trials are shown in the table at the right.

A	B	C	D	E
5	3	2	6	4

Find the experimental probability for each event. Write each as a fraction, a decimal, and a percent.

1. $P(A)$

$\dfrac{5}{20} = \dfrac{1}{4} = 0.25 = 25\%$

2. $P(B)$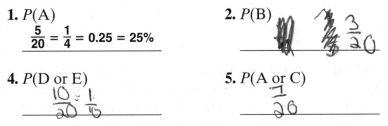

$\dfrac{3}{20}$

3. $P(C)$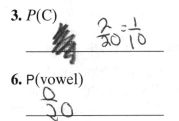

$\dfrac{2}{20} = \dfrac{1}{10}$

4. $P(D \text{ or } E)$

$\dfrac{10}{20} = \dfrac{1}{2}$

5. $P(A \text{ or } C)$

$\dfrac{7}{20}$

6. P(vowel)

$\dfrac{9}{20}$

Based on the table above, predict how many times Abby would pick the given letter(s) in 80 trials.

7. B.

$\dfrac{3}{20} = \dfrac{x}{80}$, $x = 12$ times

8. D.

$\dfrac{6}{20} = \dfrac{}{80} = 24$

9. E.

$\dfrac{4}{20} = \dfrac{}{80}$ 12

10. A or B.

$\dfrac{8}{20} = \dfrac{}{80} = 32$

11. C or E.

24

12. B or C.

20

13. A or D.

44

14. A or B or E.

48

15. B or D or E.

52

Use the information below for exercises 16–19.
Marlene uses a spinner divided into equal sections to decide her
afternoon snack. The results for 25 days are shown in the table.
Find the experimental and theoretical probabilities for landing
on the given snack(s). Write as a fraction and a decimal.

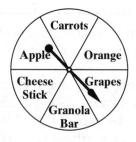

Apple	Carrots	Orange	Grapes	Granola Bar	Cheese Stick
5	3	2	4	4	7

16. apple

experimental probability = $\dfrac{5}{25} = \dfrac{1}{5} = 0.2$

theoretical probability = $\dfrac{1}{6} = 0.1\overline{6}$

17. cheese stick

experimental probability = _____

theoretical probability = _____

18. not an orange

experimental probability = _____

theoretical probability = _____

19. granola bar or carrots

experimental probability = _____

theoretical probability = _____

Roll a number cube 20 times and record the results on a separate
sheet of paper. Find the experimental probability of rolling each number.
Use your results to *predict* the outcome of the following events.

20. Some light bulbs may break before being
shipped from a factory. If the number of times
you rolled a 6 represents the number of broken
bulbs in 100 light bulbs, predict the number
of broken bulbs out of 1000 light bulbs.

_____

21. If the number of times you rolled an even
number represents the number of goals
a soccer team makes out of 20 attempts,
predict the number of goals made out of
60 attempts.

_____

Problem Solving

22. There are 3 blue marbles, 2 red marbles, and
4 yellow marbles in a bag. Bob picks one
marble, returns it to the bag, and records the
result. He repeats this 9 more times. He finds
the experimental probability of picking blue is
$\dfrac{9}{10}$. Do you think the outcome is reasonable?

_____

23. Cindy flips a coin 50 times and lands on tails
28 times. Compare the experimental and
theoretical probabilities. Do the results of
the experiment seem reasonable?

_____

MENTAL MATH

A vendor sells 18 red, 30 blue, 20 green, and 32 pink balloons. Find the experimental
probabilities of selling a balloon of the given color(s). Give your answer as a percent.

24. $P(\text{green}) = $ _____

25. $P(\text{red or blue}) = $ _____

26. $P(\text{pink or green}) = $ _____

12-5 Odds and Fairness

Name _____   Date _____

The likelihood of an event can also be represented by the *odds,* which is the ratio of the number of favorable outcomes to the number of unfavorable outcomes. *Unfavorable outcomes* are any outcomes that are not represented by the event.

$$\text{odds in favor of an event} = \frac{\text{number of favorable outcomes}}{\text{number of unfavorable outcomes}}$$

$$\text{odds against an event} = \frac{\text{number of unfavorable outcomes}}{\text{number of favorable outcomes}}$$

Remember: The sum of the number of favorable outcomes and the number of unfavorable outcomes equals the total number of possible outcomes.

A game is *fair* if the number of favorable outcomes equals the number of unfavorable outcomes.

Peter and Bradford roll a number cube. If an even number is rolled, Peter gets a point. If an odd number is rolled, Bradford gets a point. Describe the odds in favor of getting a point for each player.

odds in favor of Peter getting a point $= \frac{3}{3} = \frac{1}{1}$, or 1 : 1, or 1 to 1.

odds in favor of Bradford getting a point $= \frac{3}{3} = \frac{1}{1}$, or 1 : 1, or 1 to 1

A marble is chosen from a bag containing 3 red marbles, 4 blue marbles, and 5 white marbles. Find the odds in favor of and the odds against each event. Write each pair of odds as a fraction and a ratio in simplest form.

1. Choose a red marble.

   odds in favor: $\frac{3}{9} = \frac{1}{3}$, or 1 : 3 or 1 to 3

   odds against: $\frac{9}{3} = \frac{3}{1}$, or 3 : 1 or 3 to 1

2. Choose a blue marble.

   odds in favor: _____

   odds against: _____

3. Choose a red or blue marble.

   odds in favor: _____

   odds against: _____

4. Choose a white or blue marble.

   odds in favor: _____

   odds against: _____

Each letter in the word MISSISSIPPI is written on a card. One card is picked at random. Write the odds in favor of and the theoretical probability of each event as fractions.

5. Pick M.

   odds in favor: $\frac{1}{10}$

   theoretical probability: $\frac{1}{11}$

6. Pick I.

   odds in favor: _____

   theoretical probability: _____

7. Pick M or I.

   odds in favor: _____

   theoretical probability: _____

8. Pick a consonant.

   odds in favor: _____

   theoretical probability: _____

Identify the type of likelihood for each event as theoretical probability, experimental probability, odds in favor, or odds against. Explain how you know.

9. A coin lands on heads 6 times out of 10 flips.

Experimental probability. It compares outcomes to trials.

10. Voters approve a candidate $\frac{2}{1}$.

11. The chance of not winning a game after winning 7 of 10 games is 3 : 7.

Determine if the game is *fair*. If not, which player is more likely to win? Explain.

12. Pull from a stack of cards labeled A–Z. If a consonant (including Y) is pulled, Player 1 gets a point. If a vowel (not including Y) is pulled, Player 2 gets a point.

13. Roll a number cube labeled 1–6. If a multiple of 6 is rolled, Player 1 gets a point. Otherwise, Player 2 gets a point.

Problem Solving

14. Damien, Jared, Lucy, Jill, Becky, and Jeremiah have each of their names on one of 6 different cards. The cards are placed in a hat. One name is drawn at random. What are the odds in favor of drawing a girl's name? If a card with Andy's name is added to the hat, how would it change the odds of drawing a girl's name?

15. Tara has a set of tiles. Each tile shows one letter of the alphabet. There are 3 tiles each for the letters A, E, I, O, and U, and 5 tiles for every other letter. What are the odds in favor of her choosing a tile that shows A, B, C, D, or E? How many times out of 200 picks would you expect her to choose one of these tiles?

CRITICAL THINKING

16. Write the odds in favor of and the odds against rolling a 5 on a number cube as fractions. Then find the theoretical probability of rolling a 5. Which fraction is greater? Is this always true when comparing odds and probability? Explain.

12-6 Compound Events

Name _____ Date _____

A *compound event* consists of two or more simple events. Compound events are *independent events* if the occurrence of one does not affect the likelihood that the other will occur. *Dependent events* do affect the likelihood of each other.

Probability of Independent Events	**Probability of Dependent Events**
If A and B are independent events, then $P(A \text{ and } B) = P(A) \bullet P(B)$	If A and B are dependent events, then $P(A, \text{ then } B) = P(A) \bullet P(B \text{ after } A)$

A gumball machine contains 7 red gumballs, 5 green gumballs, and 10 blue gumballs. Anthony will put a coin in, hoping to get a red gumball. Then Nick will put a coin in to get a gumball. What is the probability that Nick will get a blue gumball after Anthony gets a red gumball?

Anthony did not put his gumball back into the machine. The events are dependent because there is 1 less gumball that Nick can receive.

$$P(\text{red, then blue}) = P(\text{red}) \bullet P(\text{blue after red}) = \frac{7}{22} \bullet \frac{10}{21} = \frac{70}{462} = \frac{5}{33}$$

The probability that Nick will get a blue gumball after Anthony gets a red gumball is $\frac{5}{33}$.

Determine whether the events are *dependent* or *independent*.

1. Rolling two number cubes and getting a 4 on each

_____**independent**_____

2. Picking a green marble from a bag, and, without replacing it, picking another green marble

_____dependent_____

3. Picking Jim's name from a hat first, then picking Judy's name second, to determine teams for gym class

_____dependent_____

4. Choosing tuna for a sandwich and milk for a drink for lunch

_____independent_____

Jon has a drawer containing 2 blue pens, 2 red pens, 2 orange pens, and 2 green pens. He picks one pen from the drawer, does not replace it, and then picks a second pen. Use a formula to find the probability for each event.

5. P(blue, then red)

$\frac{2}{8} \bullet \frac{2}{7} = \frac{4}{56} = \frac{1}{14}$

6. P(blue, then blue)

$\frac{2}{8} \bullet \frac{2}{7} = \frac{1}{14}$

7. P(green, then orange)

$\frac{2}{8} \bullet \frac{2}{7} = \frac{1}{14}$

8. P(green, then purple)

$\frac{2}{8} \bullet \frac{0}{7} = \frac{2}{64} = \frac{1}{37}$

Mary has a drawer containing 3 blue pens, 4 red pens, 1 orange pen, and 2 green pens. She picks a pen from the drawer. Later, without replacing the first pen, she picks a second pen from the drawer. Use a formula to find the probability for each event.

9. P(blue, then red)

$\frac{3}{10} \bullet \frac{4}{9} = \frac{12}{90} = \frac{2}{15}$

10. P(blue, then blue)

$\frac{3}{10} \bullet \frac{3}{9} = \frac{9}{90} = \frac{1}{10}$

11. P(red, then blue)

$\frac{4}{10} \bullet \frac{3}{9} = \frac{12}{90} = \frac{2}{15}$

12. P(green, then orange)

$\frac{2}{10} \bullet \frac{1}{9} = \frac{2}{90} = \frac{1}{45}$

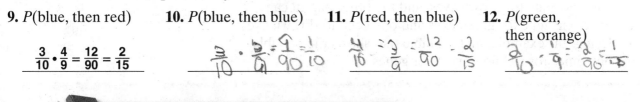

Joe spins the spinner shown then flips a coin.

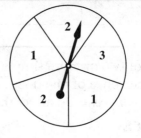

13. Make a table to show the total number of all possible outcomes.

14. Draw a tree diagram to show all of the different possible outcomes.

There are 6 maple leaves, 4 oak leaves, and 5 birch leaves in a bag. Jay picks one leaf from the bag, does not replace it, and then picks another. Write the probability of each event in decimal form, rounded to the nearest hundredth.

15. P(maple, then not maple)

P(maple) • P(not maple after maple)

$$\frac{6}{15} \cdot \frac{9}{14} = \frac{54}{210} = \frac{9}{35} \approx 0.26$$

16. P(maple, then oak)

17. P(oak, then not maple)

18. P(birch, then birch)

Problem Solving

19. You are given five cards numbered 1 through 5. You select a card, do not replace it, and select again. Draw a tree diagram to represent the situation, then find P(2, then 5)

20. A set of 4 cards consists of 1 green card, 1 red card, and 2 blue cards. Phil randomly picks a card and keeps it. Then Pat picks a card. What is the probability that Phil picks a blue card and Pat picks a green card?

CHALLENGE

21. Every person has two genes for eye color. Each parent randomly gives one of his or her eye color genes to a child. For example, one parent can have one gene for blue eyes and one gene for brown eyes, and the other parent can have one gene for green eyes and one gene for brown eyes. Using this example, make a table that shows the possible outcomes for a child's eye color genes.

12-7 Permutations

Name _____ Date _____

Permutations are arrangements of items or objects in which the order is important. To find the number of permutations, you can use an organized list, a tree diagram, the fundamental counting principle, and sometimes, a factorial.

A bag contains a blue marble, a red marble, and a green marble. Judy pulls all three marbles out, one at a time, without looking. How many different ways can she choose the marbles?

Method 1: Make an organized list.

BRG RBG GBR
BGR RGB GRB

Method 2: Use a tree diagram.

```
    B        R        G
   ↙↘      ↙↘      ↙↘
  R   G    B   G    R   B
  ↓   ↓    ↓   ↓    ↓   ↓
  G   R    G   B    B   R
```

Method 3: Use the Fundamental Counting Principle.

1st chosen   2nd chosen   3rd chosen
    ↓   ↓   ↓
3 choices • 2 choices • 1 choice = 6

There are 6 different ways Judy can choose the marbles.

Make an organized list to determine the number of possible permutations.

1. the number of different arrangements of a pencil, a crayon, and a marker on a desk

   arrangements: _____

   number of permutations: _____

2. the number of different 2-letter arrangements of letters chosen from the word ORANGE

   arrangements: _____

   number of permutations: _____

On a separate sheet of paper, draw a tree diagram to find the possible permutations.

3. the number of ways to arrange 3 pictures on a table

   number of permutations: **6;** P1 ⟨ P2 → P3 / P3 → P2   P2 ⟨ P1 → P3 / P3 → P1   P3 ⟨ P1 → P2 / P2 → P1

4. the number of ways to arrange 2 out of 4 books on a shelf

   number of permutations: _____

5. the number of ways to arrange the ends of a row of 5 different tulip bulbs

   number of permutations: _____

Use the fundamental counting principle to determine the number of possible permutations.

6. the number of ways 6 CDs can be played

7. the number of ways 10 horses can be arranged in 10 different stalls

_____

_____

Use an organized list, a tree diagram, or the fundamental counting principle to find the number of permutations.

8. the number of ways 7 students can stand in line

_____

9. the number of ways 6 shirts can be arranged in a closet

_____

10. the number of ways 3 out of 8 differently-shaped blocks can be stacked

_____

11. the number of ways first through fourth place winners can be chosen out of 10 dogs at a dog show

_____

Determine whether a single factorial can be used to find the number of possible permutations for the situation. Explain.

12. Sam's mother is driving Sam and 3 of his friends home. How many different ways can the 4 friends sit in the 4 remaining seats in the car?

_____

13. Mary needs to pick 3 different ribbons to wrap 3 different gifts. She has 16 choices of ribbons. How many different ways can she choose the ribbons?

_____

Problem Solving

14. Henry's niece has 6 stuffed animals arranged on her bed. In how many different ways can the animals be arranged?

_____

15. Martha is making a CD of her favorite songs. She has 15 songs she would like to put on it. In how many different ways can she order the first 5 songs?

_____

16. Kristin's locker combination consists of 4 different numbers between 0 and 9. She remembers that the first number is 8, but cannot remember the last 3 numbers. How many different arrangements are there of the last 3 numbers?

_____

17. Ten players, including Tom, need a ride home from football practice. Tom's father has room to take Tom and 6 others. If Tom sits next to his father, in how many different ways can the others sit in the car's 6 other seats?

_____

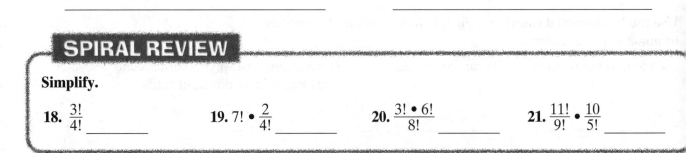

SPIRAL REVIEW

Simplify.

18. $\dfrac{3!}{4!}$ _____

19. $7! \cdot \dfrac{2}{4!}$ _____

20. $\dfrac{3! \cdot 6!}{8!}$ _____

21. $\dfrac{11!}{9!} \cdot \dfrac{10}{5!}$ _____

12-8 Combinations

Name _____ Date _____

A *combination* is a group of items in which order does not matter.
To find the number of different combinations, make an
organized list and exclude repeats, or use permutations.

> **Remember:** You can use the fundamental counting principle to find the number of permutations.

At a restaurant you may pick two different side dishes from the
5 choices they have: carrots, mashed potatoes, French fries, salad,
or pasta. How many combinations of side dishes can you choose?

Method 1: Make an organized list and cross
out repeats.

CM	CF	CS	CP
~~MC~~	MF	MS	MP
~~FC~~	~~FM~~	FS	FP
~~SC~~	~~SM~~	~~SF~~	SP
~~PC~~	~~PM~~	~~PF~~	~~PS~~

Method 2: Use permutations. Divide the
number of permutations of picking 2 side
dishes from 5 by the number of permutations
of 2 side dishes.

$$\frac{\text{permutations of 2 from 5}}{\text{permutations of 2}} = \frac{5 \cdot 4}{2 \cdot 1} = 10$$

There are 10 combinations of side dishes that you can choose.

Make an organized list to determine the number of combinations.

1. Choose 2 letters from the word MAT.

2. Choose 3 out of 4 balloons.

3. Choose 2 out of 6 pens.

_____   _____   _____

Use permutations to determine the number of combinations.

4. Choose 4 out of 8 numbers.

5. Choose 5 out of 15 apples.

6. Choose 6 out of 22 blocks.

_____   _____   _____

Determine whether a tree diagram or permutations can be used to find the number of possible combinations.

7. Choose 2 letters from the word MATH.

8. Choose 15 pencils from a pack of 24.

_____   _____

9. Complete the table showing the products of the possible outcomes of rolling 2 number cubes.

	1	2	3	4	5	6
1	$1 \times 1 = 1$					
2						
3						
4						
5						
6						

10. Complete the table showing the sums of the possible outcomes of rolling 2 number cubes.

	1	2	3	4	5	6
1	$1 + 1 = 2$					
2						
3						
4						
5						
6						

Use the tables from exercises 9 and 10 to answer the questions.

11. What permutations of the outcomes of the rolls result in a product greater than 17? How many permutations are there?

12. What combinations of outcomes results in a product and a sum that are less than 10?

Problem Solving Use a calculator to solve.

13. A school is choosing 2 new school colors. They can choose from red, blue, green, gold, maroon, silver, orange, white, black, and purple. How many different combinations could serve as the new school colors?

14. Rhonda has 8 shirts, 7 pairs of pants, and 5 sweaters in a drawer. She randomly chooses 2 of each item. How many combinations of each item could she choose? If she packs all 6 items in a suitcase, how many different ways can she pack?

15. Mr. Jackman is packing 60 different lunches belonging to students on a field trip in 4 different boxes. How many combinations of lunches can he pack in the first box?

16. A gym class of 26 students divides into 2 teams. How many different combinations of students could make up one team?

TEST PREPARATION

17. Jed picks 6 colored pencils from a pack containing 24. How many combinations of colors can he choose?

   A. 4   **C.** 134,596

   B. 144   **D.** 96,909,120

18. Reba can bring 5 friends to the movies for her birthday. If she has 14 friends she will choose from, how many combinations of friends could she bring?

   F. 70   **H.** 2002

   G. 1680   **J.** 240,240

12-9 Problem-Solving Strategy:
Review of Strategies

Read ▸ **Plan** ▸ **Solve** ▸ **Check**

Name _____   Date _____

Solve.

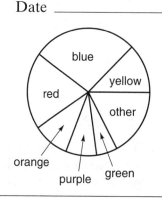

1. This pie chart shows the favorite color of 400 middle-school students. However, the percents associated with each slice failed to print. Approximately how many students selected yellow as their favorite color? Explain.

2. The diagram at the right shows two parallel ladders. The bottom of the shorter ladder is 3 feet from the base of the wall. The ladder leans against the wall at a point 4 feet above the base. The bottom of the taller ladder is 6 feet from the base of the wall. The ladder leans against the wall at a point 8 feet above the base. What is the distance d between the ladders?

3. Your neighbor's living room has an area of 360 square feet. The store sells carpet for $6.50 per square yard. Because there are 3 feet in a yard and $360 \div 3 = 120$, your neighbor thought the cost of carpet for this room would be $120 \cdot \$6.50$, or $780. What is the actual cost, and how can you explain this to your neighbor?

4. Find the *median* of the fifteen scores seen here:
28, 54, 32, 46, 51, 37, 29, 63, 60, 47, 49, 51, 60, 38, 53.

5. Determine the area of the grassy (shaded) region that does not include the four identical circular concrete patio sections in the 40-by-60 foot rectangular yard. Use the diagram at the right.

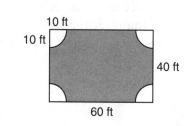

6. You stand in front of a row of numbered squares. You may move forward or backward, but only 3 or 5 squares at a time. Describe two different ways you might get to Square 4.

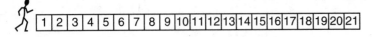

7. You stand in front of a row of numbered squares. You may move forward or backward, but only 4 or 6 squares at a time. Can you get to Square 7? Explain.

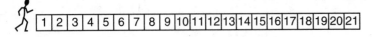

8. If their shorter dimensions must be less than 13, how many other rectangles with whole number length and width measures are similar to this rectangle?

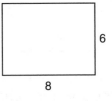

9. Using the fact that $\frac{4}{9} = 0.\overline{4}$, express $0.2\overline{4}$ as a ratio of integers.

10. A jar had $40 in it. Shawna took $6 from the jar. Monika then took twice as much as Shawna took. Next, Sasha added $8 to the jar. Finally, Jorge took some money from the jar. The jar now holds $22. How much money did Jorge take from the jar?

Enrichment:
Pascal's Triangle

Name _____ Date _____

A friend asks you to draw four marbles from a bag containing 10 marbles of different types. How many different four-marble combinations are possible?

- Since there are a total of 10 marbles to choose from, look at row 10.

- To take out four marbles at a time, start from the left side and count as you move to the right: *0 at a time, 1 at a time, 2 at a time, 3 at a time,* and *4 at a time.*

- You should be pointing to the number 210. Therefore, there are 210 different four-marble combinations that can be drawn from the bag.

```
                  1           Row 0
                1   1         Row 1
              1   2   1       Row 2
            1   3   3   1     Row 3
          1   4   6   4   1   Row 4
        1   5  10  10   5   1
      1   6  15  20  15   6   1
    1   7  21  35  35  21   7   1
  1   8  28  56  70  56  28   8   1
1   9  36  84 126 126  84  36   9   1
1  10  45 120 210 252 210 120  45  10   1
1  11  55 165 330 462 462 330 165  55  11   1
1 12  66 220 495 792 924 792 495 220  66  12  1
1 13 78 286 715 1287 1716 1716 1287 715 286 78 13 1
```

Use the diagram to answer the following problems.

1. Amanda has a set of 8 magnetic pictures to display on the door of her locker. She displays 3 of these a day. How many different combinations of pictures can she display?

_____

2. Suppose you have 4 baseball cards, and you asked a friend to choose 3 of them. How many different three-card combinations could your friend choose?

_____

3. Sal has 12 extra shirts that he will let his best friend borrow, but only 5 at a time. How many different combinations could Sal's friend borrow?

_____

4. Ms. Chung has a set of 10 markers in different colors. She asks her class to use two to complete an assignment. How many different color combinations could the class use?

_____

CRITICAL THINKING

5. Look at Row 7 of the triangle which shows combinations of 7 things. Notice that the number of *1 at a time* combinations is equal to the number of *6 at a time* combinations. The number of *2 at a time* combinations is equal to the number of *5 at a time* combinations. The number of *3 at a time* combinations is equal to the number of *4 at a time* combinations. In general, for combinations of 7 things, the number of n *at a time* combinations is the same as the number of *(7 − n) at a time* combinations. Why is this true?

_____

Name _____ Date _____

Chapter 12 Vocabulary

certain   favorable outcomes   outcome
combination   Fundamental Counting   overlapping events
complementary event   Principle   permutation
compound event   impossible   probability
dependent event   independent event   sample space
equally likely   likelihood of an event   simulation
event   mutually exclusive events   theoretical probability
experiment   not equally likely   tree diagram
experimental probability   odds   trial
factorial   odds against   unfavorable outcomes
fair   odds in favor

From the vocabulary list above, choose the term(s) that best complete each sentence. Write the term(s) in the space(s) provided.

1. The number of ways 6 people can sit in 6 chairs is the number of _____.

2. A(n) _____ is the collection of all possible outcomes in an experiment.

3. A game is said to be fair if the number of _____ is equal to

   the number of _____.

4. The number of ways to choose 8 people out of 24 to attend a meeting is

   the number of _____.

5. When flipping a coin, having it land on heads and having it land on tails are

   _____ events.

6. The sum of the probabilities of an event and its _____ is equal to 1.

7. A spinner is labeled with the letters A–E. When spinning the spinner twice, having it land

   on C on the first spin and having it land on E on the second spin are _____.

Choose two terms from the list above that you did not use in Questions 1–7. For each term, write a definition in your own words and give an example.

8. _____

   _____

   _____

Test Prep: Extended-Response Questions

Strategy: Organize Information

Name _____ Date _____

Create an organized list to help you systematically keep track of information you need to answer an extended-response question.

To solve the problem, try using these strategies:
- Reread the item.
- Use the Test-Prep Strategy.
- Apply appropriate rules, definitions, properties, or strategies.
- Analyze your answers.

Solve. *TIP: Write down all of your computations and steps.*

1. A spinner is divided into three equal sections labeled 1, 2, and 3. Jeff spins the spinner twice. He records the product of the two numbers he lands on.

   Part A
   What are the possible products of Jeff's spins?
   Show all your work.

   Part B
   What is the probability that the product is an even number?
   Show all your work.

   Answer _____

   Answer _____

2. Use the numbers 600 and 1260.

   Part A
   Write the prime factorization of each number in exponential form.
   Show all your work.

   Part B
   Find the greatest common factor and the least common multiple of the numbers.
   Show all your work.

   Answer _____

   Answer _____

3. At Armstrong Middle School, a total of 43 students participate in soccer. A total of 31 students participate in tennis. There are 7 students who participate in both sports.

Part A

Use the data in the problem to complete the Venn diagram. Be sure to title the diagram, label each circle, and place a number in each section of the diagram.

Show all your work.

Answer _____

Part B

What is the total number of students who participate in these sports?

Show all your work.

Answer _____

---

4. Granger Middle School has 6 student council representatives from the seventh grade.

Part A

The seventh grade wants to send two representatives to the school board meeting. How many combinations of two representatives can be selected from the 6 members?

Show all your work.

Part B

The seventh grade student council wants to elect a president and vice president from its members. Four students volunteer for the positions. How many combinations of president and vice president can be selected from the 4 members?

Show all your work.

Answer _____   **Answer** _____

Practice Chapter 12 Test

Name _____   Date _____

Make a tree diagram, table, or organized list to show the sample space for the given experiment.

1. Toss a coin three times.

2. Spin a spinner labeled X through Z, then toss a coin twice.

_____   _____

Find the size of the sample space for the given situation.

3. the number of ways 4 students can be assigned the offices of president, vice president, secretary, and treasurer

4. the number of ways to choose a drink, a sandwich, and a piece of fruit from 4 drinks, 4 sandwiches, and 3 pieces of fruit

_____   _____

Based on the spinner shown, write the theoretical probability of the event as a fraction in simplest form.

5. $P(\text{odd})$

_____

6. $P(not \text{ vowel})$

_____

7. $P(\text{consonant and even})$

_____

8. $P(\text{vowel and odd})$

_____

During one day, a store sells 6 small shirts, 12 medium shirts, 14 large shirts, and 8 extra-large shirts. For exercises 9 and 10, write your answers as a fraction and a percent.

9. What is the experimental probability that a person bought an extra-large shirt?

10. What is the experimental probability that a person bought a small or medium shirt?

_____   _____

Determine the odds in favor and the odds against the event when tossing a coin three times.

11. landing on heads at least once

Odds in favor: _____

Odds against: _____

12. landing on tails exactly twice

Odds in favor: _____

Odds against: _____

13. landing on tails on the second toss

Odds in favor: _____

Odds against: _____

14. If the events described in exercises 11–13 represent the ways for a player to score points in three different games, which one(s) would describe a fair game?

_____

Determine whether the events are independent or dependent. Then find the probability of the compound event. Write your answer as a fraction.

15. Choose a black chip from a bag containing 12 white and 8 black chips, replace it, then choose another black chip.

Independent or dependent: _____

Probability: _____

16. Choose an apple from a basket containing 3 apples, 5 bananas, and 4 oranges, do not replace it, and then choose an orange.

Independent or dependent: _____

Probability: _____

17. Draw a 2, do not replace it, and then draw a 4 from a hat that contains cards that show 5 different numbers.

Independent or dependent: _____

Probability: _____

18. Roll an odd number on a 6-sided number cube, then roll a multiple of 3.

Independent or dependent: _____

Probability: _____

Tell whether the situation describes a permutation or a combination. Then find how many ways it can be done.

19. Arrange 7 people in a row.

Permutation or combination: _____

Number: _____

20. Choose 2 pizza toppings out of 10.

Permutation or combination: _____

Number: _____

21. Choose 4 campers out of 12 to stay in the first tent.

Permutation or combination: _____

Number: _____

22. Award first, second, and third place trophies to 9 competitors.

Permutation or combination: _____

Number: _____

Tell About It

Explain how you solve the problem. Show all your work.

23. Bryce randomly chooses a card from a standard deck of 52 containing 13 of each suit. He records the suit of each card in the tally chart at the right. What are the experimental probabilities that Bryce chooses each suit? How do these compare to the theoretical probabilities?

Clubs	ЖҤ I
Diamonds	ЖҤ III
Hearts	ЖҤ III
Spades	ЖҤ ЖҤ

_____

_____

_____

_____

_____

_____

Cumulative Review: Chapters 1–12

Name _____ Date _____

Circle the best answer.

1. When a pair of parallel lines are cut by a transversal, what is always true about the alternate interior angles?

   A. They are complementary.
   B. They are congruent.
   C. They are supplementary.
   D. None of the above.

2. What percent of 60 is 75?

   F. 0.8%
   G. 1.25%
   H. 80%
   J. 125%

3. What is the least common multiple of 63, 90, and 105?

   A. 3   B. 63
   C. 315   D. 630

4. What are the coordinates of point A?

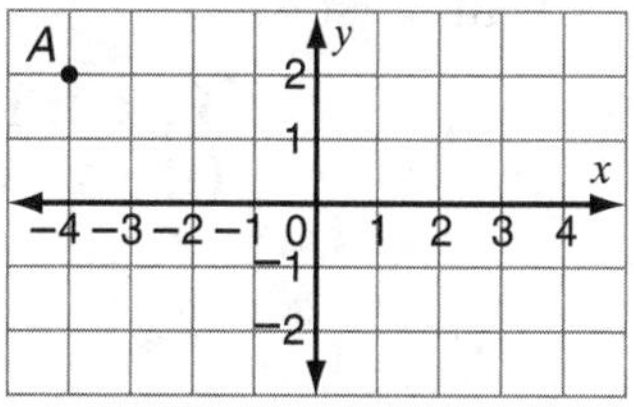

   F. $(2, -4)$
   G. $(-2, -4)$
   H. $(-4, -2)$
   J. $(-4, 2)$

5. Sean tosses a coin twice and rolls a 6-sided number cube. How many possible outcomes are there?

   A. 3   B. 10
   C. 12   D. 24

6. The mean of 6 numbers is 627. Five of the numbers are 650, 753, 602, 418, and 839. What is the sixth number?

   F. 500
   G. 604
   H. 627
   J. 650

7. Reggie is standing near a tree and casts a shadow that is 4 feet long. At the same time, the tree casts a shadow that is 12.8 feet long. If Reggie is 5 feet tall, what is the height of the tree?

   F. 10.24 feet   G. 16 feet
   H. 51.2 feet   J. 64 feet

8. The graph shows the solution of which inequality?

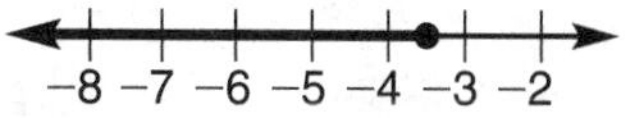

   A. $-2x + 1 \geq 10$ B. $-2x + 1 \leq 10$
   C. $-2x + 3 \geq 10$ D. $-2x + 3 \leq 10$

9. Four students are speaking at a meeting: Margo, Glen, Billy, and Marcia. If the order of the speeches is chosen at random, what is the probability that Glen speaks first or last?

   F. $\frac{1}{128}$ G. $\frac{1}{32}$ H. $\frac{1}{12}$ J. $\frac{1}{2}$

10. Edward invests $12,000. He earns interest that is compounded annually. At the end of 5 years, his investment is worth $16,400. To the nearest tenth, what was the interest rate that his investment earned?

    A. 1.4%   B. 2.7%
    C. 3.7%   D. 6.5%

11. Simplify: $9\frac{5}{12} - \frac{5}{18}\left(6\frac{2}{3}\right) + 4\frac{7}{9}$

    F. $2\frac{5}{24}$ G. $8\frac{23}{36}$
    H. $12\frac{37}{108}$ J. $65\frac{19}{27}$

12. What is the volume of the pyramid?

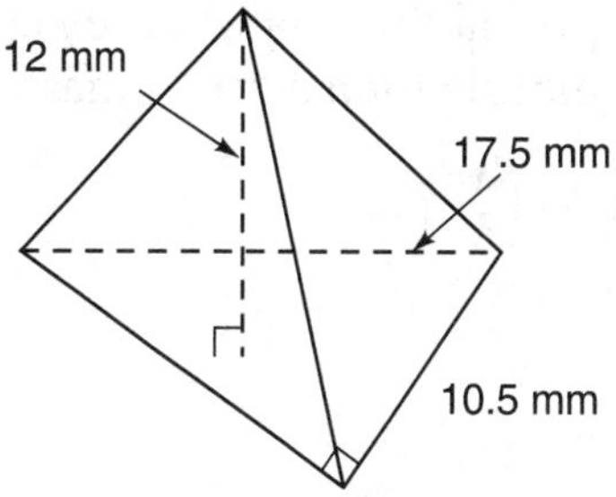

    A. 294 mm³
    B. 882 mm³
    C. 367.5 mm³
    D. 1102.5 mm³

13. A spinner that is evenly divided and numbered from 1 through 8 is spun twice. What is the probability that it lands on an even number first and then on a number less than 4?

    A. $\frac{3}{16}$ **B.** $\frac{3}{8}$

    C. $\frac{1}{2}$ **D.** $\frac{7}{8}$

14. What is the circumference of a circle with a radius of 6 feet?

    F. 6π ft   **G.** 9π ft
    H. 12π ft   **J.** 36π ft

15. In one year, the value of a home changed from $175,000 to $200,000. To the nearest tenth of a percent, what was the percent increase?

    A. 8.8%   **B.** 12.5%
    C. 14.3%   **D.** 114.3%

16. Simplify: $12b - 8a + 9 - 7b - 2(b - 5a)$

    F. $-18a - 3b + 9$
    G. $-18a + 3b + 9$
    H. $2a - 3b + 9$
    J. $2a + 3b + 9$

17. Jackie rides her bike for 2.25 miles in 18 minutes. What is her speed in miles per hour?

    A. 0.125 mi/h
    B. 4.5 mi/h
    C. 7.5 mi/h
    D. 13.5 mi/h

18. Jonathan wants 6 different DVDs. He only has enough money to buy 3. How many ways can he choose the 3?

    F. 6   **G.** 18
    H. 20   **J.** 120

19. Solve: $2.5x + 13.9 = -1.1$

    A. $x = -6$
    B. $x = -5.12$
    C. $x = 5.12$
    D. $x = 6$

20. Which inequality is the solution of the statement? Twice the difference of 22 and x is at least 42

    F. $x \geq 1$ **G.** $x \leq 1$
    H. $x \geq 43$ **J.** $x \leq 43$

Tell About It

Explain how you solve each problem. Show all your work.

21. There are 6 marbles in a bag, 3 blue, 2 red, and 1 green. Aubrey reaches into the bag and pulls out a marble, does not replace it, then chooses another. What is the probability that Aubrey chooses a blue marble then a green marble?

22. Kelsey creates a 2-player game in which the odds in favor of winning if you go first are 4 : 5. Is this a fair game? If Liz plays the game and goes first, what is the probability that she loses?

13-1 Arithmetic Sequences and Geometric Sequences

Name _____ Date _____

Determine if the sequence is arithmetic or geometric. Then find the next 2 terms.

−2, 4, 10, 16, …

$4 − (−2) = 6; 10 − 4 = 6; 16 − 10 = 6$

Each pair of numbers has a *constant difference* of 6. So this is an *arithmetic sequence*. Find the next two terms.

Add 6 ⟶ **16 + 6 = 22**

Add 6 ⟶ **22 + 6 = 28**

The next two terms are 22 and 28.

2, 7, 24.5, 85.75, …

$\frac{7}{2} = 3.5; \frac{24.5}{7} = 3.5; \frac{85.75}{24.5} = 3.5$

Each pair of numbers has a *constant ratio* of 3.5. So this is a *geometric sequence*. Find the next two terms.

Multiply by 3.5 ⟶ **(85.75)(3.5) = 300.125**

Multiply by 3.5 ⟶ **(300.125)(3.5) = 1050.4375**

The next two terms are 300.125, and 1050.4375.

Describe each sequence as arithmetic, geometric, or neither.
(*Hint*: If there is a pattern, it involves only one rule.)

1. 5, 10, 15, 20, …

_____**arithmetic**_____

2. 14, –7, 3.5, –1.75, …

_____

3. 64, 66, 70, 76, …

_____

4. $−\frac{3}{5}, −\frac{3}{25}, −\frac{3}{125}, −\frac{3}{625}, …$

_____

5. $24, 24\frac{2}{3}, 25\frac{1}{3}, 26, …$

_____

6. 202, 218.8, 235.6, 252.4, …

_____

Write a rule for each arithmetic or geometric sequence. Then find the 7th term.

7. 2187, 729, 243, 81, …

constant ratio: $\frac{729}{2187} = \frac{1}{3}$

$81 • \frac{1}{3} = 27; 27 • \frac{1}{3} = 9; 9 • \frac{1}{3} = 3$

rule: multiply by $\frac{1}{3}$; 7th term: 3

8. 2, 6, 18, 54

_____

9. 52, 63, 74, 85, …

_____

10. 7, −7.4, −21.8, −36.2, …

_____

11. 41, −18, −77, −136

_____

12. 81, 92.56, 104.12, 115.68

_____

13. 2, 2.2, 2.42, 2.662, …

_____

14. $−\frac{1}{216}, \frac{1}{36}, −\frac{1}{6}, 1, …$

_____

15. $3, 2, 1\frac{1}{3}, \frac{8}{9}, …$

_____

Find the missing term for each sequence.

16. −24, −12, −6, −3, ?, …
Constant ratio: $\frac{-12}{-24} = \frac{1}{2}$
Multiply −3 by $\frac{1}{2}$: $-3 \cdot \frac{1}{2} = -1.5$
  The missing term is −1.5.

17. 75, 15, 3, ?, 0.12, …

18. 52, ?, 40.5, 34.75, …

19. −3.64, −2.24, ?, 0.56, …

20. $\frac{4}{50}$, $1\frac{16}{25}$, ?, $4\frac{19}{25}$, $6\frac{16}{50}$

21. 2, ?, $\frac{5}{6}$, $\frac{1}{4}$, $-\frac{1}{3}$, …

Determine if the statement is *true* or *false*. Explain.

22. A sequence always follows a pattern.

23. The fifth term in the sequence 625, −125, 25, −5, … is 1.

24. −4, 6, −8, 10, … is an arithmetic sequence

Problem Solving

25. Nora is saving money for a new MP3 player. The first week, she saves $20. Each week after she adds $7 to her savings. Write a sequence to show the total amount of money she has saved each week. How much has she saved after 8 weeks?

26. Mr. Peterson has a timer on his heater so that every hour the temperature will drop 2 degrees during the day. The heat is set to 76°F at 7:00 A.M. Write a sequence to show the temperature every hour until noon.

CHALLENGE

27. A checkerboard has 64 squares. Al places 1 penny on the first square, 2 pennies on the second square, 4 pennies on the third square, and so on, doubling the number of pennies on each square. If he uses this sequence to fill the entire checkerboard, how many pennies would be on the 64th square? How many dollars is this? Give your answers in scientific notation, rounding the first number to the nearest tenth. Use a scientific calculator.

13-2 Algebraic Patterns and Sequences

Name _____ Date _____

Determine the pattern rule for the sequence. Then find the 7th term.

2, 6, 14, 30, …

(3)2 = 6. (7)2 = 14; and (15)2 = 30 ← Each term is the sum of
the previous and 1, times two.

The pattern rule is: Add 1 to the previous term. Then multiply by 2.

Extend the pattern to find the 7th term:

(1 + 2)2   (1 + 6)2   (1 + 14)2   (1 + 30)2   (1 + 62)2   (1 + 126)2

2   6   14   30   62   126   254

The 7th term is 254.

Determine the pattern rule.

1. 5, −5, 10, −10, 20, −20,…

Multiply by −1, then
multiply by −2.

2. 2.8, 7.8, 3.3, 8.3, 3.8,…

3. 100, 102, 51, 53, 26.5,…

4. −10.9, −9.9, −11.9, −8.9,…

5. $\frac{1}{9}, -\frac{1}{3}, -\frac{1}{6}, \frac{1}{2}, \frac{1}{4},\dots$

6. $99, 49\frac{1}{2}, 16\frac{1}{2}, 4\frac{1}{8},\dots$

Determine whether the sequence has an increasing or decreasing difference or ratio. Then find the next 3 terms in the sequence.

7. 7, 14, 42, 168,…

8. −20, −18, −14.4, −10.08,…

9. 1492.7, 1291.7, 1089.7, 886.7,…

Use the table to relate each term in the sequence to its position.

10.

Position	1	2	3	4	5
Term	2	6	24	120	720

11.

Position	1	2	3	4	5
Term	−6	−3	−2	−1.5	−1.2

12.

Position	1	2	3	4	5
Term	−2	−8	−18	−32	−50

13.

Position	1	2	3	4	5
Term	3	9	19	33	51

Describe the sequence represented in each visual pattern.
Then draw the next two terms on a separate sheet of paper.

14.

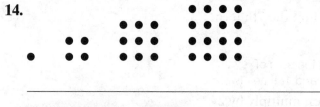

15.

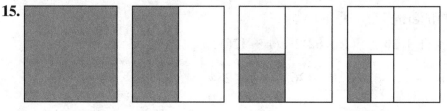

Determine if the statement is *true* or *false*. Explain.

16. If a sequence has an increasing difference, then each term is less than the previous.

17. An exponential sequence is neither arithmetic nor geometric.

18. A sequence can be both arithmetic and geometric.

Problem Solving

19. A pattern consists of concentric circles. The radius of the innermost circle is 1 cm. The radius of each successive circle is 1 cm greater than the one it surrounds. Starting with the innermost circle, approximate the first four areas for each concentric circle. Then find the area of the 10th circle.

20. Using a pattern, what is the sum of:
$\frac{1}{1} \cdot \frac{1}{2} + \frac{1}{2} \cdot \frac{1}{3} + \frac{1}{3} \cdot \frac{1}{4} + \ldots + \frac{1}{99} \cdot \frac{1}{100} + \frac{1}{100} \cdot \frac{1}{101}$? (*Hint:* Start with $\frac{1}{1} \cdot \frac{1}{2}$. Then write the sum as you add each product of fractions.)

TEST PREPARATION

21. What is the 10th term in the sequence 1, 1, 2, 3, 5, 8, 13, …?

    A. 13   **B.** 28   **C.** 34   **D.** 55

13-3 Conjectures and Counterexamples

Name _____ Date _____

> Determine if the *conjecture* is true or false.
> Conjecture: The product of two odd numbers is always odd.
> $1 \cdot 1 = 1$ $1 \cdot 3 = 3$ $3 \cdot 5 = 15$ ← start with a few tests
> So far the conjecture has not been proven false.
> Think more generally: If a number is odd, then all of its prime factors are odd.
> So the product of two odd numbers must have all odd prime factors.
> For a number to be even, 2 must be a factor of the number.
> So the product of two odd numbers cannot be even, and therefore must be odd.
> The conjecture is true.

> **Remember:** A counterexample is a case that proves that the conjecture is false.

**Test each conjecture to decide whether it is *true* or *false*.
If true, explain why. If false, provide a counterexample.**

1. The product of a negative number and a nonnegative number is always negative.

_____ False; $(-1)(0) = 0$ _____

2. All negative numbers are less than their absolute value. _____

3. For every integer, $n^2 + 1$ is odd. _____

**Make a conjecture based on the given sequence, and test your conjecture.
Explain your reasoning and the steps you took to reach your conclusion.**

4. 5, 10, 20, 35, 55, …

Conjecture: _____

Reason: _____

5. 124, −62, 31, −15.5, 7.75, …

Conjecture: _____

Reason: _____

6. $\frac{1}{3}, \frac{0}{4}, \frac{-2}{6}, \frac{-5}{9}, \frac{-9}{13}, \ldots$

Conjecture: _____

Reason: _____

7.

Conjecture: _____

Reason: _____

8.

Conjecture: _____

Reason: _____

Make a conjecture based on the information given, and test your conjecture.
Explain your reasoning and the steps you took to reach your conclusion.

9. $\frac{1}{2} - \frac{1}{3} = \frac{1}{6}$; $\frac{1}{3} - \frac{1}{4} = \frac{1}{12}$; $\frac{1}{4} - \frac{1}{5} = \frac{1}{20}$; $\frac{1}{5} - \frac{1}{6} = \frac{1}{30}$

Conjecture: _____

Reason: _____

10. $1 + 2 = \frac{2(3)}{2}$, $1 + 2 + 3 = \frac{3(4)}{2}$, $1 + 2 + 3 + 4 = \frac{4(5)}{2}$, $1 + 2 + 3 + 4 + 5 = \frac{5(6)}{2}$

Conjecture: _____

Reason: _____

11.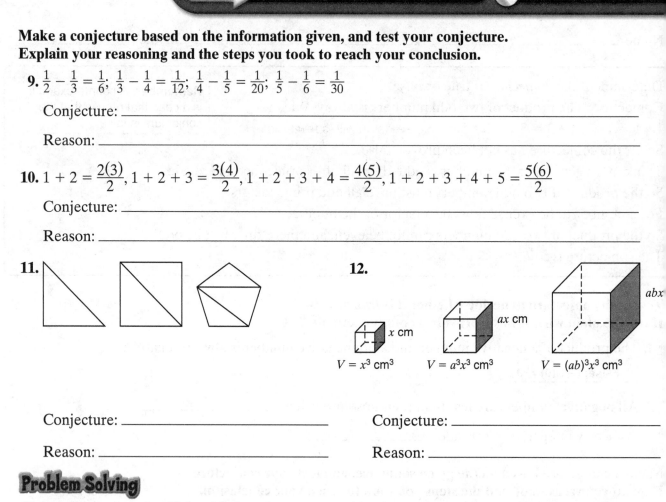

12.

x cm
$V = x^3$ cm^3

ax cm
$V = a^3x^3$ cm^3

abx
$V = (ab)^3x^3$ cm^3

Conjecture: _____

Reason: _____

Conjecture: _____

Reason: _____

Problem Solving

13. A student says that if the side lengths of a rectangle are doubled then the area is multiplied by four. Is the conjecture correct? Explain your reasoning and give a counterexample if it is false.

14. The pattern below is known as Pascal's Triangle. Make a conjecture about how each number in the triangle is found. Then complete the next row.

```
            1
          1   1
        1   2   1
      1   3   3   1
    1   4   6   4   1
  1   5  10  10   5   1
1                       1
```

_____

_____

SPIRAL REVIEW

Find the missing term for each sequence.

15. $-34, \underline{\ ?\ }, -18, -10, \ldots$

16. $48, 52, 56, \underline{\ ?\ }, 64, \ldots$

17. $5, 52.5, \underline{\ ?\ }, 5788.125, \ldots$

_____   _____   _____

13-4 Relations and Functions

Name _____ Date _____

Determine if each relation is a function. If possible, define the function rule.

Hours Worked (x)	1	2	3	4	5
Amount Earned (y)	$6	$12	$18	$24	$30

Number of Students (x)	2	6	6	4	2
Number of Siblings (y)	0	1	2	3	4

1	→	6
2	→	12
3	→	18
4	→	24
5	→	30

The relation is *one to one*.
So it is a function.
The function rule is $y = 6x$.

2	→	0
6	→	1
4	→	2
	→	3
	→	4

The relation is *one to many*.
So it is not a function.

Identify the *domain* (*x*-values) and *range* (*y*-values) of each relation.
Is the relation a function? Explain your answer.

1. $(1, 2), (4, 8), (9, 2), (16, 8)$

Domain _____

Range _____

Function? _____

2. $(0.5, 1), (0.5, 6), (-1.1, 1), (-1.1, 6)$

Domain _____

Range _____

Function? _____

Match each type of relation with the tables of information.

3. one-to-one   **4.** one-to-many   **5.** many-to-one   **6.** many-to-many

_____b_____   _____   _____   _____

a.

Name	Mary	Dan	Jane	Bob	Victor
Number of Pets	3	4	3	2	2

b.

Number of pens	1	2	3	4	5
Cost	$1.50	$3.00	$4.50	$6.00	$7.50

c.

Test scores	100	90	90	95	100
Name	Jack	Fred	Mike	Nick	Robert

d.

Name	Abby	Abby	Claire	Leah	Claire
Type of Pet	cat	dog	dog	cat	dog

Classify the relation and determine if it is a function. If possible,
write a function rule.

7.

x	1	2	3	4
y	5	10	15	20

_____

8.

x	5	10	15	20
y	3	5	7	9

_____

9.

x	5	5	6	6
y	1	2	3	4

_____

10.

x	−1	0	1	2
y	3	5	3	5

_____

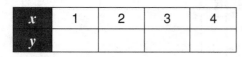
Complete the function table.

11. $y = 2x$

x	1	2	3	4
y	2	4	6	8

12. $y = \frac{1}{2}x$

x	1	2	3	4
y				

13. $y = -3x + 1$

x	1	2	3	4
y				

14. $y = 4x - 2$

x	0.1	0.2	0.3	0.4
y				

15. $y = -\frac{3}{4}x + 1$

x	1	2	3	4
y				

16. $y = -\frac{1}{2}x + 2$

x	0.2	0.4	0.6	0.8
y				

Find the function rule and answer the questions.
(*Hint:* Write the next three pairs of values for each function.)

17.

feet	1	2	3	4	5	6	7
yards	$\frac{1}{3}$	$\frac{2}{3}$	1	$1\frac{1}{3}$			

function rule: _____

How many yards are in 7 feet? _____

18.

feet	6.2	7.2	8.2	9.2	10.2	11.2
yards	6200	7200	8200			

function rule: _____

How many yards are in 11.2 feet?

_____

Problem Solving

19. A pound of peanuts costs $2.45. Write a function rule for the relation between weight and cost. Then find the cost of 6 pounds of peanuts.

20. Write a situation that can be represented by the function $y = 5x - 3$.

_____

_____

CHALLENGE

Determine if each relation is a function. Find the function rule.

21.

x	−3	−2	−1	0	1	2	3
y	9	4	1	0	1	4	9

22.

x	−3	−2	−1	0	1	2	3
y	−27	−8	−1	0	1	8	27

_____

_____

13-5 Functions

Name _____ Date _____

Mel is riding a bike at a rate of 6 miles per hour.
Write a function rule to represent the situation.

Create a *function table*.
Let x = time in hours.
Let y = distance in miles.

x	1	2	3	4	5	6
y	6	12	18	24	30	36

+6 +6 +6 +6 +6 ← The constant difference is 6.

So the function rule is $y = 6x$.

Evaluate the function for a domain
of {5, 10, 15}. Then identify the range.

So the range of the function $y = 6x$
for the given domain is {30, 60, 90}.

x	$y = 6x$	y
5	$y = 6(5)$	30
10	$y = 6(10)$	60
15	$y = 6(15)$	90

Write a function rule to represent each situation. (*Hint*: Make a function table.)

1. The space shuttle can fly 3500 miles per hour. What is the relationship between
time and distance?
x = time in hours; y = distance in miles
Each value of y in the table is 3500 times
the value of x. The function is $y = 3500x$.

x	1	2	3	4
y	3500	7000	10,500	14,000

2. A commercial jet can fly 700 miles per hour. What is the relationship between
time and distance?

_____

3. Apples cost $1.49 per pound. What is the relationship between weight and cost?

_____

4. Oranges cost $2.50 per pound. What is the relationship between weight and cost?

_____

5. Randy can make 8 napkins from 1 yard of fabric. What is the relationship
between length of fabric and number of napkins?

_____

6. Lauren can make 5 doll dresses from 1 yard of fabric. What is the relationship
between length of fabric and number of dresses?

_____

7. A taxi cab has an initial fee of $2.00. Passengers are charged $0.80 for every
minute that a ride takes. What is the relationship between the number of
minutes a ride takes and the cost of a ride?

_____

8. A phone service charges a $7 fee and $1 for each minute of the call. What is the relationship between the number of minutes and the cost of the call?

_____

Evaluate the given functions for a domain of $(-2, -1, 0,$ and $1)$.
Then identify the range of the function. (*Hint*: Make a function table.)

9. $y = 6x + 3$ **10.** $y = 2x + 2$ **11.** $y = 2.3x - 4$

12. $y = -1.5x + 4$ **13.** $y = \frac{1}{4}x + 1$ **14.** $y = \frac{1}{2}x + 6$

On a separate sheet of paper, make a table for each function.
Then evaluate the functions for three values of x. (*Hint*: The domain is the set of real numbers.)

15. $y = 5x - 1$ **16.** $y = -4x - 2$ **17.** $y = 1.5x + 3$

18. $y = -3.4x - 5$ **19.** $y = -\frac{1}{3}x + 5$ **20.** $y = -\frac{3}{4}x + 3$

Problem Solving

21. Bob can snowshoe at a rate of 2 miles per hour. Frank can only snowshoe at a rate of 0.75 mile per hour. Write a function rule that relates elapsed time and distance for both Bob and Frank. How much farther does Bob travel in 3 hours than Frank?

22. Gas station A is selling gas for $3.01 per gallon. Gas station B is selling gas for $2.95 per gallon. Write a function rule that relates the number of gallons and cost for each gas station. How much more does it cost to buy 6 gallons of gas at gas station A than at gas station B?

_____ _____

MENTAL MATH

Complete each function table.

23. $y = 2x$

x	1	2	3	4	5
y					

24. $y = 5x$

x	1	2	3	4	5
y					

13-6 Graph Linear Functions

Name _____   Date _____

You can rent a canoe for $2 per hour plus a $4 fee. Write a linear function to represent the situation, then graph the function. How much will you pay if you rent a canoe for 4 hours?

Let x = number of hours the canoe is rented.
Let y = total cost of renting a canoe.
So the function rule is $y = 2x + 4$.
Use the function rule to make a function table:

x	1	2	3
y	6	8	10

← Substitute the input values (x) to find the output values (y).

Use the values from the table to graph the function.
Using the graph, the cost of renting a canoe for 4 hours is $12.

$y = 2x + 4$

Complete the table of values to find ordered pairs.
On a separate sheet of paper, graph each linear function.

1.

x	$y = 3x + 5$	y	(x, y)
0			
1			
2			
3			

2.

x	$y = -2x + 3$	y	(x, y)
0			
2			
4			
6			

3.

x	$y = \frac{1}{2}x + 1$	y	(x, y)
−4			
−2			
0			
2			

4.

x	$y = 6x$	y	(x, y)
−1			
0			
1			
2			

5.

x	$y = -2x$	y	(x, y)
−2			
−1			
0			
1			

6.

x	$y = -\frac{1}{3}x - 4$	y	(x, y)
−6			
−3			
0			
3			

For exercises 7–22, graph each linear function on a separate sheet of paper. For exercises 7–14, use the graph to find y when $x = 3$.

7. $y = 2x + 7$ **8.** $y = 3x - 2$ **9.** $y = -5x$ **10.** $y = 4x$

_____ _____ _____ _____

11. $y = \frac{1}{3}x + 1$ **12.** $y = -\frac{1}{4}x + 2$ **13.** $y = -0.5x - 5$ **14.** $y = -0.4x + 2$

_____ _____ _____ _____

For exercises 15–22, use the graph to find y when $x = -2$.

15. $y = 4 - x$ **16.** $y = 6 - 5x$ **17.** $y = \frac{1}{2}x - 1$ **18.** $y = \frac{5}{2}x - 2$

_____ _____ _____ _____

19. $y = -1.5x + 4$ **20.** $y = -2.7x + 6$ **21.** $y = 0.4 - \frac{1}{5}x$ **22.** $y = 0.5 - \frac{1}{4}x$

_____ _____ _____ _____

Problem Solving

23. A car travels 55 miles per hour. Write a linear function to represent the situation. Graph the function on a separate sheet of paper. How far will the car travel in 7 hours?

_____

24. A loaf of bread costs $2.50 and apples cost $1.29 per pound. Write a linear function to represent the price of a loaf of bread and some apples. Graph the function on a separate sheet of paper. How much will you pay if you buy 3 pounds of apples?

_____

CRITICAL THINKING

25. Graph the functions $y = x$, $y = 2x$, $y = 3x$, $y = 5x$. What do you notice about the graphs? Make a conjecture about the relationship between x-coefficients and the graphs.

_____

_____

_____

13-7 Slope

Name _____ Date _____

Find the slope of each graph. Classify each slope as positive, negative, zero, or undefined.

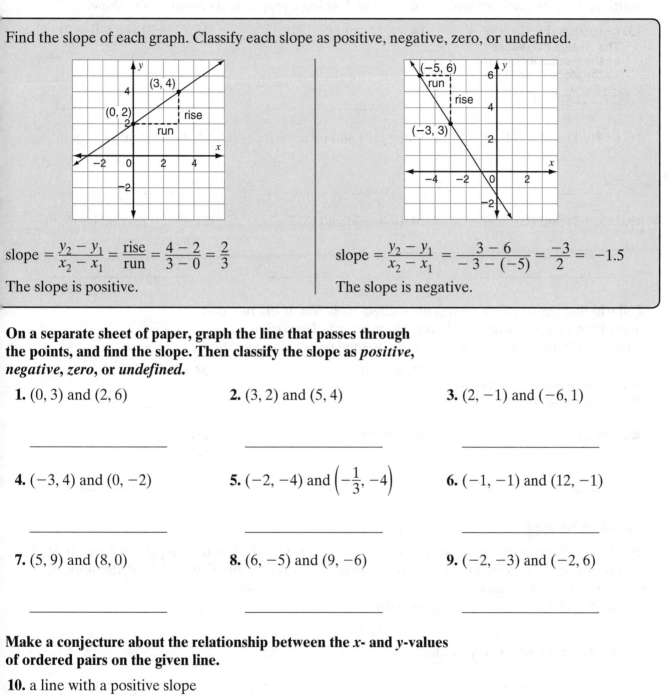

slope $= \dfrac{y_2 - y_1}{x_2 - x_1} = \dfrac{\text{rise}}{\text{run}} = \dfrac{4 - 2}{3 - 0} = \dfrac{2}{3}$

The slope is positive.

slope $= \dfrac{y_2 - y_1}{x_2 - x_1} = \dfrac{3 - 6}{-3 - (-5)} = \dfrac{-3}{2} = -1.5$

The slope is negative.

On a separate sheet of paper, graph the line that passes through the points, and find the slope. Then classify the slope as *positive, negative, zero,* or *undefined.*

1. $(0, 3)$ and $(2, 6)$

2. $(3, 2)$ and $(5, 4)$

3. $(2, -1)$ and $(-6, 1)$

_____ _____ _____

4. $(-3, 4)$ and $(0, -2)$

5. $(-2, -4)$ and $\left(-\dfrac{1}{3}, -4\right)$

6. $(-1, -1)$ and $(12, -1)$

_____ _____ _____

7. $(5, 9)$ and $(8, 0)$

8. $(6, -5)$ and $(9, -6)$

9. $(-2, -3)$ and $(-2, 6)$

_____ _____ _____

Make a conjecture about the relationship between the *x*- and *y*-values of ordered pairs on the given line.

10. a line with a positive slope

_____

11. a line with a negative slope

_____

12. a line with a slope that is undefined

_____

Examine each set of ordered pairs and classify the slope of the graph of the line as positive, negative, zero, or undefined without drawing a graph. Then compute the slope.

13. $(-6, 0)$ and $(-1, -5)$
The y-value decreases as the x-value increases, so the slope is negative.
$$\frac{-5 - 0}{-1 - (-6)} = \frac{-5}{5} = -1$$

14. $(4, 12)$ and $(9, 12)$

15. $(2, -2)$ and $(10, -7)$

16. $(-16, 1)$ and $(-11, 16)$

17. $(-1, 8)$ and $(-1, -5)$

18. $(7, 19)$ and $(11, 5)$

19. $(13, -3)$ and $(20, -3)$

20. $(-8, -7)$ and $(8, 7)$

21. $(-25, 18)$ and $(-15, 8)$

Tell whether the function represents a direct variation. If the function represents a direct variation, identify the constant of variation.
(*Hint:* In a funtion in the form of $y = kx$, k is the constant of variation.)

22. $y = -3x$
$x = 0, y = 0$; graph goes through the origin; Direct variation; $k = -3$

23. $y = 6.7x$

24. $y = 2.5x + 2.5$

25. $y = \frac{7}{9}x$

26. $y = \frac{1}{5}x - 3$

27. $y = \frac{5}{8}x$

Problem Solving

28. If the following situations were graphed on a coordinate grid, would the slopes be positive, negative, zero, or undefined?
  a. A rocket is shot straight up into the air.

  b. Rachel runs the 50-yard dash.

29. The vertices of triangle ABC are $A(-6, 5)$, $B(1, 2)$ and $C(0, -4)$. Find the slope of each side.

WRITE ABOUT IT

30. Graph the lines $y = 2x$, $y = -\frac{1}{2}x$, $y = 3x$, and $y = -\frac{1}{3}x$, and find their slopes. What is the relationship between the lines and their slopes?

13-8 Nonlinear Functions

Name _____ Date _____

Use the table to determine if the function is linear or nonlinear.
If the function is nonlinear, decide if it could be quadratic.

x	-2	-1	0	1	2
y	5	2	1	2	5

Method 1 Find the slope.

Choose any two points from the data and
find the slope. Then find the slope of a
different pair of points.

For $(-2, 5)$ and $(-1, 2)$:
$$\frac{2-5}{-1-(-2)} = \frac{-3}{1} = -3$$

For $(0, 1)$ and $(-1, 2)$:
$$\frac{2-1}{-1-0} = \frac{1}{-1} = -1$$

The slopes are different so the data
represents a *nonlinear function*.

Method 2 Examine the graph.

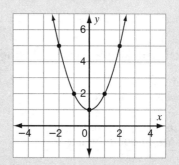

The graph is not a straight line, so
it is the graph of a *nonlinear function*.
The graph is *quadratic* because
the graph forms a U-shaped parabola.

**Examine each graph. Determine if the graph is *linear* or *nonlinear*.
If the graph is nonlinear, decide if it could be *quadratic*.**

1.

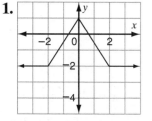

2.

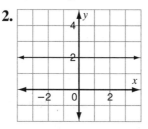

3.

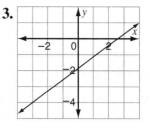

The graph is nonlinear. It is not a
parabola, so it is not quadratic.

_____ _____

4.

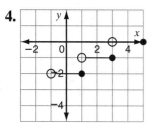

5.

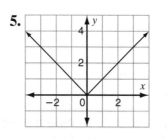

6.

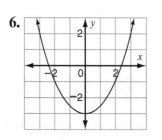

_____ _____ _____

Use the table of values to determine if each function is linear or nonlinear.

7.

x	1	2	3	4	5
y	3	4	5	6	7

The graph is a straight line, so the function is linear.

8.

x	−2	−1	0	1	2
y	−9	−7	−5	−3	−1

9.

x	−2	−1	0	1	2
y	2	1	0	1	2

10.

x	−4	−3	−2	1	2
y	8	3	0	3	8

Determine if the graph passing through the points could be of a linear function.

11. $(2, 2), (4, 3), (6, 4)$

$$\frac{3 - 2}{4 - 2} = \frac{1}{2}; \frac{4 - 3}{6 - 4} = \frac{1}{2}$$

The slope is constant.
The graph could be linear.

12. $(1, 1), (2, 4), (3, 9)$

13. $(-3, 3), (-2, 2), (-1, 1)$

14. $(1, 5), (2, 7), (3, 9)$

15. $(-1, 2), (0, 1), (1, 2)$

16. $(-4, 6), (-2, 6), (0, 6)$

17. $(2, 2.1), (3, 4.2), (4, 4.3)$

18. $(5, 1.5), (10, 15), (15, 150)$

19. $(-20, -5.75), (0, 0), (20, 5.75)$

Problem Solving

20. A store sells bags of rice for $7 each. Graph the function relating the number of bags to the total cost on a separate sheet of paper. Is the graph linear or nonlinear? If it is nonlinear, is the function quadratic?

21. Graph the functions $y = \frac{x^2}{2} + 1$, $y = \frac{x^3}{2} + 1$ and $y = \frac{x^4}{2} + 1$ on the same coordinate grid. Are the functions linear or nonlinear? If they are nonlinear, which (if any) are quadratic?

SPIRAL REVIEW

On a separate sheet of paper, make a function table to model each linear function. Then, for each equation, find y for x = 10.

22. $y = 2x + 3$

23. $y = \frac{1}{4}x - 6$

24. $y = 1.3x + 1$

25. $y = \frac{3}{5}x - 9$

13-9 Graph a Situation

Kami and Jeanne are going on a trip. Kami drives from New Hampshire to New York to pick up Jeanne. They then fly to North Carolina and stay for a week. After they fly back to New York, Kami stays with Jeanne for two days before driving back to New Hampshire. Make a graph to represent the situation.

Break the situation into separate events. Then determine the type of change and slope.

Event 1: Kami drives to New York:
increasing distance from home ◂— positive slope
Event 2: Kami and Jeanne fly to North Carolina:
fast increasing distance from home ◂— steep positive slope
Event 3: Kami and Jeanne stay in North Carolina for a week: distance from home doesn't change ◂— horizontal line
Event 4: Kami and Jeanne fly back to New York:
fast decreasing distance from home ◂— steep negative slope
Event 5: Kami stays at Jeanne's for two nights:
distance from home doesn't change ◂— horizontal line
Event 6: Kami drives to New Hampshire:
decreasing distance from home ◂— negative slope

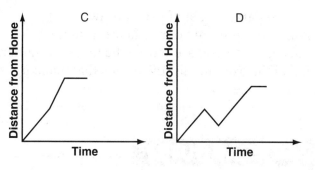

For exercises 1–4, the graphs below represent various events that happen on different days when Marcello walks to the bus stop. Select the graph that best represents each situation.

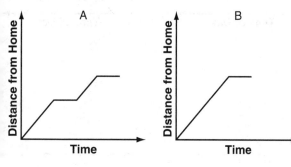

1. Marcello leaves his house and walks directly to the bus stop.

   B; The rate of change is constant.

2. Marcello stops to talk to a friend on the way to the bus stop.

   _____

3. Marcello starts walking to the bus stop, looks at his watch, and realizes that he is late. He runs the rest of the way to the bus stop.

   _____

4. Marcello realizes he forgot his lunch on his way to the bus stop. He turns around and starts walking home. On the way home, he finds his lunch is in his backpack and heads back to the bus stop.

   _____

Use the graph at the right representing Billy's canoe trip to a lake to answer the exercises.

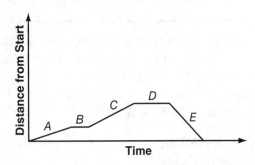

5. When was Billy traveling back to where he started?

_____

6. When was Billy not canoeing?

_____

7. When might Billy have been traveling against the current?

_____

8. Billy stopped for a brief time on his way to the lake to watch a hawk flying in the air. When was this?

_____

Problem Solving

9. Jack and Peter work at the same company, but have different schedules. They both work 8 hours each day and have one 15 minute break and an hour lunch break. Compare their work schedules.

_____

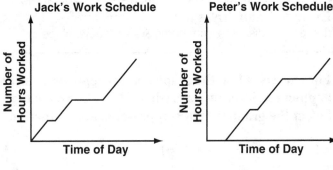

10. On a separate sheet of paper, draw a graph to represent your distance from the kitchen when you are setting the table for dinner. Label the axes and list the events that make up the graph.

_____

WRITE ABOUT IT

On a separate sheet of paper, give an example of a situation that might be represented by the graph.

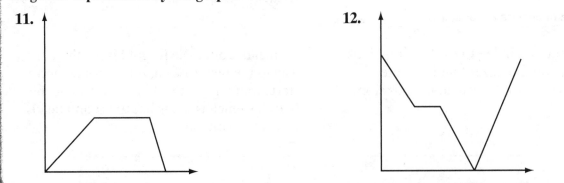

11.

12.

13-10 Graph Translations and Reflections

Name _____   Date _____

Translate the figure 2 units left and 4 units down. | Reflect the figure over the *x*-axis.

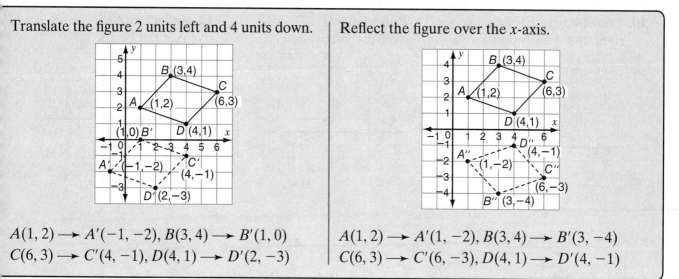

$A(1, 2) \rightarrow A'(-1, -2), B(3, 4) \rightarrow B'(1, 0)$
$C(6, 3) \rightarrow C'(4, -1), D(4, 1) \rightarrow D'(2, -3)$

$A(1, 2) \rightarrow A'(1, -2), B(3, 4) \rightarrow B'(3, -4)$
$C(6, 3) \rightarrow C'(6, -3), D(4, 1) \rightarrow D'(4, -1)$

Graph each point and its image on the coordinate plane. Label the points and write the coordinates of the image.

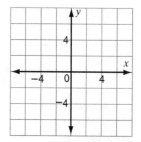

1. Translate $A(2, 3)$ four units up. _____

2. Reflect $B(5, -4)$ over the *x*-axis. _____

3. Translate $C(-6, 5)$ 1 unit down and 5 units right. _____

Write the rule for the transformation of the original figure.

4.
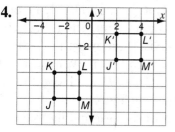

_____

5.
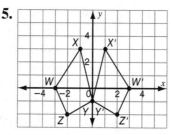

_____

6.
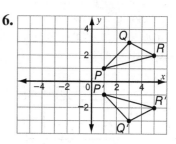

_____

7.
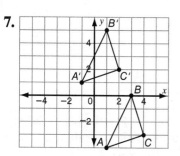

_____

8.
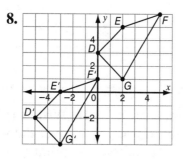

_____

9.
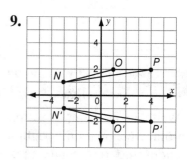

_____

Graph the transformation of each triangle. Give the coordinates of the vertices of the original figure and its image.

10. Translate △*ABC* 7 units right and 4 units down.

11. Reflect △*LMN* over the *y*-axis

12. Reflect △*QRS* over the *x*-axis.

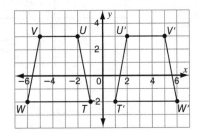

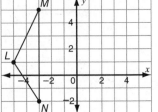

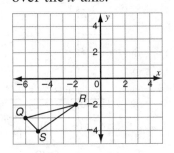

_____   _____   _____

Determine if the statement is *true* or *false*. If it is false, explain why.

13. When a figure is translated left, its side lengths decrease.

_____

14. The areas of a figure and its image when reflected over the *x*-axis are equal.

_____

Problem Solving

15. A student looks at the transformation of the trapezoid below and states that the original trapezoid is translated 7 units right. Is the student correct?

16. Nadia plots and connects the points $A(-3, 3)$, $B(-2, 4)$, $C(-1, 3)$, $D(-1, 1)$, and $E(-3, 1)$ to form a pentagon. She reflects the figure over the *y*-axis, then over the *x*-axis, then over the *y*-axis, and then over the *x*-axis to form the image $A'B'C'D'E'$. How do the coordinates of the new figure relate to the coordinates of the original figure?

_____

_____   _____

CRITICAL THINKING

17. Write a rule using coordinates to translate a point $M(x, y)$ *a* units right and *b* units down and a rule to translate a point $N(x, y)$ *a* units left and *b* units up.

18. Write a rule to reflect a point $P(x, y)$ over the *y*-axis, and a rule to reflect a point $Q(x, y)$ over the *x*-axis.

_____   _____

13-11 Graph Rotations

Name _____ Date _____

Rotate triangle ABC 90° counterclockwise around the origin.

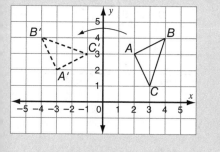

Remember: Rotation rules
90° rotation: $(x, y) \longrightarrow (-y, x)$; A quarter turn
180° rotation: $(x, y) \longrightarrow (-x, -y)$; A half a turn
270° rotation: $(x, y) \longrightarrow (y, -x)$; A three-quarter turn

$A(2, 3) \longrightarrow A'(-3, 2)$
$B(4, 4) \longrightarrow B'(-4, 4)$
$C(3, 1) \longrightarrow C'(-1, 3)$

Write the coordinates of the image of $P(x, y)$ for the given counterclockwise rotation around the origin.

1. $P(3, 8)$; 180° **2.** $P(12, -2)$; 90° **3.** $P(10, -10)$; 270° **4.** $P(-7, -1)$; 90°

180° rotation:
$P(x, y) \longrightarrow P'(-x, -y)$
$P(3, 8) \longrightarrow P'(-3, -8)$ _____ _____ _____

Describe the rotation around the origin by direction and degree.

5.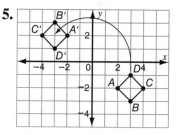

6.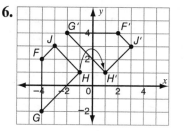

7.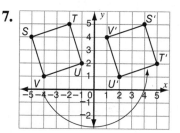

_____ _____ _____

Draw the image of the line segment for the given rotation around the origin. Label the endpoints.

8. 90° counterclockwise **9.** 180° counterclockwise **10.** 270° counterclockwise

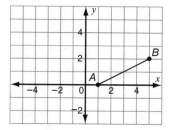 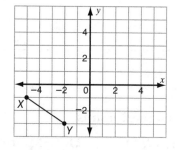 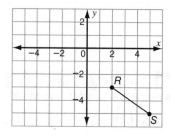

_____ _____ _____

**Draw the image of the figure for the given rotation around the origin.
Label the vertices.**

11. 90° counterclockwise

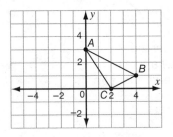

90° rotation: $(x, y) \longrightarrow (-y, x)$
$A(0, 3) \longrightarrow A'(-3, 0)$
$B(4, 1) \longrightarrow B'(-1, 4)$
$C(2, 0) \longrightarrow C'(0, 2)$

12. 180° counterclockwise

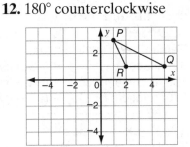

13. 270° counterclockwise

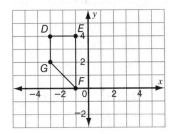

14. 90° clockwise

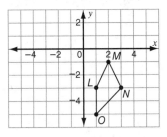

15. 180° clockwise

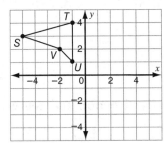

16. 270° clockwise

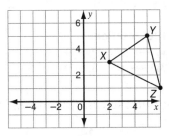

Problem Solving

17. The point $X(5, 5)$ is rotated 90° counterclockwise around the origin. What other transformations, besides rotation, would produce the same image?

18. Triangle LMN has coordinates $L(-3, 2)$, $M(-1, 4)$ and $N(2, 3)$. The triangle is translated 3 units up and 4 units right, then rotated 180° around the origin. What are the vertices of the image?

SPIRAL REVIEW

For each exercise find the slope between the 2 points.

19. $(3, 0)$ and $(4, -2)$ **20.** $(6, 3)$ and $(9, 5)$ **21.** $(-5, -6)$ and $(1, 1)$ **22.** $(-4, 8)$ and $(5, 5)$

13-12 Graph Dilations

Name _____ Date _____

Enlarge rectangle $ABCD$ using a scale factor of 2.
Then find the area of the dilation.

> **Remember:**
> Scale factor > 1; dilation is an *enlargement*.
> $0 <$ Scale factor < 1; dilation is a *reduction*.

To enlarge $ABCD$, multiply each vertex by 2.
$$P(x, y) \longrightarrow P'(2x, 2y)$$
$A(-1, 3) \quad \longrightarrow A'(2 \bullet -1, 2 \bullet 3) = A'(-2, 6)$
$B(3, 3) \quad \longrightarrow B'(2 \bullet 3, 2 \bullet 3) = B'(6, 6)$
$C(3, -2) \quad \longrightarrow C'(2 \bullet 3, 2 \bullet -2) = C'(6, -4)$
$D(-1, -2) \longrightarrow D'(2 \bullet -1, 2 \bullet -2) = D'(-2, -4)$

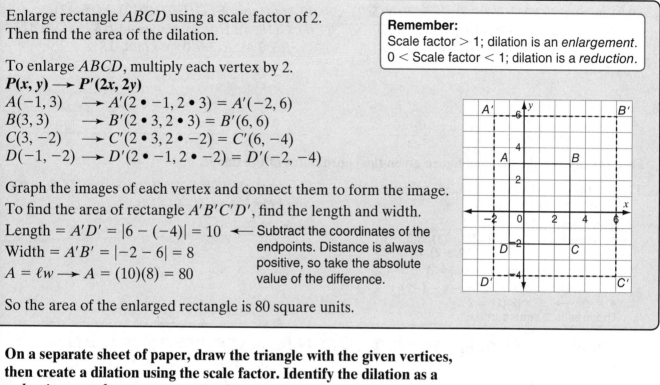

Graph the images of each vertex and connect them to form the image.
To find the area of rectangle $A'B'C'D'$, find the length and width.
Length $= A'D' = |6 - (-4)| = 10$ ← Subtract the coordinates of the
Width $= A'B' = |-2 - 6| = 8$ endpoints. Distance is always
$A = \ell w \longrightarrow A = (10)(8) = 80$ positive, so take the absolute
value of the difference.

So the area of the enlarged rectangle is 80 square units.

On a separate sheet of paper, draw the triangle with the given vertices, then create a dilation using the scale factor. Identify the dilation as a *reduction* or *enlargement*.

1. $A(1, 2)$, $B(2, 2)$, $C(1, -2)$
scale factor: 3

_____

2. $X(-6, 0)$, $Y(3, 3)$, $Z(0, -9)$
scale factor: $\frac{1}{3}$

_____

3. $D(2, 8)$, $E(4, -4)$, $F(-4, 0)$
scale factor: $\frac{1}{4}$

_____

4. $L(-1, 1)$, $M(1, 1)$, $N(-1, -1)$
scale factor: 6

_____

5. $P(3, 2)$, $Q(5, 1)$, $R(2, -4)$
scale factor: $6\frac{1}{2}$

_____

6. $J(-8, 6)$, $K(-2, 4)$, $L(-4, -8)$
scale factor: $\frac{3}{4}$

_____

Graph the figures on a separate sheet of paper. If the second figure is a dilation of the first, find the scale factor.

7. square $IJKL$: $I(6, 4)$, $J(10, 4)$, $K(10, 0)$, $L(6, 0)$
square $MNOP$: $M(3, 2)$, $N(5, 2)$, $O(5, 0)$, $P(3, 0)$

8. triangle QRS: $Q(-3, 2)$, $R(1, 3)$, $S(-1, -1)$
triangle TUV: $T(6, 4)$, $U(2, 6)$, $V(-2, -3)$

_____

Graph the figures on a separate sheet of paper. If the second figure is a dilation of the first, find the scale factor.

9. trapezoid $WXYZ$: $W(0, 7)$, $X(5, 7)$, $Y(5, 2)$, $Z(-3, 2)$, trapezoid $ABCD$: $A(0, 10.5)$, $B(7.5, 10.5)$, $C(7.5, 3)$, $D(-4.5, 3)$

10. trapezoid $EFGH$: $E(10, 12)$, $F(15, 12)$, $G(18, 4)$, $H(9, 4)$, trapezoid $IJKL$: $I(2, 2.4)$, $J(3, 2.4)$, $K(3.6, 0.8)$, $L(1.8, 0.8)$

Find the area of the original figure given the coordinates of the image.

11. rectangle $A'B'C'D'$: $A'(3, -3)$, $B'(9, -3)$, $C'(9, -6)$, $D'(3, -6)$
    scale factor: 3
    coordinates of original: $A(1, -1)$, $B(3, -1)$, $C(3, -2)$, $D(1, -2)$
    length $= AB = DC = |1 - 3| = 2$
    width $= AD = BC = |-1 - (-2)| = 1$
    $A = \ell w \longrightarrow A = (2)(1) = 2$
    The area is 2 square units.

12. rectangle $E'F'G'H'$: $E'(6, -10)$, $F'(18, -10)$, $G'(18, -14)$, $H'(6, -14)$
    scale factor: 2

13. triangle $I'J'K'$: $I'(-7, 4)$, $J'(18, -9)$, $K'(-7, -9)$
    scale factor: 0.5

14. square $O'P'Q'R'$: $O'(-15, 5)$, $P'(5, 5)$, $Q'(5, -15)$, $R'(-15, -15)$
    scale factor: 2.5

Problem Solving

15. Brian has a 6 ft by 5 ft rectangular vegetable garden. He enlarges it by 1.5. On a separate sheet of grid paper, draw a rectangle to represent the original garden. Then dilate the rectangle and find the area of each garden.

16. Julie plots and connects the points $(3, 3)$, $(5, 3)$, $(5, 1)$, and $(3, 1)$ to form a square. Veejay plots and connects the points $(6, 6)$, $(10, 6)$, $(10, 2)$, and $(6, 1)$. Is his square a dilation of Julie's square?

WRITE ABOUT IT

17. If figure $ABCD$ is a rectangle with vertices $A(1, 5)$, $B(6, 5)$, $C(6, 1)$ and $D(1, 1)$, how does the area of the rectangle change when it is dilated with a scale factor of c? Explain.

13-13 Problem-Solving Strategy:
Consider Extreme Cases

Name _____ Date _____

Solve by using the strategy Consider Extreme Cases.

1. Provide an example of a rectangle whose perimeter is more than twice its area. (*Hint:* Consider the numeric value of the measure, not the units.)

_____

2. All hexagons have interior angles that sum to the same number of degrees. What is that degree measure?

_____

3. A *chord* is a line segment joining any two points of a circle. What is the length of the *longest* chord of a circle with circumference 40 cm?

_____

4. Henry has an average of 96 on four 100-point exams. What is the lowest possible average he can finish the year with if there is only one more 100-point exam remaining?

_____

5. All seven-sided polygons have interior angles that sum to the same number. What is that number?

_____

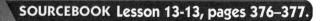

6. One side of a parallelogram has length 4 cm, and an adjacent side has length 6 cm. Is it possible for the area of this parallelogram to be less than 0.2 cm².

_____

7. A drawer holds 4 blue socks, 6 black socks, and 6 brown socks. How many socks must be randomly pulled from the drawer in order to be *sure* of obtaining two of the same color?

_____

8. A drawer holds 4 blue socks, 6 black socks, and 6 brown socks. How many socks must be randomly pulled from the drawer in order to be *sure* of obtaining two *brown* socks?

_____

9. Kelly scored a 62 on her first exam. All exams have 100 possible points. What is the highest average she can obtain if there are five exams in all?

_____

10. Suppose you know the area formula for parallelograms. Prove that the area A of the obtuse triangle below is given by $A = \frac{1}{2}bh$.

_____

Enrichment:
Combining Transformations

Name _____   Date _____

What two transformations might have been applied to rectangle ABCD to get the final image of rectangle A″B″C″D″?

There are several ways to combine transformations to get the image. One way is to reflect ABCD across the x-axis and rotate the image A′B′C′D′ counterclockwise 270°.

In exercises 1–4, describe a combination of two transformations that would create the final image. Use grid paper if needed.

1.

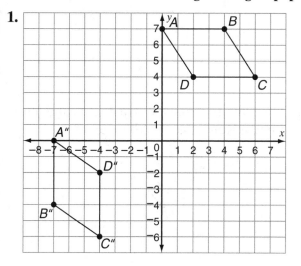

Reflect across x-axis and rotate 270° counterclockwise about the origin.

2.

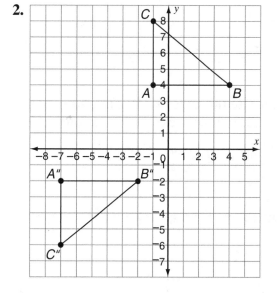

_____

3.

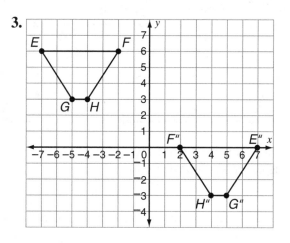

_____

4.

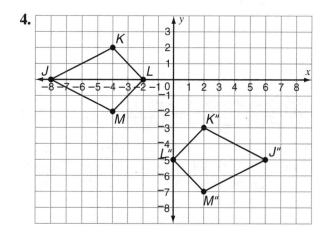

_____

In exercises 5–8 the first image is given. Follow the steps listed below to create the image. Use graph paper to help you find the answer if needed.

5. Translate the image right 8 units. Reflect across the *x*-axis.

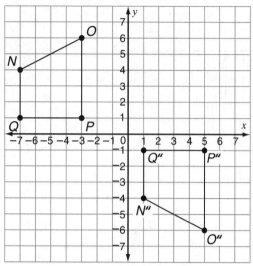

6. Translate the image down 4 units. Rotate counterclockwise 90° about the origin.

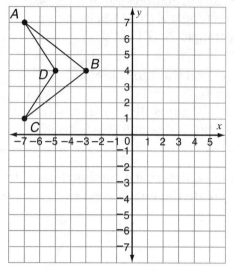

7. Translate the image up 8 units and right 4 units. Rotate counterclockwise 180° about the origin.

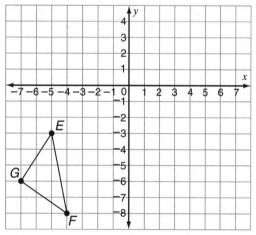

8. Translate the image down 4 units and left 5 units. Reflect across the *x*-axis.

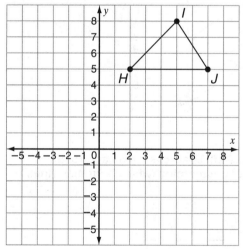

WRITE ABOUT IT

9. In exercises 1–4, you were asked to describe a combination of transformations that would result in the final image. Choose one of these exercises and describe a different combination that would also work.

_____

_____

Test Prep: Gridded-Response Questions

Strategy: Apply Mathematical Reasoning

Name _____ Date _____

When deciding how to approach a problem, sometimes it is helpful to *solve a simpler problem*.	To solve the problem, try using these strategies. • Reread the item. • Use the Test-Prep Strategy. • Apply appropriate rules, definitions, properties, or strategies. • Analyze your answer.

Record your answers on the gridded-response answer sheet. Explain how you used strategies. *TIP: If you have time, check your work.*

1. Jake earns $54 when he works 4.5 hours. How many hours would he have to work to earn $108?

Show all your work.

Answer _____

2. The Sandwich Cart offers 4 choices of bread, 6 choices of meat, and 3 choices of cheese. How many different sandwiches can be made from one type of bread, meat, and cheese?

Show all your work.

Answer _____

3. If you enlarge a square by multiplying the lengths of its sides by 5, what is the ratio of the area of the smaller square to the area of the larger square? Write the answer as a fraction.

Show all your work.

Answer _____

4. What is the 25th term in this sequence?

2.5, 5, 7.5, 10, 12.5, …

Show all your work.

Answer _____

5. Sasha's car averages 23 miles per gallon of gas. She plans to drive 210 miles today and 158 miles tomorrow. How many gallons of gas will she use?

Show all your work

Answer _____

6. A square table can seat two people on each side. For larger groups, the tables can be pushed together, as shown. How many people will 7 tables pushed together seat?

Show all your work

Answer _____

Vocabulary Development

Name _____ Date _____

Chapter 13 Vocabulary

arithmetic sequence	geometric sequence	quadratic function
center of rotation	image	range
conjecture	inputs	reduction
constant difference	iteration	reflection
constant ratio	line of reflection	relation
counterexample	linear equation	rotation
dilation	linear function	sequence
direct variation	nonlinear function	slope
domain	outputs	term
enlargement	parabola	transformation
function	pattern rule	translation

From the vocabulary list above, choose the term(s) that best complete each sentence. Write the term(s) in the space(s) provided.

1. The set of inputs in a relation is called the _____.

2. _____ is a measure of the steepness of a line.

3. A _____ is a U-shaped graph.

4. An enlargement is a type of _____.

5. A line that passes through the origin is the graph of a _____.

6. The graph of a _____ is *not* a line.

7. The following sequence is _____: $-2, 4, -8, 16, -32, \ldots$

8. You can use a _____ to show that a conjecture is false.

9. The sequence $10, 7.5, 5, 2.5, 0, \ldots$ has a _____ of 2.5.

10. One-to-one and many-to-one relations are examples of _____.

11. A _____ flips a figure over a _____.
    Its image has a different orientation.

Choose two terms from the list that you did not use in Questions 1–12. For each term, write a definition in your own words and give an example.

12. _____

_____

_____

Practice Chapter 13 Test

Name _____   Date _____

**Describe the sequence as arithmetic, geometric, or neither.
If arithmetic or geometric, find the 8th term.**

1. $14.5, 13, 11.5, 10, \ldots$ **2.** $-1, -2, -6, -24, \ldots$ **3.** $100, -25, \frac{25}{4}, -\frac{25}{16}, \ldots$ **4.** $0.4, 1.2, 3.6, 10.8, \ldots$

_____   _____   _____   _____

Find the missing term for each sequence.

5. $656, 627, 598, \underline{\hspace{1cm}}, 540$ **6.** $\underline{\hspace{1cm}}, 324, 108, 36, 12$ **7.** $720, 360, \underline{\hspace{1cm}}, 30, 6$

8. $14, \underline{\hspace{1cm}}, 29, 38, 48$ **9.** $7, 25, 79, \underline{\hspace{1cm}}, 727$ **10.** $\frac{4}{5}, 1\frac{4}{5}, \underline{\hspace{1cm}}, 5\frac{1}{5}, 7\frac{1}{5}$

**Determine whether the conjecture is true or false. If true, explain
why. If false, give a counterexample.**

11. The sum of two fractions is always greater than 1.

_____

12. The product of 2 prime numbers is never prime.

_____

**Identify the input and output values of each relation and determine
if it is a function.**

13. $(9, 30), (4, 30), (2, 28), (2, 29), (1, 31)$

  inputs: _____

  outputs: _____

  function? _____

14. $(4, 16), (2, 4), (5, 25), (1, 1), (8, 64)$

  inputs: _____

  outputs: _____

  function? _____

15. $(42, 14), (65, 9), (97, 9), (38, 12), (81, 42)$

  inputs: _____

  outputs: _____

  function? _____

16. $(38, 7), (39, 7), (40, 7), (41, 7), (42, 7)$

  inputs: _____

  outputs: _____

  function? _____

Complete the function table.

17. $y = 6x + 3$

x	1	2	3	4
y				

18. $y = -3x + 15$

x	4	6	8	10
y				

19. $y = -x - 4$

x	5	10	15	20
y				

20. $y = 2x - 5$

x				
y	-9	-7	-5	-3

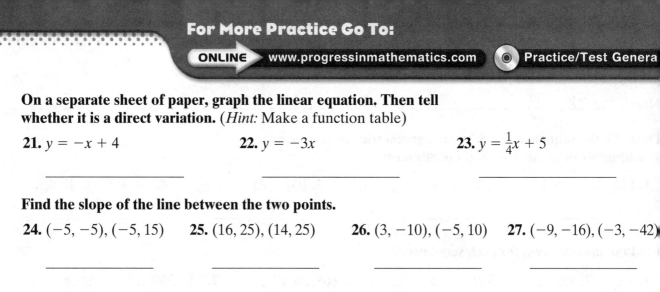
On a separate sheet of paper, graph the linear equation. Then tell whether it is a direct variation. (*Hint:* Make a function table)

21. $y = -x + 4$ **22.** $y = -3x$ **23.** $y = \frac{1}{4}x + 5$

_____   _____   _____

Find the slope of the line between the two points.

24. $(-5, -5), (-5, 15)$ **25.** $(16, 25), (14, 25)$ **26.** $(3, -10), (-5, 10)$ **27.** $(-9, -16), (-3, -42)$

_____   _____   _____   _____

Decide if the graph is of a linear or nonlinear function. If nonlinear, determine if it is a parabola.

28. 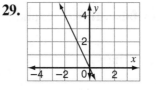   **29.** 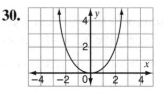   **30.**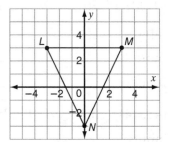

_____   _____   _____

Graph the transformation of the figure. Write the coordinates for each vertex of the image.

31. Reflect trapezoid $DEFG$ over the y-axis.

32. Rotate parallelogram $WXYZ$ 90° counterclockwise around the origin.

33. Dilate triangle LMN with a scale factor of $\frac{1}{3}$.

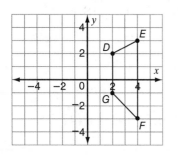   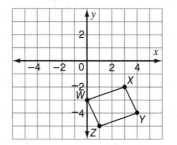   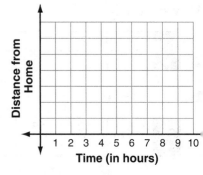

_____   _____   _____

Tell About It

Explain how you solve the problem. Show all your work.

34. Melanie walks from home to school in 15 minutes. After 7 hours at school, she walks 10 minutes to her babysitting job, which is on her way home. She babysits for 2 hours, and then walks home. Make a graph relating the time to the distance that Melanie is from home.

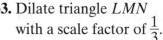

_____

_____

_____

Cumulative Review: Chapters 1–13

Name _____   Date _____

Circle the best answer.

1. Simplify: $\dfrac{a^{-5}b^4}{a^{-10}b^{-12}}$.

A. $\dfrac{1}{a^5b^{16}}$ **B.** $\dfrac{a^2}{b^3}$

C. $\dfrac{b^3}{a^2}$ **D.** a^5b^{16}

2. The mean score for a group of 4 golfers was 92. Three of the scores were 90, 86, and 97. What was the fourth score?

F. 92   **G.** 93
H. 94   **J.** 95

3. Solve: $2x - 7 = -6\frac{1}{2}$.

A. $x = -5$ **B.** $x = -\frac{1}{4}$

C. $x = \frac{1}{4}$ **D.** $x = 5$

4. Rectangles $ABCD$ and $EFGH$ are similar. What is the value of l?

F. 1 cm
G. 1.375 cm
H. 1.75 cm
J. 1.875 cm

5. What is the eighth term in the sequence $256, -128, 64, -32, \ldots$?

A. -2 **B.** -1
C. 1 **D.** 2

6. Which point lies in Quadrant II?

F. $(-5, -5)$ **G.** $(-5, 5)$
H. $(5, -5)$ **J.** $(5, 5)$

7. AB is parallel to CD. What must be true about $\angle 2$ and $\angle 7$?

A. They are congruent.
B. They are complementary.
C. They are supplementary.
D. None of the above.

8. What is the slope of the line that passes through $(-4, 8)$ and $(2, 7)$?

F. -6 **G.** $-\dfrac{1}{6}$

H. $\dfrac{1}{6}$ **J.** 6

9. Justin buys a DVD player that originally cost $90. It is on sale for 15% off. He then is charged 6% sales tax. How much does Justin pay for the DVD player?

A. $76.50   **B.** $81.09
C. $81.90   **D.** $95.40

10. The base of a rectangular pyramid has length 25 yd and width 17 yd. The height of the pyramid is 12 yd. What is the volume of the pyramid?

F. 1275 yd^3
G. 1700 yd^3
H. 2550 yd^3
J. 5100 yd^3

11. The legs of a right triangle measure 2 meters and 4 meters. What is the length of the hypotenuse?

A. $2\sqrt{3}$ m   **B.** $2\sqrt{5}$ m
C. 6 m   **D.** 20 m

12. Evaluate: $x^2 - \dfrac{x^3}{x} + \dfrac{x}{3}$ when $x = -3$.

F. -19 **G.** -1
H. 1 **J.** 17

13. The perimeter of a regular octagon is 116 ft. What is its side length?

    A. $11\frac{2}{3}$ ft   **B.** $14\frac{1}{2}$ ft

    C. $19\frac{1}{3}$ ft   **D.** 29 ft

14. What is the area of the figure?

    F. 72 in.^{2} **G.** 81 in.^{2}

    H. 84 in.^{2} **J.** 96 in.^{2}

15. Which equation is a direct variation?

    A. $y = x + 7$ **B.** $y = x - 14$

    C. $y = 9x$ **D.** $y = \dfrac{5}{x}$

16. Solve: $4x + 12 = 22.8$

    F. $x = -6.3$ **G.** $x = 2.7$

    H. $x = 8.7$ **J.** $x = 17.7$

17. How many pounds are in 2 lb 10 oz?

    A. 2.625 lb   **B.** 3.25 lb

    C. 26 lb   **D.** 42 oz

18. Solve: $-16x - 5 \le -197$.

    A. $x \le -12$

    B. $x \ge -12$

    C. $x \le 12$

    D. $x \ge 12$

19. What type of transformation is shown?

    A. dilation   **B.** reflection

    C. rotation   **D.** translation

20. 213.94 is what percent of 112.6?

    F. 1.9%   **G.** 53%

    H. 90%   **J.** 190%

21. What is 4.608×10^{-5} written in standard form?

    A. $-4,608,000$ **B.** $-460,800$

    C. 0.00000408   **D.** 0.00004608

22. What is the greatest common factor of 540, 550, and 660?

    F. 10   **G.** 45

    H. 660   **J.** 29,700

Tell About It

Explain how you solve the problem. Show all your work.

23. A yoga club charges a $40 monthly membership fee and $8 for each yoga class you take. You can also take a yoga class for $20 without becoming a member. Graph the equations representing the two situations on a coordinate plane. How many classes would you need to take a month for it to be less expensive to become a member than to pay for each class?

14-1 Polynomials

Name _____   Date _____

A *polynomial* is an algebraic expression that is the sum or difference
of terms. Each term is called a *monomial*. A polynomial that has exactly
two terms is called a *binomial*, and a polynomial with exactly three terms
is called a *trinomial*.

$\frac{k}{4}$ ← monomial

$xy^2 + 2x$ ← binomial

$a^2b - c + \frac{1}{2}$ ← trinomial

The *degree of a monomial* is the sum of the
exponents of the variables in the term. The largest
degree of any of the monomial terms that make
up an expression is the *degree of the polynomial*.

$x^3y - 13x^2 + 17$ ← The degrees of the monomials
                    are 4, 2, and 0.

The degree of the polynomial is 4 because it is
the largest degree of any of the monomial terms.

Write the polynomial in descending order for x:

$17x + 3x^3 - 12$

$3x^3 + 17x - 12$ ← Degrees of x are from
                      greatest to least. This is
                      known as *standard form*.

Classify each expression as *monomial*, *binomial*, or *trinomial*.

1. $-2xy$

     __monomial__

2. $a^3 + b^2$

3. 13

4. $-16x + y$

5. $x^2 - 8x + 16$

6. $-6x^2y$

7. $\frac{1}{2}y^4 - 6y^2 + 9$

8. $\frac{3}{4}t + \frac{3}{4}$

**Give the degree of each term in the polynomial. Then give the
degree of the polynomial.**

9. $-7x^2 + 7xy$

degrees: __2, 2__
degree of
the polynomial: __2__

10. $2x^3y^2 + 8x^2y$

degrees: _____
degree of
the polynomial: _____

11. $6m^4 + (-2m^3) + 3m$

degrees: _____
degree of
the polynomial: _____

12. $-3x^2 + 5x$

degrees: _____
degree of
the polynomial: _____

13. $\frac{3}{7}a^2b + (-a)$

degrees: _____
degree of
the polynomial: _____

14. $\frac{3}{7}a^5 + b$

degrees: _____
degree of
the polynomial: _____

Write the polynomial in standard form.

15. $t + t^5 + 25$

     $t^5 + t + 25$

16. $-x^3 + 7 + x + 2x^2$

17. $9 - r$

18. $s + 2s^2 + 7$

19. $16 - 20k + 11k^2$

20. $p^4 + p^3 + 8 - p$

Write the polynomial in descending order for x.

21. $5x^3y^2 - 18xy + 10x^2y + y^3$ **22.** $y^2 + 11x - 2x^2$ **23.** $9 - 3x^2y + 10xy$

$5x^3y^2 + 10x^2y - 18xy + y^3$ _____   _____

24. $7x^2 + 21 - 19xy$ **25.** $xy^3 + x^2y + 7 + x^3$ **26.** $x^4y + x^2y^2 + x^3y^3 + 11x$

_____   _____   _____

Evaluate each expression for $a = 2$, $b = -1$, $c = 3$, and $d = 5$.

27. $(ab)^2$ **28.** $ab^2 + c$ **29.** $bc^2 + a$ **30.** $(ac)^2$

$\dfrac{[2 \cdot (-1)]^2}{(-2)^2}$
4
_____   _____   _____   _____

31. $d^2 - bc$ **32.** $(a^2b)^3 + d$ **33.** $a^2d + bc$ **34.** $dc^2 + bd$

_____   _____   _____   _____

Problem Solving

35. Mark works two different jobs, one that pays $6 an hour, and one that pays $7 an hour. Write a polynomial that describes the total amount Mark earns. Then use the polynomial to find how much Mark gets paid in a week if he works three hours at his first job and four hours at the second job.

36. Ramona has been saving up coins. She has pennies, nickels, dimes, and quarters. Write a polynomial that represents the total amount of money (in cents) Ramona is saving. Then find the total amount if she counts 95 pennies, 35 nickels, 50 dimes, and 40 quarters. How much is this in dollars?

_____   _____

WRITE ABOUT IT

37. On a small airplane, the average passenger weighs 80 kg, and has 10 kg of luggage. The pilot weighs 62 kg. There are also several boxes of supplies that weigh about 8 kg each. Explain why the polynomial $90x + 8y + 62$ can be used to estimate the weight the plane carries on the trip (not including the weight of the fuel and other necessary components).

_____

_____

_____

4-2 Model Polynomials

Name _____ Date _____

You can use algebra tiles to help write polynomials in simplest form. The key shows what each tile represents.

$\blacksquare = 1$ $| = x$ $\blacksquare = x^2$

$\blacksquare = -1$ $| = -x$ $\blacksquare = -x^2$

Remember: When you have a positive tile and a negative tile of the same type, they form a zero pair.

Use models to write the polynomial $3x^2 + 2x - 7 - 5x^2 + 3$ in simplest form.

$3x^2 + 2x + (-7) + (-5x^2) + 3$ ← Write the polynomial as an addition expression, and represent the terms with algebra tiles.

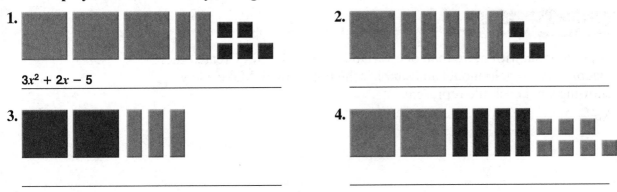

← Rearrange tiles so that like terms are next to each other to indicate zero pairs.

← Remove the zero pairs.

$-2x^2 + 2x - 4.$ ← Write the polynomial for the resulting model.

Write the polynomial modeled by the algebra tiles.

1.
$3x^2 + 2x - 5$

2.
_____

3.
_____

4.
_____

Draw a model using algebra tiles that aligns "like tiles" and places zero pairs, if any, together. Write the resulting polynomial in simplest form. (*Hint:* Write polynomials in descending order.)

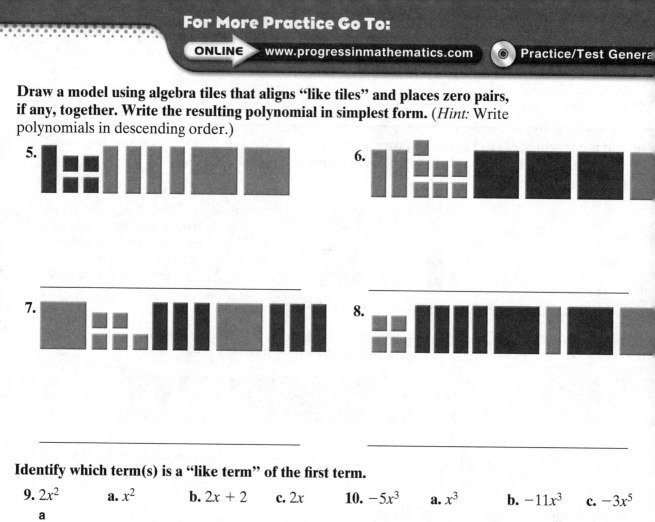

5.

6.

7.

8.

Identify which term(s) is a "like term" of the first term.

9. $2x^2$ **a.** x^2 **b.** $2x + 2$ **c.** $2x$ **10.** $-5x^3$ **a.** x^3 **b.** $-11x^3$ **c.** $-3x^5$
a

11. $5x$ **a.** $x + 3x$ **b.** $-x$ **c.** 15 **12.** -107 **a.** x^3 **b.** $107x$ **c.** 3

Write each polynomial in simplest form. Use algebra tiles to help.
(*Hint:* First rewrite the polynomial as an addition expression.)

13. $3x^2 + 2x - 5 - x^2 + x + 2$ **14.** $-x^2 + 4x + 2 + 2x^2 - x$ **15.** $2x^2 + 7 + 5x$

      $2x^2 + 3x - 3$

16. $2x - 3 + x^2 + 2 - 2x$ **17.** $-3x + 5 + 2x^2 - 5 + x$ **18.** $-7x + 2 + 3x^2$

CHALLENGE

19. A polynomial with more than one variable is given below. Create other algebra tiles to help model and simplify the polynomial. Make a key showing what each tile represents.

$3x^2 - 2y^2 + 2x + 4y - 1 + x^2 + y^2 - 2x + 5$

4-3 Add Polynomials

Name _____ Date _____

You can use algebra tiles to add polynomials the same way you used them to simplify.
You can also use the *horizontal method* and the *vertical method* to add
polynomials algebraically.

Find the sum of the polynomials $3x^2 + 5x$ and $x^2 + 1 - 3x$.

Horizontal Method

$(3x^2 + 5x) + [x^2 + 1 + (-3x)]$ ←—Write each expression as an addition expression.

$3x^2 + 5x + x^2 + 1 + (-3x)$ ←—Remove grouping symbols.

$3x^2 + x^2 + 5x + (-3x) + 1$ ←—Group like terms.

$[3 + 1]x^2 + [5 + (-3)]x + 1$ ←—Use the Distributive Property to combine like terms.

$4x^2 + 2x + 1$ ←—Simplify.

Vertical Method

Write each expression as an addition expression in standard form. Arrange like terms
in columns. If a polynomial does not have one of the terms, write a zero in its place,
then add the terms in each column.

$$\begin{array}{rrr} 3x^2 + & 5x & + 0 \\ + x^2 + & (-3x) & + 1 \\ \hline 4x^2 + & 2x & + 1 \end{array}$$

The sum of $3x^2 + 5x$ and $x^2 + 1 - 3x$ is $4x^2 + 2x + 1$.

**Use algebra tiles to combine like terms for each addition exercise.
Then write the sum in standard form.**

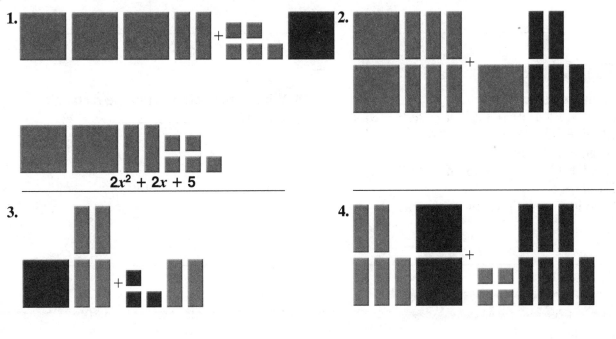

1.

$2x^2 + 2x + 5$

2.

3.

4.

_____   _____

Use the horizontal method to find the sum. Write each sum in standard form.

5. $(14x + 9) + (27x - 15)$

$(14 + 27)x + [9 + (-15)]$
$\underline{\qquad 41x - 6 \qquad}$

6. $(-6t + 40) + (15t - 35)$

7. $(-4m^2 - m) + (-6m^2 + 7m$

8. $(8k^2 - 14k + 3) + (-12k^2 - 5)$

9. $(3x - 11x^2) + (-x + 6x^2 + 5)$

10. $(31x^2 - 15x + 2) + (-16x^2 +$

Use the vertical method to find the sum. Write each sum in standard form.

11. $(77a^2 + 25a) + (44a^2 + 75a)$

$$\begin{array}{r} 77a^2 + 25a \\ + 44a^2 + 75a \\ \hline 121a^2 + 100a \\ \mathbf{121a^2 + 100a} \end{array}$$

12. $(10m^2 - 19m) + (31m^2 - 24m)$

13. $(-43c^2 - 29c + 17) + (15c - 58c^2)$

14. $(15x + 27) + (5x^2 - 3x + 12)$

15. $(35c^2 - 5c + 10) + (18 - 14c)$

16. $(a^2 + a) + (4a - 6a^2 + 20)$

Problem Solving

17. Sophie says that
$(7c^2d + 12cd^2 + 3) + (5c^2d - 2cd^2 - 8) =$
$12c^2d + 10cd^2 - 5$.
Angela says that
$(7c^2d + 12cd^2 + 3) + (5c^2d - 2cd^2 - 8) =$
$22c^2d^2 - 5$.
Who is correct? Explain the error.

18. What is the perimeter of the rectangle shown?

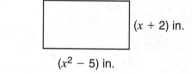

$(x + 2)$ in.

$(x^2 - 5)$ in.

TEST PREPARATION

19. Find the sum.

$(5a^3b - 7a^2b^2) + (3ab^3 + 12a^2b^2)$

A. $8a^3b^3 + 5a^2b^2$ **B.** $8a^3b^3 + 5a^4b^4$ **C.** $5a^3b + 5a^4b^4$ **D.** $5a^3b + 5a^2b^2 + 3ab^3$

14-4 Subtract Polynomials

Name _____ Date _____

Find the difference of $3x^2 - 4$ and $2x^2 + 3$. Use both algebra tiles and the vertical method.

Method 1: Use Algebra tiles.

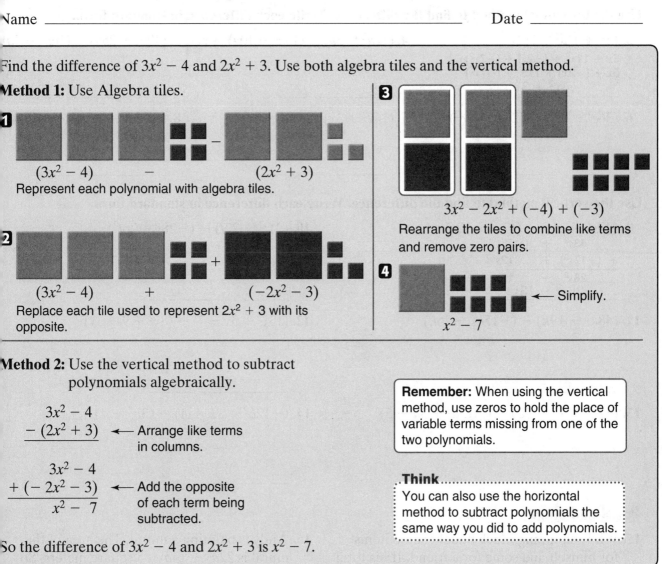

1
$(3x^2 - 4)$ − $(2x^2 + 3)$
Represent each polynomial with algebra tiles.

2
$(3x^2 - 4)$ + $(-2x^2 - 3)$
Replace each tile used to represent $2x^2 + 3$ with its opposite.

3
$3x^2 - 2x^2 + (-4) + (-3)$
Rearrange the tiles to combine like terms and remove zero pairs.

4
← Simplify.
$x^2 - 7$

Method 2: Use the vertical method to subtract polynomials algebraically.

$$3x^2 - 4$$
$$- (2x^2 + 3)$$ ← Arrange like terms in columns.

$$3x^2 - 4$$
$$+ (-2x^2 - 3)$$
$$\overline{\quad x^2 - 7 \quad}$$ ← Add the opposite of each term being subtracted.

So the difference of $3x^2 - 4$ and $2x^2 + 3$ is $x^2 - 7$.

Remember: When using the vertical method, use zeros to hold the place of variable terms missing from one of the two polynomials.

Think
You can also use the horizontal method to subtract polynomials the same way you did to add polynomials.

Draw algebra tiles to combine like terms. Then write the difference in standard form.

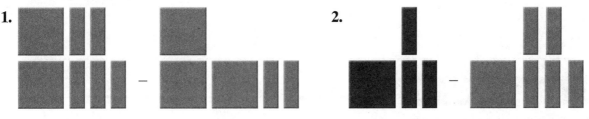

1.   −

2.   −

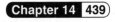

Use the horizontal method to find the difference. Write each difference in standard form.

3. $(5x + 11x^2) - (2x + 7x^2)$
$5x + 11x^2 + (-2x) + (-7x^2)$
$5x + (-2x) + 11x^2 + (-7x^2)$
$4x^2 + 3x$

4. $(12a^2 - 3a) - (15a^2 + 10a)$

5. $(40a^2 - 25a) - (16a^2 - 5a)$

6. $(36e^2 - 29e) - (28e - 19e^2)$

7. $(14x^2 + 3x) - (5x^2 - 2x)$

8. $(-22a^2 - 4a) - (-8a + 4a$

Use the vertical method to find the difference. Write each difference in standard form.

9. $(43s^2 - 25s) - (17s^2 - 12s)$
$43s^2 + (-25s)$
$+ (-17s^2) + 12s$
$26s^2 - 13s$
$26s^2 - 13s$

10. $(21t^2 - 27t) - (-28t - 76t^2)$

11. $(48k^2 + 19k) - (-15k^2 - 26k)$

12. $(13x^2 + 5x - 7) - (8x^2 + 9 - 3x)$

13. $(52a^2 + 15 - 7a) - (-13a^2 + 3a - 5)$

14. $(-12b^2 + 7b + 4) - (3b^2 + 4)$

Problem Solving

15. While shopping, Zack bought some items for himself and some for a friend. If his total purchase was $15x^2 + 2x - 3$ dollars and his friend's portion cost $3x^2 + x + 15$ dollars, how much did Zack spend for his items?

16. Andy is painting a mural. The area of the mural is $22a^2 + 14a + 5$ square meters. So far, he has painted a section with an area of $13a^2 - 12a - 5$ square meters. What area does Andy have left to paint?

CRITICAL THINKING

17. Write two binomials whose difference is a trinomial. Explain your reasoning.

18. Write two binomials whose difference is a monomial. Explain your reasoning.

19. Write two binomials whose difference is zero. Explain your reasoning.

14-5 Multiply and Divide Monomials

Name _____ Date _____

When multiplying and dividing monomials, use the appropriate Laws of Exponents.
You can also model multiplication and division of monomials using algebra tiles.

Multiply: $2x(5x)$

Place two x-tiles vertically to represent $2x$ and five x-tiles horizontally to represent $5x$.

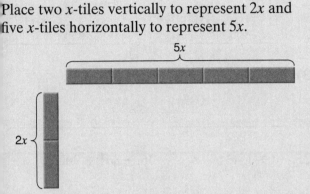

Create a rectangle with dimensions $2x$ and $5x$.

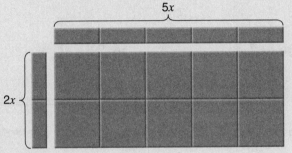

The area of the rectangle represents the product of the monomials.
There are 10 x^2-tiles in the rectangle, so $2x(5x) = 10x^2$.

Find the quotient $\dfrac{26x^4}{13x^2}$ algebraically.

$\dfrac{26x^4}{13x^2} = \dfrac{26}{13} \bullet \dfrac{x^4}{x^2}$ ← Regroup to divide like terms.

$\quad = 2x^{(4-2)}$ ← Apply the Law of Exponents for Division.

$\quad = 2x^2$ ← Simplify.

Remember:
Laws of Exponents
$a^m \bullet a^n = a^{(m+n)}$
$(a^m)^n = a^{mn}$
$a^m \div a^n = \dfrac{a^m}{a^n} = a^{m-n}$

Multiply algebraically. Use algebra tiles to help.

1. $8x(5x)$
$(8 \bullet 5)(x)(x) = 40x^{(1+1)}$
$\qquad 40x^2$

2. $-7(y^2)$

3. $8d \bullet 4d^3$

4. $12a^4 \bullet 3a^2$

5. $-20b^2 \bullet b^5$

6. $9m^2 \bullet (-5m^3)$

7. $(6b^2)(-4b)$

8. $15x \bullet 3x$

9. $-7c \bullet 8c^3$

10. $(-9x^3)(-3)$

11. $15k^2 \bullet k^6$

12. $(14b)(-3b^6)$

13. $(6p^4)(-2p^2)$

14. $\frac{1}{2}p^5 \bullet (-40p^3)$

15. $\frac{2}{3}x^2 \bullet 15x^3$

16. $\frac{3}{4}m^2 \bullet 8m^3 \bullet (-5)$

17. $-15x^2 \bullet \frac{2}{3}x^3 \bullet x^2$

18. $2x^3 \bullet (-3x)$

19. $4n^4 \bullet 4n^2$

20. $\left(\frac{1}{2}a^2\right)^2 \bullet 24a^3$

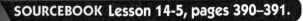

Divide algebraically. Use algebra tiles to help.

21. $18b^2 \div 2b$

$$\frac{18b^2}{2b} = \frac{18}{2} \cdot \frac{b^2}{b} = 9b$$

22. $-21y \div 3y$

23. $50x^3 \div (-10x)$

24. $-45r^2 \div (-3r^2)$

25. $\dfrac{60e^5}{-12e^4}$

26. $\dfrac{27b^3}{9b^3}$

27. $\dfrac{-33t^6}{-11t^4}$

28. $\dfrac{-71r^3}{71r^2}$

29. $\dfrac{72h^7}{12h^2}$

30. $\dfrac{63t^5}{-9t}$

31. $(-13p^2) \div (-13p^2)$

32. $56w^4 \div 8w$

33. $\dfrac{-21e^2}{3e^6}$

34. $\dfrac{4a^3}{8a^5}$

35. $5y \div 15y^3$

36. $-3n^4 \div 9n^5$

Problem Solving

37. Martin is painting a picture on a rectangular canvas that has an area of $15a^2$ square centimeters and a width of $3a$ centimeters. What is the length of the canvas?

38. A large storage box is 5 feet long and $3x^4$ feet wide. The box has a volume of $30x^5$ ft³. What is its height?

39. Charlene has a mirror in the shape of a regular hexagon. It has a perimeter of $24n$ inches. What is the length of each side of her mirror?

40. Michelle has a triangular banner hanging in her room. It has an area of $12y^4$ meters. The base of the triangle measures $4y^2$ meters. What is its height?

SPIRAL REVIEW

Find the sum or difference.

41. $(3x^2 + 5x) + (2x^2 + 5)$

42. $(5b + 3b + 1) + (-3b + 5b)$

43. $(-4n^2 + 3) - (2n^2 - 2 + 8)$

44. $(4x^3 - 5x + 9) - (-2x^3 + x + 1)$

14-6 Multiply Polynomials by Monomials

Name _____ Date _____

Find the product $(3x)(2x - 4)$ using algebra tiles.

Place three x-tiles vertically to represent $3x$. Then place two x-tiles and four -1-tiles horizontally to represent $2x - 4$.

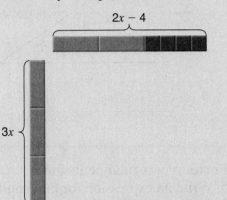

Create a rectangle with dimensions $3x$ and $(2x - 4)$.

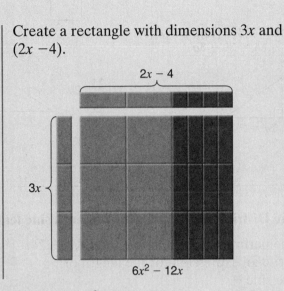

The area of the rectangle represents the product. There are six x^2-tiles and twelve $-x$-tiles in the rectangle, so $(3x)(2x - 4) = 6x^2 - 12x$.

Multiply algebraically: $(4x)(2x^2 + 6)$

$$
\begin{aligned}
(4x)(2x^2 + 6) &= (4x)(2x^2) + (4x)(6) &&\longleftarrow \text{Use the Distributive Property.}\\
&= (4)(2)(x)(x^2) + (4)(6)(x) &&\longleftarrow \text{Group coefficients and variables.}\\
&= 8x^{(1+2)} + 24x &&\longleftarrow \text{Use the Law of Exponents.}\\
&= 8x^3 + 24x &&\longleftarrow \text{Simplify.}
\end{aligned}
$$

Multiply algebraically. Use algebra tiles to help.

1. $10(a + 2)$

$10(a) + 10(2) = 10a + 20$

2. $3(b + 7)$

3. $m(15 - m)$

4. $r(2 - 8r)$

5. $-2d(7 + d)$

6. $5y^2(-8 + y)$

7. $a^2(-a + 5)$

8. $-x^3(x - x^2)$

9. $-2a(a^2 + 3a - 7)$

10. $-5x(2x^2 - 3x + 1)$

11. $-b(4b^2 - 5b)$

12. $x^2(2x + 6x^4)$

Simplify the expression.

13. $m(4 - 3m) + 2m$

$m(4) - m(3m) + 2m = 4m - 3m^2 + 2m = 6m - 3m^2$

14. $a(3a^2 - 2a + 7) - a$

15. $4x^2(2x + 3 - 5) + 8x^2$

16. $\frac{1}{2}c(2 + 4c^3 - 6c) - c^2$

Find the area of each figure.

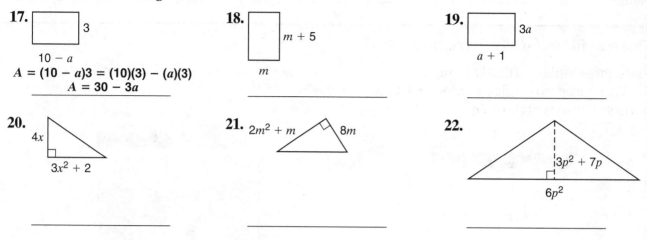

17.

3

10 − a

$A = (10 - a)3 = (10)(3) - (a)(3)$

$A = 30 - 3a$

18.

m + 5

m

19.

3a

a + 1

20.

4x

3x² + 2

21. 2m² + m   8m

22.

3p² + 7p

6p²

Use the Distributive Property to find each side length.

23. The perimeter of a square equals $8m + 24$. Write an expression for the length of one side.

24. The perimeter of a regular pentagon is $15a - 35$. Write an expression for the length of one side.

Problem Solving

25. The radius of a circular pool is $6 + 2n$ feet. What is its circumference in terms of π?

26. A rectangular field has a width of $3x$ meters and a length of $x^2 + 6x$ meters. What is its area?

27. The price of a binder is $4x^2 - 3$ dollars. A teacher buys one for each of the y students in the class. What is the total cost?

28. A refrigerator has a base with an area of $x^2 + 5x + 6$ square feet. The height of the refrigerator is $4x^2$ feet. What is volume of the refrigerator?

MENTAL MATH

Find the product.

29. $m(m^2 + 7)$

30. $-5(x^3 + 3)$

31. $a^5(-a + 19)$

32. $-y^7(y^2 + y)$

14-7 Divide Polynomials by Monomials

Name _____ Date _____

To find the quotient of a polynomial and a monomial, multiply the polynomial by the reciprocal of the monomial.

Divide: $(8x^3 - 20x) \div 4x$

$$\frac{8x^3 - 20x}{4x} = \frac{1}{4x}(8x^3 - 20x)$$ ◄— Rewrite division as multiplication.

$$= \frac{8x^3}{4x} - \frac{20x}{4x}$$ ◄— Apply the Distributive Property.

$$= 2x^{(3-1)} - 5x^{(1-1)}$$ ◄— Divide the coefficients and apply the Law of Exponents.

$$= 2x^2 - 5$$ ◄— Simplify.

You can also use algebra tiles to model division. If you are given the area of a rectangle, you can find the length by dividing the area by the width.

Find the quotient $(6x^2 - 12x) \div 3x$ using algebra tiles.

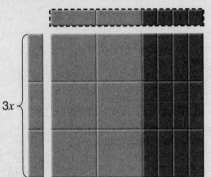

Use algebra tiles to model the dividend, $6x^2 - 12x$, as the area of a rectangle. One side of the rectangle should be the same length as the divisor, $3x$.

To find the quotient, determine the length of the other side of the rectangle.

$$(6x^2 - 12x) \div 3x = 2x - 4$$

Draw a model of algebra tiles to find the quotient.

1. $(4x^2 - 6x) \div 2x$

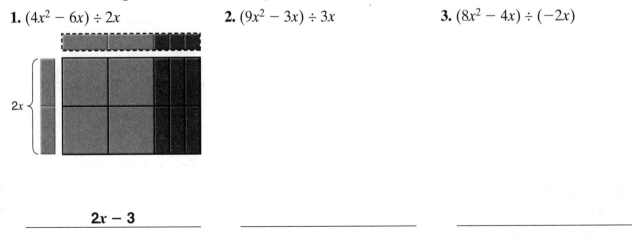

_____ **2x − 3** _____

2. $(9x^2 - 3x) \div 3x$

_____

3. $(8x^2 - 4x) \div (-2x)$

_____

Find the missing factor. (*Hint:* Write a related division sentence.)

4. $t^2 \cdot$ _____ $= 3t^2 + 8t^2v$

_____

5. $x^3 \cdot$ _____ $= 7x^3 + 9x^3y^3$

_____

Divide. Use the product of the quotient and the divisor to check your solution.

6. $(a^2 + 3a) \div a$

$$(a^2 + 3a)\frac{1}{a} = a + 3$$

7. $(x^3 - 5x) \div x$

8. $(4m^2 + m) \div (-m)$

9. $(5y + 20) \div (-5)$

10. $(18b^2 - 12b) \div 6b$

11. $(14r + 21r^2) \div 7r$

12. $(45d^3 - 36d^2) \div 3d^2$

13. $(16y^5 - 8y^4) \div 2y^2$

14. $\dfrac{18n^3 - 3n^2 + 6n^5}{3n^2}$

15. $\dfrac{4b^7 - 6b^3 + 10b^2}{-2b^2}$

16. $\dfrac{16x^5 + 8x^4 - 72x^3}{8x^3}$

17. $\dfrac{12m^7 + 6m^5 - 42m^6}{6m^4}$

18. $\dfrac{9f^5 - 3f^4 - 33f^3}{-3f^3}$

19. $\dfrac{14k^6 + 42k^4 + 56k^2}{-14k^2}$

20. $\dfrac{3d^3 + 5d^2 - d^2}{(-d)^2}$

21. $\dfrac{16y^5 - 4y^3 + 20y^2}{(-2y)^2}$

Problem Solving

22. A case of yogurt cups costs $(15x^2 - 21x)$ dollars. If a case contains $3x$ cups of yogurt, how much does each cup cost?

23. A soccer league has $(25a^3 + 15a^2 - 10a)$ players. Each team has the same number of players. If there are $5a$ teams, how many players are on each team?

24. A triangular sail has a base of $3b$ meters and an area of $(6b^2 + 12b)$ square meters. What is the height of the sail?

25. A storage box has a volume of $(4x^3 + 6x^2 + 8x^4)$ cubic inches, a length of $2x$ inches, and a width of x inches. What is the height of the box?

CRITICAL THINKING

26. Complete the steps to solve the division problem using long division.

$$x + 1 \overline{)\, 2x^2 + x - 1}$$

14-8 Solve Multistep Equations

Name _____ Date _____

You may need to use more than one operation or property to solve an equation.
Multistep equations may also have variables on both sides. To solve these,
you need to isolate the variable on the same side of the equal sign.

Solve.

$5a - 12 + 6a + 13 = 34$

$\qquad 11a + 1 = 34$ ◄— Combine like terms.

$11a + 1 - 1 = 34 - 1$ ◄— Subtract 1 from both sides.

$\qquad 11a = 33$ ◄— Simplify.

$\qquad \dfrac{11a}{11} = \dfrac{33}{11}$ ◄— Divide both sides by 11.

$\qquad a = 3$ ◄— Simplify.

Solve.

$3(-5x + 3) = 34 - 10x$

$\qquad -15x + 9 = 34 - 10x$ ◄— Apply the Distributive Property.

$-15x + 9 + 10x = 34 - 10x + 10x$ ◄— Add $10x$ to both sides.

$\qquad -5x + 9 = 34$ ◄— Simplify.

$\qquad -5x + 9 - 9 = 34 - 9$ ◄— Subtract 9 from both sides.

$\qquad -5x = 25$ ◄— Simplify.

$\qquad \dfrac{-5x}{-5} = \dfrac{25}{-5}$ ◄— Divide both sides by -5.

$\qquad x = -5$ ◄— Simplify.

Solve the equation. Check to justify your answer.
(*Hint:* Combine like terms then follow the order of operations.)

1. $4c + 6c + 5 + 2c = 17$
$\qquad 12c + 5 = 17$
$\qquad 12c = 12$
$\qquad c = 1$

2. $-2a - 8 + 5a = 19$

3. $t + 9 + 5t - 2t = -51$

4. $3x + 6 + 7x - 2 + 5x = -26$

5. $3y - 10 + 5y + 3y = 45$

6. $4p - 7 - 5p + 2p = -3$

7. $8s + 5 - 5s = -1$

8. $-10m + 6 + 4m - 10 = 14$

9. $4g - 8 + 6g + 6 = 22$

Solve the equation. Check to justify your answer. (*Hint:* Use the
Distributive Property, then follow the order of operations.)

10. $-2(x + 5) = 6$
$\qquad -2x - 10 = 6$
$\qquad -2x = 16$
$\qquad x = -8$

11. $-4(c - 3) = 48$

12. $2(3z + 4) = 20$

13. $3(2d + 3) = 39$

14. $9 - 5(p + 2) = -16$

15. $-2 + 6(r - 7) = 10$

Solve the equation. Check to justify your answer. (*Hint:* Use properties to move and combine like terms on opposite sides of the equation.)

16. $5x + 10 = -9x - 4$

$14x + 10 = -4$
$14x = -14$
$x = -1$

17. $-3t + 7 = 2t + 32$

18. $8p - 6 = 54 - 2p$

19. $9 + 2a = 4a + 15$

20. $-5(3n + 2) = -12n + 8$

21. $2(b + 3) = 3b + 6$

22. $3(2m + 1) + 4 = 4m + 21$

23. $-(9 - 5n) + n = -4n + 71$

24. $-4(5x + 7) + 11x = x + 4$

Problem Solving

25. The drama club is making signs for its play. Cindy made a total of 18 signs, which was 2 more than 4 times the number that Jane made. Jane made 3 more signs than Sam. How many signs did Sam make?

26. Margaret's class is running a car wash. It costs $85 to rent the space. Supplies cost $0.75 for each car the students wash. The students will make $5 for each car they wash. How many cars does the class need to wash for their total cost to equal the total amount they make?

27. Marlene is going on a camping trip with a group of friends. She brings 3 boxes of granola bars, plus 3 extra bars. Robyn brings 2 boxes of granola bars and Wendy brings one box. They have a total of 57 granola bars. If each box contains the same number of bars, how many bars are in each box?

28. Mr. Robinson bought 3 boxes of crayons for an art class he teaches, but had to throw 7 crayons away because they were broken. He received two donations from parents: Mrs. Bruce gave 2 boxes of crayons and Mrs. Rockwood gave 5 boxes. Mr. Robinson had a total of 153 crayons. If each box had contained the same number of crayons, how many were in a box?

CHALLENGE

Solve.

29. $\dfrac{5}{x^2}(2x^3 + 3x^2) = -5$

30. $\dfrac{1}{3x^2}(6x^3 - 33x^2) = -1$

14-9 Addition and Subtraction: Inequalities with Rational Numbers

Name _____ Date _____

You can solve inequalities involving addition and subtraction with rational numbers the same way you solve these types of inequalities with integers.

Remember: When graphing the endpoints of inequalities, use a dot for $\geq$ and $\leq$, and use a circle for $>$ and $<$.

Solve and graph the solution on a number line.

$q + 6.8 > 23$

$q + 6.8 - 6.8 > 23 - 6.8$ ← Subtract 6.8 from both sides.

$q > 16.2$ ← Simplify.

16   16.1   16.2   16.3   16.4   16.5   16.6

$2t - t - \frac{1}{4} \leq -1\frac{3}{8}$

$t(2 - 1) - \frac{1}{4} \leq -1\frac{3}{8}$ ← Use the Distributive Property to combine like terms.

$t - \frac{1}{4} \leq -1\frac{3}{8}$ ← Simplify.

$t - \frac{1}{4} + \frac{1}{4} \leq -1\frac{3}{8} + \frac{1}{4}$ ← Add $\frac{1}{4}$ to both sides.

$t \leq -1\frac{1}{8}$ ← Simplify.

-2 $-1\frac{3}{4}$ $-1\frac{1}{2}$ $-1\frac{1}{4}$ -1 $-\frac{3}{4}$ $-\frac{1}{2}$

Solve the inequality and graph the solution on a number line. Then answer the questions.

1. $48.7 + x < 112.4$

$48.7 + x - 48.7 < 112.4 - 48.7$

$x < 63.7$

63.5   63.6   63.7   63.8   63.9   64   64.1

Is 63.6 a solution? __Yes__   Is 63.7 a solution? __No__   Is 63.8 a solution? __No__

2. $a + 24.6 \geq 19.2$

_____

Is -5 a solution? _____

Is -5.4 a solution? _____

Is -6 a solution? _____

3. $d + 9\frac{3}{5} \leq 6\frac{2}{5}$

_____

Is -3 a solution? _____

Is -4 a solution? _____

Is $-3\frac{1}{10}$ a solution? _____

4. $\frac{7}{10} + r > \frac{9}{10}$

_____

Is 0 a solution? _____

Is $\frac{1}{10}$ a solution? _____

Is $\frac{1}{5}$ a solution? _____

Find the solution for exercises 5–19. Check to justify your answer.

5. $y + 192.6 > 153.3$

$y + 192.6 - 192.6 > 153.3 - 192.6$

$y > -39.3$

6. $x + 88.8 \geq 99.9$

_____

7. $15.92 + g \geq 15.8$

_____

8. $x - 79.2 < 1.9$

9. $m - 210.2 \leq 58.8$

10. $s - 16.95 < -19.26$

_____

_____

_____

11. $-47.99 + v + 16.72 > 1.68$

12. $h - 79.2 - 98.5 < 167.73$

13. $258.75 - 298.45 + w > -46.95$

_____

_____

_____

14. $r - 1.57 - 2.46 \leq -4.84$

15. $-(6.03 - 2p) - p < -68.19$

16. $5(0.9 + 0.2k) - 4.6 \geq -0.12$

_____

_____

_____

17. $4\frac{1}{4}\left(\frac{8}{15} + \frac{4}{17}b\right) - 5 > 1\frac{4}{5}$

18. $\frac{4}{21}\left(10\frac{1}{2}n - 7\right) - n \leq -1\frac{2}{3}$

19. $3\frac{2}{3} - 6\left(4\frac{1}{9} - \frac{1}{6}y\right) \geq -42\frac{1}{5}$

_____

_____

_____

Problem Solving

20. Vehicles traveling through a tunnel must have a height that is less than 13.5 feet. A truck's cab has a height of 9.25 feet. How much taller can the truck's trailer be than the cab to fit through the tunnel? Write an inequality to answer the question.

21. Bernard has $25.75. He buys a gift for his mother that costs $14.99. He still has to buy a gift for his sister with his remaining money. Write and solve an inequality to find the amount of money he can spend on his sister's gift.

_____

_____

22. Charles is $3\frac{3}{4}$ feet tall. A roller coaster has a height restriction that riders must be at least $4\frac{1}{6}$ feet tall. Write and solve an inequality to find the amount that Charles must grow in order to ride the roller coaster.

23. Brandy goes to the store to buy apples to make apple pie and apple cider. She uses 3.2 pounds in the pies, and 4.1 pounds for the apple cider. She has over 1 pound left. Write and solve an inequality to find the weight of the apples she bought.

_____

_____

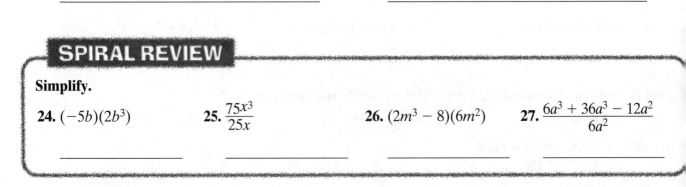

SPIRAL REVIEW

Simplify.

24. $(-5b)(2b^3)$

25. $\dfrac{75x^3}{25x}$

26. $(2m^3 - 8)(6m^2)$

27. $\dfrac{6a^3 + 36a^3 - 12a^2}{6a^2}$

_____

_____

_____

_____

14-10 Multiplication and Division: Inequalities with Rational Numbers

Name _____ Date _____

You can solve inequalities involving multiplication and division with rational numbers the same way you solve these types of inequalities with integers.

> **Remember:** If you multiply or divide an inequality by a negative number, you need to reverse the inequality symbol.

Solve each inequality and graph the solution on a number line.

$0.1(14y + 16) \le 10$

$\qquad 1.4y + 1.6 \le 10 \quad \leftarrow$ Apply the Distributive Property.

$\qquad\qquad 1.4y \le 8.4 \quad \leftarrow$ Subtract 1.6 from both sides.

$\qquad\qquad \dfrac{1.4y}{1.4} \le \dfrac{8.4}{1.4} \quad \leftarrow$ Divide both sides by 1.4.

$\qquad\qquad\qquad y \le 6 \quad \leftarrow$ Simplify.

$-\dfrac{x}{8} < 1\tfrac{1}{2}$

$(-8)\left(-\dfrac{x}{8}\right) > 1\tfrac{1}{2}(-8) \quad \leftarrow$ Multiply both sides by -8 and reverse the inequality symbol.

$\qquad\qquad x > -12 \quad \leftarrow$ Simplify.

Solve the inequality and graph the solution on a number line. Then answer the questions.

1. $5.5x < 38.5$

$\qquad \dfrac{5.5x}{5.5} < \dfrac{38.5}{5.5}$

$\qquad\qquad x < 7$

Is 7.7 a solution? __No__   Is 7 a solution? __No__   Is 6.4 a solution? __Yes__

2. $6.25a > 50$

3. $\dfrac{8}{15}c \ge -2\tfrac{2}{3}$

4. $-14\tfrac{1}{6} \le -1\tfrac{5}{12}d$

_____   _____   _____

Is 7.9 a solution? _____   Is −6 a solution? _____   Is −2 a solution? _____

Is 8.2 a solution? _____   Is 0 a solution? _____   Is 0 a solution? _____

Is 8.1 a solution? _____   Is −5 a solution? _____   Is 12 a solution? _____

Find the solution. Check to justify your answer.

5. $11z - 5.5 > 93.5$
$\qquad 11z > 99$
$\qquad\qquad z > 9$

6. $388.8 \ge 32.4x - 97.2$

7. $2(-8.69y - 1.21) \le -37.18$

8. $-26.31 < -2.95 + 2.4q + 3.4$

9. $-40.32x + 6.748 + 6.56x \ge 57.388$

_____   _____

Find the solution. Check to justify your answer.

10. $\dfrac{p}{10.8} - 12.2 > -7.2$

$\dfrac{p}{10.8} > 5$

$p > 54$

11. $3.6 - \dfrac{f}{3.6} > -6.4$

12. $\dfrac{x}{5.2} + 7 \geq 9.5$

13. $-5.4 > -9 + \dfrac{z}{1.05}$

14. $\dfrac{c}{15.75} - 1.8 \geq -3.8$

15. $6\left(22.7 - \dfrac{y}{5.1}\right) \leq 112.2$

16. $-21.63 < \left(\dfrac{h}{3.75} + 8.9\right)(-2.1)$ **17.** $\dfrac{d}{1.6} + 2 - \dfrac{d}{3.2} > 7.3$

18. $19 - \dfrac{t}{12.12} + 0.5 > 11$

19. $\dfrac{x}{30.4} - 3\left(\dfrac{x}{15.2} + \dfrac{1}{3}\right) - 0.8 \leq -44.05$

20. $12.3 + \dfrac{m}{9.3} - 2.3\left(\dfrac{m}{4.65} + \dfrac{1}{4.6}\right) \geq 2.8$

Problem Solving

21. The ratio of the horizontal length that a wheelchair ramp extends from a building to its height should be no greater than 12 : 1. The height of a wheelchair ramp is $5\frac{1}{3}$ feet. Write and solve an inequality to show the maximum length.

22. A fitness club charges members $29.20 a month, plus a small fee for each class. Margie has set a limit on her cost per month to $52. She wants to take 8 classes each month, and each class has the same cost. Write and solve an inequality to find the greatest amount it could cost per class for Margie to be able to take the 8 classes and stay within her budget. What other restriction on the cost of each class is needed?

WRITE ABOUT IT

23. Let a, b, c and d be positive numbers. Explain the steps to solve the inequality $a - \dfrac{x}{b} > \dfrac{c}{d}$.

Name _____   Date _____

Solve by reviewing the strategies.

1. A machine stamps out a fixed number of plastic washers at a time.
   The number of washers produced is the fewest that can be distributed
   evenly in 2, 3, 4, 5, or 8 packages.

   a. What is this number of washers?

   b. What other numbers of same-sized packages would work?
   Give all possibilities less than 21.

2. Of the concentric circles seen here at the right, any consecutive two
   are 1 cm apart. What is the difference in the circumference of any two
   such adjacent circles?

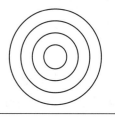

3. The circumference of Earth is approximately 132,000,000 feet.
   Imagine that a 132,000,000 foot-long rope is snuggly tied around Earth.
   Suppose a second rope is placed, using stakes, exactly 1 foot above
   the first rope all the way around Earth. How much longer than
   the first rope would this second rope have to be?

4. Determine the area of the
   shaded region at the right.

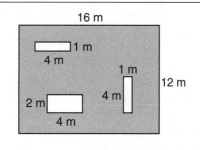

5. What is the next number in the sequence below? (*Hint:* Look at the
   partial sums—the sum of the first term, the sum of the first two terms,
   the sum of the first three terms, etc.)

   2, 1, 2, 2, 4, 2, 4, 2, 4,...

6. Suppose you start with a nonsquare rectangular blanket and fold it in half three times. Note that you have a choice each time about which way to fold (the "long way" or the "short way"). The final shape will also be a rectangle.

  a. Does the area of the resulting rectangle depend on how you fold the blanket?

  b. Does the perimeter of the resulting rectangle depend on how you fold the blanket?

7. Without using a calculator, determine the decimal representation for the product $0.66 \times 0.\overline{3}$.

8. What digit is in the 94th place after the decimal in the decimal representation of the number $\frac{5}{37}$?

9. The bar graph at the right represents the sales of a new breakfast cereal in both 2006 and 2007 plotted on the same graph. The actual numbers of sales were inadvertently left off! By about what percent did sales increase between 2006 and 2007? (Assume the bars start at 0.)

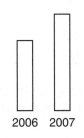

2006 2007

10. Phil tries to mail a 5-foot-long fishing rod in a box that is 5 feet long, but he is told that no box can be mailed with a side length longer than 4.5 feet. He purchases a new box for the fishing rod, returns to the post office, and mails the 5-foot-long fishing rod in the new box without any difficulty. What dimensions of box could allow him to meet the post office's requirements?

Enrichment:
Graphing with Absolute Values

Name _____ Date _____

The graph of the function $f(x) = |x|$ is shown below.

$f(x) = |x|$	
x	$f(x)$
4	$|4| = 4$
2	$|2| = 2$
0	$|0| = 0$
−2	$|-2| = 2$
−4	$|-4| = 4$

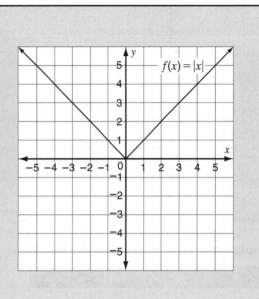

How does $f(x) = -|x| + 4$ compare to $f(x) = |x|$?

First, make a table to identify coordinates for the graph.

Next, graph the function. $f(x)$ is the same
as the y-coordinate. So the table shows that if $x = 4$,
then $f(x) = 0$ and the coordinate point is $(4, 0)$.

$f(x) = -|x| + 4$	
x	$f(x)$
4	$-|4| + 4 = 0$
2	$-|2| + 4 = 2$
0	$-|0| + 4 = 4$
−2	$-|-2| + 4 = 2$
−4	$-|-4| + 4 = 0$

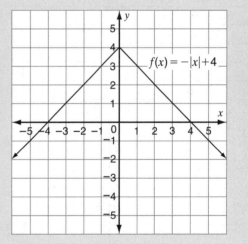

The graph of $f(x) = -|x| + 4$ is shown at the right.

The graph of $f(x) = -|x| + 4$ opens
down and the vertex has been moved up 4 units.

For exercises 1–4, describe how the graph of each function compares
to the graph of $f(x) = |x|$.

1. $f(x) = |x| + 3$

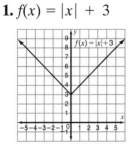

_____

_____

2. $f(x) = 3 - |x|$

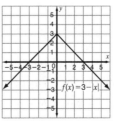

_____

_____

3. $f(x) = |x - 3| + 2$

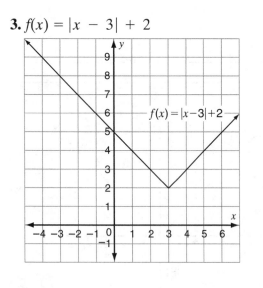

4. $f(x) = -|x - 2| + 3$

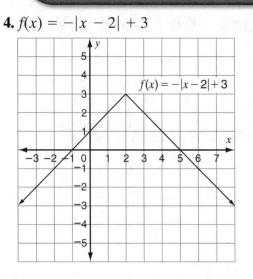

_____   _____

Complete the table and graph the function.

5.

$f(x) = |x + 4|$	
x	$f(x)$
0	
−2	
−4	
−6	
−8	

6.

$f(x) = 4 - |x - 4|$	
x	$f(x)$
8	
6	
4	
2	
0	

CHALLENGE

7. Compare the graph of $g(x) = |kx|$ to the graph of $f(x) = |x|$ for several different values of k. How do the graphs compare when k is greater than 1? How do the graphs compare when k is less than 1 but greater than 0?

_____

_____

_____

Test Prep: Short-Answer Questions
Strategy: Show All Your Work

Name _____   Date _____

When completing a short-answer question, *justify your steps* as part of showing your work. Explain how you used properties, rules, and definitions.

To find the answer, try using these strategies:
- Reread the item.
- Use the Test-Prep Strategy.
- Apply appropriate rules, definitions, properties, or strategies.
- Analyze your answers.

Sample Test Item

Evaluate the polynomial below for $y = 3$.

$$4y^2 - 6y - 1$$

Show all your work.

$4(3)^2 - 6(3) - 1$ ◀— Substitute 3 for y.

Follow the order of operations.

$4(9) - 6(3) - 1$ ◀— Evaluate the power.
$36 - 18 - 1$ ◀— Multiply left to right.
17 ◀— Subtract left to right.

Answer: 17

Solve. *TIP: Think before you answer. Be sure you understand the question.*

1. The table below shows the number of chaperones, y, needed for x students, on a field trip.

Field Trip				
Number of Students (x)	24	60	84	96
Number of Chaperones (y)	2	5	7	8

How many chaperones are needed for a field trip that has 180 students?
Show all your work.

2. The table below shows the prices of three different-sized packages of almonds.

Almonds		
Package	Weight (in ounces)	Package Price
A	6	$3.90
B	9	$4.68
C	14	$5.74

Which has the least cost per ounce?
Show all your work.

Answer _____

Answer _____

---

3. What is the volume of Amber's cylinder, shown at the right? Use 3.14 for π. Round your answer to the nearest tenth.
Show all your work.

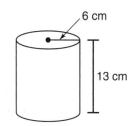

6 cm

13 cm

Answer _____

Vocabulary Development

Name _____ Date _____

Chapter 14 Vocabulary

binomial	descending order	standard form
degree of a monomial	monomial	trinomial
degree of a polynomial	polynomial	

From the vocabulary list above, choose the term(s) that best complete each sentence. Write the term(s) in the space(s) provided.

1. For the term x^3y^3, 6 is the _____.

2. Each term in an algebraic expression is a(n) _____.

3. A(n) _____ is an algebraic expression with 2 terms.

4. The greatest degree of a term of an algebraic expression that is the sum or difference of terms is the _____.

5. A(n) _____ is an algebraic expression that is the sum or difference of terms.

6. The expression $3x^3 + 4x - 6$ is written in _____;

the terms are written in _____ for the variable x.

7. An algebraic expression with 3 terms is a(n) _____.

Tell whether each statement is true or false. If the statement is false, change it to make it true.

8. x^2 is a binomial.

_____

9. In the expression $5x + 9$, 9 is a monomial.

_____

10. The degree of the polynomial $-6x^4 + 2x^3 + 4$ is 3.

_____

11. $9 + 3x - 6x^2 + x^3$ is in standard form.

_____

Practice Chapter 14 Test

Name _____   Date _____

**Classify the expression as a *monomial*, *binomial*, or *trinomial*.
Then give its degree.**

1. $2x + 4$

2. $-6x^2 + y - 7$

3. $4x^2y^4$

4. $14a^5 + 9$

_____   _____   _____   _____

5. $-22a^5b^2$

6. $-11mn - 3m + 15n$ **7.** $x + y$

8. $20x^4y^4 + 15x^5y^2 - 5x$

_____   _____   _____   _____

Evaluate the expression for $x = 3$ and $y = -2$.

9. $3x^2 + 10y$

10. $4x^2 - 2y$

11. $-x^2 + 4y^2 + 25$

12. $y^2 - 2x^2 - 9$

_____   _____   _____   _____

13. $-x^2y + 6$

14. $2x^2y^2 + xy + 5y$

15. $4y^2 + 5xy - 3x$

16. $2x^3y - 2x^2y^3 + y$

_____   _____   _____   _____

Find the sum or difference. Write your answer in standard form.

17. $(-2x + 4x^2 - 8) + (2 - 2x^2 + x)$

18. $(9 + 14x + x^2) + (-9x + -x^2 + 11)$

_____   _____

19. $(8x + 7x^2) + (6x + 22)$

20. $(12x - 4 - 5x^2) - (-9x^2 + 15x - 6)$

_____   _____

21. $(3x^2 - 9x + 7) - (x^2 + 10x + 2)$

22. $(-5x + 14 - 4x^2) - (-2x^2 + 3x + 8)$

_____   _____

Multiply or divide.

23. $(-3x^4)(10x^2)$

24. $6x^2(8x^3 - 4)$

25. $5x^6(2x^3 - 7x^2 + 5x)$

_____   _____   _____

26. $\dfrac{35x^9}{7x^7}$

27. $\dfrac{4x^3 - 12x}{2x}$

28. $\dfrac{-42x^9 + 15x^8 + 21x^6}{3x^3}$

_____   _____   _____

Solve the equation.

29. $3x - 8 + 9x = 40$

30. $5x + 5 - 2x = -10$

31. $20 - 2x = 5x - 36$

_____   _____   _____

32. $x + 4 = 32 - 3x$

33. $5(4x + 5) = 4x - 23$

34. $-2(x + 40) = 4(5 - x)$

_____   _____   _____

Solve the inequality and graph the solution.

35. $x + 1.6 > 14.2$

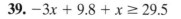

36. $\frac{3}{8} + x \leq \frac{5}{16}$

37. $14.7x < 72.03$

38. $-\frac{x}{10} > \frac{24}{25}$

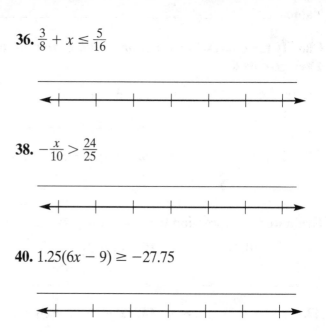

39. $-3x + 9.8 + x \geq 29.5$

40. $1.25(6x - 9) \geq -27.75$

Problem Solving

41. Harrison is saving money to buy new speakers that cost at least $120.25. He earns $6.50 per hour working at a grocery store. Write and solve an inequality to find the number of hours he must work to earn enough money for the speakers.

42. A company has a goal of manufacturing more than 48 thousand products per day. Each machine can produce about 1.6 thousand products each day. Write and solve an inequality to find the number of machines the company should have in order to reach its goal.

Tell About It

Explain how you solve each problems. Show all your work.

43. A square prism with a base side length of s has a volume of $6s^3 + 3s^2$ square centimeters. What is its height?

44. Lacey is making a birthday card for her friend. She has 19.8 inches of ribbon to use as a border. She wants the length of the card to be 1.2 times its width. Write and solve an inequality to find the largest dimensions she can use for the card if she adds the border.

Cumulative Review: Chapters 1–14

Name _____   Date _____

Circle the best answer.

1. The legs of the base of a right triangular prism measure 9 in. and 12 in. The prism has a height of 5 in. What is the surface area of the prism?

    A. 270 in.^{2} **B.** 288 in.^{2}
    C. 318 in.^{2} **D.** 396 in.^{2}

2. What is the 8th term is the sequence 4, 7, 12, 19, 28…?

    F. 36
    G. 39
    H. 55
    J. 67

3. At dinner, Ray's bill is $32. He leaves the server a 20% tip. He also has to pay 5% tax on the amount of the bill. What is the total amount that Ray pays?

    A. $32.32   **B.** $34.24
    C. $40   **D.** $40.32

4. Curtis is choosing 5 mugs from a shelf containing 7. How many possible combinations of mugs can he choose?

    F. 21   **G.** 35
    H. 42   **J.** 120

5. Which is the graph of the solution of $5 - 2x \le 3$?

  A.

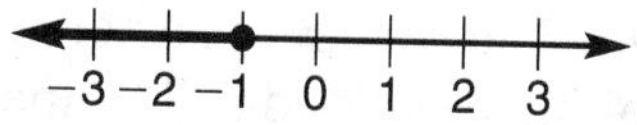

  B.

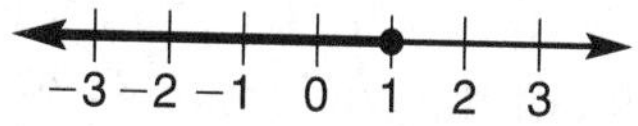

  C.

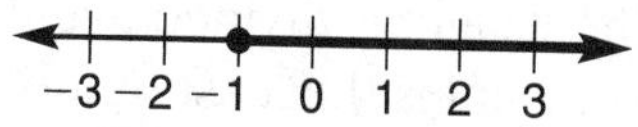

  D.

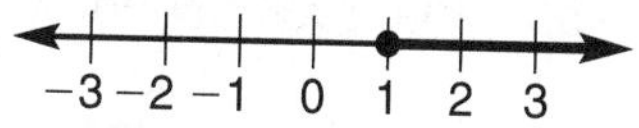

6. Simplify: $38 - |-16| + \dfrac{-10^2}{(-5)^2}$

    F. 18   **G.** 26
    H. 50   **J.** 58

7. The Venn diagram shows the number of students who take each type of class at a dance school. How many students take tap and at most one other class?

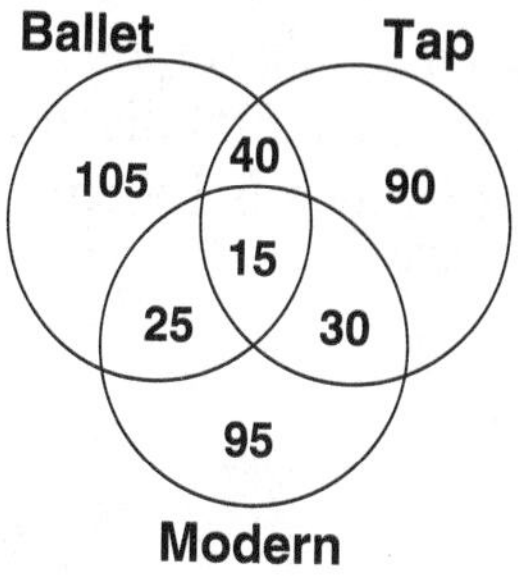

    A. 120
    B. 130
    C. 160
    D. 175

8. Solve: $-4x + 6 = 14$.

    F. −5
    G. −2
    H. 2
    J. 5

9. The hypotenuse of a right triangle measures 6 feet. One leg measures 2 feet. What is the length of the other leg?

    A. 2 ft   **B.** 4 ft
    C. $4\sqrt{2}$ ft   **D.** $2\sqrt{10}$ ft

10. Miranda jogs 2 miles in 15 minutes. How far would you expect her to walk in 1 hr 20 min?

    F. $\frac{2}{25}$ mi   **G.** $\frac{4}{25}$ mi

    H. $10\frac{2}{3}$ mi   **J.** 18 mi

11. $(-8)(8) = (8)(-8)$ is an example of which property?

   A. Associative Property of Multiplication
   B. Commutative Property of Multiplication
   C. Identity Property of Multiplication
   D. Inverse Property of Multiplication

12. Solve $4(2 - x) - 8 = 84$.

   F. $x = -37$
   G. $x = -21$
   H. $x = 21$
   J. $x = 37$

13. The scale on a map is 1 cm = 500 km. What is the actual distance in meters if the map distance is 1.9 cm?

   A. 950 m
   B. 9,500 m
   C. 95,000 m
   D. 950,000 m

14. In 2002, the value of a house was $250,000. In 2007, the same house had a value of $305,000. What was the percent increase in the value of the house?

   F. 18%
   G. 22%
   H. 55%
   J. 82%

15. Divide $30x^3 - 18x^2 + 12x$ by $6x$.

   A. $5x^3 + 3x^2 + 2x$
   B. $5x^3 - 3x^2 + 2x$
   C. $5x^2 - 3x + 2$
   D. $2x + 2$

16. Find the product $20(9.58 \times 10^{-9})$

   F. 1.916×10^{-9}
   G. 1.916×10^{-7}
   H. 1.916×10^{-8}
   J. 1.916×10^{-9}

17. Jerry has 4 black socks, 4 blue socks, and 2 white socks in a drawer. He reaches in at random and chooses a sock, does not replace it, and then chooses another. What is the probability he chooses 2 blue socks?

   A. $\dfrac{3}{25}$ **B.** $\dfrac{2}{25}$

   C. $\dfrac{4}{25}$ **D.** $\dfrac{2}{5}$

18. What is the volume of the figure?

   F. 24π mm^3 **G.** 28π mm^3
   H. 32π mm^3 **J.** 38π mm^3

Tell About It

Explain how you solve each problem. Show all your work.

19. Marissa is 3 years older than her younger brother. Her older brother is twice as old as her younger brother. Her older brother is 18. How old are Marissa and her younger brother?

20. A fitness center is moving equipment using an elevator. The movers load the equipment into the elevator and send it up, where other movers are waiting to unload it. The maximum weight the elevator can hold is 750 kilograms. The total weight of the equipment is 3937.5 kilograms. If the weight is divided evenly among the trips, what is the least number of trips up the elevator that are needed?